113 Springer Series in Solid-State Sciences
Edited by Hans-Joachim Queisser

Springer Series in Solid-State Sciences

Editors: M. Cardona P. Fulde K. von Klitzing H.-J. Queisser

Managing Editor: H. K.V. Lotsch

Volumes 1–89 are listed at the end of the book

90 **Earlier and Recent Aspects of Superconductivity** Editors: J. G. Bednorz and K. A. Müller

91 **Electronic Properties of Conjugated Polymers III** Basic Models and Applications
Editors: H. Kuzmany, M. Mehring, and S. Roth

92 **Physics and Engineering Applications of Magnetism** Editors: Y. Ishikawa and N. Miura

93 **Quasicrystals** Editors: T. Fujiwara and T. Ogawa

94 **Electronic Conduction in Oxides** By N. Tsuda, K. Nasu, A. Yanase, and K. Siratori

95 **Electronic Materials** A New Era in Materials Science
Editors: J. R. Chelikowsky and A. Franciosi

96 **Electron Liquids** By A. Isihara

97 **Localization and Confinement of Electrons in Semiconductors**
Editors: F. Kuchar, H. Heinrich, and G. Bauer

98 **Magnetism and the Electronic Structure of Crystals**
By V. A. Gubanov, A. I. Liechtenstein, and A.V. Postnikov

99 **Electronic Properties of High-T_c Superconductors and Related Compounds**
Editors: H. Kuzmany, M. Mehring, and J. Fink

100 **Electron Correlations in Molecules and Solids** By P. Fulde

101 **High Magnetic Fields in Semiconductor Physics III**
Quantum Hall Effect, Transport and Optics By G. Landwehr

102 **Conjugated Conducting Polymers** Editor: H. Kiess

103 **Molecular Dynamics Simulations** Editor: F. Yonezawa

104 **Products of Random Matrices in Statistical Physics**
By A. Crisanti, G. Paladin, and A. Vulpiani

105 **Self-Trapped Excitons** By K. S. Song and R. T. Williams

106 **Physics of High-Temperature Superconductors** Editors: S. Maekawa and M. Sato

107 **Electronic Properties of Polymers** Orientation and Dimensionality of Conjugated Systems
Editors: H. Kuzmany, M. Mehring, and S. Roth

108 **Site Symmetry in Crystals** Theory and Applications
By R. A. Evarestov and V. P. Smirnov

109 **Transport Phenomena in Mesoscopic Systems** Editors: H. Fukuyama and T. Ando

110 **Symmetry and Optical Phenomena in Superlattices and Other Heterostructures**
By E. L. Ivchenko and G. E. Pikus

111 **Low-Dimensional Electronic Systems** New Concepts
Editors: G. Bauer, F. Kuchar, and H. Heinrich

112 **Phonon Scattering in Condensed Matter VII**
Editors: M. Meissner and R. O. Pohl

113 **Electronic Properties of High-T_c Superconductors**
Editors: H. Kuzmany, M. Mehring, and J. Fink

H. Kuzmany M. Mehring
J. Fink (Eds.)

Electronic Properties of High-T_c Superconductors

The Normal and the Superconducting State of High-T_c Materials

Proceedings of the International Winter School, Kirchberg, Tyrol, March 7–14, 1992

With 286 Figures

Springer-Verlag
Berlin Heidelberg New York
London Paris Tokyo
Hong Kong Barcelona
Budapest

Professor Dr. Hans Kuzmany

Institut für Festkörperphysik, Universität Wien, Strudlhofgasse 4,
A-1090 Wien, Austria

Professor Dr. Michael Mehring

2. Physikalisches Institut, Universität Stuttgart, Pfaffenwaldring 57,
W-7000 Stuttgart, Fed. Rep. of Germany

Dr. Jörg Fink

Kernforschungszentrum Karlsruhe, Institut für Nukleare Festkörperphysik, Postfach 3640,
W-7500 Karlsruhe, Fed. Rep. of Germany

ISBN 3-540-56195-1 Springer-Verlag Berlin Heidelberg New York
ISBN 0-387-56195-1 Springer-Verlag New York Berlin Heidelberg

Library of Congress Cataloging-in-Publication Data. Electronic properties of high-Tc superconductors : the normal and the superconducting state of high-tc materials : proceedings of the international winter school, Kirchberg, Tyrol, March 7-14, 1992 / H. Kuzmany, M. Mehring, J. Fink, eds. p. cm. – (Springer series in solid-state sciences ; 113) Includes bibliographical references and index. ISBN 0-387-56195-1 (New York). – ISBN 3-540-56195-1 (Berlin) 1. High temperature superconductors–Congresses. 2. Electronic structure–Congresses. I. Kuzmany, H. (Hans), 1940- . II. Mehring, M., 1937- . III. Fink, J. (Jörg), 1938- . IV. Series. QC611.98.H54E35 1993 537.6'23–dc20 92-37326

Typesetting: Camera ready copy from the authors/editors
54/3140 – 5 4 3 2 1 0 – Printed on acid-free paper

Preface

The *International Winter School on Electronic Properties of High-Temperature Superconductors*, held between March 7–14, 1992, in Kirchberg, (Tyrol) Austria, was the sixth in a series of meetings to be held at this venue. Four of the earlier meetings were dedicated to issues in the field of conducting polymers, while the winter school held in 1990 was devoted to the new discipline of high-T_c superconductivity. This year's meeting constituted a forum not only for the large number of scientists engaged in high-T_c research, but also for those involved in the new and exciting field of fullerenes. Many of the issues raised during the earlier winter schools on conducting polymers, and the last one on high-T_c superconductivity, have taken on a new significance in the light of the discovery of superconducting C_{60} materials.

The Kirchberg meetings are organized in the style of a school where experienced scientists from universities, research laboratories and industry have the opportunity to discuss their most recent results, and where students and young scientists can learn about the present status of research and applications from some of the most eminent workers in their field.

In common with the previous winter school on high-T_c superconductors, the present one focused on the electronic properties of the cuprate superconductors. In addition, consideration was given to related compounds which are relevant to the understanding of the electronic structure of the cuprates in the normal state, to other oxide superconductors and to fulleride superconductors. Contributions dealing with their preparation, transport and thermal properties, high-energy spectroscopies, nuclear magnetic resonance, inelastic neutron scattering, and optical spectroscopy are presented in this volume. The theory of the normal and superconducting states also occupies a central position. In this school, particular attention was paid to the application of high-T_c superconductors and the preparation of thin-film high-T_c cuprates. The discussion session was devoted to the topic of spin and charge separation in high-T_c superconductors.

This volume summarizes the tutorial and research lectures presented at the 1992 winter school at Kirchberg. We acknowledge all the authors for their contributions, and all those whose stimulating remarks in the discussions made this meeting such an exciting and informative event.

As in previous years, the 1992 winter school in Kirchberg was organized in cooperation with the "Bundesministerium für Wissenschaft und Forschung" in Austria. We are particularly grateful to this ministry, to the "Kulturamt der Tiroler Landesregierung" in Austria, to the "Kernforschungszentrum Karlsruhe in Germany and to the "US-Army Research, Development and Standardisation Group" in the United Kingdom, as well as to the sponsors from industry for the substantial financial support without which the organization of such a successful winter school would have been impossible.

Finally, we thank the manager of the Hotel Sonnalp, Herrn J.R. Jurgeit, and his staff for their continuous support and for their patience with the many special arrangements required during the meeting.

Vienna	*H. Kuzmany*
Stuttgart	*M. Mehring*
Karlsruhe	*J. Fink*
October 1992	

Contents

Part III Transport Properties, Thermal Properties

Part VI Optical Spectroscopy, Raman Scattering

Part VII **Theory**

High-Temperature Superconductors in 1992
Welcome Address

K.A. Müller

IBM Research Division, Zurich Research Laboratory,
CH-8803 Rüschlikon, Switzerland

Much to my regret, a serious illness prevented me from attending the 1990 Kirchberg workshop. Therefore I am all the more grateful to the organizers, Profs. H. Kuzmany, M. Mehring and Dr. J. Fink for renewing their invitation to attend this promising workshop on "Electronic Properties of High Temperature Superconductors," the scope of which is described as follows:

> The winterschool will be focused on electronic properties of high temperature superconductors and their potential applications. Particular attention will be paid to the anisotropy of the electronic system, to the influence of defects and to the electronic structure in chains, planes and 3D clusters. The relevance to conductivity, magnetic and optical properties including IR, magnetic resonance, Raman scattering, high energy spectroscopy, and in particular to T_c and to superconducting fluctuations will be discussed. Oxidic and carbon superconductors (C_{60}) in the neutral and doped state will be covered and the status of our present theoretical understanding of the corresponding systems will be reviewed.

At the Kanazawa Conference in Japan in July of 1991, and more recently in greater detail at the Nobel Symposium in Göteborg, Sweden, in December of 1991, I summarized the first five years of the development of the high-T_c superconductors since their discovery. Therefore, I shall not reiterate it here, as quite a number of you were present at one or the other of these events, but let me briefly recall the conclusions I had reached then.

The microscopic interactions due to which the high superconducting transition temperatures of over 100 K occur are not yet understood. Nevertheless, applications are becoming realizable, as will be presented in the course of this winterschool in an overview and status reports of these various aspects. However, the main emphasis here is on the microscopic interactions that take place, because essential progress has been made in the past two years in identifying the nature of these interactions, both on the experimental as well as the theoretical side. In a way, the high-T_c situation reminds me of the critical phenomena field in 1970, where the universality hypothesis as exemplified by the liquid-to-gas and paramagnetic-to-antiferromagnetic phase transitions were experimentally proven and discussed during an Enrico Fermi

School in Varenna, which I attended at the suggestion of Toni Schneider. On the theoretical side, the notion of self-similarity, especially with the famous Kadanoff construction in real space, was presented. Less than two years elapsed until Wilson's formulation of the renormalization theory and the diagrams for the evolution of a system towards a fixed point became available, thus determining the critical properties near a transition. With this my experiments on critical and multicritical behavior in structural phase transitions could be quantitatively accounted for. On the other hand, new phenomena had been predicted by theory, which we subsequently verified quantitatively. Scientifically this interplay of experiment and theory was one of the most gratifying periods in my scientific career. To this remark I attach the hope that some of you may in the future experience similar satisfaction in the field of high-T_c superconductivity.

Where have we made progress? Certainly in preparation processes, with respect to the epitaxial growth of multilayers. Also, the kind of layers we generate is becoming increasingly better understood. We are now in a position where the more demanding molecular-beam chemical vapor deposition (MOCVD) and chemical-beam epitaxy (CBE) techniques are mastered. Atomic layer-by-layer growth is now feasible, at least in our laboratory. The influence of the substrates is being actively investigated. In characterizing the structures, we have attained a substantially higher degree of proficiency. An example of this will be presented to you in the next lecture.

Our understanding of the electronic properties, the main scope of this winterschool, is much better, both experimentally and theoretically. A partial description of the interactions occurring in the CuO_2 planes has been achieved and more convergence in understanding these essential mechanisms appears to be imminent. The coupling between the CuO_2 planes is also substantial, both on the superconducting multilayers by 2D-to-3D crossover scaling as well as magnetically by the presence of antiferromagnetic correlations along the c-axial direction. On the other hand, a systematic investigation of the anharmonicity and the isotope effect has not yet been undertaken. This is also the case for experiments on excitonic excitations. The characterization of flux creep and its relation to high current transport is, as you will see, important for applications. The use of cuprate superconductors in microelectronics and microwave technology is also making good progress.

Last year, the fullerene-based high-T_c superconductors were discovered. It is amazing how fast they could be characterized structurally and electronically. In this workshop those of you who have not been so close to this field will find themselves in a position to obtain comprehensive and expert information. I am sure you will greatly enjoy this workshop and contribute to its success.

Part I

General Properties, Preparation, Structure

Charge Dynamics in Metallic CuO_2 Layers

B. Batlogg, H. Takagi, H.L. Kao, and J. Kwo

AT&T Bell Laboratories, Murray Hill, NJ 07974, USA

Abstract. A short overview with quantitative comparisons, including several recent results, is given on the charge dynamics in metallic cuprates. The in-plane charge response, studied by dc transport and optical techniques, varies systematically with carrier concentration. Near the concentration for optimal superconductivity, $\rho_{ab}(T)$ and the scattering rate $\Gamma^*(\omega)$ increase nearly linearly over wide temperature and frequency ranges, respectively. The corresponding slopes $d\rho_{ab}/dT$ and $d\Gamma^*/d\omega$ are essentially the same for the different compound families even when the optimized T_c's are very different. The close connection between resistivity and scattering rate is also found to hold in the "overdoped" range, where the super-linear increase of $\rho_{ab}(T)$ and $\Gamma^*(\omega)$ has been studied in detail recently. A novel power-law dependence $\rho_{ab} \propto T^{1.5\pm0.1}$ was observed from 4K to ~1000K in overdoped $La_{1.66}Sr_{0.34}CuO_4$.

1. Introduction

Understanding the normal state charge and spin dynamics of cuprates is closely tied to an explanation of high temperature superconductivity[1] in layered cuprates. Various experiments suggest that the normal state properties of metallic cuprates are indeed different from that of conventional metals, e.g. Aluminum or Lead.[2–7] This may not be surprising considering the importance of correlation effects. The purpose of this short overview is to present recent experiments that shed light on the charge dynamics in cuprates, particularly the temperature and frequency dependent electrical superconductivity along the CuO_2 planes as the carrier concentration is systematically changed by chemical means. We shall demonstrate, using up-to-date results, the great quantitative similarity among the various structural families despite the much different T_c's, and highlight the most unusual charge dynamics in the metallic "overdoped," but not superconducting composition range.

2. In-Plane Resistivity $\rho_{ab}(T)$

The nearly linear temperature dependence of the resistivity has been recognized as one of the characteristics of cuprate superconductors even in the early days of this field when only polycrystalline samples, although of high quality, were available. [8] Now that crystals of good quality exist for several compounds, a quantitative comparison of the in-plane resistivity ρ_{ab} is revealing. In Fig. 1, ρ_{ab} is shown for Bi2201, $YBa_2Cu_3O_7$ (123 O_7), $La_{1.85}Sr_{0.15}CuO_4$ (214 LSCO), and Bi2212. (See e.g. Refs. [9-13]). Besides the remarkably similar magnitude and T-dependence of ρ_{ab}, one also observes deviations from linearity, albeit on a fine scale, mainly close to T_c, due to

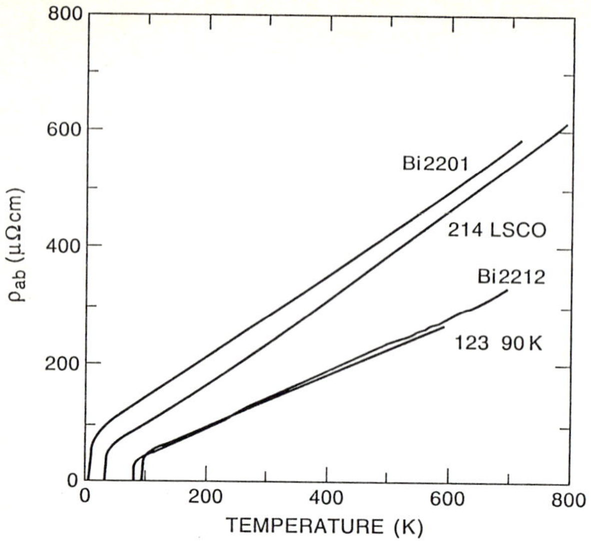

Fig. 1 Temperature dependence of the in-plane resistivity ρ_{ab} measured on crystals of various cuprate superconductors.

superconducting fluctuation effects, and at highest temperatures. When these ρ_{ab} curves are converted to ρ_{ab} at constant volume, the slight upward curvature at high T will be decreased. This effect is estimated to be less than 10% at highest temperatures in $La_{1.85}Sr_{0.15}CuO_4$.[13] In good quality samples, there is no indication of flattening of $\rho_{ab}(T)$ at low temperatures, which is particularly well expressed in Bi2201 with T_c's below 10K. These nearly-linear $\rho_{ab}(T)$ curves are only observed very close to the composition (carrier concentration) with maximal T_c. When the chemical composition deviates from the optimal, the $\rho(T)$ curves are no longer linear over an extended T range and change in a characteristic way. A recent result will be discussed below. We should add that $\rho_{ab}(T)$ will not follow the near-linear T dependence when structural elements other than the CuO_2 layers also contribute metallic conduction. This is most clearly visible in compounds with metallic double-chains, such as $YBa_2Cu_4O_8$ (124 or 248) or $Y_2Ba_4Cu_7O_{15}$ (247), where $\rho_{ab}(T)$ can be lower in magnitude and also resembles $\rho(T)$ of a conventional metal's s-shaped curve, suggesting perhaps saturation at highest T.[14,15]

A point of further research will be the in-plane anisotropy, i.e. ρ_a vs. ρ_b. It will be interesting to separate the effects of orthorhombicity from the contributions due to the chains, particularly in the best crystals of 123.[16,17] Systematic studies of Bi2212 or Bi2201 crystals might be useful in this respect since a significant anisotropy has been found in these materials also, despite the absence of CuO chains.[14,18–19]

The near-linear in-plane resistivities are conveniently parameterized by the slope of $d\rho_{ab}/dT$, which is given in Fig. 2 for those compounds for which reasonable reliable data are available. Worth noting is that the slopes for the optimized T_c samples are all near $0.5(\pm 0.2)\,\mu\Omega cm/K$ with no clear dependence on T_c (solid symbols); at least it is obvious that $d\rho/dT$ is not larger in the compounds with higher T_c. The close similarity is striking considering the different phonon spectra in these

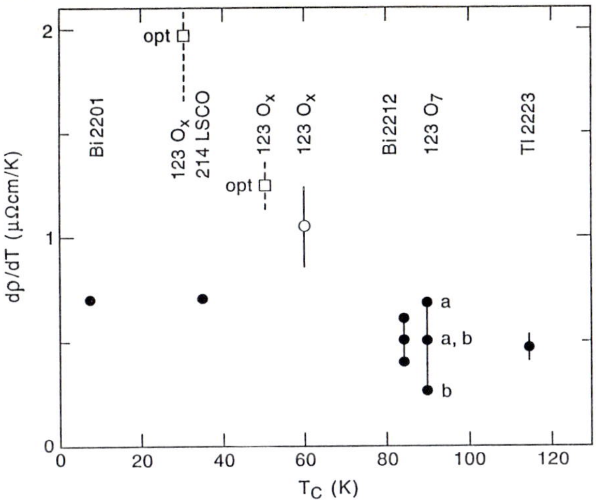

Fig. 2 Temperature coefficient $d\rho_{ab}/dT$ of the in-plane resistivity of several cuprate superconductors. The solid symbols represent values for optimized T_c materials and fall in a narrow range ($0.5\pm0.2\Omega$cm/K), independent of T_c. The open symbols indicate the steeper $\rho_{ab}(T)$ curves when the carrier concentration is sub-optimal in $123O_x$, but $\rho_{ab}(T)$ in those compounds is more non-linear than shown in Fig. 1. The in-plane anisotropy (ρ_a vs. ρ_b) is indicated for $123O_7$ and Bi2212.

compounds and also the greatly varying degree of crystal imperfections, suggesting that scattering by phonons and defects is not dominating $\rho_{ab}(T)$.

Also included in Fig. 2 are open symbols which represent $d\rho/dT$ for crystals of 123 with reduced oxygen content and thus reduced T_c. While the near-linearity of $\rho(T)$ is less well documented for those compositions, nevertheless $d\rho/dT$ is generally larger for sub-optimal T_c's. The squares are results from optically determined $\rho(\omega,T)$, extrapolated to $\omega=0$. (In the same set of data, the agreement between the optical and dc measurements was confirmed for the samples with T_c near 90K).[20] At this point, the higher values of $\rho(T)$ in non-optimized samples can be interpreted as either due to a reduction of carrier concentration or increased scattering, or both. A partial answer to this question comes from a comparison, in the next chapter, of the optically measured $\sigma(\omega,T)$ and $\rho_{dc}(T)$.

3. Relationship Between Temperature and Frequency Dependence of $\sigma(\omega,T)$

Going beyond the dc limit of the charge response in cuprates, substantial progress has been made in the past year in measuring the conductivity $\sigma(\omega,T)$ at optical frequencies. Instead of following a simple Drude model with a constant scattering rate τ_0 that leads to $\sigma(\omega)\sim1/\omega^2$, the conductivity decreases much more slowly with ω, actually very close to $1/\omega$ in the photon energy range up to a fraction of 1eV. Thus, a generalized Drude model with a frequency dependent $\tau^*(\omega)$ (or scattering rate $\Gamma^*(\omega)$) has been widely used to parameterize the measurements.[20–27] Fig. 3 is a summary of the resulting scattering rate $\Gamma^*(\omega)$ calculated from $\sigma(\omega)$, for a selection of compounds, including compositions with optimized and non-optimized transition temperatures

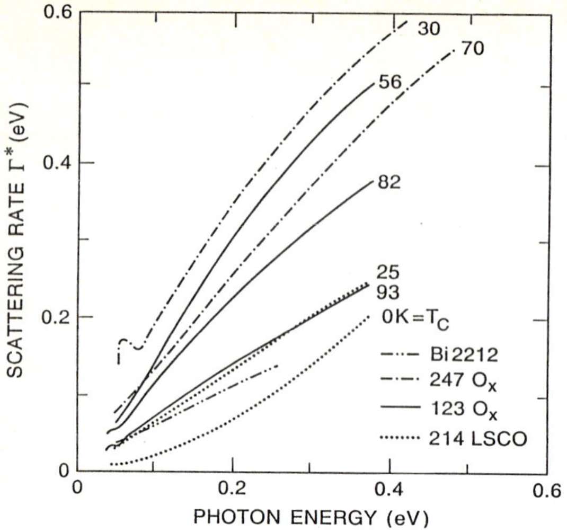

Fig. 3 The frequency dependent scattering rate obtained from a fit of a generalized Drude expression to the optically measured conductivity up to ~0.4eV photon energy, for four compound families. Noteworthy is the very close similarity and near-linearity of $\Gamma^*(\omega)$ for the compositions with optimized T_c. In the compositions with reduced hole concentration (and lower T_c), $\Gamma^*(\omega)$ is larger and assumes a sub-linear T dependence. In overdoped non-superconducting $La_{2-x}Sr_xCuO_4$, $(x \approx 0.34)$ $\Gamma^*(\omega)$ is significantly smaller and it is worth comparing the super-linear T dependence with the corresponding $\rho_{ab}(T)$ curve in Fig. 5. Both of them follow a power law ω^n and T^n with $n \approx 1.5$. (See text for refs.)

(T_c's are given next to the curves).[24-27] After recognizing the strong frequency dependence of $\Gamma^*(\omega)$ in all compositions, we point to the three nearly linear curves for Bi2212, 123 O_x (T_c=93K) and 214 LSCO. Noteworthy is the large energy range over which this nearly linear increase of $\Gamma^*(\omega)$ is observed, and it is reminiscent of the $\rho(T)$ data in Fig. 1. The photon energy scale of 0.4-0.5eV compares well with the temperature scale of ~1000K since resistivity measurements probe electronic states in an energy window around E_F that is several times kT wide. (For instance, approximately 75% of the weight function lies within 4kT around the Fermi level). The optical data, combined with the dc resistivity, then reveal the unusual feature of charge dynamics, characterized by a scattering rate $\Gamma^*(\omega,T)$ that is given either by $\approx kT$ (for $\hbar\omega \ll kT$) or by $\beta\hbar\omega$ with $\beta \approx 0.5-0.7$ for $\hbar\omega \gg kT$.

For samples with reduced T_c, the scattering rate is higher and grows sub-linearly with energy. In $Y_2Ba_4Cu_7O_{15-x}$, $\Gamma^*(\omega)$ is not quite linear in samples with a T_c of 70K, consistent with the fact that 70K is not the optimal T_c for this compound.[27] It will be necessary to clarify in future studies to what degree the so-called mid-infrared absorption feature, which is best seen at several tenths of an eV photon energy in lightly doped non-metallic cuprates, can influence a parameterization in terms of a generalized Drude model in metallic samples with less than optimal hole concentration.[20,21,24]

The comparison of the scattering rate results strongly suggests a trend among the metallic cuprates which closely resembles the temperature dependence of $\rho(T)$: (1) $\Gamma^*(\omega)$ increases nearly linearly with frequency (if T_c is optimized); (2) The slope $d\Gamma^*(\omega)/d\omega$ is 0.5-0.7 and seems to be independent of T_c (as long as T_c is optimized)

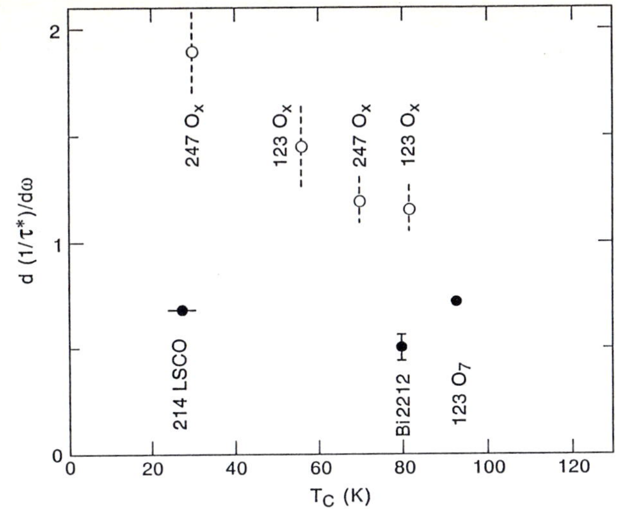

Fig. 4 Slope $d\Gamma^*(\omega)/d\omega$ near 0.1-0.2eV of the scattering rates shown in Fig. 3. For the optimized compositions (solid circles) $d\Gamma^*(\omega)/d\omega$ is in the range of 0.5-0.8 and depends not on T_c, while $d\Gamma^*(\omega)/d\omega$ is significantly larger in non-optimized compositions. This systematics, combined with Fig. 2, captures an essential aspect of the in-plane charge dynamics.

in analogy to the $d\rho_{ab}/dT$ values. (3) In both "under" and "overdoped" crystals, $\Gamma^*(\omega)$ deviates in a characteristic way from the nearly linear $\Gamma^*(\omega)$.

Fig. 4 summarizes the frequency dependence of Γ^* in a simplified way by plotting the slopes in the low energy range (0.1-0.2eV) for the various compounds, as function of T_c. Solid symbols represent optimized compositions. The similarity with Fig. 2 is striking and strongly suggests that the scattering mechanism determining the electrical conductivity in the CuO_2 planes is *qualitatively* and *quantitatively* the same in all cuprates with optimized carrier concentration. When the hole concentration is smaller, the scattering rate appears to be larger. Therefore, the increased resistivity (open symbols Fig. 3) is at least partly due to increased scattering, in addition to reduction of carrier concentration.

4. Variation of $\rho_{ab}(T)$ with Carrier Concentration

While the previous discussions were focused mainly on the various superconducting compounds near their optimal composition, we will now present an example where the hole concentration is varied chemically over a wide range. In $La_{2-x}Sr_xCuO_4$ the substitution of Sr for La offers a relatively convenient way to explore the transport properties both in the "underdoped" and in the "overdoped" region.

Fig. 5 shows some of the results of a recent transport study involving high quality epitaxial thin films.[13] The overall values of the resistivities are significantly lower than for samples studied earlier, including crystals. The x=0.07 composition exhibits a metal-like $\rho_{ab}(T)$ with indication of resistivity saturation at the highest temperatures, and an upturn of ρ_{ab} at low temperatures reminiscent of localization. For

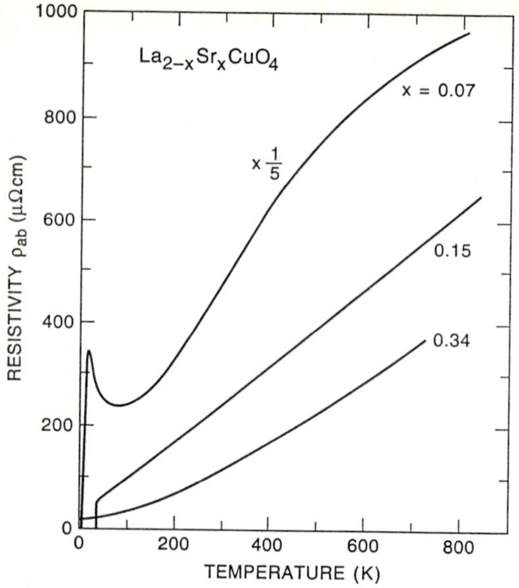

Fig. 5 Variations with hole concentration of the in-plane resistivity in high quality thin films of $La_{2-x}Sr_xCuO_4$ over a wide temperature range. The near-linearity is observed only close to the optimal composition ($x \approx 0.15$). In the overdoped range ($x=0.34$), $\rho_{ab}(T)$ follows a power law $T^{1.5\pm0.1}$ from 4K to the highest temperatures. (Ref. 13). Of particular significance is the observation of the same power law in $\Gamma^*(\omega)$ shown in Fig. 3, (Ref. 25), which we analyze as $\Gamma^*(\omega) \propto \omega^{1.6\pm0.1}$.

the optimal composition (x=0.15), the near-linear temperature dependence is observed again over the wide T-range explored in this study. Particularly interesting is the super-linear T dependence in the overdoped region, x=0.34, which follows a power law $T^{(1.5\pm0.1)}$ over a wide temperature range from 4K to nearly 800K (1000K in polycrystals). Even at these high temperatures $d\rho_{ab}/dT$ keeps increasing.

In an independent study on different samples, the optical properties of a crystal with the same composition (x=0.34) revealed the frequency dependent scattering rate $\Gamma^*(\omega)$ shown in Fig. 3.[25] Up to 0.4eV $\Gamma^*(\omega)$ is proportional to ω^n with $n=1.6\pm0.1$. The close link between $\rho(T)$ and $\Gamma^*(\omega)$ is thus also demonstrated in the overdoped range. This $T^{3/2}$ power law in overdoped $La_{2-x}Sr_xCuO_4$ is equally unusual as the linear T-dependence near the optimal carrier concentration, and it remains to be investigated whether or not the charge dynamics in "overdoped" cuprates is that of a "conventional Fermi liquid." Earlier resistivity results below room temperature on Tl2201[28] with different amounts of oxygen excess and on thin films of $Nd_{2-x}Ce_xCuO_4$[29] also show a super-linear $\rho(T) \propto T^n$ with n approaching ~2, which was interpreted as a continuous transition to a Fermi liquid behavior. Those resistivities, however, were up to an order of magnitude higher than the ones on the $(La,Sr)_2CuO_4$ film. It would be very interesting to measure $\Gamma^*(\omega)$ in these two systems to high frequencies to probe the range of these power laws in relation to the estimated Fermi energies.

5. Summary

Through advances in materials preparation and systematic optical and dc transport measurements, significant progress has been made in elucidating the charge dynamics in metallic CuO_2 layers. What had been recognized early as typical transport properties of cuprate superconductors is now being put on solid quantitative footing. Among the outstanding features is the close correspondence between the temperature dependent in-plane resistivity and the frequency dependent scattering rate over wide frequency and temperature ranges. This holds true not only for optimal compositions, but also in the "overdoped" range, where unusual power laws have been found for $\rho \propto T^n$ and $\Gamma^* \propto \omega^n$.

References

[1] J. G. Bednorz and K. A. Müller, *Z. Phys.* **B64,** 189 (1986).

[2] See e.g. Proc. Los Alamos Symposium 1989 on High Temperature Superconductivity, K. S. Bedell, D. Coffey, D. E. Meltzer, D. Pines and J. R. Schrieffer eds., Addison-Wesley Publishing Co., 1990.

[3] For a short overview, see e.g. B. Batlogg, *Physics Today,* June 1991, p. 44; also in "Physics of High-Temperature Superconductors," eds. S. Maekawa and M. Sato, p. 219, Springer Series in Solid-State Sciences, Vol. 106, Springer-Verlag 1992; also in Ref. 2, p 37-82.

[4] P. A. Lee, Ref. 2, p. 96-116.

[5] K. Levin, Ju H. Kim, J. P. Lu and Aimioro Si; *Physica C* **175,** 449 (1991).

[6] P. W. Anderson, *Science,* **256,** 1526 (1992). (A most recent discussion of experimental data as they constrain the theory of high T_c superconductivity).

[7] For overviews on transport, see e.g. N. P. Ong in "Physical Properties of the High Temperature Superconductors," edited by D. M. Ginsberg (World Scientific, Singapore 1990), Vol. II, p. 459 and Yosuhiro Iye, in Studies of High Temperature Superconductors: Advances in Research and Applications, A. Narlikar, ed. (Nova Science, NY, 1991) p. 199.

[8] R. J. Cava, B. Batlogg, R. B. van Dover and E. A. Rietman, *Phys. Rev. Lett.* **58,** 408 (1987), and R. J. Cava et al., *Phys. Rev. Lett.* **58,** 1676 (1987).

[9] S. Martin, A. T. Fiory, R. M. Fleming, G. P. Espinosa and A.S. Cooper, *Appl. Phys. Lett.* **54,** 72 (1989), and S. Martin et al., *Phys. Rev.* **B41,** 846 (1990).

[10] A. T. Fiory, S. Martin, R. M. Fleming, L. F. Schneemeyer, J. V. Waszczak, A. F. Hebard and S. A. Sunshine, *Physica C* **162-164,** 1195 (1989).

[11] J. P. Rice, J. Giapintzakis, D. M. Ginsberg and J. M. Mochel, *Phys. Rev.* **B44,** 9743 (1991).

[12] N. P. Ong, T. W. Jing, T. R. Chien, Z. Z. Wang, T. V. Ramakrishnan, J. M. Tarascon and K. Remschnig, *Physica C,* **185-189,** 34 (1991) and references therein.

[13] H. Takagi, B. Batlogg, H. L. Kao, J. Kwo, R. J. Cava, J. J. Krajewski and W. F. Peck, Jr., (to be published).

[14] J. Schoenes, J. Karpinski, E. Kaldis, J. Keller and P. de la Mora, *Physica C* **166,** 145 (1990) and B. Bucher, J. Karpinski, E. Kaldis and P. Wachter, *Physica C* **167,** 324 (1990).

[15] P. Berghuis, P. H. Kes, G. M. Stollman and J. Van Bentum, *Physica C* **167,** 348 (1990).

[16] T. A. Friedmann, M. W. Rabin, J. Giapintzakis, J. P. Rice and D. M. Ginsberg, *Phys. Rev.* **B42,** 6217 (1990).

[17] U. Welp, S. Fleshler, W. K. Kwok, J. Downey, Y. Fang, G. W. Crabtree and J. Z. Liu, *Phys. Rev.* **B42,** 10189 (1990).

[18] S. Martin, A. T. Fiory, R. M. Fleming, L. F. Schneemeyer and J. V. Waszczak, *Phys. Rev. Lett.* **60,** 2194 (1988).

[19] K. Yamaya, T. Haga, T. Honnma, Y. Abe, F. Minami, S. Takegawa, Y. Tajima and Y. Hidaka, *Physica C* **162-164,** 1009 (1989).

[20] J. Orenstein, G. A. Thomas, A. J. Millis, S. L. Cooper, D. H. Rapkine, T. Timusk, L. F. Schneemeyer and J. V. Waszczak, *Phys. Rev.* **B42,** 6342 (1990).

[21] For a recent overview, see e.g. G. A. Thomas, in "High Temperature Superconductivity", p. 169, ed. D. P. Tunstall and W. Barford, (Adam Hilger, Bristol, England 1991) and T. Timusk and D. B. Tanner, in "Physical Properties of High Temperature Superconductors," D. M. Ginsberg (ed.) World Scientific Publishing Co., (1989), p. 339.

[22] J. Schützmann, W. Ose, J. Keller, K. F. Renk, B. Roas, L. Schultz, and G. Saemann-Ischenko, *Europhys. Lett.* **8,** 679 (1989).

[23] B. Koch, H. P. Geserich and T. H. Wolf, *Solid State Comm.* **71,** 495 (1989).

[24] L. D. Rotter, Z. Schlesinger, R. T. Collins, T. Holtzberg, C. Field, U. W. Welp, G. W. Crabtree, J. Z. Liu, Y. Fang, K. G. Vandervoort, S. Fleshler *Phys. Rev. Lett.* **67,** 2741 (1991).

[25] S. Uchida, *Physica C* **185-189,** 28 (1991).

[26] Z. Schlesinger, *Physica C* **185-189,** 57 (1991) and refs. therein.

[27] B. Bucher, J. Karpinski, E. Kaldis and P. Wachter, *Phys. Rev.* **B45,** 3026 (1992).

[28] Y. Kubo, Y. Shimakawa, T. Manako and H. Igarashi, *Phys. Rev.* **B43,** 7875 (1991).

[29] C. C. Tsuei, A. Gupta and G. Koren, *Physica C* **161,** 415 (1989).

Superconductivity in the Infinite-Layer Phase Stabilized Under High Pressure

M. Takano, Z. Hiroi, and M. Azuma

Institute for Chemical Research, Kyoto University,
Uji, Kyoto-fu 611, Japan

Cupric-oxide superconductors are complex oxides involving counter cations like rare-earth and alkaline-earth ions. Counter cations and cupric ions compromise with each other to coexist in a crystal by adjusting their coordination numbers, bond lengths, and bond angles. Pressure and temperature evidently influence these parameters, and so, depending upon pressure and temperature, different compositions would be stabilized in a given structure and different structures would appear for a given composition. By applying 6GPa to the alkaline-earth-copper-oxygen system a new superconductor family with the highest T_c of 110K has been found.

1. High Pressure, Why?

All the known cupric oxide superconductors are made of negatively charged two-dimensional (2D) CuO_2 sheets and positively charged counter layers which are stacked alternatively along a crystallographic axis. Experimentally alkaline-earth (A) and rare-earth (R) ions work as counter cations (C.C.'s), which are larger in size and more spherical in electronic state than the cupric ions. Since the Cu-O and C.C.-O bonds should thus have different compressibilities and different thermal expansion coefficients, the lattice matching between the CuO_2 sheets and the counter layers and, therefore, the structural stability would by strongly influenced by pressure and temperature.

We have studied high-pressure effects upon complex cupric oxides for the purpose of finding new compositions and new structures [1]. As a part of this study we report here a new superconductor found in the A-Cu-O system.

2. Infinite-Layer Structure

The 'infinite-layer' structure illustrated in Fig. 1a is the simplest structure containing the CuO_2 sheets [2]. At ambient pressure only $Ca_{1-x}Sr_xCuO_2$ with $x \sim 0.1$ can be stabilized in this structure [2,3], but we found that the composition range could be widened at high pressures so that it covered from $Ba_{1/3}Sr_{2/3}CuO_2$ to $Ca_{2/3}Sr_{1/3}CuO_2$ through $SrCuO_2$ [4]. The lattice constants are plotted against the average A-ion radius (r_A) in Fig. 1b. Both a and c increase as r_A increases, while the rate for the c axis is almost three

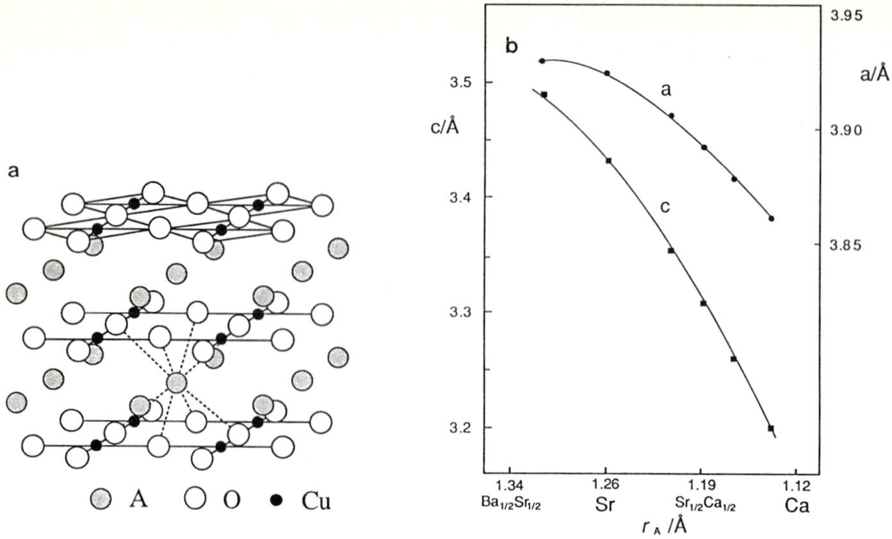

Fig. 1 Infinite-layer structure (a) and lattice constants plotted against the average A-ion radius (b).

times as large as that for the *a* axis, and for $r_A > r_{Sr}$ the *a* axis is almost saturated. This points out the stiffness of the Cu-O bond. If it were soft, large A-ions would not expand the structure so anisotropically and the composition range would be widened towards $BaCuO_2$.

There is a chance to inject carriers into the CuO_2 sheets where there is a structural instability. One way to relax the structural instability caused by large A-ions is to inject excess electrons into, or reduce, the CuO_2 sheets and, thereby, make the Cu-O bond longer. Another way is to partially remove the large A-ions, or introduce A-ion vacancies, and, thereby, make r_A smaller. These two ways might lead us to finding *n*-type and *p*-type superconductors.

Smith et al. [5] and Er et al. [6] succeeded in preparing an *n*-type superconductor $Sr_{1-x}R_xCuO_2$ with R=Nd, La and $T_c \leq 43$K. We recently obtained $(Ca_{1-x}Sr_x)_{1-y}CuO_2$ (y~0.1) with T_c up to 110K [7]. Previously we had reported superconductivity with T_c=40~100K in the Ba-Sr-Cu-O system [8,9] and suggested that a modulated, not simple, infinite-layer structure was responsible [8]. However, the chemistry of even the simple Sr-Cu-O system under pressure turned out to be complex [1,10] and it was not possible to isolate the superconducting phase. Substitution of Ca^{2+} for Sr^{2+} as above has proved to make it easy.

3. Experimental

Samples were prepared starting from metallic compositions of $Ca_{1-x}Sr_x$: Cu=1-y : 1 with $0.4 \leq x \leq 0.7$ and $0 \leq y \leq 0.1$. Starting oxide powder was filled in a gold capsule, pressed almost isostatically up to 6 GPa using a classical cubic-anvil-type apparatus, and heated at 1273 K with a graphite-sleeve heater under the pressure for 30 min. $KClO_4$ that releases oxygen at high temperature was added in the bottom of the capsule when oxidizing atmosphere was applied. Samples used for various measurements were ascertained by using a scanning electron microscope (SEM) equipped with an energy-dispersive X-ray analyzer to be free from potassium and chlorine within experimental error. It was also confirmed that the Ca : Sr : Cu ratio was in agreement with the mixing ratio. Magnetic susceptibility was measured for crushed sample powder on cooling in an applied field of 10 Oe, and resistance was measured by a usual four terminal method. X-ray diffraction (XRD), electron diffraction (ED), and transmission electron microscopy (TEM) were used for a structural characterization.

4. Results and Discussion

Superconductivity was found for the wide Ca : Sr ratio mentioned above, if the samples were treated with $KClO_4$. Typical data for $(x, y)=(0.7, 0.1)$ are shown in Fig. 2. The magnetic data indicate that the transition occurs in two steps, one at 110 K and the other at 75 K. The multiplicity has been attributed to a specific microstructure to be described later. A volume fraction of ~10% was estimated at 5 K, which was reasonably large for the fine particle size of $\leq 1\mu m$ as measured by SEM. Resistance begins to drop at ~110 K and becomes zero within experimental error at 65 K. The transition temperature of 110K is comparable with those of the "2223" phases in the Tl-Ba-Ca-Cu-O and Bi-Sr-Ca-Cu-O systems.

Figure 3a shows the XRD pattern of this sample. Most peaks can be indexed assuming the tetragonal infinite-layer structure with a = 3.902 Å and c = 3.350 Å. Small amounts of CuO (marked with stars) and unknown phases (marked with open circles) which probably formed as a result of

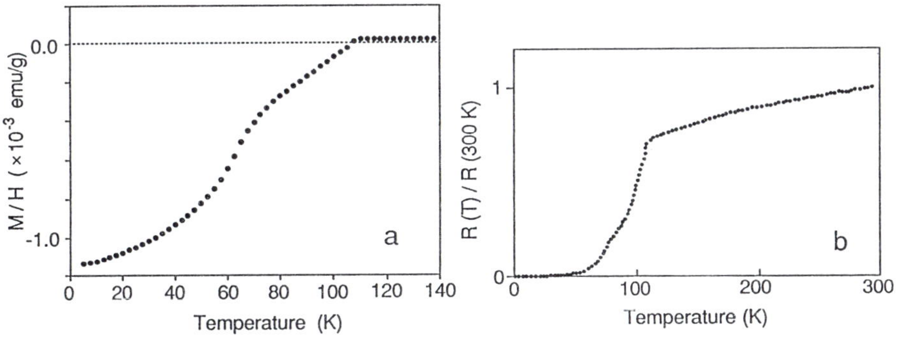

Fig. 2 Temperature dependence of susceptibility ($M/H, H$=10 Oe) measured for a powdered sample of $(Ca_{0.3}Sr_{0.7})_{0.9}CuO_2$ on cooling (a) and the temperature dependence of resistance of the same composition (b).

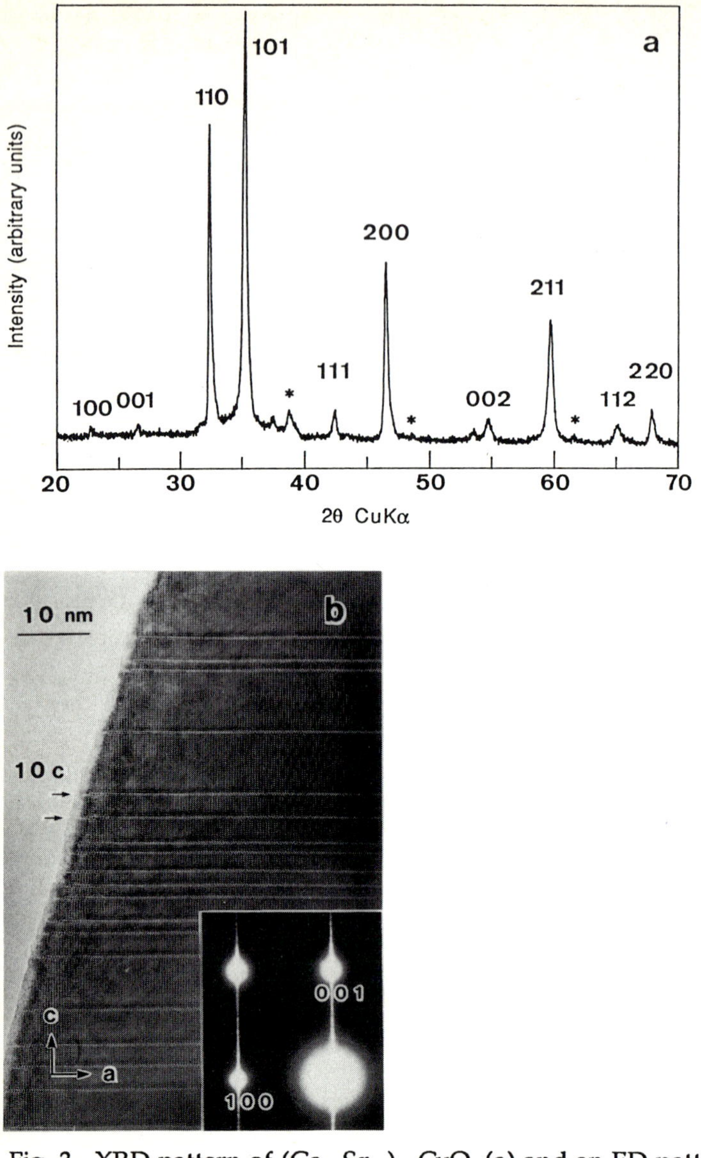

Fig. 3 XRD pattern of $(Ca_{0.3}Sr_{0.7})_{0.9}CuO_2$ (a) and an ED pattern and the corresponding HREM image for $A = Ca_{0.4}Sr_{0.6}$, $y = 0.1$ (b).

slight reaction with the sample container are mixed, but these are not relevant to superconductivity. It is interesting to note here that the XRD pattern of the superconducting sample is characterized by index-dependent peak broadening, though the peak positions remain the same as those for the stoichiometric (y=0) sample. The broadening is index-dependent, quite light for (h k 0)'s but serious for (0 0 l)'s.

Typically shown in Fig. 3b are an ED pattern and the corresponding high-resolution electron microscopic (HREM) image for a sample with $(x, y)=(0.4, 0.1)$. The ED pattern is streaked along the c^* axis, and in the HREM image "defect" layers occur rather randomly. The randomness explains both the broadening of the (00*l*) XRD peaks and the streaking of the ED spots. The density of the defect layers was found to increase as the A/Cu ratio decreases but does not depend upon oxygen content: We treated various samples in an oxidizing atmosphere using $KClO_4$, in an inert atmosphere without using $KClO_4$, and also in a strongly reducing atmosphere created by the graphite-sleeve heater by using a porous sample holder made of BN instead of an gas-tight gold capsule, while essentially the same microstructures were observed, though electrical and magnetic properties varied remarkably. It has thus been considered that A-ion vacancies are not distributed randomly but are concentrated in the defect layers. Even the sample with a starting composition of $y=0$ is slightly defective, because the temperature of the high-pressure treatment was high enough to drive the system towards a slightly A-deficient composition [9, 10].

Two most important features of the defect layer found at a higher magnification are that triple Cu-O sheets involved in each defect layer have an elongated intersheet distance of about 3.7 Å, longer by 10 % in comparison with the normal distance, and that the contrast of the oxygen sites within the central Cu-O sheet specifically changes depending remarkably upon the atmosphere during the high pressure treatment. Oxygen released from $KClO_4$ can fill the oxygen vacancies within the central sheet which are stabilized in the inert or reducing atmosphere. It is reasonable to assume that the inter-CuO_2-sheet distance is elongated if the *A*-ion vacancies are concentrated in the defect layer : The deficiency enhances the electrostatic repulsion between the negatively charged CuO_2 sheets. We can formulate the defect layer as $CuO_2/A_{1-z}/CuO_{2-\delta}/A_{1-z}/CuO_2$ $(y<z)$, where δ (≥ 0) is variable depending upon the atmosphere. The superconductivity appearing at $\delta \sim 0$ should be of *p*-type with hole carriers created by the A-deficiency. And this would be the first *p*-type superconductor in which cupric ions have no apical oxide ions. The multiplicity in transition should have resulted from the inhomogeneity in defect density within a crystal.

5. Concluding Remarks

$Sr_{1-x}R_xCuO_2$ and $(Ca_{1-x}Sr_x)_{1-y}CuO_2$ are *n*-type and *p*-type superconductors, respectively, both crystallizing basically in the infinite-layer structure. Application of high pressure has thus proved to be useful to finding new cupric-oxide superconductors. Non-superconducting but new cupric oxides have been reported elsewhere [1,10].

Acknowledgements

The authors express their hearty thanks to O. Ohtaka, S. Kume, and T. Yamanaka of Osaka University for permitting us to use their high pressure apparatus. This study was partly supported by a Priority-Areas Grant from the Ministry of Education, Science, and Culture of Japan.

References

[1] M. Takano, Z. Hiroi, M. Azuma and Y. Takeda in *Chemistry of High Temperature Superconductors*, edited by C. N. R. Rao (World Scientific, Singapore, 1991), p.243.

[2] T. Siegrist, S.M. Zahurac, D.W. Murphy and R.S. Roth, *Nature* **334**, 231 (1988).

[3] H. Yamane, Y. Miyazaki and T. Hirai, *J. Cer. Soc. Jpn.* **97**, 143 (1989) (in Japanese).

[4] M. Takano, Y. Takeda, H. Okada, M. Miyamoto and K. Kusaka, *Physica* **C 159**, 375 (1989).

[5] M.G. Smith, A. Manthiram, J. Zhou, J.B. Goodenough and J.T. Market, *Nature* **351**, 549 (1991).

[6] G. Er, Y. Miyamoto, F. Kanamaru and S. Kikkawa, *Physica* **C 181**, 206 (1991).

[7] M. Azuma, Z. Hiroi, M. Takano, Y. Bando and Y. Takeda, *Nature* **356**, 775 (1992).

[8] M. Takano, M. Azuma, Z. Hiroi, Y. Bando and Y. Takeda, *Physica* **C 176**, 441 (1991).

[9] M. Takano, Int. Workshop on Electrical Properties and Mechanisms in High-T_c Superconductors (July, 1991, Tsukuba), in press.

[10] Z. Hiroi, M. Azuma, M. Takano and Y. Bando, J. *Solid State Chem.*, **95**, 230 (1991).

Crystal Chemistry and Superconductivity in $M(Ba_{1-y}Sr_y)_2RECu_2O_x$

X.Z. Wang and B. Hellebrand

Angewandte Physik, Johannes-Kepler Universität Linz, A-4040 Linz, Austria

The crystal chemistry and superconductivity have been investigated for compounds of the type of $REBaSrCu_3O_x$ (RE ≡ La, Ce, Pr, Nd, Sm, Eu, Gd, Tb, Dy, Y, Ho, Er, Tm, Lu) and $MA_2RECu_2O_{8-y}$ (M ≡ Nb or Ta, A ≡ Ba or Sr and RE ≡ Pr or Sm). The powder X-ray diffraction analysis of $REBaSrCu_3O_x$ revealed a structural phase transition from tetragonal to orthorhombic, when the ionic radius of the RE^{3+} decreases. The $MSr_2RECu_2O_{8-y}$ compounds crystallized in a tetragonal structure similar to that of Y-123.

Introduction

All known copper oxide superconductors contain layers of copper-oxygen squares, pyramids, or octahedrons as electronically active structural components [1]. The layers of these structural components are intergrown with oxide layers such as Ba(Sr)-O, RE-O, Bi-O, and Tl-O. By proper doping these layer compounds can be varied from insulators to semiconductors, metallic or even superconductors.

When searching for new superconducting layer compounds it is interesting to investigate the intergrown system with different kind of oxide layers. In this work we synthesized 1-2-1-2 type compounds of the $REBaSrCu_3O_x$ (RE ≡ La, Pr, Nd, Sm, Eu, Gd, Dy, Y, Ho, Er, Tm) and $MA_2RECu_2O_{8-y}$ (M ≡ Nb or Ta, A ≡ Ba or Sr and RE ≡ Pr or Sm).

Experimental

The preparation of $REBaSrCu_3O_x$ and $MA_2RECu_2O_{8-y}$ compounds by solid-state reactions has been reported in [2, 3]. Structural analysis was carried out by powder X-ray diffraction (XRD) at room temperature using Cu-K_α radiation. The instrument was calibrated with silicon powder. The XRD intensity was measured from 6° to 100° (2θ) at a speed of 0.25 degrees per minute. The lattice parameters were calculated by a least squares refinement. The oxygen content of all samples was determined by iodometric titration or by thermal gravimetry (TG) analysis. The temperature dependence of the electrical resistance was measured by employing a standard DC four-point probe technique from room temperature down to 10 K. The room temperature resistivity was determined by using the Van de Pauw method [4] on a thin pellet.

Results and discussion

Figure 1 shows the unit cell volume of different $REBaSrCu_3O_x$ compounds as a function of ionic radius of the RE^{3+} ion. Ionic radii for RE^{3+} considered

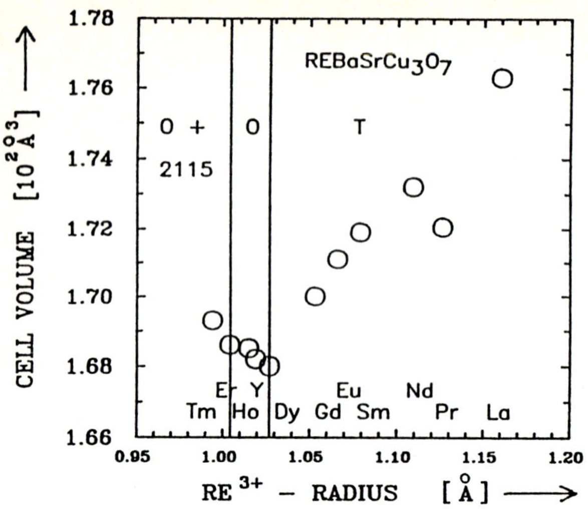

Fig. 1. Dependence of the unit cell volume and the phase formation region of $REBaSrCu_3O_x$ on the ionic radius of the RE^{3+} ion [5]. The abbreviations denote O = orthorohmbic, T = tetragonal, and 2115 = RE_2BaCuO_5 .

in this paper were taken from [5]. The different $REBaSrCu_3O_x$ compounds are isostructural with $YBa_2Cu_3O_7$ or similar to it [6]. For RE ≡ Ce and Tb, no Y-123 phase was formed. For RE ≡ Lu there was also no strong evidence for a Y-123 phase. The compounds with rare-earth elements with an ionic radius smaller than that of erbium, $r_{RE} \le r_{Er}$, contain the so-called green phase, RE_2BaCuO_5 , and $Ba(Sr)CuO_2$ as impurities. Samples with ionic radius $r_{RE} < r_{Dy}$ show orthorhombic structure, while those with $r_{RE} > r_{Dy}$ are tetragonal. At the phase boundary, i.e. with $DyBaSrCu_3O_x$, both the tetragonal and the orthorhombic phase were obtained, depending on the particular thermal treatment [7]. For single-phase $REBaSrCu_3O_x$ the oxygen content, determined by iodometric titration experiments, was between x ≃ 6.93 and 6.94. All of these compounds were found to be superconductors with transition temperature T_c between 54K and 86K, except of RE = Pr, which is semiconducting. Further details on this system have been reported previously [2, 7, 8]. When $YBa_2Cu_3O_7$ is heated to above 1000°C, it decomposes into Y_2BaCuO_5 and other phases [9]. In the Y-123 structure the RE^{3+} ion is coordinated by 8 oxygen ions, while in RE_2BaCuO_5 it is coordinated by only 7 oxygen ions [10]. Thus, 8-fold and 7-fold oxygen coordination of the RE^{3+} ions competes in these systems. The results shown in Fig.1, in particular the occurrence of the RE_2BaCuO_5 phase observed with $r_{RE} \le r_{Er}$, may be interpreted along these lines. For the smallest rare-earth ion, Lu^{3+}, 8-fold coordination becomes impossible with the preparation conditions employed. Partial substitution of Ba by Sr results in a shrinkage of the cell volume. In addition, it favors the formation of RE_2BaCuO_5 , in particular for the compounds with the small radius of the RE^{3+} ion. It has been reported that in $YBa_{2-x}Sr_xCu_3O_7$ the substitution of

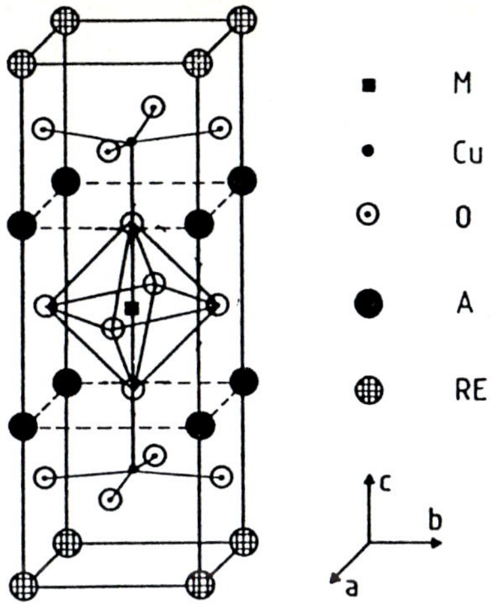

Fig. 2. Crystal structure of $MA_2RECu_2O_8$, M ≡ Nb or Ta, A ≡ Ba or Sr and RE ≡ rare earth.

Ba by Sr is possible only up to about 50 % by standard solid-state reactions [11]. This cannot be understood from simple geometrical considerations. It may be related to the deformation of the Y-123 structure with respect to the normal perovskite structure. The Ba ion is moved out of the oxygen plane, and the Cu-O_2 planes are buckled [6]. It has been demonstrated that pulsed-laser deposition permits to fabricate both single phase $LuBaSrCu_3O_7$ and $YBa_{2-x}Sr_xCu_3O_7$ with Sr-content up to x = 1.8 in the form of thin films [12, 13]. These results prove that it is possible to stabilize $RESr_2Cu_3O_7$ at room temperature by special preparation methods. A mixed valence of Pr has already been discussed for $PrBa_2Cu_3O_7$ [14]. The deviation in the data shown in Fig.1 for the case of Pr are tentatively ascribed to the presence of both Pr^{3+} and Pr^{4+} ions. We denote also that the ionic radius of Sr^{2+}(r_{Sr} ≅ 1.26 Å) is smaller than that of Ba^{2+}(r_{Ba} ≅ 1.42 Å) and it is thus closer to the ionic radius of the RE^{3+} ions. Sr has an electronegativity closer to that of RE ions as well. These circumstances may cause site mixing between Sr^{2+} and lager RE^{3+} ions, as already reported in [2]. This has still to be clarified .

The $MSr_2RECu_2O_{8-y}$ and $NbBa_2PrCu_2O_{8-y}$ compounds investigated are single phase. The oxygen content for $MSr_2SmCu_2O_{8-y}$ and $NbBa_2PrCu_2O_{8-y}$ as estimated from the TG analysis is about y ≃ 0.05. These compounds turn out to have the same crystal structure as $TaBa_2LaCu_2O_8$ reported in [15, 16]. This structure is quite similar to that of Y-123 (Fig.2). The Sr or Ba ions occupy Ba site and the unit cell has a tripled c-axis with respect to the perovskite lattice. The M-ions with 6-fold oxygen coordination occupy Cu(1) sites. Thus, the CuO2-RE-CuO2 layers are retained. The detailed structural investigation by XRD will be reported in [3]. Fabrication of single-phase $MBa_2RECu_2O_{8-y}$, except for $NbBa_2PrCu_2O_8$, was not successful. The XRD spectra revealed a mixed phase consisting of Ba_2REMO_6 and CuO. The situation is similar to that reported for $NbBa_2NdCu_2O_8$ (17). The room temperature resistivities of the different compounds are given in Table 1.

Table 1
Structural parameters and resistivities for $MA_2RECu_2O_{8-y}$ at room temperature

Compound	a(Å)	c (Å)	ρ(Ωcm)
$NbSr_2SmCu_2O_{8-x}$	3.877(1)	11.636(1)	0.98
$TaSr_2SmCu_2O_{8-x}$	3.872(1)	11.676(3)	4.79
$NbSr_2PrCu_2O_{8-x}$	3.892(1)	11.681(2)	0.67
$TaSr_2PrCu_2O_{8-x}$	3.890(2)	11.713(5)	0.77
$NbBa_2PrCu_2O_{8-x}$	3.950(2)	11.947(4)	544

All of these compounds show a semiconducting behavior from room temperature down to 10K. Preliminary results from Hall effect measurements for $MSr_2RECu_2O_{8-y}$ give a positive hall coefficient which indicates that the materials are hole conductors. Thus the charge carriers seems to locate in the double CuO2 layers.

In summary, we have shown that the $REBaSrCu_3O_X$ compounds show a structural phase transition from tetragonal to orthorhombic when the radius of the rare-earth ion decreases. These compounds were found to be superconductors with T_c between 54K and 86K, except of RE = Pr, which is semiconductor. The $MSr_2RECu_2O_{8-y}$ and $NbBa_2PrCu_2O_{8-y}$ compounds investigated are non-superconductors from room temperature to 10K.

Acknowledgements: We wish to thank the "Forschungsförderungsfonds für die Gewerbliche Wirtschaft in Österreich" for financial support.

References

[1] R.J. Cava, Science 247, 656(1990).
[2] X.Z. Wang and D. Bäuerle, Physica C 176, 507(1991).
[3] B. Hellebrand, X.Z. Wang and D. Bäuerle, to be published
[4] L.J. van der Pauw, Philips Res.Rep. 13, 1(1958).
[5] R.D. Shannon, Acta. Cryst. A32, 751(1976).
[6] J.D. Jorgensen, B.W. Veal, W.K. Kwok, G.W. Crabtree, A. Umezawa, L.J. Nowicki, and A.P. Paulikas, Phys. Rev. B 36, 5731(1987).
[7] X.Z. Wang, P.L. Steger, M. Reissener, and W. Steiner, to be published in Physica C, 1992.
[8] X.Z. Wang, B. Hellebrand, and D. Bäuerle, to be published
[9] K. Oka, K. Nakane, M. Ito, M. Saito and H. Unoki J. J. of Appl. Phys. 27, L1065(1988).
[10] C. Michel and B. Raveau, J. of Sol. State Chem. 43, 73(1982).
[11] A. Ono, T. Tanaka, H. Nozaki and Y. Ishizawa, J. J. of Appl. Phys. 26, L1687(1987).
[12] P. Schwab, X.Z. Wang, and D. Bäuerle, to be published in Appl. Phys. Lett., (1992).

[13] P. Schwab, X.Z. Wang, and D. Bäuerle, to be published
[14] L. Soderholm and G.L. Goodman, J. of Sol. State Chem. 81, 121(1989).
[15] N. Murayama, E. Sudo, K. Kani, A. Tsuzuki, S. Kawakami, M. Awano, and Y. Torii, J. J. Appl. Phys. 27, L1623(1988).
[16] C. Greaves and P.R. Slater, Physica C 161, 245(1989).
[17] C. Greaves and P.R. Slater, IEEE Trans. Magnetics 27, 1174(1991).

Superconducting Mixed-Metal Oxide Compounds of the Type $Sr_2Ln_{1.5}Ce_{0.5}MCu_2O_{10-\delta}$, Ln = Sm, Eu, M = Nb, Ta

N. Brnicevic[1], *I. Basic*[1], *P. Planinic*[1], *M. Paljovic*[1], *M. Pozek*[1], *B. Ravkin*[1], *A. Dulcic*[1], *U. Desnica*[1], *D. Desnica*[1], *M. Reissner*[2], *W. Steiner*[2], *M. Forsthuber*[3], *G. Hilscher*[3], *and H. Kirchmayr*[3]

[1]Rudjer Boscovic Institute, Bijenicka 54, 41000 Zagreb, Croatia
[2]Institut für Angewandte und Technische Physik, TU Wien, A-1040 Wien, Austria
[3]Institut für Experimentalphysik, TU Wien, A-1040 Wien, Austria

Abstract. - A simple method is developed for the preparation of good quality superconducting samples of the composition $Sr_2(Ln,Ce)_2MCu_2O_{10-\delta}$, Ln = Sm, Eu; M = Nb, Ta. Structural, microwave absorption, magnetic and superconducting properties are reported.

1. Introduction

During the course of our investigations concerning the superconducting properties in the Sr-(Ln,Ce)-Ta-Cu-O systems, the preparation procedure and crystal structure of the compound $Sr_2Nd_{1.5}Ce_{0.5}TaCu_2O_{10-\delta}$ has been reported [1]. The structure was related to that of the Tl-1222 phase consisting of TaO_6 octahedra sharing two apical oxygen atoms with apices of (CuO_5) pyramidal planes. Very recently the procedure for the preparation of bulk superconductivity samples was discovered for $Sr_2Nd_{1.5}Ce_{0.5}NbCu_2O_{10-\delta}$ and for the Ta analog as well [2].

Here we report on the procedure for the preparation of the new isostructural series of the composition $Sr_2(Ln,Ce)_2MCu_2O_{10-\delta}$, Ln = Sm, Eu; M = Nb, Ta. Their structural and physical properties are compared with those of the $Sr_2Nd_{1.5}Ce_{0.5}NbCu_2O_{10-\delta}$ analog.

2. Materials and Methods

The samples were prepared from stoichiometric amounts of $SrCO_3$, Ln_2O_3, (previously fired at 800° C) and freshly dried CeO_2, Nb_2O_5 (Ta_2O_5) and CuO. Mixed powders were pelletized and heated to 1000° C with a rate of 200°C/hour. At this temperature the samples were left for 24 hours. After cooling and mechanical grinding the pellets were heated at 1100° C for 24 hours, slowly cooled (100°/h) to 800° C and left at this temperature for 6 hours. Subsequently the specimens were cooled to 630° C and kept in oxygen atmosphere for 10 hours before furnace cooling to room temperature.

Springer Series in Solid-State Sciences, Vol. 113 Electronic Properties of High-T_c Superconductors
Editors: H. Kuzmany, M. Mehring, J. Fink

The X-ray powder diffraction patterns were recorded with a Philips counter diffraction using Cu Kα radiation whereby the powdered samples contained Mo powder as an external standard. Modulated microwave absorption was detected using an ESR spectrometer. Magnetisation, DC- and AC-susceptibility measurements were performed with a vibrating sample magnetometer and an AC-susceptometer, respectively.

3. Results and Discussion

Different thermal treatments of the starting components were applied for the preparation of $Sr_2(Ln, Ce)_2MCu_2O_{10-\delta}$ superconducting samples. A minor fraction of superconducting phase was often formed but the superconducting samples related in their properties to the recently reported superconducting $Sr_2Nd_{1.5}Ce_{0.5}NbCu_2O_{10-\delta}$ were obtained only by the thermal treatments described above.

A typical X-ray powder diffraction pattern of $Sr_2Sm_{1.5}Ce_{0.5}TaCu_2O_{10-\delta}$ is presented in Fig. 1. The position of all diffraction lines is related to the bodycentered tetragonal phase found for $Sr_2Nd_{1.5}Ce_{0.5}TaCu_2O_{10-\delta}$ [1]. A minor fraction of impurity phase with the main diffraction line located at $2\Theta = 30.05°$ is due to the presence of $Sr_3TaO_{5.5}$ [3]. The unit cell parameters are: a = 3.873 Å , c = 28.831 Å and a = 3.868 Å, c = 28.828 Å for $Sr_2Sm_{1.5}Ce_{0.5}TaCu_2O_{10-\delta}$ and $Sr_2Eu_{1.5}Ce_{0.5}TaCu_2O_{10-\delta}$ respectively.

Superconductivity was indicated by the intensity of the field modulated microwave absorption which saturates at lower temperatures and attains

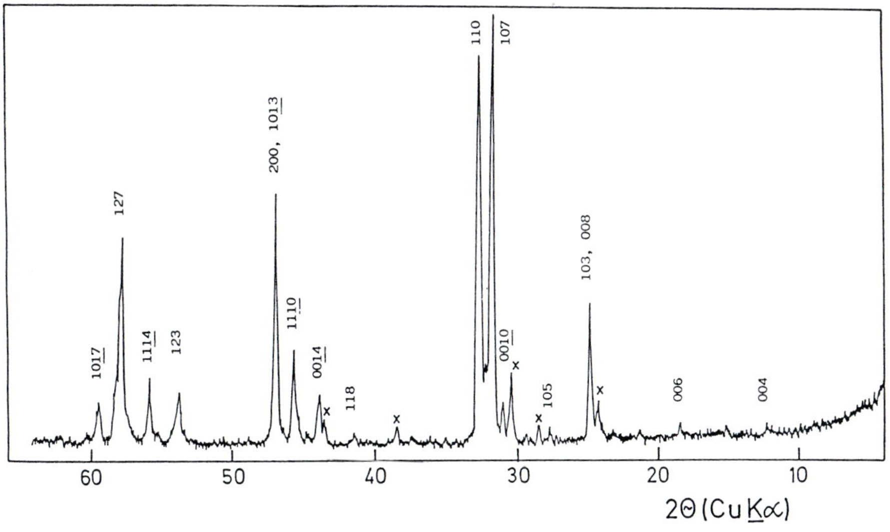

Fig.1: X-ray diffraction pattern of $Sr_2Sm_{1.5}Ce_{0.5}TaCu_2O_{10-\delta}$ at room temperature; reflections labeled with x correspond to the impurity phase.

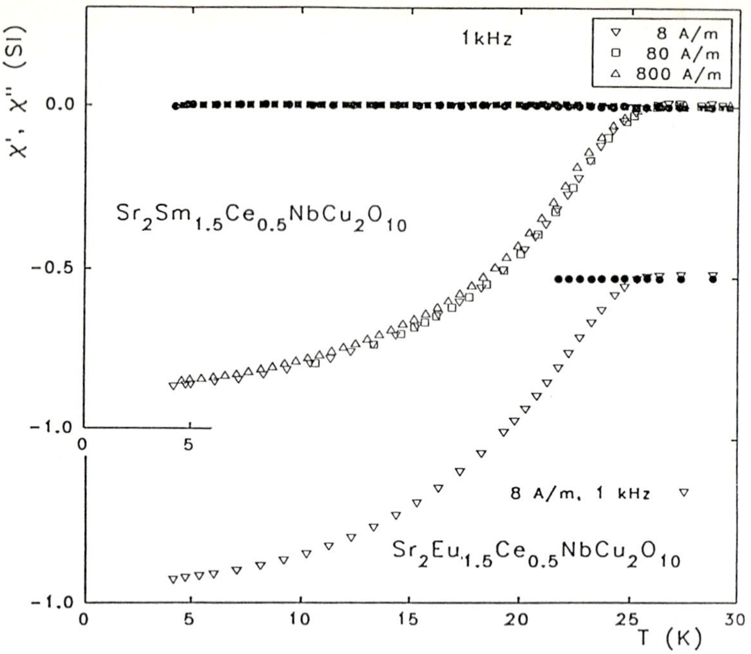

Fig.2: AC susceptibility of $Sr_2Ln_{1.5}Ce_{0.5}NbCu_2O_{10-\delta}$, Ln = Eu, Sm as a function of temperature; the signal is nor- malized to the maximal value at low temperatures.

values of the same order of magnitude as observed for other ceramic high-Tc materials. The signal shape, however, shows only a weak hysteresis at low fields which means that the coupling between the grains in these samples is rather weak.

From the AC susceptibility measurements, displayed in figs. 2 and 3, we estimate the superconducting fraction by comparing the density deduced from the normalised signal with an assumed density of $6g/cm^3$: For both the Ta and the Nb compounds the Eu samples systematically exhibit a larger superconducting fraction (17 - 25 %) than the Sm samples (7 - 14 %). This results are in good agreement with DC susceptibility measurements where no saturation of the diamagnetic shielding signal down to 4.2K was achieved in a measuring field of 0.16 mT. Furthermore the diamagnetic signal of the Ta compounds is approximately by a factor of two larger than those of the Nb-compounds. Within a series of Nb or Ta compounds the Eu-containing sample systematically exhibits a significantly larger diamagnetic signal than the corresponding Sm sample which is in accordance with the AC measurements. The superconducting shielding seems mainly to be caused by intragranular currents since the AC susceptibility shows hardly a dependence upon the AC field amplitude except for $Sr_2Sm_{1.5}Ce_{0.5}TaCu_2O_{10}$.

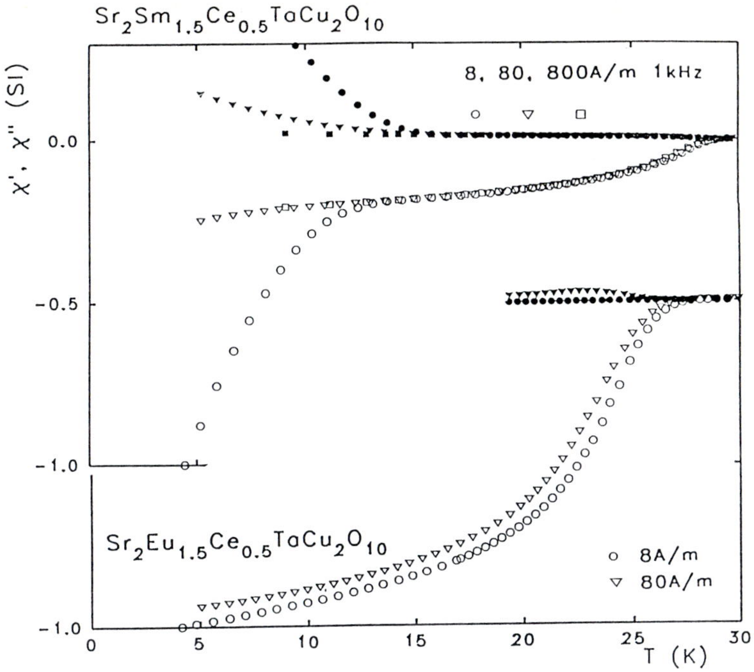

Fig.3: Normalized AC susceptibility as a function of temperature for $Sr_2Ln_{1.5}Ce_{0.5}TaCu_2O_{10-\delta}$, Ln = Eu, Sm.

This is also in accordance with resistivity measurements which show above Tc a weak semiconducting behaviour with resistivities up to 80 mΩcm at 30K indicating a rather poor connectivity between the superconducting grains. While for both Nb compounds the onset of superconductivity apears at 25K, the onset of the transition occurs for the Ta-based system at 27 and 28K for the Eu and Sm sample, respectively. AC hysteresis measurements at 1kHz and field amplitudes up to 1500 A/m (1.8 mT) indicate that the superconducting fraction is rather homogeneous and that H_{c1} of $Sr_2Eu_{1.5}Ce_{0.5}NbCu_2O_{10}$ at 5K is larger than the field amplitude used.

The hysteresis loops in DC fields up to 7T demonstrate that above 1T the magnetisation becomes reversible and minor loops on the other hand, point to very low H_{c1} values (fig. 4). For the Nb-containing series the width of the loops at comparable fields is larger for the Eu compound than for Sm. Exchanging Nb by Ta increases the width of the loops again. Presuming that the samples investigated exhibit similar grain size distributions, the larger width of the hysteresis is indicative for a larger critical current density. From the present state of the experiments we conclude that these new synthesized ceramic oxides are bulk superconductors and that among them the Ta containing compounds are more easily prepared than the analogous Nb compounds and exhibit the better superconducting properties .

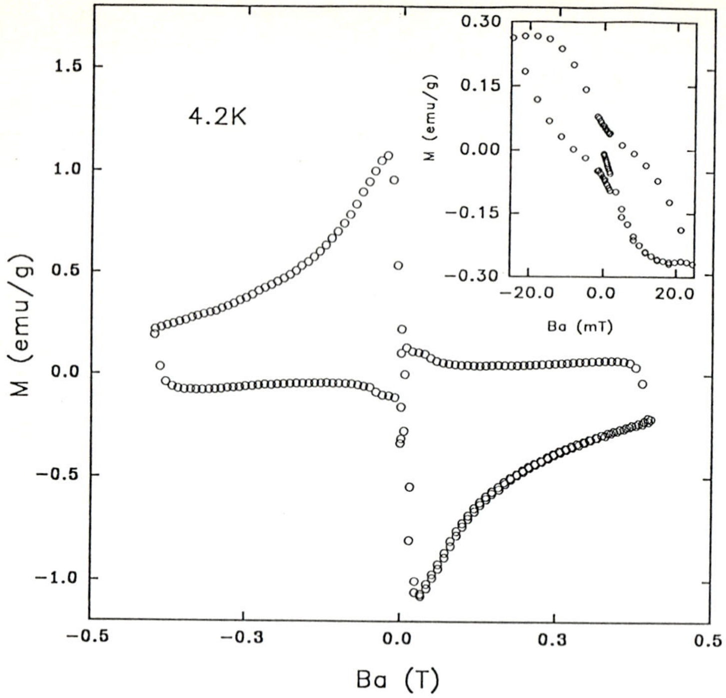

Fig.4: Field dependence of the magnetisation $Sr_2Eu_{1.5}Ce_{0.5}TaCu_2O_{10-\delta}$, at 4.2 K. Insert low field hysteresis loop.

Acknowledgement: This work was partly supported by the Ministry for Science, Technology and Informatics of the Republic of Croatia under project 1-07-166 and by the Austrian Science Foundation Fonds under project P-8173 and P8174.

References:

[1] L.Rukang, Z.Yingije and C. Zuyano, Physica C 176 (1991) 19

[2] R.J.Cava, J.J.Krajewski, H.Takagai, H.W.Zandbergen, R.B. van Dover, W.F.Peck and B.Hessen, preprint.

[3] L.H.Brixner, J. Am. Chem. Soc. 80 (1958) 3214

Part II

Applications, Film Preparation

High-T_c Superconductivity: Present Status of Applications

H. Rietschel[1], *R. Hott*[2], *and M. Sander*[2]

[1]Kernforschungszentrum Karlsruhe, Institut für Nukleare Festkörperphysik, W-7500 Karlsruhe, Fed. Rep. of Germany
[2]Gesellschaft für Angewandte Supraleitung, Postfach 36 40, W-7500 Karlsruhe 1, Fed. Rep. of Germany

Abstract: This lecture reviews the present status of applications of high-T_c superconductivity (HTSC). Rather than discussing selected topics in detail, it is intended to give an overview over a wide spectrum of applications in such various fields as microwave applications, electronics, infrared detection, energy technology and magnetic sensors (SQUIDs).

1. HTSC Families: Characteristics and Preparation

Virtually all applications of high-T_c cuprate superconductors are restricted to cuprates with superconducting transition temperatures $T_c >$ 77 K, thus allowing the maintenance of superconductivity by cooling with liquid nitrogen. These materials may roughly be grouped into four families. The most prominent members of these families are listed in the table, together with their short-hand notations and the maximum T_c reached up to the present time [1]

With respect to applications, the most important (and detrimental) characteristics of these compounds are the high anisotropy of the critical current density, J_c, and the very short coherence length, ξ, $2A < \xi < 20A$. In polycrystalline samples, this leads to weak-link behaviour at the grain boundaries, with J_c strongly reduced in comparison to its intragrain value ("granularity"). This is the actual reason that in ceramic samples, J_c (77 K, OT) is always found to be below ~ 1000 A/cm^2 , and in magnetic fields, is reduced even further. Thus for most applications, ceramic (or "granular") HTSCs are completely useless.

At present, two strategies are pursued to reach higher J_c values in cuprate superconductors:

i) preparation of epitaxial films and
ii) preparation of highly textured bulk samples.

Both methods aim at a reduction in the number of grain boundaries by single-crystallinity and at the alignment of the CuO_2 -planes in the most favourable direction, i.e., parallel to the transport currents.

Epitaxial films are grown on single-crystalline substrates like $SrTiO_3$, $LaAlO_3$ or Al_2O_3 with matching cuts. Currently, the growth and processing procedures for YBCO-films are the furthest advanced. Various techniques such as laser ablation, sputtering or MOCVD allow the repro-

Formula	Short hand	MaximumT_c
$REBa_2Cu_3O_7$ (RE="Rare Earth" = Y,Eu,Gd,...)	"RE BCO" or "123"	92 K (YBCO)
$Bi_2Sr_2Ca_{n-1}Cu_nO_{2n+4}$ (+ Pb doping)	"BSCCO" or "Bi-22(n-1)n"	90 K (Bi-2212) 122 K (Bi-2223) 90 K (Bi-2234)
$Tl_2Ba_2Ca_{n-1}Cu_nO_{2n+4}$	"TBCCO" or "Tl-22(n-1)n"	110 K (Tl-2212) 127 K (Tl-2223) 119 K (Tl-2234)
$Tl_1A_2Ca_{n-1}Cu_nO_{2n+3}$ (A=Sr,Ba)	"Tl-12(n-1)n"	90 K (Tl-1212) 122 K (Tl-1223) 122 K (Tl-1234) 110 K (Tl-1245)

ducible preparation of films with $T_c > 90$ K and J_c (77 K, OT) $> 10^6$ A/cm^2 [2]. Meanwhile, high-J_c films based on of Tl- and Bi-HTSCs have been prepared, but their J_c-values are much more sensitive to applied magnetic fields.

Texturing of HTSC bulk-samples, wires or tapes can be achieved by a number of methods: for example, crystallization from the melt in a temperature gradient or mechanical treatments like pressing and rolling. At the moment, the main progress in melt texturing has been achieved for YBCO bulk samples, while for future applications in conductors, tapes or wires containing textured Bi-2212 or Bi-2223 material seem to be particularly promising.

2. Applications of Films

Passive microwave devices (filters, delay lines) designed in stripline technology based on YBCO and Tl-2223 thin-films (d < 3000 A) will form the first HTSC applications [3]. As a result of their electronic energy gap, HTSCs exhibit much lower rf-losses than normal conductors, at least in the frequency range below about 100 GHz. Therefore, superconducting resonators - the basic component of these devices - can be made considerably smaller and lighter than their normal conducting counterparts for a given performance. Superconducting multipole filters in the 10 GHz range have already been put up for sale.

Similar arguments hold for small microwave antennas which are also composed of resonators. Miniaturized planar antennas manufactured from

HTSC thin-films show losses considerably reduced in comparison to normal conducting models of equal size [4]. This is particularly advantageous if highly directional antenna arrays are considered. Only recently, a group antenna consisting of 64 Tl-HTSC thin-film elements was successfully tested in the USA.

Not only the lower rf losses but also the lower dispersion of short pulses in superconducting striplines is an essential feature for certain applications, e.g., as the interconnects between semiconducting chips in ultra high-speed computers. In those cases where the computers are already cooled by liquid nitrogen, such a semiconductor-superconductor hybrid technology does not require additional cryogenics and is thus particularly straightforward. A USA research program has been initiated which aims at the development of such HTSC multi-chip modules.

HTSC thin-films can also form the basis of highly sensitive IR sensors. Making use of the steep R(T)-characteristic at the superconducting transition temperature, T_c , HTSC bolometers are the most sensitive IR detectors in the far infrared, where semiconductors with sufficiently small energy gap are not available. Work on integration of many of such pixels into position sensitive IR detectors has already been initiated [5].

Finally, let us briefly discuss HTSC thick-film applications ($d > 1$ μm). Lifting the requirement of epitaxy, much simpler preparation methods (e.g., electrophoresis, sol-gel, spreading of pastes) may be applied which lend themselves also to large or curved surfaces. Although with respect to critical currents and rf losses these polycrystalline thick-films are by far inferior to epitactic thin-films, they may still be used advantageously for coating rf devices, a good example being the HTSC-coated cavity for a hydrogen maser [6].

However, the main application of HTSC thick-films is magnetic shielding. Several Japanese companies have already developed shielding chambers based on the use of Bi-HTSC thick-films. A system consisting of a cylindrical chamber 40 cm long and 15 cm in diameter which attenuates magnetic background fields by a factor of 10^4 to 10^5 is already on the market.

3. Textured Current Leads and Bulk Samples

Regarding the development of HTSC current leads, present interest is focused on Bi-HTSC wires or tapes. Here, the Bi-2212 phase offers extraordinarily favourable conditions for its use in helium-cooled high-field magnet coils: with J_c (4.2 K, 25 T) = 140,000 A/cm^2, its criticial current-density in high magnetic fields surpasses that of any classical superconductor (e.g., NbTi or Nb_3Sn). For cooling under liquid nitrogen, on the other hand, the Bi-2223 phase is superior: with J_c (77 K, 0 T) ~ 50,000 A/cm^2, it is suitable for use in high current leads at low fields; in high fields, however, its J_c rapidly decreases [7].

To manufacture such wires or tapes, silver tubes filled with HTSC powder or silver tapes spread with HTSC pastes are subjected to consecutive steps of tempering, followed by pressing or rolling. The role of the silver is not yet clear: it is assumed that it not only supports the alignment of HTSC crystallites but also helps to avoid cracking as a result of its plasticity. By adding finely dispersed Ag powder to the precursor material, wires have been produced which can be stretched up to 2 % without irreversible degradation of J_c. In view of all this progress, industrial production and technical use of HTSC current leads may be expected in the near future.

Until now, all fabricated magnet coils based on HTSC materials have only been "demonstrators" and are without practical use. There is one major hurdle which must yet be overcome, and this is the phenomenon of flux creep. Even in low magnetic fields (e.g., self field of the transport current), thermally activated flux lines move under the Lorentz force of the transport current, thus leading to dissipation. Even in the Bi-HTSC tapes and wires described above, flux creep still remains a problem. This excludes operation of the magnet without external current source (persistent mode). Very recently it was discovered that in the Tl-1223 phase, magnetic flux can be pinned much more effectively than in the Bi-based HTSC so that flux creep sets in only above $B \sim 10$ T [9]. In fact, short Tl-1223 wires with J_c (77 K, 1,5 T) = 8000 A/cm^2 have already been produced by similar techniques as were developed for the Bi-HTSCs.

By means of a rather slow procedure which is commonly called "melt texturing" and which consists of a sequence of melting and cooling steps, highly textured plates or disks of YBCO can be produced with up to several hundred grams of weight. In these melt-textured YBCO samples, magnetic flux is pinned very efficiently, and high critical currents can be reached at high fields. Presently, typical values are J_c (77 K, 1 T) = 30000 A/cm^2 and J_c (77 K, 5 T) = 15000 A/cm^2. As a result of its time consuming nature, this process is hardly suited for making wires or tapes, but the melt-textured disks or plates do offer a very interesting potential application as magnetic bearings. If such a sample is cooled below T_c in the field of a permanent magnet, magnetic flux gets frozen in. Due to the strong flux pinning, any attempt to displace the magnet will result in a restoring force (present maximum: ~ 10 N/cm^2) which allows fabrication of stable passive magnetic bearings [9]. Heavy-duty bearings for high loads (up to 100 kg) as well as high-speed bearings reaching 500000 rpm have already been designed and realized based on melt-textured YBCO. One particularly interesting application of superconducting magnetic bearings could be their use with energy storing flywheels.

A further application of HTSCs in energy technology is their use in current limiters. In this case, a superconducting line is pushed by shock currents or shock fields into its highly resistive normal state thus limiting possible short circuit currents in the network. However, for more demanding applications in energy technology like superconducting transformers, generators or magnetic energy storage devices, HTSC materials are presently far from being worth discussing.

4. Josephson Contacts

A number of potential applications for superconductivity results from the Josephson effects which occur at two weakly coupled superconductors (the Josephson contact). The high sensitivity of the dc Josephson-current to magnetic fields is exploited in SQUIDs, which are presently by far the most sensitive detectors of magnetic fields. Designed in classical Nb-technology, SQUIDs are widely used in science and more recently even in medical diagnostics for both magnetoencephalography and cardiography. Besides SQUIDs, oscillators and mixers for ultrahigh frequencies are further devices where Nb Josephson-contacts are employed advantageously. For the ac Josephson effect, the realization of high-precision voltage standards is the most important application.

Various different methods have been developed to prepare Josephson contacts based on HTSC thin-films. These are reviewed elsewhere in these Proceedings together with special designs for HTSC SQUIDs and their properties such as sensitivity and noise figures. Summarizing these discussions one can state that now, HTSC SQUIDs already come close to commercially fabricated Nb SQUIDs in their performance. The progress achieved in this field is perhaps illustrated best by the on-chip integration of SQUID and flux transformer by CONDUCTUS [10]. Although not yet optimized in sensitivity and noise figure, with its 15 different HTSC and buffer layers this device represents the state-of-the-art of HTSC thin-film technology. Similar integrated SQUID chips in somewhat simpler design are already offered at low price for practical training of students.

SQUIDs may also be considered an intermediate step towards digital electronics based on Josephson contacts. There appears to be decreasing support for the concept of using hysteretic Josephson contacts as flip-flops in fast computers. This concept, which has been pushed ahead in the past, particularly by the Japanese, does not offer much faster clock speeds than advanced semiconductor technology. Much faster superconducting logical components may be expected from the various concepts based on rapidly moving single flux quanta ("RSFQ"), but these new and futuristic ideas have yet to be realized in classical Nb technology, let alone in HTSC! What can be expected in the near future, however, is the development of small scale integrated Josephson circuitry (e.g., fast AD-converters) to be used, for instance, as the read-out electronics of a SQUID located on the same cold chip [11].

5. Conclusions

Within a remarkably short time, HTSCs have reached a stage of development for which classical superconductors have needed a much longer period. Although some of the first dreams and hopes have turned out to be unrealizable, at least in the near future (this regards in particular energy technology), the already realized ideas such as SQUIDs, microwave components or magnetic bearings demonstrate that HTSCs will find wide applications in future technologies.

References

[1] K. Wasa et al., J. Mater. Res. **6** (1991) 1595

[2] J. Geerk et al., Mat. Sci Rep. 4, (1989) 193

[3] R.W. Ralston, Supercond. Sci. Technol. 4 (1991) 386

[4] H. Chaloupka et al., IEEE Trans. Microwave Theory Tech. **39** (1991) 1513

[5] S. Verghese et al., IEEE Trans. Magn. **27** (1991) 3077

[6] D. Opie et al., IEEE Trans. Magn. **27** (1991) 2944

[7] K. Sato et al., J. Appl. Phys. **70** (1991) 6484

[8] R.S. Liu et al., Appl. Phys. Lett. **60** (8) 24.2.1992

[9] M. Murakami et al., IEEE Trans. Magn. **27** (1991) 1479

[10] R. Simon, Physics Today, June 1991, 64

[11] K.K. Likharev et al., IEEE Trans. Appl. Supercond. 1 (1991) 3

Recent High-T_c-SQUID Developments

C. Heiden

Institut für Schicht- und Ionentechnik, Forschungszentrum Jülich GmbH, W-5170 Jülich, Fed. Rep. of Germany

Abstract. Progress in the preparation of epitaxial high-T_c perovskite films on suitable substrates, their patterning into microstructures, and recent progress in Josephson junction technology using grain boundary engineering resulted in SQUID magnetometers with attractive noise performance for operation at liquid nitrogen temperature. DC- as well as RF-SQUIDs using Josephson junctions made on artificial step edges in the substrate surface exhibit a rather low 1/f excess noise. Values well below $10^{-4}\ \Phi_0/Hz^{1/2}$ for the spectral flux noise at frequencies down to a fraction of 1 Hz, and of the order of several 10^{-30} J/Hz for the spectral energy resolution in the white noise region have been observed at 77 K. Using flux focussing, this leads to magnetometers with a field sensitivity of several 100 fT/$Hz^{1/2}$ that are sufficiently sensisitive for the detection of several human biomagnetic signals.

1. Introduction

Shortly after the discovery of cuprates that are superconducting in liquid nitrogen, successful attempts were made to demonstrate quantum interference effects [1] and the feasibility of high-T_c-SQUIDs [2-7]. The early SQUIDs were made of bulk samples, the SQUID-hole and the weak links being prepared by mechanical machining using drilling, sawing, and grinding. SQUIDs with adjustable weak links also were made, that could be operated over a wide temperature range from 4.2 K up to over 100 K [8]. All these SQUIDs usually being of the rf-type had in common a rather pronounced low frequency excess noise. Equivalent spectral flux noise densities of the order of 10^{-5} - $10^{-4}\ \Phi_0^2$/Hz at a signal frequency of 1 Hz were typical for such devices at an operating temperature of 77 K. A possible reason for this effect lies in the polycrystalline nature of the weak links that provides many possibilities for the supercurrent to choose a percolative path, the switching from one path to another giving rise to the observed excess noise. A natural alternative to improve the noise performance of high-T_c SQUIDs therefore was to create thin film devices with a locally well defined weak link structure. Epitaxial film growth on suitable substrates [9,10] as well as the developement of appropriate micro-patterning methods were necessary steps towards improved SQUIDs.

2. Grain boundary engineering

Up to now, grain boundaries are the most widely used kind of weak links, whose current-voltage-characteristics exhibit a Josephson type behavior. In order to avoid percolation, it is necessary to create at will individual grain boundaries at predetermined locations. Three different ways to achieve this have been developed recently: A) the bicrystal method [11], B) the biepitaxial method [12], and C) the step edge method [13,14]. In method A), the film is deposited epitaxially on a substrate that is made by fusing together two single crystals thus forming a bicrystal. A grain boundary thus is formed also in the epitaxial cuprate film just at the location of the grain boundary in the substrate. DC-SQUIDs made of such films by an appropriate patterning procedure [11] led to a significant improvement in noise performance. In method B) a template (seed film) first is deposited covering part of the substrate. This template film grows with an orientation that is rotated with regard to the orientation of the substrate (at present usually rotated by 45°). A high-T_c cuprate film then grows epitaxially with different orientations on the template and on the substrate thus forming a grain boundary at the borderline of the template. This technique has been used to make DC-SQUIDs in a multilayer structure with integrated coupling coils [15]. Finally, by depositing a $YBa_2Cu_3O_{7-x}$-film on a substrate with a step in its surface, two grain boundaries can be formed just at the edges of the step (fig. 1). SQUIDs having grain boundaries as weak links made with this technique will be dealt with in some more detail in the following, because the highest field sensitivity so far has been achieved with such devices at signal frequencies that are important for applications in the biomedical field.

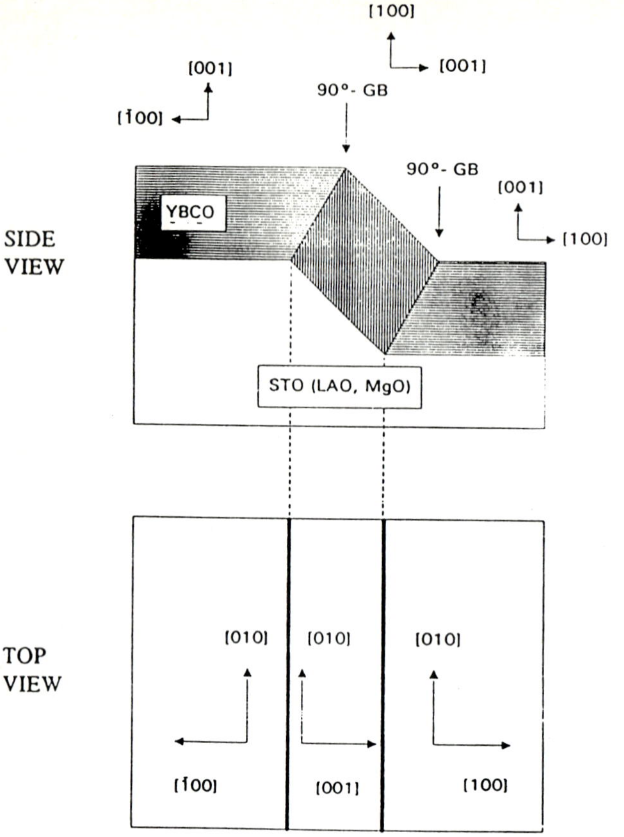

Fig. 1: Step edge junction with two 90° grain boundaries in the YbCo-film.

3. Fabrication of step edge junctions

Fig. 2 shows a method used to create step edge junctions [16]. First a metal mask (Nb) is prepared on top of the substrate. Using Ar^+-ion milling, the step in the substrate then can be eroded, after which the metal mask is removed by reactive ion etching. A high temperature anneal in oxygen atmosphere follows in order to repair to a certain extent the surface damage caused by the ion bombardment. The following epitaxial deposition of the high-T_c film usually is done by laser ablation, the film thickness being of the order of the step height. In the final procedure, lateral patterning is accomplished using low energy (500 eV) Ar^+-ion milling. The resulting width of the junction is of the order of a few microns. After the ion milling, the remaining photoresist can be left on top of the film and the junction as a protective coating.

It was found that such junctions exhibit RSJ-like behavior. High resolution micrographs show a difference in the fine structure of the two grain boundaries at the step [17]. It is now established that the critical currents I_{c1} and I_{c2} of the two grain boundaries usually differ significantly i.e. $I_{c1} << I_{c2}$.

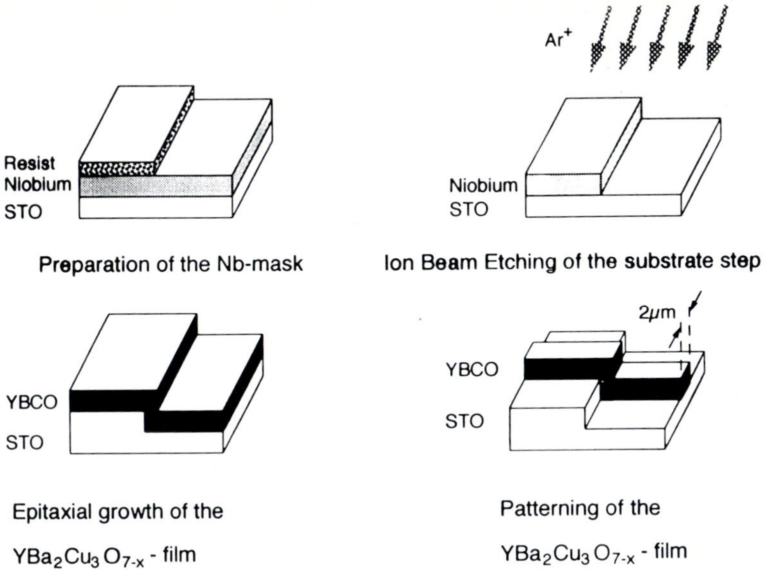

Fig. 2: Preparation steps for step edge junctions.

4. SQUIDs with step edge junctions

4.1 RF-SQUID

A washer type structure (fig. 3) was used for the planar RF-SQUID, the details of fabrication being given in Ref. [18]. The hole of the washer ranged between 100x100μm^2 and 300x300μm^2 corresponding to a geometrical SQUID inductance L_s between 120 pH and 400 pH. In order to have a well localized weak link structure in the superconducting ring produced by the hole, two step edge junctions were created in close vicinity to each other using a few μm wide trench in the substrate near the rim of the hole. The width of these step edge junctions usually was 2.0-2.5 μm. The outer dimensions of the washer varied between 1,4x1,4 mm^2 and 8x8mm^2. The epitaxial $YBa_2Cu_3O_{7-x}$-films were pulsed-laser deposited on 10x10mm^2 (100) $SrTiO_3$ substrates.

The SQUIDs were driven by lumped tank circuits. Matching to the 50 Ohm transmission line to the room temperature electronics was achieved by means of a capacitive tap. Fig. 4 shows noise data, measured in flux-locked-loop operation of the SQUIDs. One spectrum is measured at a tank circuit frequency of 20 MHz whereas the other noise spectrum was obtained at a resonance frequency of the tank circuit of 160 MHz. As predicted by theory [19], the SQUID noise is reduced significantly when using the higher frequency. This is not only true for the white noise, but also for the low frequency excess noise that becomes visible only well below 1 Hz.

Due to the flux focussing effect of the washer geometry, the field sensitivity can assume attractive values below 1 pT/Hz$^{1/2}$. In fig. 5, the spectral flux noise is given for different SQUID with L_s-values between 25 pH and 380 pH. Also the spectral field sensitivity for the 190 pH SQUID is shown with a white noise value of 170 fT/Hz$^{1/2}$, and the low frequency excess noise starting at about 1 Hz.

4.2 Microwave biased Rf-SQUID

Further reduction of RF-SQUID noise can be expected by raising the bias frequency to even higher values. This has been demonstrated by planar microwave biased SQUIDs made of niobium film [20]. Instead of a tank circuit consisting of lumped elements, a micro strip line resonator can be used, and the SQUID ring can be integrated into the resonator to achieve adequate coupling. Fig. 6 shows such a structure designed

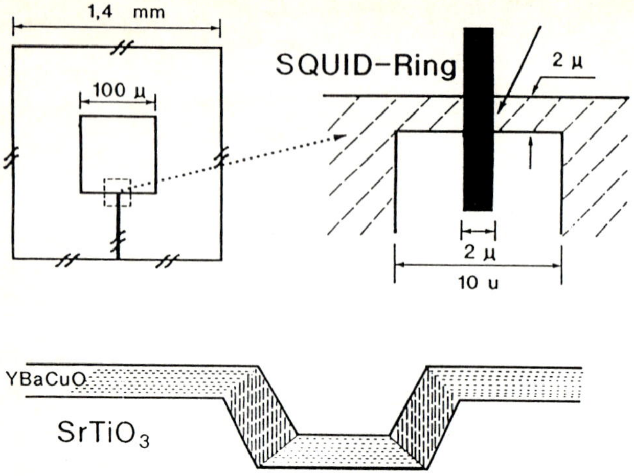

Fig. 3: Washer type rf-SQUID using a double step edge junction as weak link. Outer dimensions of up to 8x8 mm^2 for the flux focussing washer have been used for the most sensitive SQUIDs.

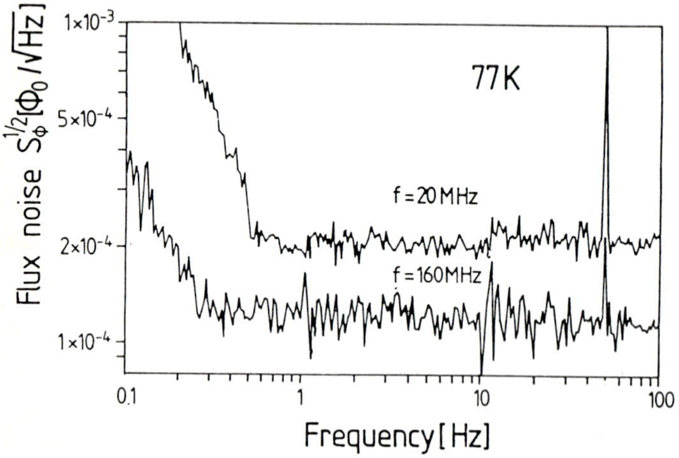

Fig. 4: Spectral flux noise of a washer type rf-SQUID operated at 77 K with two different tank circuit frequencies, 20 MHz and 160 MHz.

for an operating frequency near 3 GHz. It is made of epitaxial $YBa_2Cu_3O_{7-x}$-film deposited on a 0.5 mm $LaAlO_3$ substrate on top of a copper ground plane. The resonator is capacitively coupled to a 50 Ohm coaxial cable leading to the room temperature electronics. The coupling could be varied in order to obtain the highest signal output from the SQUID.

In fig. 7, the white flux noise $(7\pm1)\times10^{-5}\ \phi_0/Hz^{1/2}$ is shown for the best device, made so far [21]. The low frequency excess noise level of this device, with crossover to the white noise level well below 0.1 Hz, is probably the lowest ever recorded at 77 K for a high-T_c RF-SQUID. However the white noise level is still comparable to that for the 160 MHz washer type SQUIDs of similar inductance L_s. This result was traced down to the transfer function $dV/d\phi$, whose value at 77 K was by an order of magnitude lower than expected. It is hoped that this situation can be improved in the near future, such that a white flux noise in the lower $10^{-5}\ \phi_0/Hz^{1/2}$ range, or even smaller, will be achieved.

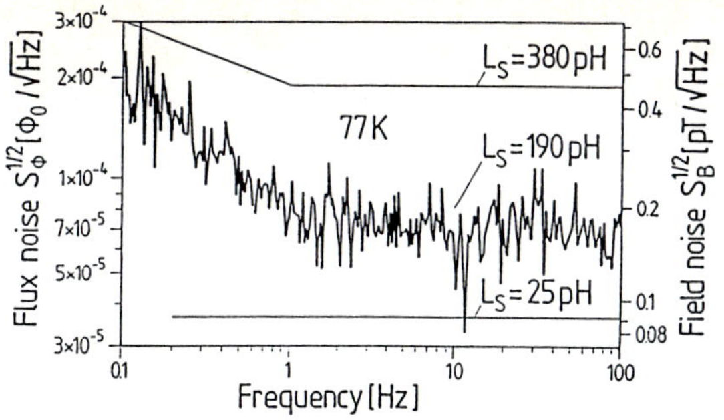

Fig. 5: Spectral flux noise and field sensitivity of a washer type rf-SQUID with a 150x150 μm^2 hole which corresponds to an inductance of 190 pH. The outer dimensions are 8x8 mm^2. Also indicated are the spectral flux values (not the spectral field sensitivity!) for SQUIDs with an inductance of 380 pH and 25 pH. The data are taken at a tank circuit frequency of 160 MHz.

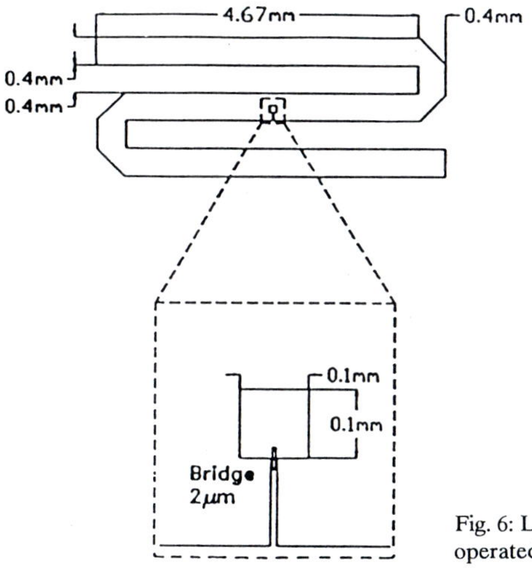

Fig. 6: Lay-out of a planar integrated microwave-SQUID operated at a frequency near 3 GHz.

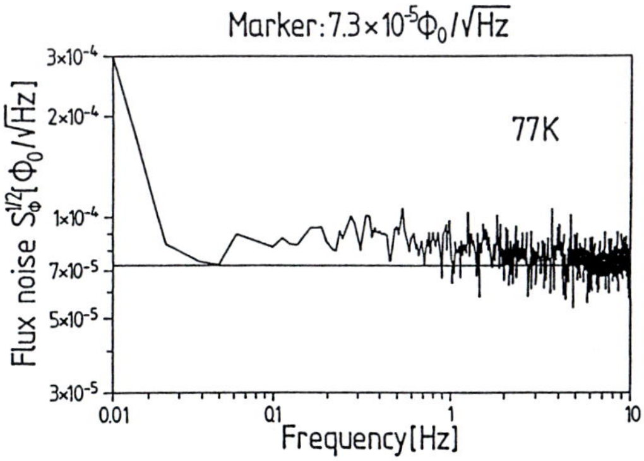

Fig. 7: Spectral flux noise of a YBCO thin film microwave-SQUID whose lay-out is given in fig. 6. The weak link is a double step edge junction as shown in fig. 3.

4.3 DC-SQUIDs

DC-SQUIDs employing step edge junctions also were made recently. Record low values near $6x10^{-6}$ $\Phi_o/Hz^{1/2}$ have been reported for the white flux noise [22] with a crossover to low frequency excess noise of the order of 1 Hz. With an inductance of the device (5x5 μm^2 hole) of 20 pH this corresponds to a spectral energy resolution of the order of $4x10^{-30}$ J/Hz. This is the lowest value demonstrated so far for dc-SQUIDs with step edge junctions at 77 K for low signal frequencies. Due to the small hole area, the field sensitivity is less than that of the aforementioned washer type rf-SQUID, despite its better flux sensitivity.

5. Magnetometers

In order to create magnetometers with high field sensitivity a good field to flux conversion is needed; A simple method to achieve this is to use flux focussing as has been demonstrated with the washer type SQUIDs. Flux concentration ratios of the order of 100 easily can be achieved using this method [23]. This may already be sufficient to register stronger biomagnetic signals like that of the human heart. Fig. 8 shows a human heart signal recorded with diagnostically relevant detail over a band width of 30 Hz. In fig. 8a the signal is recorded in normal laboratory environment using an electronically compensated gradiometer consisting of two washer type SQUIDs. Fig. 8b shows the magnetocardiogram from the same male person recorded one day later in a magnetically shielded room using the 380 pH RF-SQUID of fig. 5.

In principle, higher flux concentration ratios can be achieved using flux transformers with superconducting coils. These flux transformers have to be well designed in order not to deteriorate the overall noise performance. The combination of thin film low noise high-T_c SQUIDs with low noise high-T_c flux transformers undoubtedly will lead to magnetometers, that at 77 K have a field sensitivity coming within one order of magnitude close to that of conventional helium cooled magnetometers. Magnetoencephalography therefore should be feasible with high-T_c SQUID magnetometers. Acoustically stimulated brain signals recently could be made visible with a washer type rf-SQUID at 77 K (fig 9) using signal averaging over 80 individual recordings.

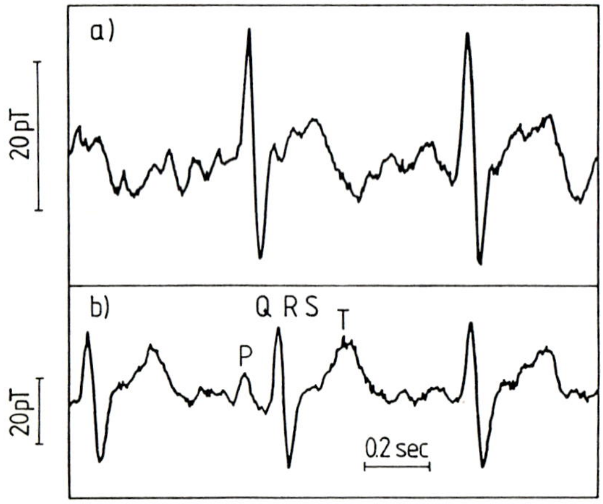

Fig. 8: Real-time magnetic signal of one male subject's heart recorded a) using a first order rf-SQUID gradiometer in normal laboratory environment without any magnetic shielding, b) using one channel of the gradiometer inside a magnetically shielded room (measurement done one day later at the Institute of experimental Audiology of the University of Münster, Germany

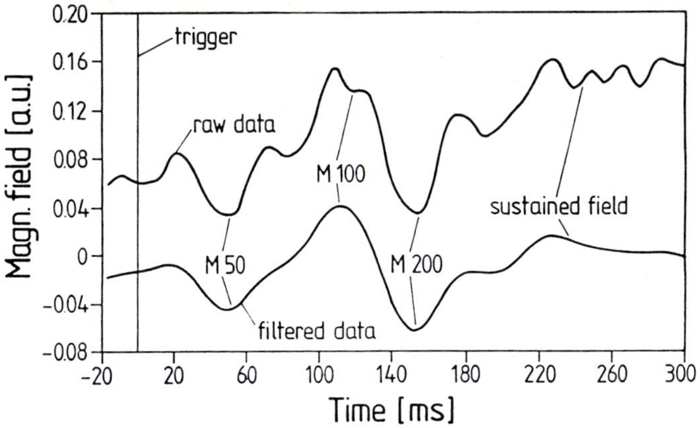

Fig. 9: Averaged signal (x80) of acoustically evoked brain signal. Upper trace: raw data, lower trace: filtered data.

6. Conclusion

The noise performance obtained with SQUIDs using step edge junctions justifies expectations, that SQUID-magnetometers operated at liquid nitrogen temperatures soon - if not for the most demanding applications - can replace those made of conventional superconductors which need liquid helium for cooling. This does not mean however that step edge junctions, or, more general, by grain boundaries, will be the final answer to the quest for low noise high-T_c Josephson junctions. Also the issue of reproducibility with narrow tolerances for instance may favor a different type of junction, e.g. those of the SNS-type (see [24]).

Acknowledgements

Results quoted in this report that were obtained at the research center Jülich are mainly due to the invaluable work and enthusiasm of the following colleagues: A.I. Braginski, K. Herrmann, C.L. Jia, B. Kabius, M. Mueck, M. Siegel, J. Schubert, K. Urban, W. Zander, and Y. Zhang. Part of the work has been supported by the German Minister of Science and Technology (BMFT) within the Consortium "First Applications of HTS in Micro- and Cryoelectronics". This support is gratefully acknowledged.

5. References

[1] C.E. Gough et al., Nature **326**,855(1987)
[2] R.H. Koch et al., Appl. Phys. Lett., **51**, 200(1987)
[3] J.E. Zimmermann et al., Appl. Phys. Lett. **51**, 617(1987)
[4] M.S. Colclough et al., Nature **328**,47(1987)
[5] C.M. Pegrum et al., Appl.Phys.Lett. **51**,617(1987)
[6] N.V. Zavaritzki and V.N. Zavaritzki, Physica **C 153-155**,1405(1988)
[7] V.N Polushkin, B.V. Vasiliev, Mod. Phys. Lett. **B3**,1327(1989)
[8] Y. Zhang, Y. Xu, and C. Heiden, Appl. Phys. Lett., **56**,1579(1990)
[9] J. Geerk, G. Linker and O. Meyer, Mat. Sci. Rep. **4**,193(1989)
[10] B. Stritzker, et al., J.Less-Common Metals **164&165**,279(1990)
[11] R. Gross, et al., IEEE Trans. Magn. **MAG-27**, 3227(1991)

[12] K. Char et al., Appl. Phys. Lett. **58**, 2168(1991)
[13] K.P. Daly et al., Appl. Phys. Lett. **58**, 543(1991)
[14] C.L. Jia et al., Physica C **175**, 545(1991)
[15] L.P. Lee et al., Appl. Phys. Lett., **59**, 3051(1991)
[16] K. Herrmann et al., Supercond. Sci. and Techn., **4**, 583(1991)
[17] C.L. Jia et al., Physica **C 196**, 212(1992)
[18] Y. Zhang, et al., Appl. Phys. Lett. **60**, 645(1992)
[19] J. Kurkijärvi, J. Appl. Phys. **44**, 3729(1973)
[20] M. Mück and C. Heiden, ISEC `89, Extended Abstracts, Japan Society of Applied Physics, Tokyo, Japan, 199(1989)
[21] Y. Zhang et al., Appl. Phys. Lett., **60**, 2303(1992)
[22] G. Friedl, et al., Appl. Phys. Lett., to be published (June 1992), and unpublished data
[23] M.B. Ketchen et al., in "SQUID`85 - Superconducting Interference Devices and their Applications", H.D. Hahlbohm and H. Lübbig, eds., W. de Gruyter, Berlin, 865(1985)
[24] M.S. DiIorio et al., Appl. Phys. Lett. **58**, 2552(1991)

Epitaxial YBCO Films on MgO, $SrTiO_3$, Si, and GaAs by Thermal Coevaporation

H. Kinder[1], *F. Baudenbacher*[1], *P. Berberich*[1], *S. Corsepius*[1], *O. Eibl*[2], *H.J. Güntherodt*[3], *K. Hirata*[1], *H.P. Lang*[3], *W. Prusseit*[1], *and M. Zwerger*[1]

[1]Physik Department E 10, Technische Universität München, W-8046 Garching, Fed. Rep. of Germany
[2]Siemens Research Laboratories, W-8000 München, Fed. Rep. of Germany
[3]Institut für Physik, Universität Basel, CH-4056 Basel, Switzerland

Abstract. The technique of thermal coevaporation for the preparation of thin $YBa_2Cu_3O_7$ films yields excellent superconducting properties and, at the same time, very smooth surfaces. Scanning tunnelling microscopy (STM) reveals tiny growth spirals with extremely high density on MgO, and layer-by-layer growth on $SrTiO_3$. On $SrTiO_3$ we also observe very pronounced RHEED-oscillations. The relatively low substrate temperatures of 600 to 650°C for optimum epitaxial growth allow film preparation also on semiconductor substrates. On silicon with buffer layers of yttria stabilized zirconia (YSZ), we have grown epitaxial films with $T_c = 87..89K$, $j_c(77K) = 2.5 \cdot 10^6 A/cm^2$, $\rho(100K) = 40 \mu\Omega$, and a high degree of smoothness. Recently we have also succeeded to grow epitaxial films on GaAs with buffer layers of MgO, with $T_c = 86.8K$, $j_c(77K) = 7 \cdot 10^5 A/cm^2$, and $\rho(100K) = 100 \mu\Omega$ cm. These values are markedly better than those obtained with pulsed laser ablation by Fork, Nashimoto, and Geballe. Integrated superconducting and semiconducting devices have now come in sight.

1. Introduction

A prerequisite for basic science as well as for applications of high temperature superconductors (HTSC) is the materials science. Thin films of HTSC are used in basic research, e.g. in tunnelling experiments and for studies of flux pinning. Applications of thin film HTSC include SQUIDs, microelectronics, and microwave devices. The requirements for these purposes are: high critical temperature, high critical current density, and low microwave resistance. Most applications like tunnel junctions or multilayer packaging require surfaces as smooth as possible.

Furthermore, there is a strong need to grow such films not only on standard substrates like $SrTiO_3$, MgO, Al_2O_3, or $LaAlO_3$, but also on semiconductors. Substrates such as Si and GaAs allow "super-semi" technology, i.e. a true integration of superconducting and semiconducting circuits. In addition, semiconductors are simply high quality substrates which are available in large areas and at relatively low cost.

2. Thermal coevaporation technique

At present there are basically four different techniques for the preparation of HTSC films, namely pulsed laser ablation, sputtering, chemical vapour deposition, and reactive coevaporation. Among these, evaporation techniques require the least elevated substrate temperatures, around 600 to 650°C, whereas the other methods require 750 to 800°C. This is probably due to the higher surface mobility of the metal atoms as compared with the larger composites deposited by the other methods. A second advantage of the evaporation technique is that the composition can be easily varied in a controlled manner. This is essential for obtaining smooth films.

Among the various ways of evaporation by electron guns, Knudsen cells, or current heated metal boats we are employing the latter because it is insensitive to the oxygen background pressure, it is simple, stable, and cheap. Our system is described in more detail elsewhere [1] [2] We are controlling the evaporation rates by a cross-beam quadrupole mass spectrometer or, in another system, by quartz crystal monitors. Both methods work equally well with reproducibilities of the composition of a few percent. The sample is radiation heated inside a small oven which also serves as inlet of the molecular oxygen to obtain an enhanced pressure of $5 \cdot 10^{-3}$mbar near the sample surface. A hole in the bottom of the oven allows the metal vapours to enter. The chamber is equipped with a reflection high energy electron diffraction system to study the film growth in situ.[2]

An important issue is the absolute determination of the composition of the finished samples to calibrate the rate control. We use Rutherford backscattering spectroscopy (RBS) using ^{16}O ions.[3] The spectra of all three metals are then well separated and can be directly integrated without fitting. This yields an accuracy of about 1% for the content of each metal.

3. Smooth $YBa_2Cu_3O_7$ films

Since it is easy to vary the composition by varying the evaporation rates we have made a careful study relating the composition to the growth mechanism on MgO as observed by RHEED, to the resulting surface morphology observed by scanning electron microscopy (SEM), and to the superconducting properties.[3] It turned out that the surface morphology depends in a reproducible way on composition variations of a few percent only. In fact, looking at the surface by SEM we can fairly well predict the composition and we use this correlation for the optimization. Films whose composition deviates no more than 3% from ideal stoichiometry generally do not exhibit any outgrowth, and still have the best superconducting properties.

The smoothest film with no visible structure at SEM resolution was the ideally stoichiometric one within the 1% accuracy of the ^{16}O-RBS measurement. Therefore we looked on this film by STM.[4] The result is reproduced in Fig. 1. The large magnification in *z*-direction reveals a high density of fine growth spirals of an average height of only 4 unit cells or 5nm. In fact, this means that the film was extremely smooth. Growth spirals in $YBa_2Cu_3O_7$ films were first reported on by Gerber et al.[5] who speculated that the associated screw dislocations might act as strong pinning centers. The density in Fig. 1 is two orders of magnitude higher than that of Gerber et al. This would provide pinning centers for fields up to about 1 Tesla. $J_c(B)$ measurements are under way.

On MgO substrates we obtain always spirals, however small. In contrast, we observe on $SrTiO_3$ under suitable conditions layer-by layer growth. This is demonstrated in

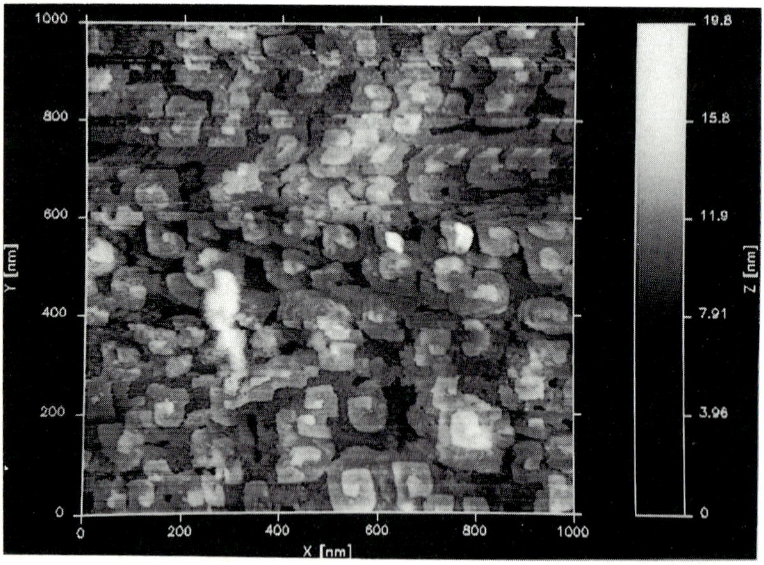

Fig. 1. STM image of a $YBa_2Cu_3O_7$ film with ideal stoichiometry on MgO

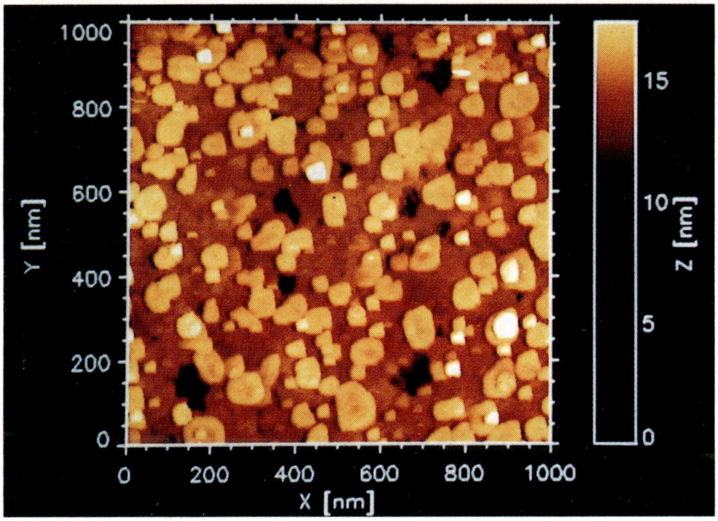

Fig. 2. Growth on $SrTiO_3$ substrate is layer-by-layer rather than in spirals.

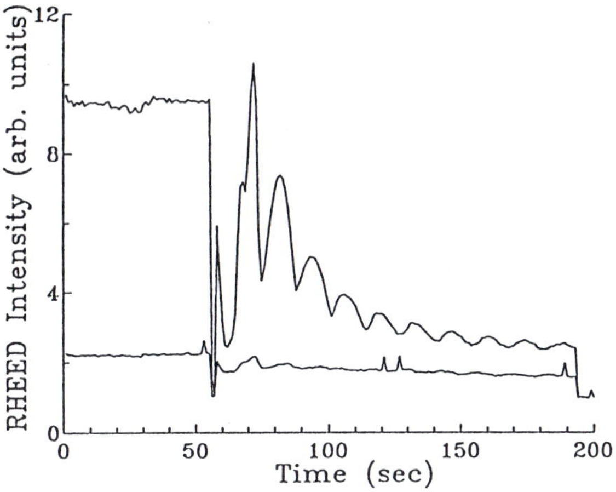

Fig. 3. RHEED-oscillations confirming layer-by layer-growth on $SrTiO_3$.

Fig. 2, again by an STM image. The islands on the dominant surface plane are one unit cell high. So this film is even smoother than that of Fig. 1. The layer-by layer growth is also nicely demonstrated by the appearance of RHEED oscillations. Fig. 3 shows the intensity of a specularly reflected 20KeV-electron beam *vs.* time during the deposition. On completion of a monolayer of unit cells the surface is smoothest, so that periodic maxima occur. Presently we study the surface morphology after a growth stop at a defined phase of the oscillation. On MgO the oscillations are hardly observable, consistent with the observed spiral growth. We conclude that the spirals are forming in the first monolayers already, probably due to the larger lattice misfit of the MgO.

4. Epitaxial $YBa_2Cu_3O_7$ films on semiconductor substrates

Early on we have evaporated YBCO directly onto bare silicon wafers[1]. These films had fairly high T_c's, and they were c-axis textured. However, they were not epitaxial in the a-b-plane and, hence, j_c was low. With buffer layers of YSZ, deposited by electron gun at 800°C, we were able to grow epitaxial films with $j_c = 2.5 \cdot 10^6 A/cm^2$ and very smooth surfaces, comparable to those on MgO.[6] A cross section of the layer sequence is shown in Fig. 4. Between the Si substrate and the YSZ layer, there is an additional layer of amorphous SiO_2. This must have formed after the epitaxy of the YSZ had been established. YSZ is a good ionic oxygen conductor at elevated temperatures, so that oxygen is highly mobile. In fact, we were able to reinforce this layer up to several 100nm by treating the YSZ-film with atomic oxygen. The SiO_2 can serve as a good insulator between the superconductor and a prospective semiconductor circuit underneath.

A difficulty of silicon as a substrate is its extremely low thermal contraction in view of the strong contraction of the YBCO. This leads to stresses which can be sustained only by films thinner than 70nm. Above this thickness we observe inevitably cracks and a degradation of j_c within a few days. Another disadvantage of the silicon is that it is not well suitable for microwave applications, were the YBCO would have its strongest potential of beeing applied. Therefore, we have also grown YBCO on gallium arsenide.

GaAs is mainly used for microwave applications, and it has also the advantage of a thermal contraction coefficient that is comparable to that of MgO or $SrTiO_3$. So cracks and degradation are not expected. On the other hand, it has the great difficulty of loosing arsenic at temperatures above 480°C. This means that YSZ or other oxides with high deposition temperatures could not be used as buffer layers.

Fork, Nashimoto, and Geballe were the first to prepare epitaxial YBCO films on GaAs with relatively good quality by using MgO buffer layers which can be prepared epitaxially at relatively low temperatures.[7] But for the YBCO deposition they still had to apply 700°C-somewhat too low for their technique of pulsed laser ablation, and somewhat too high in view of the arsenic problem. As a consequence, the electronic properties, $\rho(100K) = 500\ \Omega cm$ and $j_c = 1.5 \cdot 10^5 A/cm^2$ were not yet satisfactory.

We recently applied our technique to this problem and used only 620°C. Even then some arsenic evaporates from the free sample surfaces and is partly incorporated in the YBCO film where it has a negative effect on the electronic properties. The resistive transition of an epitaxial film of very good crystallinity is shown in Fig. 5,trace (a). By encasing the sample with the help of silicon wafers we were able to reduce the arsenic contamination considerably. This has resulted in trace(b) of Fig. 5, which now nicely extrapolates back to zero. The maximum T_c we have reached so far was 86.8K, and the maximum j_c was $7 \cdot 10^5 A/cm^2$. We are confident that we can optimize the process further to obtain the full performance of YBCO known from the standard substrates.

Fig. 4. TEM image of $YBa_2Cu_3O_7$on Si with YSZ/Y_2O_3 buffer

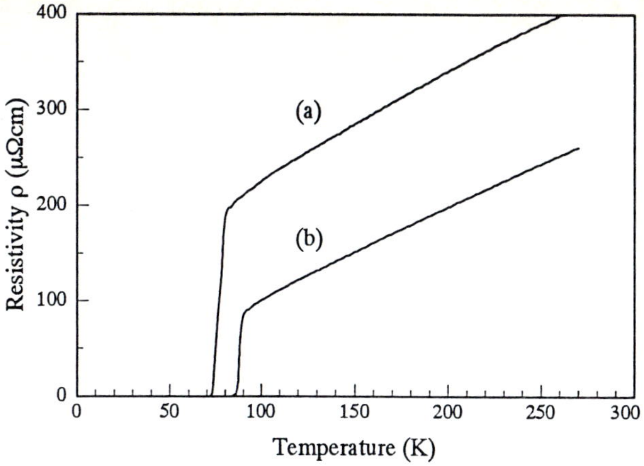

Fig. 5. Resistive transition of epitaxial YBCO on GaAs (a) without and (b)with encasing

5. Conclusion

Thermal co-evaporation of the metals in oxygen atmosphere has several advantages which make the technique well suited for the preparaion of thin films which are almost atomically smooth on $SrTiO_3$ and have high performance also on Si and GaAs substrates.
This work was supported by the Budesminister für Forschung und Technologie.

References

1. P. Berberich, J. Tate, W. Dietsche, and H. Kinder, Appl. Phys. Letters **53**, 925 (1988); J. Tate, P. Berberich, W. Dietsche, and H. Kinder, J. Less-Common Metals **151**, 311 (1989).
2. F. Baudenbacher, H. Karl, P. Berberich, and H. Kinder, J. Less-Common Met. **164 & 165**, 269 (1990); F. Baudenbacher, H. Karl, P. Berberich, and H. Kinder in: Science and Technology of Thin Film Superconductors 2, ed. by R. D. McConnell and R. Noufi (Plenum Press 1990), p. 351.
3. F. Baudenbacher, K. Hirata, P. Berberich, H. Kinder, and W. Assmann, in: High T_c Superconductor Thin Films, ed. by L. Correra (Elsevier 1992), p. 365.
4. F. Baudenbacher, K. Hirata, P. Berberich, H. Kinder, W. Assmann, and H.P. Lang, Physica **C 185-189**, 2177 (1991).
5. Ch. Gerber, D. Anselmetti, J.G. Bednorz, J. Mannhart, D.G. Schlom, Nature **350**, 279 (1991).
6. W. Prusseit, S. Corsepius, M. Zwerger, F. Baudenbacher, K. Hirata, P. Berberich, O. Eibl, and H. Kinder, to be publ.
7. D.K. Fork, K. Nashimoto, and T.H. Geballe, to be publ. in Appl. Phys. Letters.

Preparation and Patterning of (110) Oriented YBaCuO Thin Films

B. Elkin[2], *H.-U. Habermeier*[1], *B. Leibold*[1], *and D. Shen*[1]

[1]Max-Planck-Institut für Festkörperforschung, Heisenbergstr. 1, W-7000 Stuttgart 80, Fed. Rep. of Germany

[2]On leave from: A.F. Ioffe Physico-Technical Institute, Politekhnicheskaya 26, 194021 St. Petersburg, Russia

Abstract. Epitaxial YBaCuO films with (110) orientation (c-axis in plane) were made by laser deposition and magnetron sputtering and characterized by X-ray and optical methods. Problems associated with patterning of these films are discussed and solutions to these problems are presented. Measurements of transport properties along *c*-axis, and along *ab* planes, on the patterned films, showed a pronounced anisotropy.

1. Introduction

(110) oriented YBaCuO films are unique in the respect that the *c*-axis is macroscopically aligned along the substrate (001) axis in the film plane, while the *ab* plane is perpendicular to the film surface; the *a* and *b* axes are at 45° to the film surface (Fig. 1). These films, in contrast to more common "*c*-axis" (100) and "*a*-axis" ((010), (001)) films, possess a pronounced anisotropy, particularly in optical and electrical properties.

Two features of the (110) films make them a promising object for basic studies, as well as for future electronic applications - the aforementioned anisotropy, and the fact that the longer (in *ab*-planes) coherence length (ξ_{ab}=1.5 nm, while ξ_c=0.2 nm) is perpendicular to the film plane, which makes them attractive for various multilayer structures, e.g. for planar Josephson junctions. *A*-axis films, though also have the longer coherence length perpendicular to the film plane, consist of mixture of crystallites with *c*-axis orientated along the (010) and (001) axes of the substrate because of 90° symmetry of the substrate surface.

Many of the experiments to study *c*-axis vs. *ab*-plane anisotropy of YBaCuO films which can be done on the (110) films, are impossible or difficult to perform on single crystals, because of their small size, especially along the *c*-axis (typical single crystal thickness is 10 μm). First works to study the optical [1-3] and electrical [3] anisotropy on the (110) YBaCuO films have already been done. In [2], the changes in the optical anisotropy were used to monitor accumulation of the amorphous phase upon the film irradiation by energetic ions.

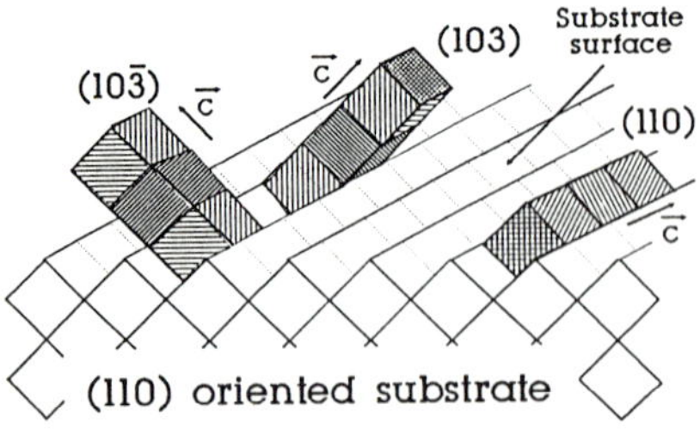

Fig. 1. Possible epitaxial orientations of YBaCuO on (110) oriented substrate.

Springer Series in Solid-State Sciences, Vol. 113 Electronic Properties of High-T_c Superconductors
Editors: H. Kuzmany, M. Mehring, J. Fink

Preparation and patterning of (110) films is associated with a number of problems. First, on the (110) substrates, (103) and $(10\bar{3})$ film epitaxy (Fig. 1) is possible, along with (110) one. Therefore, films consisting of crystallites of all three orientations are often obtained. Moreover, by the standard X-ray diffractometry it is difficult to distinguish between these orientations.

When standard photolithographic process, giving excellent results for *c*-axis films, was applied to the (110) films, tremendous degradation of the T_c occurred (this was observed also in [4] for (103) films). Also, we found that the patterned films tend to crack after thermocycling. In the present work, the ways to overcome these problems are presented.

2. Film preparation

To obtain (110) YBaCuO films, (110) oriented cubic or tetragonal (usually $SrTiO_3$) substrates are used. The films were obtained by pulsed laser deposition as well as DC magnetron sputtering. The temperature regime is crucial for the film quality. At low deposition temperature T_d, films with low T_c are obtained, while high T_d promotes (103) vs. (110) growth. The later is thought [3] to be due to the fact that at high temperature, the thermal expansion of YBaCuO along the *c*-axis is very high, and the misfit for the *c*-axis in-plane epitaxy (i.e. for (110) orientation) increases dramatically.

Pulsed laser deposition. The description of the experimental setup and the details of the process are given elsewhere [1, 5]. Eximer KrF laser (248 nm) is used, the deposition is performed in the O_2 atmosphere at 1 mbar. In our setup, the substrate lies on the bottom of homogeneously heated metallic cavity, so that the substrate temperature is really close to the cavity temperature as measured by a thermocouple (this was checked with a pyrometer). The deposition begins at $T_d \cong 660^{\circ}C$, and after deposition of about 50 nm YBaCuO the temperature is increased to $720^{\circ}C$ without interrupting the deposition. The low initial temperature is favorable for (110) epitaxy of YBaCuO on $SrTiO_3$, and then this crystalline orientation is retained at the higher T_d, resulting in a (110) film with a high T_c (zero resistance at 83 - 87 K).

Magnetron sputtering. Hollow cathode DC magnetron [3] as well as planar DC magnetron [2] were used. We [2] used on-axis substrate position, and a special designed magnet system. In the central area of the target, opposite to the substrate, there was no discharge - the discharge formed a narrow ring with inner diameter 40 mm. This is favorable for avoiding the resputtering effects. In both works, Ar/O_2 mixture was used at the total pressure of 0.4 mbar. Also, in the both works, the substrate was clamped to a heating block. We suppose, that absence of good thermal contact was crucial for obtaining (110) films. The heat transfer from the block to the substrate was mainly radiative. The growing film increases the absorption of the radiation, and the T_d rises during the process. So, the temperature regime is like the one used for laser ablated films. This supposition is supported by the fact that the thinner (120 nm) films we obtained displayed T_c below 78 K, while for 200 nm and thicker films the T_c (R=0) was 82 - 90 K.

Diagnostics. The standard tool to characterize film crystal orientation is X-ray θ-2θ scan. However, this technique does not discriminate between (110) and (103) orientations. In [3], the ϕ scan was used for this purpose.

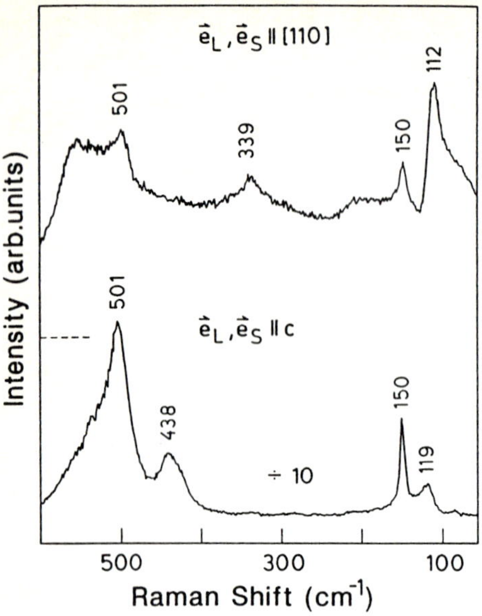

Fig. 2. Raman spectra of (110) YBaCuO film [1]. Lower spectrum: the incident and scattered light polarized along the *c*-axis; upper one: the polarization perpendicular to it. Note the scale factor applied to the lower spectrum.

A fast and informative technique for characterization of (110)/(103) oriented YBaCuO films is Raman scattering [1, 2]. On Fig. 2, Raman spectra for polarization of incident and scattered light parallel to *c*-axis (lower curve) and parallel to ab-plane (upper curve) are presented. The features proving the (110) orientation of the film are: anisotropy of the peak at 500 cm^{-1} (it changes by a factor of 30 upon 90° rotation of the sample), and the peak at 340 cm^{-1} can not be seen in the polarization parallel to the *c*-axis, and is weak for another polarization. In the spectra, only YBaCuO lines are present, and there are no indications of foreign phases (to which Raman scattering is very sensitive). The position of the apex-oxygen peak at 501 cm^{-1} suggests that the film is fully oxygenated.

Cross-sectional TEM analysis has also been employed to prove that the *ab* planes are perpendicular to the film surface [5].

3. Patterning

Patterning of (110) films proved to be much more difficult than that of usual *c*-axis ones. Dramatic decrease of the T_c occurred after the lithography. It was found, that the step, where the degradation happened, was the application of a photoresist. The tentative explanation is that in the (110) films the *ab*-planes, in which fast diffusion is known to occur, are opened towards the surface. Extraction of oxygen from the film due to interaction with the organic photoresist is therefore possible, or, alternatively, diffusion of some impurities into the film.

To overcome this problem, we tried different protective layers. Of them, BaF_2 layer gave good results. BaF_2 is known to be inert in respect to YBaCuO even at elevated temperatures. BaF_2 is soluble in the photoresist developer and thus removed together with the exposed resist, thereby making possible wet etch of YBaCuO. If necessary, the BaF_2 layer can be removed from the top of YBaCuO structure after stripping the photoresist by a short dip into a strong (15 wt.%) KOH solution.

For etching (110) YBaCuO films, citric acid solution (0.5 wt.%, 4°C, 2.5 min) gave reasonably good results. However, when thicker films were etched, some undercutting of the edges was observed. Moreover, the etch of thicker films was anisotropic, resulting in poorly defined edges. If better resolution was necessary, ion milling was successfully applied (500V, 0.2 mA/cm^2, 5 min etch / 10 min pause cycle).

An alternative, "chemical free" process was developed, to obtain patterned film *in situ*. First, an amorphous Si layer (150 nm) was deposited onto the $SrTiO_3$ substrate by e-beam evaporation. The silicon was patterned by the wet etching (4 wt.% $Cu(NO_3)_2$ + 25 wt.% NH_4F , 38°C, 1.5 - 3 min.). After that, YBaCuO film was deposited by the laser ablation. On the spots free from silicon, an epitaxially grown superconducting film was obtained; in the other places, YBaCuO reacted with the silicon to form an insulator. The lateral resolution of this technique is at least several μm (Fig. 3). If the deposition is performed at the low 670/730°C temperature, an additional anneal *in situ* (750°C, 1 hour, 1 mbar O_2) is needed for completing the reaction between Si and YBaCuO to obtain a perfect insulation.

Another serious problem of the (110) film patterning is film cracking. For YBaCuO, the thermal expansion coefficient α in the *ab*-plane is 11 ppm/K, while along the *c*-axis it is 15 ppm/K. For $SrTiO_3$, α=10.4ppm/K. Therefore, the film tends to crack upon cooling and thermocycling. Only patterned films crack, because sharp edges serve as stress concentrators to initiate a crack. Films patterned through both routes (standard lithography and "silicon" process) crack. However, films, patterned by the Si-route seem to be somewhat more stable (a film, obtained by the standard lithography usually cracks during the first cooling to cryogenic temperatures). The problem can be alleviated by avoiding sharp edges, though for certain applications such a pattern with all edges rounded may be undesirable.

We had also a limited success with a different way of cracking prevention. A relatively thick (0.35 μm) film of MgF_2 was deposited on the top of a lithographed film. The idea was that the MgF_2 has lower expansion coefficient, and it can counterbalance the tensile stress acting the YBaCuO film when the system film/substrate is cooled. The films with MgF_2 on the top of them cracked too, but they usually survived several thermocycles from room to liquid helium temperature.

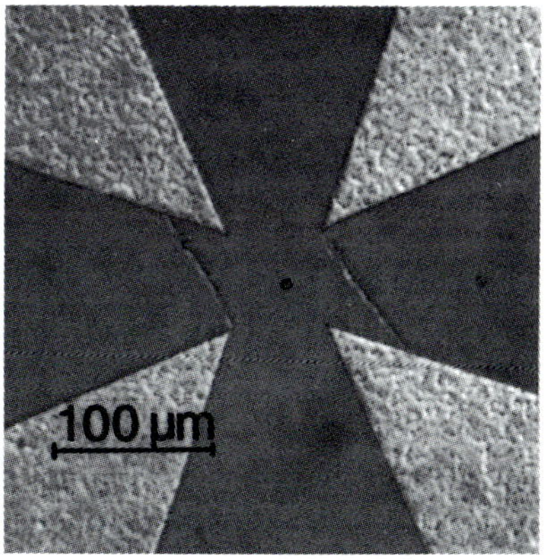

Fig. 3. A pattern made via Si-route. The cross: YBaCuO film, the grainy material outside it: insulating Y-Ba-Cu-Si-O compound. Two cracks are initiated by the sharp edges of the pattern.

4. Transport properties

With the test structure shown on the Fig. 3, we were able to measure the transport properties in both directions ($\parallel c$ and $\perp c$) on the same spot - on the central section of the cross. A pair of contacts is made to the each branch of the cross, so that 4-point measurements are possible for both directions.

Our preliminary results (on unpatterned films), as well as literature data [6, 7], indicated appreciable (1.5 - 10 K) anisotropy of T_c, which apparently does not fit into the existing theoretical conceptions.

However, when we managed to measure T_c on a structure shown on the Fig. 3, we never found any difference in T_c for different current directions. Authors of [3] have also found that the T_c is independent of the direction of the current. The aforementioned anisotropy is apparently an artifact due to measuring the T_c on different parts of an inhomogeneous film.

The anisotropy of the resistivity ρ_c/ρ_{ab} and of the critical current j_{ab}/j_c is not good reproduced and was for our films in the range 3 - 10, while for single crystals values above 30 were obtained [3]. As Wu et al. [3] argue, this property is extremely sensitive to even a small admixture of (103) phase.

5. Conclusion

The techniques are developed to grow epitaxial (110) YBaCuO films, and to pattern these films. This opens the way for many experiments to study the anisotropy of the material, which is of fundamental importance. Also, applications are now feasible using the anisotropy, and in particular the longer superconducting coherence length which in these film is normal to the surface. However, there are still some problems with traces of (103) oriented phase, which may influence dramatically the anisotropy of the electrical properties, and with cracking of the patterned films.

References

1. H.-U. Habermeier, A.A.C.S. Lourenço, B. Friedl, J. Kircher, and J. Köhler. Solid State Commun., **77**, 683 (1991).
2. M.V. Belousov, F.A. Chudnovskii, V.Yu. Davydov, B.Sh. Elkin, S.L. Shokhor, and V.Ya. Velichko. Solid State Commun., **77**, 493 (1992).
3. J.Z. Wu, P.Y. Hsieh, A.V. McGuire, D.L. Schmidt, L.T. Wood, Y. Shen, and W.K. Chu. Phys. Rev. B, **44**, 12643 (1991).
4. S. Kohjiro, T. Tachino, H. Akoh, and S. Takada. Jpn. J. Appl. Phys., **30**, L1471 (1991).
5. H.-U. Habermeier, G. Mertens, B. Leibold, G. Lu, and G. Wagner. Physica C, **180**, 17 (1991).
6. J.E. Pohl, A. Kirk, P.J. King, J.S. Lees, and W.B. Roys. Supercond. Sci. Technol., **4**, 499 (1991).
7. S. Hontsu, J. Ishii, T. Kawai, and S. Kawai. Appl. Phys. Lett., **59**, 2886 (1991).

$YBa_2Cu_3O_7/PrBa_2Cu_3O_7$ Superlattices: Properties of Ultrathin $YBa_2Cu_3O_7$ Layers

J.-M. Triscone, O. Brunner, L. Antognazza, L. Miéville, and Ø. Fischer

Département de Physique de la Matière Condensée, Université de Genève, 24, Quai E. Ansermet, CH-1211 Genève 4, Switzerland

The growth of high T_c superlattices such as $YBa_2Cu_3O_7/DyBa_2Cu_3O_7$[1] or $YBa_2Cu_3O_7/PrBa_2Cu_3O_7$[2] (YBCO/PrBCO) superlattices allows systematic studies of certain properties of this class of materials. With the YBCO/PrBCO system (PrBCO being isostructural to YBCO but not superconducting), it is for instance possible to modify the anisotropy in a controlled manner and thus investigate the role of the reduced dimensionality of the high temperature superconductors on the superconducting properties.

Using the YBCO/PrBCO system we have studied the properties of ultrathin YBCO layers as a function of the thickness of the superconductor and, as a function of the degree of decoupling (simply by varying the PrBCO insulating separation layer thickness). For the critical temperature we find that when one layer composed of one or few unit cells of YBCO is separated from the next layer by PrBCO T_c decreases markedly until a PrBCO thickness of about 70Å and then saturate[2,3]. This behavior has been confirmed by different groups[4-6] and has generated a strong theoretical effort to elucidate this T_c reduction. Particularly interesting is whether or not this reduction is due to a Kosterlitz-Thouless transition in these almost 2D layers. Although there is no firmed proof that such a transition occurs, many experiments suggest that it is so. Unfortunately this problem is complicated by the effect of PrBCO on YBCO and by the microstructure of such multilayers. It requires additional work to clarify this issue.

Another important problem of the high T_c materials, especially for applications, is the strong dissipation observed when a magnetic field is not applied perpendicular to the c-axis[7]. This dissipation is related to the motion of vortices which can be thermally activated over potential wells of typical energies U. This activation energy U is particularly low in these high T_c materials because of the strong anisotropy. To further understand the nature of the dissipative behavior it is necessary to have a model system where the anisotropy can be varied at will. YBCO/PrBCO superlattices is the ideal model system and we systematically investigated the behavior of the activation energy as a function of the YBCO thickness[8]. For magnetic fields parallel to the c-axis, and for thick PrBCO separations, we find that U scales with the YBCO thickness up to layer thicknesses of more than 200Å. Since this characteristic length is a measure of the vortex stiffness, it means that the coupling between the CuO_2 planes of different unit cells in pure YBCO is strong and that the vortices are relatively rigid in this material. As a consequence the vortex lattice is two dimensional in the individual thin YBCO layers. We observe in these superlattices that the dependence of the activation energy on the magnetic field is U~lnB, as measurement on bulk materials give $U \sim B^{\alpha}$. This behavior may be typical of a 2D vortex lattice for which, close to the melting temperature, the dissipation is essentially dominated by the motion of dislocation pairs[9].

References:

[1] J.-M. Triscone, M. G. Karkut, L. Antognazza, O. Brunner, and Ø. Fischer, Phys. Rev. Lett. 63, 1016 (1989).

[2] J.-M. Triscone, Ø. Fischer, O. Brunner, L. Antognazza, A. D. Kent, and M. G. Karkut. Phys. Rev. Lett. 64, 804, (1990).

[3] Ø. Fischer, J.-M. Triscone, O. Brunner, L. Antognazza, M. Affronte, O. Eibl, L. Miéville, T. Boichat, and M.G. Karkut, Physica B169, 116 (1991).

[4] Q. Li, X. X. Xi, X. D. Wu, A. Inam, S. Vadlamannati, W. L. McLean, T. Venkatesan, R. Ramesh, D. M. Hwang, J. A. Martinez, and L. Nazar. Phys. Rev. Lett. 64, 3086 (1990).

[5] D. H. Lowndes, D. P. Norton, and J. D. Budai. Phys. Rev. Lett. 65, 1160 (1990).

[6] T. Terashima, Y. Bando, K. Iijima, K. Yamamoto, K. Hirata, K. Hayashi, K. Kamigaki, and H. Terauchi. Phys. Rev. Lett. 65, 2684 (1990).

[7] See, for instance, Y. Iye, T. Tamegei, H. Takeya, H. Takei, Jpn. J. Appl. Phys. 27, L 1850 (1987).

[8] O. Brunner, L. Antognazza, J.-M. Triscone, L. Miéville, and Ø. Fischer, Phys. rev. Lett. 67, 1354 (1991).

[9] M. V. Feigelmann, V. B. Geshkenbein and A. I. Larkin, Physica C167, 177 (1990).

Synthesis of New HTS by Pulsed Laser Deposition

P. Schwab[1], *X.Z. Wang*[1], *B. Hellebrand*[1], *A. Kochemasov*[2], *and D. Bäuerle*[1]

[1]Angewandte Physik, Johannes-Kepler-University Linz, A-4040 Linz, Austria
[2]On leave from: Institute of Applied Physics, Russian Academy of Sciences, 603600 Nishni Nowgorod, Russia

Abstract: Thin superconducting films of single-phase $LuBa_2Cu_3O_7$ and $LuBaSrCu_3O_7$ have been synthesized by means of pulsed-laser deposition (PLD). $LuBa_2Cu_3O_7$ and $LuBaSrCu_3O_7$ films show zero resistance at 90 K and 54 K, respectively. The critical current density found with $LuBa_2Cu_3O_7$ films at 83 K is in excess of $10^6 A/cm^2$. For $YBa_{2-x}Sr_xCu_3O_7$ PLD permits to extend the solid solution range for single-phase material from $x < 1.2$ to $x = 1.8$. With increasing x, the critical temperature decreases from 79K for $x = 1$ to 57K for $x = 1.8$, and the c-axis from 11.68 Å for $x = 0$ to 11.45 Å for $x = 1.8$.

Since the discovery of high-temperature superconductors [1-4], intense efforts in the in situ fabrication of high quality thin films have been made. Among the various techniques being presently under investigation, pulsed-laser deposition (PLD) is distinguished by a number of unique properties which were reviewed in [5].

In this communication we demonstrate that PLD permits to synthesize single-phase materials that cannot be prepared by standard ceramic techniques. The model substances considered are Lu-Ba-Cu-O, Lu-Ba-Sr-Cu-O and Y-Ba-Sr-Cu-O.

It was shown in Refs. [6,7] that $LuBa_2Cu_3O_{7-x}$ prepared by standard solid-state reactions contains a second phase that accounts for at least half of the intensity in the powder X-ray diffraction (XRD) spectra. In $LuBaSrCu_3O_{7-x}$ the second phase accounts for at least 80% of the intensity in the XRD spectra [8]. For $YBa_{2-x}Sr_xCu_3O_{7-x}$ standard ceramic techniques permit to stabilize the 123-phase only for a Sr content $x < 1.2$ [9,10].

The ceramic targets employed in the present experiments have been prepared from mixtures of Y_2O_3, Lu_2O_3, $BaCO_3$, $SrCO_3$ and CuO using the standard solid-state reaction. The starting materials had a purity of better than 99.9%. Stoichiometric compositions of $LuBa_2Cu_3O_7$, $LuBaSrCu_3O_7$ and $YBa_{2-x}Sr_xCu_3O_{7-x}$ were used to produce the corresponding films. After one hour of mixing and grinding in an automatic ball mill, the corresponding powder was pressed into pellets and calcined at 900°C for 24 hours. After regrinding and repressing, pellets were subjected to a second calcination step at 920°C for 24 hours, followed by slow cooling in O_2 atmosphere. In samples of $LuBaSrCu_3O_7$ and $YBa_{2-x}Sr_xCu_3O_7$ with $x > 1$ prepared in this way, no 123-phase could be identified.

Pulsed-laser deposition was performed by means of 248nm KrF excimer-laser radiation ($\Phi = 4\ J/cm^2$, $\tau_\ell = 20$ ns, 10 pulses per second) and a gaseous atmosphere of either O_2 or N_2O ($p(O_2) = p(N_2O) = 0.4$ mbar). A schematic of the experimental setup used was shown in [5]. The substrates employed were (100) MgO and (100) $SrTiO_3$.

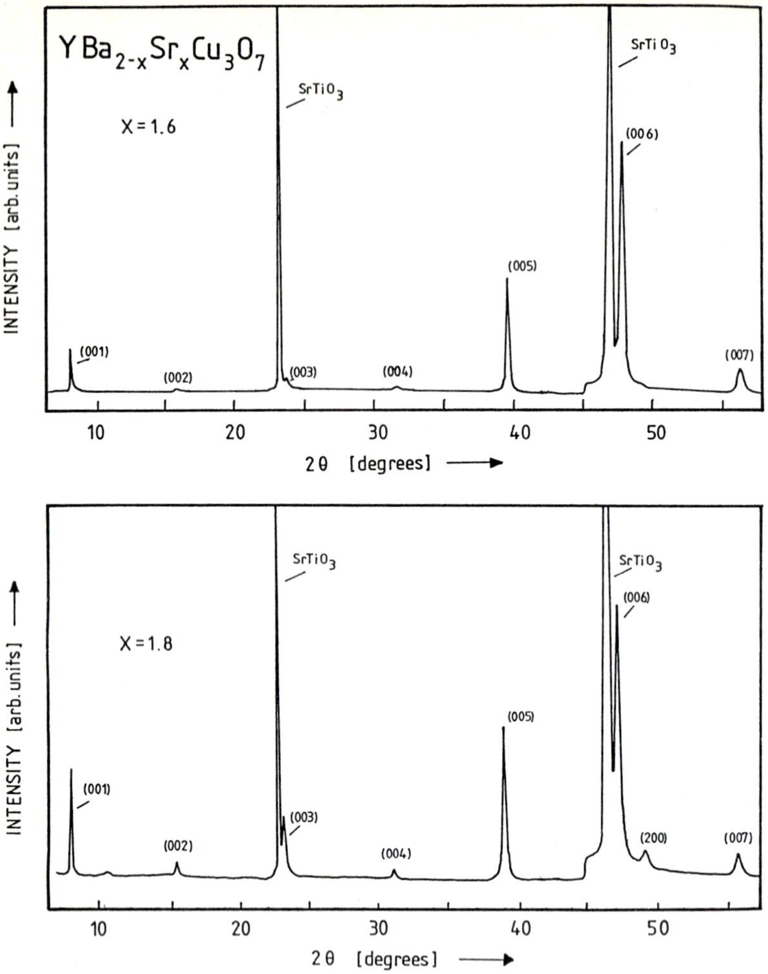

Fig. 1: X-ray diffraction spectra of $YBa_{2-x}Sr_xCu_3O_7$ films on (100) $SrTiO_3$
a) x = 1.6, T_s= 715°C. The c-axis derived is 11.48 Å.
b) x = 1.8, T_s = 720°C, c = 11.45 Å.

$LuBa_2Cu_3O_7$ films, and $YBa_{2-x}Sr_xCu_3O_7$ films containing Sr up to x = 1.8, were successfully prepared in oxygen atmosphere at substrate holder temperatures between 680°C < T_s< 750°C. $LuBaSrCu_3O_7$ could only be synthesized at lower temperatures, namely at T_s= 600°C. Because of the low oxidation force of molecular oxygen at this temperature, N_2O gas was employed (11,12). Within the temperature range 580°C < T_s < 750°C it was not possible to stabilize $YSr_2Cu_3O_7$ in considerable amounts neither in O_2 nor in N_2O atmosphere.

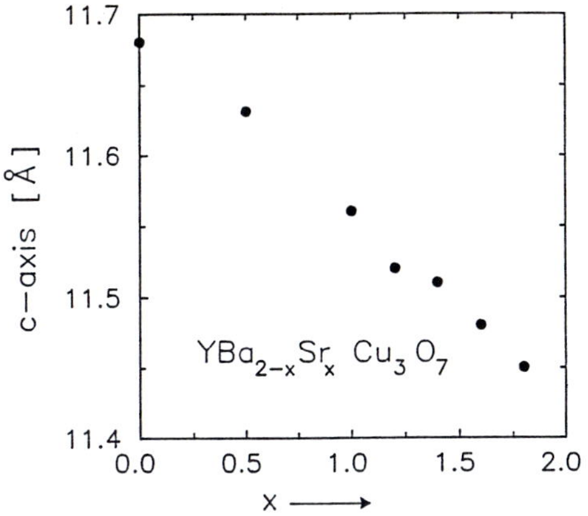

Fig. 2: Length of c-axis in single-phase $YBa_{2-x}Sr_xCu_3O_7$ films on (100) $SrTiO_3$ as a function of x; $680^{\circ}C \le T_s \le 750^{\circ}C$.

$LuBa_2Cu_3O_7$ films deposited onto (100) MgO or (100) $SrTiO_3$ substrates show only the c-oriented 123-phase and all peaks can be indexed by (001) reflections with c = 11.66 Å. From the XRD spectra of single phase $LuBaSrCu_3O_7$, with the c-axis perpendicular to the substrate surface, we derive c = 11.61 Å [13].

Figure 1 shows XRD spectra of $YBa_{2-x}Sr_xCu_3O_7$ films for two compositions and (100) $SrTiO_3$ substrates. The c-axis is oriented perpendicular to the substrate surface. With x = 1.6 the spectrum shows only the 123-phase, while with x = 1.8 (Fig.1b) small amounts of an impurity phase can be detected. Figure 2 shows the concentration dependence of the c-axis of $YBa_{2-x}Sr_xCu_3O_7$ films on (100) $SrTiO_3$ substrates. The data were derived from XRD spectra. Each data point represents an average over two measurements on at least three different samples. The figure shows that the c-axis decreases about linearly with increasing x. This can be expected when Ba is substituted by ions of smaller radius.

The chemical composition of films was analyzed by electron microprobe (EDX) analysis. This analysis proved that the films have the same chemical composition as the corresponding targets employed.

Electrical transport measurements were carried out by using the standard DC four-point-probe technique. Figure 3 shows the zero resistance temperature, T_{co}, of $YBa_{2-x}Sr_xCu_3O_7$ films as a function of x. In samples with the chemical composition $YSr_2Cu_3O_7$ only very small amounts of the 123-phase were detected. These samples were semiconducting without any onset to superconductivity.

With (100) $SrTiO_3$ substrates $LuBa_2Cu_3O_7$ and $LuBaSrCu_3O_7$ show zero resistance at temperatures of 90 K and 54 K, respectively (Fig.4). The critical current density of the $LuBa_2Cu_3O_7$ film at zero magnetic field, j_c(83K), exceeds $10^6 A/cm^2$ (Fig.5).

Techniques for synthesizing new HTS materials become more and more important. Frequently, high pressures and high temperatures are employed in such investigations [14,15]. With systems that require low pressures

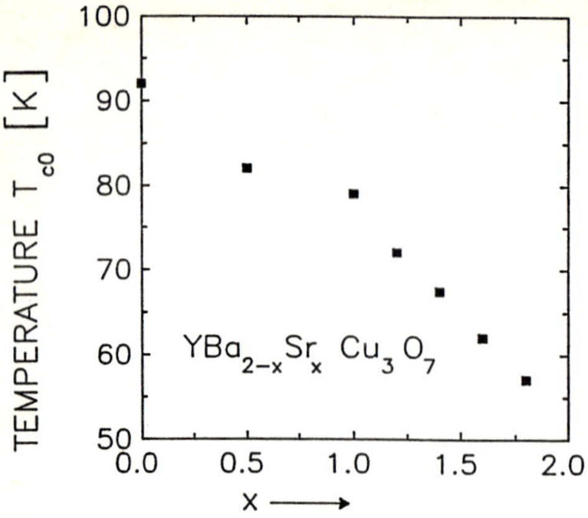

Fig. 3: Zero resistance temperature, T_{co}, of $YBa_{2-x}Sr_xCu_3O_7$ films on (100) $SrTiO_3$ as a function of x. Data refer to the highest value of T_{co} achieved for the corresponding composition.

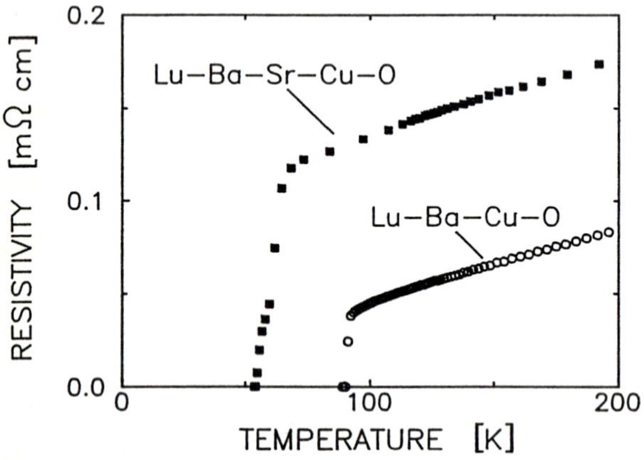

Fig. 4: Resistivity of $LuBa_2Cu_3O_7$ (o) and $LuBaSrCu_3O_7$ (■)films on (100) $SrTiO_3$ as a function of temperature (after [13]).

and low growth temperatures, as apparently the 123 - phase, PLD seems to provide a unique tool.

In summary, we have demonstrated that pulsed-laser deposition permits to extend the solid-solution range for different substitutions in various HTS compounds with 123-structure.

Acknowledgement: We wish to thank the "Fonds zur Förderung der wissenschaftlichen Forschung in Österreich" for financial support.

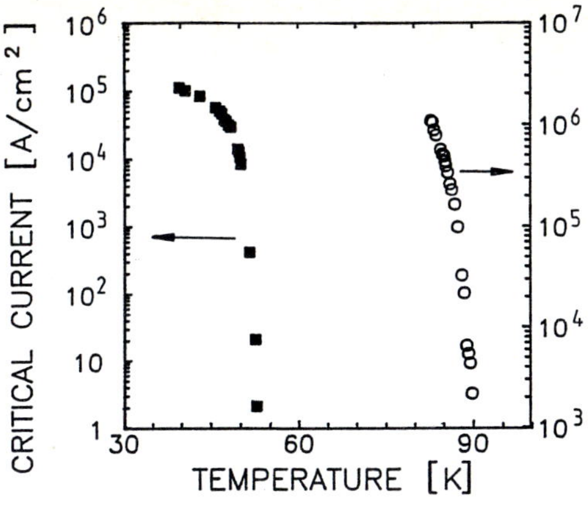

Fig. 5: Temperature dependence of the critical current density of $LuBa_2Cu_3O_7$ (o) and $LuBaSrCu_3O_7$ (■) films on (100) $SrTiO_3$ substrates (after[13]).

References:

[1] J.G. Bednorz and K.A. Müller, Z.Phys. **B 64**, 189 (1986).
[2] C.W. Chu, P.H. Hor, R.L. Meng, L. Gao, Z.J. Huang and Y.Q. Wang, Phys. Rev. Lett. **58**, 405 (1987).
[3] H. Maeda, Y.Tanaka, M. Fukutomi and T. Asano, Jpn. J. Appl. Phys. **27**, L209 (1988).
[4] Z.Z. Sheg and A.M. Hermann, Nature **332**, 138 (1988).
[5] D. Bäuerle, Appl. Phys. **A 49**, 527 (1989).
[6] P.H. Hor, R.L. Meng, Y.Q. Wang, L. Gao, Z.J. Huang, J. Bechtold, K. Forster, and C.W. Chu, Phys. Rev. Lett. **58**, 1891 (1987).
[7] J.M. Tarascon, W.R. McKinnon, L.H. Green, G.W. Hull, and E.M. Vogel, Phys. Rev. B **36**, 226 (1987).
[8] X.Z. Wang, unpublished.
[9] A. Ono, T Tanaka, H. Nozaki, and Y. Ishizawa, Jap. J. App. Phys. **26**, 1687 (1987).
[10] B.W. Veal, W.K. Kwok, A. Umezawa, G.W. Crabtree, J.D. Jorgensen, J.W. Downey, L.J. Nowicki, A.W. Mitchell, A.P. Paulikas, and C.H. Sowers, Appl. Phys. Lett **51** (4), 279 (1987).
[11] P. Schwab and D. Bäuerle, Physica C **182**, 103 (1991).
[12] P. Schwab, A. Kochemasov, R. Kullmer, and D. Bäuerle, Appl. Phys. **A 54**, 166 (1992).
[13] P. Schwab, X.Z. Wang, and D. Bäuerle, Appl.Phys.Lett. **60**, 16 (1992).
[14] R.J. Cava, B. Batlogg, R.B. van Dover, J.J. Krajewski, J.V. Waszczak, R.M. Fleming, W.F. Peck, L.W. Rupp, P. Marsh, A.C.W.P. James, and L.F. Schneemeyer, Nature **345**, 602 (1990).
[15] M.Takano, Y. Takeda, H. Okada, M. Miyamoto, and T. Kusaka, Physica C **159**, 375 (1989).

Epitaxial Growth of Thin-Film $Bi_2Sr_2CaCu_2O_{8+x}$ on $LaAlO_3(001)$, $NdGaO_3(001)$ and MgO(001)

R. de Reus[1], *M. Nielsen*[1], *R. Seemann*[2], *A. Sewing*[2], and *R.L. Johnson*[2]

[1]Department of Solid State Physics, Risø National Laboratory, DK-4000 Roskilde, Denmark

[2]II. Institut für Experimentalphysik, Universität Hamburg, Luruper Chaussee 149, W-2000 Hamburg, Fed. Rep. of Germany

Abstract. Thin-film $Bi_2Sr_2CaCu_2O_{8+x}$ was deposited onto $LaAlO_3(001)$, $NdGaO_3(001)$, and MgO(001) substrates by laser ablation. After post annealing, films were obtained exhibiting superconducting critical temperatures higher than 80 K. All films show *c*-axis growth. Oriented growth is achieved on $LaAlO_3(001)$ and $NdGaO_3(001)$ substrates, although approximately 50% and 65%, respectively, of the film is randomly oriented in the *ab*-plane. For a small fraction of the films deposited on MgO preferential orientations in the *ab*-plane with rotational angles of 11.5° and 45° are observed.

Applications of high-T_c superconductors, for example in microelectronics, demand reliable deposition processes of films thinner than 1 μm with critical currents of at least 1×10^6 A/cm^2. In a recent publication [1] it was shown that small amounts (less than 5%) of misaligned grains in epitaxial $YBa_2Cu_3O_{6+x}$ on MgO(001) and $SrTiO_3(001)$ reduce the critical current by a factor of 10. Therefore, it is of great importance to obtain a fundamental understanding of the epitaxial growth of high-T_c superconductors and the influence of different types of substrates on the growth properties. Here we report an X-ray study of the epitaxial growth of $Bi_2Sr_2CaCu_2O_{8+x}$ (BSCCO) on $LaAlO_3(001)$, $NdGaO_3(001)$, and MgO(001).

Laser ablation was used to deposit BSCCO from a stoichiometric target. The deposition took place in 0.2 mbar O_2 at a substrate temperature of 470 °C. Immediately after deposition air was let into the system and the samples were annealed for 5 min at 852 °C. By this method we succeeded in preparing thin-film BSCCO with thicknesses ranging from 250 to 5000 Å and exhibiting critical temperatures of $T_{c,0} > 80$ K. Details of the deposition process will be published elsewhere [2].

The X-ray diffraction (XRD) experiments were carried out using a rotating anode operating at 50 kV and 150 mA and a four-circle diffractometer. A graphite monochromator was used to select the Cu-K$_\alpha$ line.

Since high quality epitaxial films are expected to grow on substrates with a small lattice mismatch, we investigated the epitaxial growth of BSCCO on three different types of substrates: $LaAlO_3(001)$ (cubic,

Springer Series in Solid-State Sciences, Vol. 113 Electronic Properties of High-T$_c$ Superconductors
Editors: H. Kuzmany, M. Mehring, J. Fink

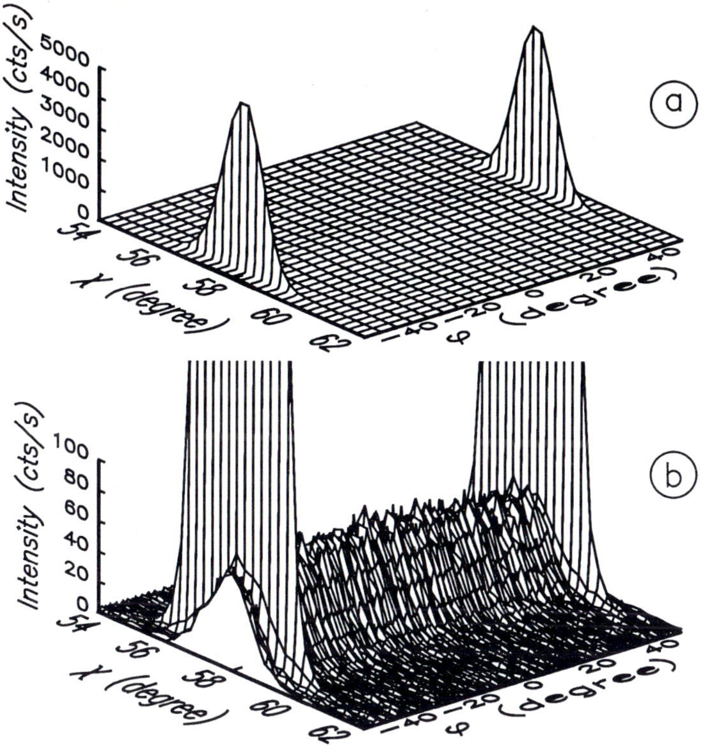

Figure 1: (a) a χ-φ scan of the BSCCO(115) reflection of a BSCCO film deposited on $NdGaO_3(001)$. The occurrence of two sharp peaks at $\varphi = -45°$ and $+45°$ indicates full epitaxial growth. However, a blowup (b) reveals a homogeneous distribution of the (115) reflection along φ, corresponding to randomly in-plane oriented BSCCO.

$a = 3.778$ Å), $NdGaO_3(001)$ (pseudocubic, $a = 3.851$ Å), and MgO(001) (cubic, $a = 4.213$ Å). Describing $Bi_2Sr_2CaCu_2O_{8+x}$ by an orthorhombic unit cell with $a = 5.4095, b = 5.4202$, and $c = 30.9297$ Å, a 45° rotation of the ab-plane would give an average mismatch of $-1.33, +0.58$, and $+10.0\%$ for $LaAlO_3$, $NdGaO_3$, and MgO, respectively.

Conventional $\theta - 2\theta$ scans in the specular reflection geometry only show (0,0,2l) reflections of BSCCO, indicating c-axis growth on all types of substrates. In some cases small amounts of impurity phases were detected due to loss of Bi during the preparation.

To examine the in-plane structure, $\chi - \varphi$ scans of several reflections were performed. In Fig. 1 such a scan of the BSCCO(115) reflection of a sample on $NdGaO_3$ is shown. χ is defined as the angle between the [110] plane of the film and the scattering plane and the angle φ as the rotation of the crystal around the [001] zone axis of the film. Thus, for full epitaxial growth, *i.e.*, alignment of the *ab*-plane with the main crystallographic axes of the substrate, four equivalent peaks at $\varphi = -135°, -45°, +45°$, and $+135°$ are expected. Indeed, these peaks are observed (see Fig. 1a). From these data it is clear that epitaxial BSCCO on $NdGaO_3(001)$ is present. However, on an expanded scale, as shown in Fig. 1b, the presence of the BSCCO(115) reflection is revealed for all values of φ. The intensity of this additional signal is independent of φ, suggesting a random distribution of BSCCO in the *ab*-plane. Although the intensity of the reflection of this randomly in-plane oriented material is only about 1% of the intensity of the peaks of the aligned material, an integration over the full range χ=[54,62] and φ=[0,360] shows that as much as 65% of the total amount of BSCCO is randomly in-plane oriented.

For the BSCCO films grown on $LaAlO_3(001)$ similar results were obtained. In this case approximately 50% of the total amount of BSCCO is epitaxial, whereas the remaining part of the film is randomly orientated in the *ab*-plane.

Although the films deposited on MgO(001) are strongly *c*-axis oriented, their in-plane structure is almost 100% random. For a small amount of the films preferential orientations corresponding to epitaxial rotations of 11.5° and 45.0° are observed. By performing glancing incidence XRD it was confirmed that the oriented parts of the BSCCO film were located at the interface with the MgO substrate.

Our observations show that BSCCO can be grown epitaxially on $LaAlO_3(001)$ and $NdGaO_3(001)$, both substrates with a good lattice match, whereas on MgO(001) predominantly random alignment of the *ab*-plane is observed. For all substrates, additional XRD spectra, taken directly after deposition at 470 °C, show the presence of amorphous Bi–Sr–Ca–Cu–O without any indication of crystalline material. Therefore, the growth of the epitaxial phase occurs via crystallization of the amorphous phase during the post-annealing at 852 °C. Since it is likely that crystallization is nucleated both at the interface with the single-crystalline substrate as well as at the free surface, epitaxial and randomly aligned BSCCO are formed simultaneously. The elongated unit cell dimensions of the BSCCO ($c > a \approx b$) favor *c*-axis growth. Assuming perfect epitaxial growth of BSCCO on $LaAlO_3$ and $NdGaO_3$, this would result in approximately 50% epitaxial and 50% randomly oriented material, as observed. In the case of MgO the lattice mismatch is approximately 10%, which apparently inhibits epitaxial growth. In order to grow fully epitaxial films of BSCCO, the substrate temperature during deposition should be high enough that crystalline BSCCO is deposited. It is then expected that this phase will grow epitaxially on $LaAlO_3$ and $NdGaO_3$ substrates, since random nucleation at a free surface is not possible. In this case, the post-annealing will not influence the growth of the film, but should enhance the superconducting properties and anneal out crystalline defects. A severe problem preparing BSCCO films this way is the loss of Bi with increasing substrate temperature.

In conclusion, XRD of post-annealed laser-ablated BSCCO showed epitaxial growth on $LaAlO_3(001)$ and $NdGaO_3(001)$ substrates of approximately 50 and 35%, respectively. The remaining part of the film is c-axis oriented, but random in the ab-plane. On MgO(001) substrates a c-axis orientation is observed, but only a small amount of epitaxial BSCCO could be detected. The difference in growth is attributed to the different lattice match between BSCCO and substrate. Crystalline BSCCO is formed during post annealing at 852 °C. Therefore, not only epitaxial material, nucleated at the substrate interface, but also randomly oriented material is formed. A more detailed analysis of our results will be published elsewhere [3].

This work was financially supported by the European Community Science Plan under contract #ERBSC1∗CT000352.

[1] R. Kromann, J.B. Bilde-Sørensen, R. de Reus, N.H. Andersen, P. Vase, and T. Freltoft, *J. Appl. Phys.* **71**, #7 (1992).
[2] R. Seemann, F. Hänisch, M. Peyerl, A. Sewing, R.L. Johnson, R. de Reus, and M. Nielsen, in preparation
[3] R. de Reus, M. Nielsen, R. Seemann, A. Sewing, and R.L. Johnson, in preparation.

Part III

Transport Properties, Thermal Properties

Aspects of Quantum Coherence in Superconducting Rings: Flux Quantisation in a Heavy Fermion/Niobium Hybrid Ring and the Origin of Noise in a HTC DC SQUID

C.E. Gough[1], *S.G. Hammond*[1], *Y. He*[1], *C.M. Muirhead*[1], *G. Geibel*[2], *C. Schank*[2], *F. Steglich*[2], *M.S. Colclough*[3], *and K. Char*[3]

[1]University of Birmingham, Superconductivity Research Group, Birmingham B15 2TT, UK
[2]Institut für Festkörperphysik, Techn. Hochschule Darmstadt, W-6100 Darmstadt, Fed. Rep. of Germany
[3]Conductus Inc., 969 West Maude Avenue, Sunnyvale, CA, USA

ABSTRACT. We report recent measurements of flux quantisation in a hybrid ring formed from niobium and the newly discovered heavy fermion superconductor UPd_2Al_3 ($T_c \sim 2K$) providing an unambiguous demonstration of quantum coherence of the superconducting wave function between the heavy fermion and the conventional BCS superconductor. I/V characteristics of the edge-contacts formed across the UPd_2Al_3/Nb contact regions suggest a relatively weak coupling of the heavy fermion/niobium superconducting wave functions. In the second experiment, a novel method for measuring noise in superconducting circuits is illustrated by measurements on a Conductus dc SQUID incorporating two bi-epitaxial weak-link junctions. The noise is shown to arise from fluctuations in critical currents across the two junctions, as independently determined by noise measurements on the junctions themselves after physical isolation from the SQUID. There was no evidence for any increase in noise in either SQUID device or constituent junctions associated with thermally induced motion of flux trapped within the device on cooling.

1. Introduction

In keeping with focus of this Winterschool, I have selected two recent Birmingham experiments which relate to the electronic properties of superconductors and their applications. The presentation will be intentionally tutorial, as detailed accounts of these measurement have already been or will soon be published elsewhere(1,3).

Springer Series in Solid-State Sciences, Vol. 113 **Electronic Properties of High-T_c Superconductors**
Editors: H. Kuzmany, M. Mehring, J. Fink

The first experiment provides the first evidence for quantum coherence in a superconducting circuit involving a heavy fermion superconductor (1). Flux quantisation and voltage-current characteristics are reported for a hybrid ring of niobium bridged by the heavy fermion superconductor UPd_2Al_3 recently discovered by Geibel et al(2). The second experiment involves a novel method for identifying the likely origin of noise in superconducting junctions and dc SQUIDs. The method is illustrated by measurements on dc SQUID rings fabricated by Conductus(3) and on the individual bi-epitaxial grain boundary weak-link junctions forming the SQUID.

2. Quantum coherence and critical currents in a heavy fermion/ niobium hybrid ring

The quantisation of flux within a superconducting ring provides an unambiguous demonstration of the quantum mechanical nature of the superconducting state. The magnitude of the flux quantum $\Phi_0 = h/q$ is determined by the effective superconducting charge q, as derived by London (4) long before it was known that superconductivity involved the pairing of electrons. Flux quantisation in units of h/2e was first demonstrated for conventional superconductors by Deaver and Fairbrother(5) and Doll and Nabauer(6), confirming the pairing of electrons predicted by the BCS theory(7).

Soon after the discovery of HTC superconductors, we were able to demonstrate the quantisation of flux in a ceramic YBCO sample(8) proving that HTC superconductivity also involved the pairing of electrons. In a subsequent experiment, flux quantisation was confirmed in a composite ring formed from a HTC superconducting ring bridged by a short section of niobium (9). This demonstrated quantum coherence of the superconducting wave functions across the interface between the two superconductors, even though the microscopic mechanism for pairing in each superconductor may be completely different.

It might be thought that the existence of such coupling implies identical symmetry for the conventional and HTC superconducting wave functions. Unfortunately, no such deduction can be made because of symmetry-breaking at any real interface between two metals, quite apart from hybridisation of electronic states by spin-orbit coupling (10). The strength of coupling across the interface, and hence the critical current is, however, expected to be significantly reduced if the wave functions of the coupled superconductors are different(11).

The question of quantum symmetry and the strength of coupling across an interface is of particular interest for heavy fermion superconductors, a number of which are candidates for non-conventional p- or d-state electron pairing, such as UPt_3 and $U_{1-x}Th_xBe_{13}$ (12,13), and the newly discovered superconductor UPd_2Al_3(2). Characteristic signatures for p- or d-state pairing include low temperature power law dependences of superconducting properties[14]. Additional evidence for non-conventional pairing has been inferred from the apparent existence of more than one superconducting phase of UPt_3 deduced from measurements including heat capacity(15), and ultrasonic attenuation (16). The splitting of the superconducting phase transition suggests an analogy with the transitions associated with the A and B phases of superfluid ^3He (see the discussion of superfluid ^3He in reference 17), which are believed to involve a superfluid p-state.

The discovery of superconductivity of the "123- high T_c" heavy fermion superconductor UAl_2Pd_3, with a transition temperature ~2K, provides an additional candidate for possible unconventional pairing in the superconducting state(18). The evidence for non-conventional pairing is suggested by the weak dependence of T_c on magnetic doping for UPd_2Al_3 in contrast to the precipitate dependence observed for the related UNi_2Al_3 compound. Because the transition temperature of UPd_2Al_3 is in the easily accessible temperature range above 1.2K, we were able to repeat our earlier experiment on quantum coherence in hybrid rings using this material as one of the superconductors.

The UPd_2Al_3 sample was prepared as described by Geibel et al (2). A 45° cone of maximum diameter 1.5mm was spark-machined from a bulk sample and was mounted in a brass holder. The cone was mechanically positioned, from outside the cryostat, to bridge a slot cut between two holes in a solid niobium block, as illustrated in figure 1. The external adjusting mechanism was withdrawn while measurements were made to avoid problems from mechanical vibrations and thermal expansion. The two-hole geometry, similar to that of the 2-hole rf

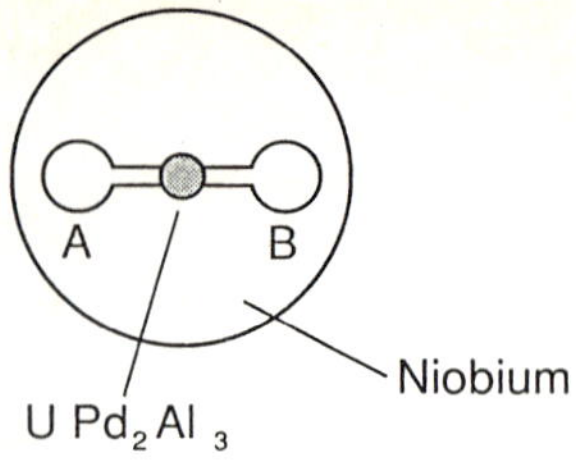

Figure 1. Schematic of the experiment. The UPd_2Al_3 pin is lowered into the slot in the niobium to form superconducting weak links at the contact points.

SQUID, provides a high degree of isolation from external magnetic noise, without affecting the essential physics.

A current is passed through a long solenoidal coil inserted into one of the holes in the niobium block to provide a known external bias flux. As the external flux is changed, currents are induced around the niobium holes and through the bridging heavy fermion material to maintain the net flux within the niobium block constant (nominally zero, if cooled through T_c in zero external field). These currents induce a signal in the pickup coil of a superconducting dc flux-transformer inserted into the second hole and connected to a conventional SQUID system. Measuring the SQUID output as a function of a known applied external flux provides an absolute calibration of the system in terms of known flux within the two holes (equal and opposite).

As the external flux is increased, a shielding current is induced to keep the total flux within the hole containing the solenoid constant until the critical current of the weakest of the two bridging UPd_2Al_3 / niobium junctions is exceeded. Flux then passes between the two holes in quanta of Φ_0 as illustrated in figure 2 by the hysteretic magnetisation loops of the SQUID output as a function of externally applied flux. Measurements at three temperatures are shown for a particular setting of the bridging cone. At 1.25K the junctions support a flux within the ring of $Li_c \sim 5\Phi_0$, corresponding to a critical current of a few μA. However, the critical current decreases rapidly with increasing temperature. By 1.28K, for this particular setting of the contacts, the magnetic properties of the ring become quasi-reversible. As the critical current becomes smaller, the transition appear more rounded- because

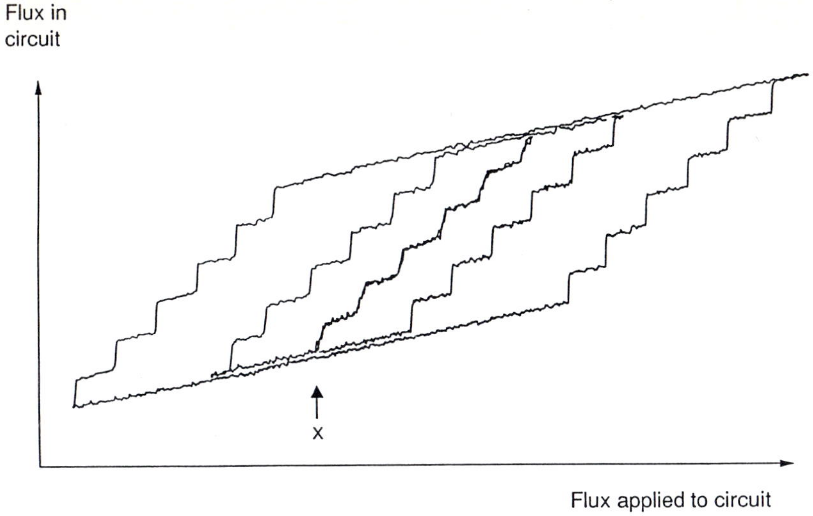

Figure 2. Flux detected by SQUID versus flux applied through the long solenoid. The outer loop is for T = 1.22K and the middle loop is for T = 1.25K. The central staircase is for T = 1.26K. The steps in both axis are at intervals of one flux quantum.

of multiple thermally activated transitions between adjacent quantum states, which occur on the time- scale of the measurements themselves.

Figure 3 illustrates transitions induced between the quantised states of the ring by periodic bursts of electromagnetic noise (a hair dryer) from outside the cryostat. The quantised flux states are separated by h/2e to within the absolute accuracy of the measurements (~ +/-2%). The observation of flux quantisation provides an unambiguous confirmation of the phase-coherence of the superconducting wave function across the niobium/ heavy-fermion interface.

The I/V characteristics for one particular point setting are shown in Figure 4 and were measured using a standard 4-point method. The current flows from the heavy fermion superconductor into the niobium block through the two contact-junctions in parallel. The characteristics are therefore dominated by the strongest of the two junctions. The inset in Figure 4 shows the temperature variation of the measured critical current. For this particular setting, J_c extrapolates to zero at around 1.8K, close to the transition temperature determined from magnetic and bulk supercurrent measurements(2). It is important to recognise that thermal fluctuations always result in "measured" critical currents,

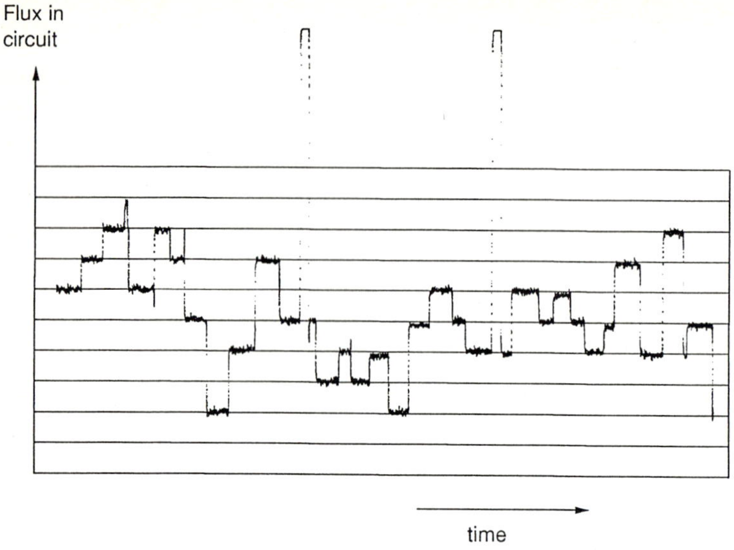

Figure 3. Flux jumps stimulated by deliberately applied electromagnetic interference when the applied flux was at point X on figure 2. The separation between the grid lines is 0.99 Φ_o. The two large jumps are due to unlocking of the measuring SQUID.

thermal fluctuations always result in "measured" critical currents, especially when very small, extrapolating to zero below the value of T_c determined from bulk properties(19,20).

A measure of the quality of a conventional superconducting junction is the I_cR product, where R is the junction resistance in the normal state. For an ideal Josephson junction well below T_c, this product is equal to $\frac{\pi}{2}\Delta$, where Δ is the superconducting energy gap in eV(21). Taking $\Delta = 1.76\ kT_c$, we would expect a product $\sim$ 2 mV, whereas measured values never exceeded 5μV. Moreover, despite many attempts, we were never able to confirm quantum coherence, nor even to observe a supercurrent, in a heavy fermion/HTC system with the niobium block replaced by a geometrically equivalent sintered block of $YBa_2Cu_3O_{7-d}$.

A present it is not possible to determine whether the weakness of coupling across the UPd_2Al_3/Nb interface and the lack of any evidence for coherence across the UPd_2Al_3/YBCO interface arises from non-conventional symmetry of the heavy fermion superconducting

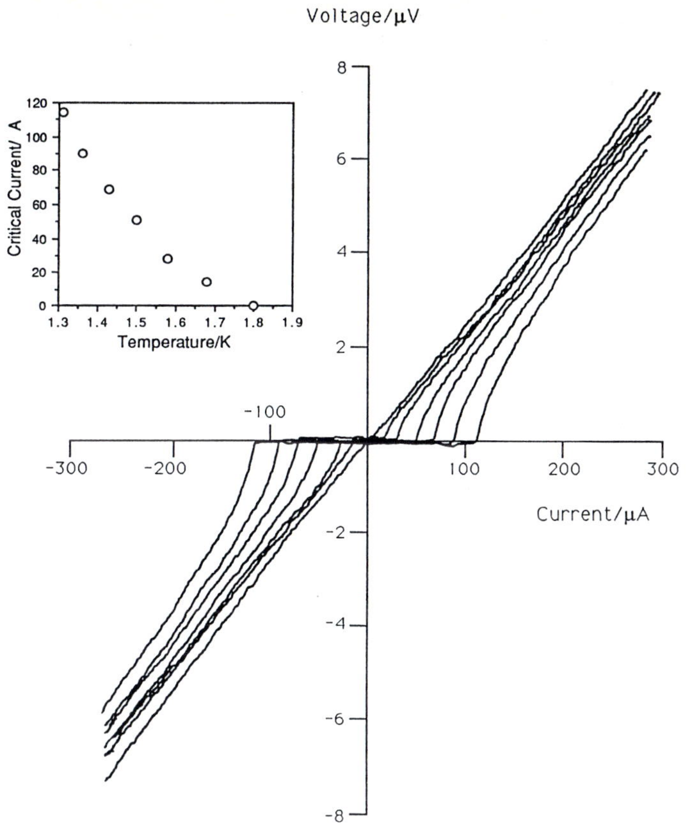

Figure 4. Voltage/current characteristics of a weak link formed between the Heavy Fermion and niobium specimens. These curves were measured at temperatures of 1.31, 1.36, 1.43, 1.50, 1.58, 1.68 and 1.8K. The inset shows the Critical Current versus temperature characteristics deduced from this data.

state wave function. The difficulty of establishing a large I_cR product may simply be a materials science problem. Further experiments on UPd_2Al_3 and on UPt_3 below 1K will hopefully clarify the experimental situation.

3. Critical Current fluctuations in HTC bi-epitaxial junctions and dc SQUIDs.

A dc SQUID consists of a superconducting ring formed by two weak-link junctions in parallel, as shown in the inset of Figure 5. We consider an

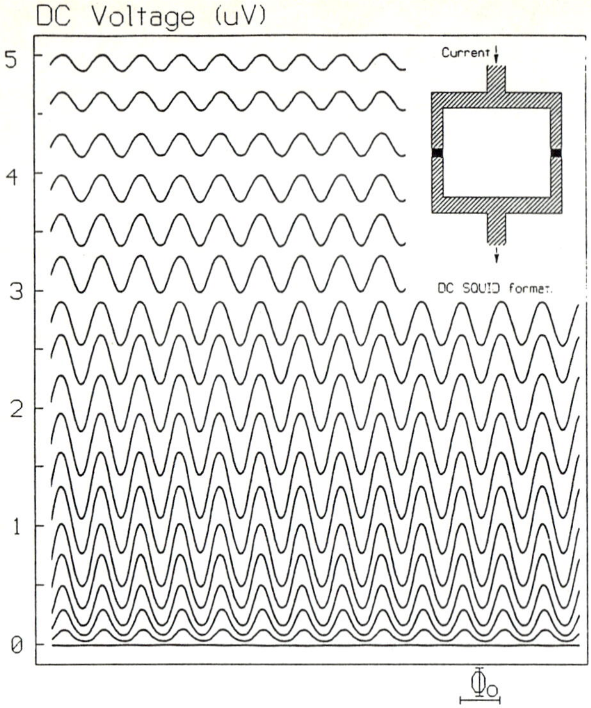

Figure 5. Voltage/field characteristics of a dc SQUID for a series of bias currents (I_{bias} increasing towards the top of the figure). The inset shows a schematic of a dc SQUID.

idealised situation with identical junctions with critical current I_c and initially neglect the influence of flux produced by currents circulating the ring. The critical current across the device is then predicted to vary with external flux linking the device as $2I_c|\cos(\pi\ \Phi/\Phi_0)|$ (see, for example (22)), where Φ is the flux passing through the ring.

A dc SQUID is operated by biasing the current slightly above $2I_c$ and observing the periodicity in voltage across the device as a function of external applied flux. Figure 5 shows a typical set of such characteristics for a Conductus dc SQUID at 77K as a function of external field for a sequence of bias currents. In operation as a SQUID magnetometer, the device is incorporated in an electronic feedback loop with the system "locked on" to one of the minima. Any subsequent change in external flux is then measured by the compensating field provided by the feedback circuitry to maintain the device at the same operating point.

In practice, there are two potentially important sources of noise in a SQUID device. The first is flux noise, caused by intrinsic thermodynamic fluctuations or thermal activation of flux lines in and out of the ring. The second arises from fluctuations in critical current δI_C. Such fluctuations could arise, for example, from aperiodic changes in the occupancy of localised electron trapping centres within the weak-link junction region. In addition to affecting the maximum critical current through the device, the current noise also leads to fluctuations in the current circulating around the ring and hence to flux-noise $L\delta I_C$, where L is the ring inductance.

The ultimate sensitivity of a SQUID is determined by the overall noise in the system, which is distributed over a wide frequency spectrum. Noise is conventionally cited in terms of the equivalent mean square flux noise measured at a specific frequency over a 1 Hz bandwidth. The sensitivity achieved for the best HTC SQUIDs at 77K already exceeds $10^{-4}\ \phi_0 / \sqrt{\ }$ Hz down to frequencies well below 1 Hz (23) . At low frequencies the performance is always limited by an approximately 1/f noise. The experiments described here involve a novel method for measuring such noise in superconducting devices.

Measurements have been made on a number of Conductus dc SQUIDs, which contain weak-link junctions patterned across 45^0 bi-epitaxial grain boundaries(24). These commercially available SQUIDs incorporate 17 epitaxial superconductor, insulator and buffer layers on a single chip(3). The superconducting flux transformer necessary to couple magnetic fields effectively to the SQUID itself is included in the integrated chip package. The field sensitivity at 77K is typically around $10^{-4}T/\sqrt{Hz}$ above 100Hz, more than sufficient to record a magnetocardiagram(25). Our noise measurements were made on partially fabricated SQUIDs before incorporation of the flux transformer.

It was initially believed that noise from thermally activated motion of external flux or vortex/anti-vortex pairs trapped in the device on cooling would limit the achievable sensitivity for HTC SQUID operation at 77K (26). Not only could such fluctuations affect the flux linkage within the ring but could also affect the performance by thermal transitions of flux within the junction regions. Recent measurements on bulk films (27) have suggested that the former source of magnetic noise

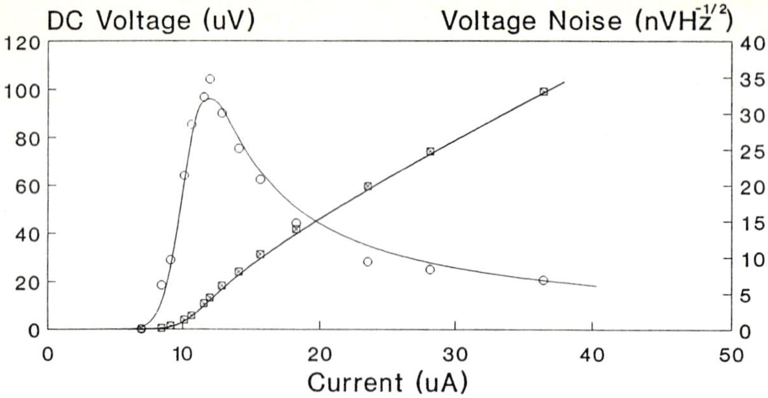

Figure 6. I/V characteristics of a dc SQUID at 20K (crossed squares) and the corresponding noise voltage at 10 Hz (open circles). The solid lines are theoretical curves and are discussed in the text.

is unlikely to be a serious problem for HTC SQUIDs fabricated from sufficiently high quality epitaxial thin films. However, thermal activation of flux in the junction regions could ultimately still prove to be a problem. In present HTC SQUIDs, the major source of noise appears to be from fluctuation in critical current. Such noise is likely to be highly dependent on the nature and quality of the weak-link junctions used, and will vary from laboratory to laboratory. It is clearly important to understand the origin of such noise in order to optimise SQUID performance.

In our measurements, a phase sensitive detector(PSD) is used to monitor the modulation of voltage, as the biasing current across the device is switched between $\pm\ i_{bias}$ at a modulation frequency of 1 kHz. Any fluctuations in the V(I) characteristics on a time-scale longer than that set by the modulation frequency is observed as noise on the in-phase signal of the PSD. The resulting noise spectrum is recorded and analysed using a HP Spectrum analyser.

We find that the noise obtained by this means is the same, within experimental error as that measured when biasing the junction with the same *dc* current, i_{bias}. This confirms that fluctuations in the critical current are the major source of noise for this junction. In Figure 6 we show the I/V characteristics at 20K, fitted to a finite temperature Resistively Shunted Junction model. The zero temperature critical

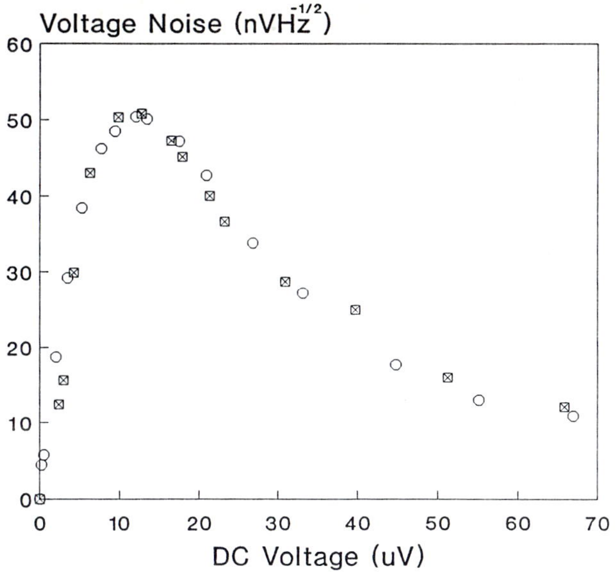

Figure 7. Noise voltage versus current at 10 Hz and 20K. Open squares are for zero applied field. Open circles are for cooling in 250 μT and adjusting the applied field to the same point on the I_c/B characteristics.

current, $I_C(0)$ can be deduced from this fit and the effect of any fluctuations in $I_C(0)$ calculated. By using δ $I_C(0)$ as the only adjustable parameter, good agreement between the theoretical and experimental noise curves is obtained. These are also shown in Figure 6.

Figure 7 shows two quite independent sets of measurements, which superimpose almost exactly on top of each other. The first was obtained after cooling the device in nominally zero field, while the second set was obtained after cooling in a field of 250μT, trapping appreciable flux within the device. In both cases the dependence of critical current on externally applied field was identical, reversible and quasi-periodic, though the field dependence was shifted by a constant small field by the trapped flux. For these latter measurements, a small external field was therefore superimposed so that the V(I) characteristics coincided exactly with the "zero- field cooled" characteristics. Despite the significant amount of trapped flux, there was no evidence for any increase in noise. Thermally activated motion of trapped flux in the junction regions or within the ring itself is therefore unlikely to be a major source of noise for this particular device.

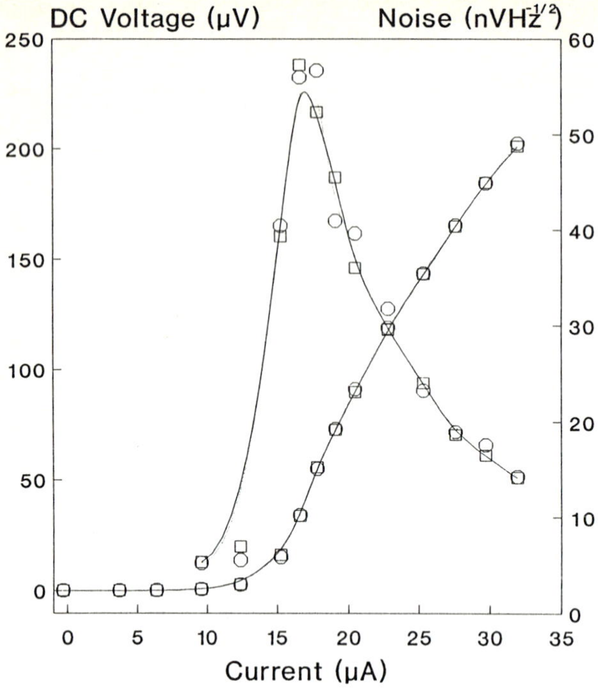

Figure 8. Noise in a complete SQUID (open circles) and noise in a single junction (crossed squares) at 10 Hz and 20K.

In Figure 8 we have plotted the noise across a complete SQUID ring and have compared it with the noise subsequently measured across one of its junctions, after isolation from the SQUID . To within experimental error, the SQUID noise can be entirely attributed to noise in the critical current of the individual junction.

As yet very little is known about the source of noise in weak-link junctions. This is clearly a major problem for both materials scientists in the preparation of "higher quality" junctions and physicists in terms of understanding the physics involved. We can almost certainly expect major advances on both fronts, as is clear from the remarkably low noise figures already being achieved, with cited sensitivities already exceeding $10^{-4}\Phi_0/\sqrt{Hz}$ down to frequencies as low as only 20mHz (see Heiden (28) in this volume). The prospect for HTC SQUID applications at liquid nitrogen temperatures is therefore already assured and performances approaching those of liquid helium cooled SQUIDs may well yet be achieved.

References

1. Y. He, C.M. Muirhead, D. Fort, C. Shank, G.B. Geibel and F. Steglich, to be published in Nature.
2. C. Geibel et al , Physica C **185-189**, 2651 (1991).
3. A.H. Miklick, J.J. Kingston, F.C. Wellstood, J. Clark, M.S. Colclough, K. Char and G. Zaharchuk, Appl. Phys. Lett. **59** 3051 (1991).
4. F. London, Superfluids, Dover Publications, New York, 1950.
5. B.S. Deaver and W.M. Fairbank, Phys. Rev. Lett. **7** (1961) 43.
6. R. Doll and M. Nabauer, Phys. Rev. Lett. 7 (1961) 51.
7. J. Bardeen, L.N. Cooper and J.R. Schrieffer, Phys.Rev. **108,** 1175 (1957).
8. C.E. Gough, M.S. Colclough, E.M. Forgan, R.G. Jordan, M. Keene, C.M. Muirhead, A.I.M. Rae, N. Thomas, J.S. Abell, S. Sutton, Nature 326 (1987) 855.
9. M.N. Keene, T.J. Jackson and C.E. Gough, Nature **340,** 855 (1989).
10. A.J. Millis, Physica **B135**, 69 (1985).
11. J.A. Dacs and W. van Haeringen, Physica **92B**, 360 (1977).
12. J. Flouquet et al, Physica C **185-189**,372 (1991).
13. T M Rice, Japanese Journal of Applied Physics **26,** Supp 26-3, 1865 (1987).
14. J. Flouquet, J.P. Brison, K. Hasselbach, L. Taillefer, K. Behnia, D. Jaccard and A. de Visser, Physica C **185-189**, 372 (1991).
15. A. Sulpice et al., J.Low.Temp.Phys. **62**, 39 (1986).
16. A. Schenstrum et al, Phys.Rev.Lett. **62**, 332 (1989).
17. D.R. Tilley and J. Tilley, *Superfluidity and Superconductivity (3rd edition)* (IOP Publishing, Bristol, 1990). Phys.Rev.Lett. **63**,1411 (1989).

18. F. Steglich, U. Ahlheim, A. Bohm, C.D. Bredl, R. Caspary, C. Geibel, A.B. Grauel, R. Helfrich, R. Kohler, M. Lang, A. Mehner, R. Modler, C. Schank, C. Wassilew, G. Weber, W. Assmus, N. Sato and T. Komotsubara, Physica C **185-189**, 379 (1991).
19. J. Manhart, P. Chaudhari, D. Dios, C.C. Tsuei and T.R. McGuire, Phys. Rev. Lett. **61**, 2476 (1988).
20. M.N. Keene, Supercon. Sci. and Technol., **3** , 312 (1990).
21. V. Ambegaokar and F.A.Baratoff, Phys. Rev. Lett. **11**, 104 (1963).
22. R. Feynman, R.B. Leighton and M. Sands, *Lectures on Physics:QuantumMechanics* (Addison-Wesley, 1965).
23. Heiden paper in these proceedings.
24. K. Char, M.S. Colclough, S.M. Garrison, N. Newman, G. Zaharchuk, Appl. Phys. Lett. **59** 733 (1991).
25. ISEC 91, Strathclyde, U.K.
26. M.J. Ferrari, M. Johnson, F.C. Wellstood, J. Clarke, P.A. Tosenthal, R.H. Hammond and M.R. Beasley, Appl. Phys. Lett. **53** 695 (1988).
27. M.J. Ferrari, M. Johnson, F.C. Wellstood, J. Clarke, A. Inam, X.D. Wu, L. Nazar, T. Verkatesan, Nature **341** (1989).
28. Heiden, see article in this volume.

Effect of Thermodynamic Fluctuations on the Transport Properties in YBaCuO Thin Films

W. Lang[1], *G. Heine*[1], *H. Jodlbauer*[1], *P. Schwab*[2], *X.Z. Wang*[2], *and D. Bäuerle*[2]

[1]Ludwig Boltzmann Institut für Festkörperphysik, Kopernikusgasse 15, A-1060 Wien, Austria and Institut für Festkörperphysik der Universität Wien, Austria

[2]Institut für Angewandte Physik, Universität Linz, A-4040 Linz, Austria

Abstract. Measurements of the electrical resistivity and the Hall effect in thin films of YBaCuO are reported. The films have been fabricated by pulsed laser deposition in oxygen atmosphere on MgO substrates. The rounding of the resistivity curve above T_C was attributed to thermodynamic fluctuations of the superconducting order parameter and analyzed in terms of Aslamazov-Larkin and Maki-Thompson theories and their extensions for 2-dimensional, layered superconductors. These fluctuation contributions were also found near the superconducting transition of the Hall effect. From the results we deduce a c-axis coherence length $\xi_{C(0)} = 1.5$ Å and a phase-relaxation time $\tau_\varphi = 8.6 \times 10^{-13}$ s at 100 K, indicating 2-dimensional transport and moderate strong pair-breaking in YBaCuO, respectively.

1. Introduction

In early investigations of the transport properties of high temperature superconductors, a remarkable rounding of the superconducting transition was observed and attributed to inhomogenities in ceramic samples. These effects, however, appeared also in both thin film and single crystal samples, and must be explained by a contribution of superconducting fluctuations to the normal state transport properties near T_C.

2. Experimental Techniques

Thin films of $YBa_2Cu_3O_{7-d}$ (thickness ≈ 0.5 μm) were fabricated on (100) MgO subtrates by reactive pulsed-laser deposition using 248 nm KrF-excimer laser radiation and stoichiometric ceramic targets. The critical current density of these films was around $j_C \geq 4 \times 10^6$ A/cm². The magnetotransport measurements were performed in a closed cycle refrigerator using lock-in technique with low current density $j = 80$ A/cm² and a magnetic field $B = 0.69$ Tesla.

In order to enhance the signal to noise ratio, the Hall effect measurements were repeated several times with both polarities of the magnetic field while sweeping the temperature very slowly.

Springer Series in Solid-State Sciences, Vol. 113 **Electronic Properties of High-T$_c$ Superconductors**
Editors: H. Kuzmany, M. Mehring, J. Fink

3. Paraconductivity

The temperature variation of the resistivity ρ_{xx} is shown in Fig.1. The width of the superconducting transition is about 0.5 K and we define a mean field critical temperature $T_C^* = 88.55$ K by the intersection point of the tangent to the transition curve with the T axis. Above T_C^* the conductivity $\sigma_{xx} = \sigma_{xx}^N + \Delta\sigma_{xx}$ is given by the sum of normal state and fluctuation contributions. Hence it is necessary for the determination of the paraconductivity $\Delta\sigma_{xx}$ to substract the extrapolated normal state contribution. Altough the mechanism responsible for the normal state transport is still controversial, we found an excellent agreement of the ρ_{xx} vs T curve with the model of Anderson and Zou [1] at temperatures above 160 K, where superconducting fluctuations should be insignificant.

Essentially there are two mechanisms for the paraconductivity, well known as direct or Aslamazov-Larkin (AL) [2] and indirect or Maki-Thompson (MT) [3,4] contributions. These formulas were extended for the case of layered superconductors by Lawrence and Doniach (LD) [5] and Hikami and Larkin (HL) [6]. If we use the c-axis lattice parameter d = 11.7 Å of YBaCuO for the interlayer distance, the zero-temperature coherence length in c-direction, $\xi_{C(0)}$, remains the only fit parameter in the LD expression. The HL term additionally contains the pair-breaking parameter $\delta = (T_{CO} - T_C^*)/T_C^*$, reflecting the shift of the transition temperature from a hypothetic intrinsic value without any pair-breaking effects T_{CO} to the lower actual value T_C^*.

The paraconductivity $\Delta\sigma_{xx}$ is plotted in Fig.2 together with the calculated contributions from the LD and HL processes using $\xi_{C(0)}$= 1.5 Å and δ = 0.35 as fit parameters. Deviations from the theory above 94 K can be related to a cutoff of the fluctuation spectrum at high energies, where the slow variation approximation of the Ginzburg-Landau theory is no longer valid [7].

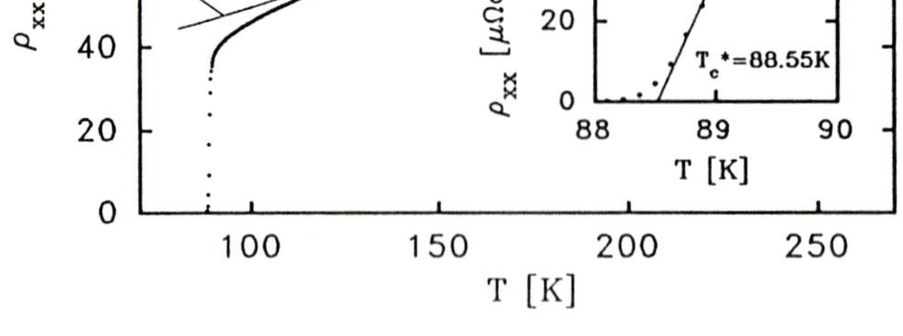

Fig.1: Temperature variation of the resistivity ρ_{xx} of an YBaCuO film.

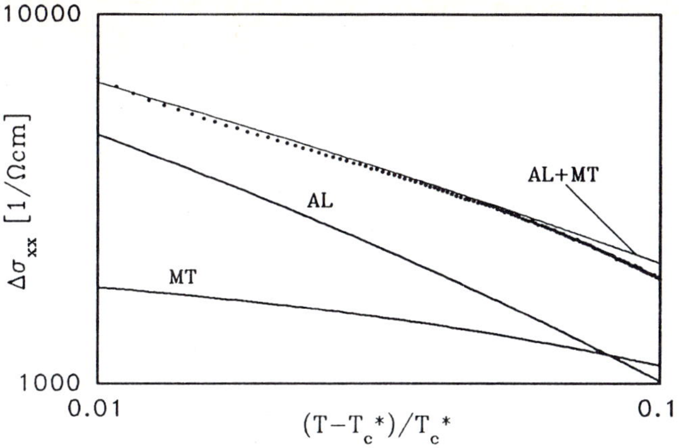

Fig.2: Paraconductivity $\Delta\sigma_{xx}$ in YBaCuO as a function of the reduced temperature $(T-T^*_C)/T^*_C$. The solid lines represent the results from the fit.

4. Hall effect in the fluctuation regime

The Hall resistivity ρ_{xy} as a function of temperature is shown in Fig.3. The negative voltage observed in the temperature range from 87 to 88.7 K will be not discussed here. T^*_C = 88.7 K was determined by the method described above. The Hall effect in the fluctuation regime can be written $\sigma_{xy} = \sigma^N_{xy} + \Delta\sigma_{xy}$ in analogy to the paraconductivity. The normal state Hall effect was subtracted using a recent theory of Anderson [8], where he proposed an additional relaxation mechanism for the Hall angle θ_H, yielding the temperature dependence cot $\theta_H = aT^2 + C$. This theorem is in good agreement with our data in the

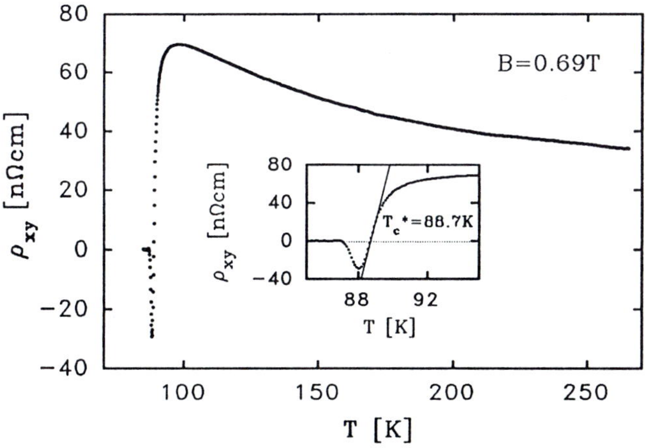

Fig.3: Hall resistivity ρ_{xy} in YBaCuO as a function of temperature.

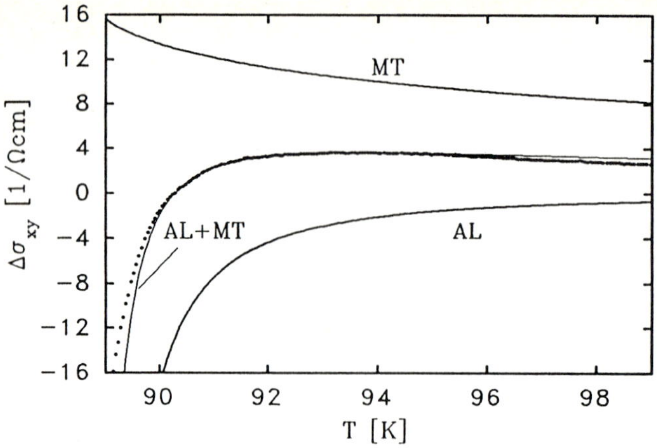

Fig.4: Excess Hall conductivity $\Delta\sigma_{xy}$ vs temperature. The solid lines are the results from the fit.

temperature range from 120 to 220 K and was also observed to hold in various cuprates [9].

The first calculation of $\Delta\sigma_{xy}$ by Fukuyama et al. [10] including both the AL and the MT contributions was recently extended for layered superconductors by Ullah and Dorsey [11] and Rice et al. [12]. Like the paraconductivity, $\Delta\sigma_{xy}$ is a function of $\xi_{C(0)}$, δ and in addition, of the parameter α, reflecting details of the band structure at the Fermi-energy [10]. The excess Hall conductivity $\Delta\sigma_{xy}$ is plotted in Fig.4 together with the calculated AL and MT contributions. A remarkably good fit including the sign change at 90 K (not to be confused with $\rho_{xy} < 0$ below 88.7 K) can be obtained using the values for $\xi_{C(0)}$ and δ previously determined and α = -0.168.

5.Conclusions

The effect of thermodynamic fluctuations on the transport properties in YBaCuO superconductors, i.e. the paraconductivity and the excess Hall effect can be both described with a consistent set of parameters. The c-axis coherence length $\xi_{C(0)}$= 1.5 Å indicates that the two CuO_2-planes within an elementary cell are tightly coupled, acting as one superconducting layer. From the magnitude of the pair-breaking parameter δ, a T_{C0} of 120 K and a phase-relaxation time [6] τ_{φ} = 8.6 x 10^{-13} s at 100 K are estimated. The latter is essentially equivalent to the transport scattering time, which may be an indication that the mechanism causing the pair-breaking is also responsible for the normal state resistivity, disfavouring any conventional phonon mechanism. Finally, the negative sign of α indicates that the fluctuations are, like the normal state transport, mediated by holes.

Acknowledgements. This work was supported by the Fonds zur Förderung der wissenschaftlichen Forschung, Austria, grant no. P8180.

References.

1. P.W.Anderson, Z.Zou: Phys.Rev.Lett. **60**, 132 (1988)
2. L.G.Aslamazov, A.I.Larkin: Sov.Phys.-Solid State **10**, 875 (1968)
3. K.Maki: Prog.Theor.Phys. **39**, 897 (1968)
4. R.S.Thompson: Phys.Rev.B **1**, 327 (1970)
5. W.E.Lawrence, S.Doniach: in Proc. of the 12th Int. Conf. on Low Temp. Phys. (Kyoto 1970), ed: E.Kanda, Keigaku, Tokyo 1971, p.361
6. S.Hikami, A.I.Larkin: Mod.Phys.Lett.B **2**, 693 (1988)
7. W.L.Johnson, C.C.Tsuei: Phys.Rev.B **13**, 4827 (1976)
8. P.W.Anderson: Physica C **185-189**, 11 (1991)
9. e.g.: N.P.Ong, T.W.Jing, T.R.Chien, Z.Z.Wang, T.V.Ramakrishnan, J.M.Tarascon, K.Remschnig: Physica C **185-189**, 34 (1991)
10. H.Fukuyama, H.Ebisawa, T.Tsuzuki: Prog.Theor.Phys. **46**, 1028 (1971)
11. S.Ullah, A.T.Dorsey: Phys.Rev.B **44**, 262 (1991)
12. J.P.Rice, J.Giapintzakis, D.M.Ginsberg, J.M.Mochel: Phys.Rev.B **44**, 10158 (1991)

Metallic Weak-Link Character of Grain Boundaries in High-T_c Materials

R. Nicolsky

Instituto de Física, Universidade Federal do Rio de Janeiro,
C.P. 68528, Rio de Janeiro 21945, Brazil

Abstract: The intrinsic current-voltage characteristics (CVC) of high-T_c materials are analysed in the frame of a recent microscopic theory of metallic (nontunnelling) Josephson junctions, suitable for SNS systems. The comparison of the theoretical model with experimental CVC of grain boundaries shows that those intrinsic juntions exhibit the essential features of metallic weak links and definitely do not act as tunnelling junctions. As a consequence, the grain boundaries are also responsible for the presence of intrinsic normal electrons in the superconducting state of high-T_c superconductors.

1. Introduction

The high temperature superconductors, the metallic copper oxides, are non homogeneous materials intrinsically, which means that the pair potential of these materials is non constant in space due to the presence of grain boundaries (GB) in the ceramics and twin planes in the single crystals, additionally to a possible spatial anisotropy of the gap in the unit cell scale. Deutscher and Müller [1] showed that the short coherence length of those materials is the responsible for those intrinsic inhomogeneities. Due to spatial inhomogeneities, the coupling between two fully superconducting regions with equilibrium pair potentials in those materials is of the Josephson type. In this paper it is shown that the nature of a particular inhomogeneity determines the charge transport process across it in the superconducting state.

If an insulator (or a semiconductor) is placed in between two fully superconducting regions, neither the Cooper pairs nor the superconducting excitations can propagate across such an inhomogeneity, because its gap is much larger than the pair potential of the superconductors with a vacuum of density of states. In this case, the only charge transport process possible is the Josephson and quasiparticle tunnelling through the barrier representing the insulating (or semiconducting) gap [2]. The inhomogeneity can be represented as a superconductor-insulator-superconductor (SIS) system and is usually called tunnel Josephson junction (TJJ).

When the inhomogeneity is due to the presence of a normal metal (or the normal state of the superconductor) in between the superconducting regions, the pair potential in the inhomogeneity decreases or vanishes forming a potential well instead of a barrier. The well exhibits a density of bound excited normal states close to the Fermi surface which accounts for the propagation of the Cooper pair and superconducting excitations [3] through the inhomogeneity. As a consequence, the charge transport process in this inhomogeneity is the metallic conductance, instead of tunnelling,

Springer Series in Solid-State Sciences, Vol. 113 Electronic Properties of High-T_c Superconductors
Editors: H. Kuzmany, M. Mehring, J. Fink

of a precise kind: the Andreev reflection (AR) mechanism [3]. All these inhomogeneities belong to superconductor-normal metal-superconductor (SNS) systems. In the literature, these systems are called weak links as well. In this paper these systems are called metallic Josephson junctions (MJJ), in order to avoid the ambiguity of the former denomination and to stress their metallic and Josephson character.

The resulting quantum mechanical models for both systems are opposite to each other: the TJJ are represented by potential barriers while the MJJ ones by potential wells. As expected, the involved physics are consequently different: *tunnelling conductance* in TJJ against *metallic conductance* in MJJ systems. Thus, the identification of whether the dominant charge transport process in GB is tunnelling or metallic conductance, is an essential step for characterizing the intrinsic nature of the electronic states which populate those GB. The search for that identification of the dominant transport process increased substantially the experimental investigation on GB [4-6] and even on the Josephson coupling between unit cells [7].

2. Identification of the GB Nature

There is a lot of controversy about the nature of the GB. This disagreement is due to the ambiguity of the method used to identify whether the GB is of the TJJ or MJJ kind. The used criteria is the temperature dependence of the critical current J_c of tunnelling or metallic junctions. The experimental data of GB, normalized to the lowest temperature value of J_c, is compared with the theoretical dependence for each kind of junction. This attempt usually results inconclusive, as shown by figure 6 of Ref. 4, due to the similarity between the temperature dependence of the critical current J_c in TJJ and MJJ systems. This ambiguity is discussed in Ref. 9.

The lack of success of the criteria based on temperature dependence of the critical current suggests the use of another physical property of both kind of junctions but with an unambiguously different behaviour. The more appropriate property, because it satisfies this condition, is the CVC of each type of junction [8,9], since they are entirely distinct in TJJ and MJJ systems, avoiding any ambiguity in almost all cases. These criteria, explained elsewhere [8,9], can be summarized as follows

$$\text{TJJ systems: } I = G_Q V_J < I_N = V_J/R_J$$

$$\text{MJJ systems: } I = I_N + I_{AR} > I_N = V_J/R_J$$

for $V_J < 2\Delta$, where I is the total current across the junction averaged in a cycle, G_Q is the quasiparticle tunnelling conductance, V_J is the junction voltage, I_N is the normal (ohmic) current, R_J is the junction resistance, I_{AR} is the additional conductance due to the Andreev reflection mechanism, which is voltage dependent [3] and non negative [8], and Δ is the pair potential or gap. Figure 1 shows the typical CVC of TJJ and MJJ systems and illustrates the above inequalities. The tunnelling CVC exhibits the characteristic hysteresis crossing the ohmic curve and the metallic CVC shows the increase of the current at low voltages, exceeding largely the critical current.

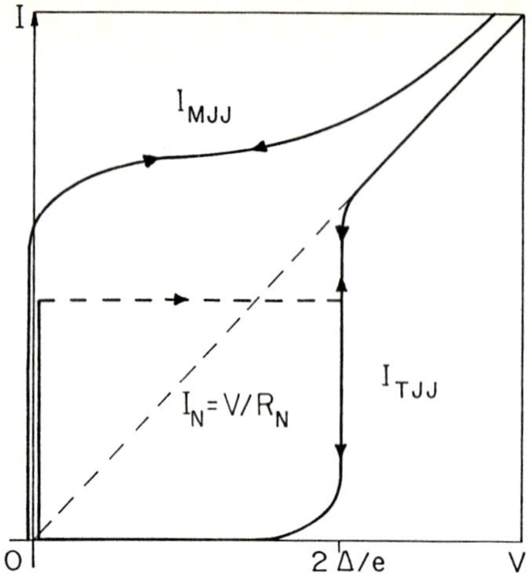

Figure 1. Typical CVC of TJJ and MJJ systems releted to the normal (ohmic) curve for the same resistance. Note that the critical current of a MJJ is larger than the one of a TJJ with the same resistance. In the MJJ systems the current response for low voltages usually exceeds the critical current and the total current exceeds the ohmic one, even at high voltages. Note the characteristic hysteresis of TJJ systems, crossing the ohmic curve.

The figure 1 and the above inequalities show that in the sub-gap voltage range, the CVCs of a TJJ and a MJJ are separated unambiguously by the normal (or ohmic) current. The TJJ exhibits a *deficient conductance* and the MJJ an *excess conductance* (where the AR contribution is the additional term) related to the metallic (ohmic) one. This excess conductance, highly nonlinear at low voltages and increasing when the temperature decreases below T_c [3], is the signature of the AR mechanism, since AR is the only charge transport process which exceeds the ohmic conductance in normal metals. The above inequalities can be used as the criteria [9] for determining whether the character of an inhomogeneity is tunnelling- or metallic-like.

Actually, a high-T_c sample is a 3-dimensional network of junctions represented by GB, where each one can be of the TJJ or MJJ kind. The above inequalities are obviously still valid for a network of only one kind of junctions. If a particular sample has both types of junctions, the summation of the currents over all junctions should be a competition between both types of conductances. The final result, when compared with the normal conductance following the above criteria, should indicate which transport process is dominant in the sample.

3. Discussion of the Experimental Data

Applying the above criteria for CVC of individual GB [4-6], we must consider first that at $V = 0$ the normal (ohmic) current crosses the origin and at finite voltages the CVC is linear in V. Under these circumstances, there is no doubt in concluding that in all cases of Ref. 4 - 6 the GB are

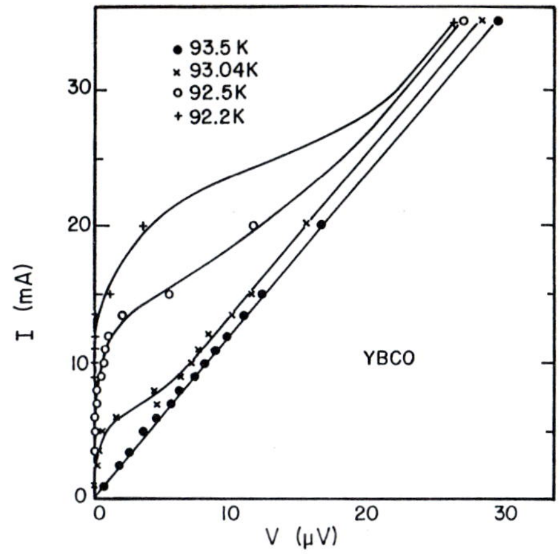

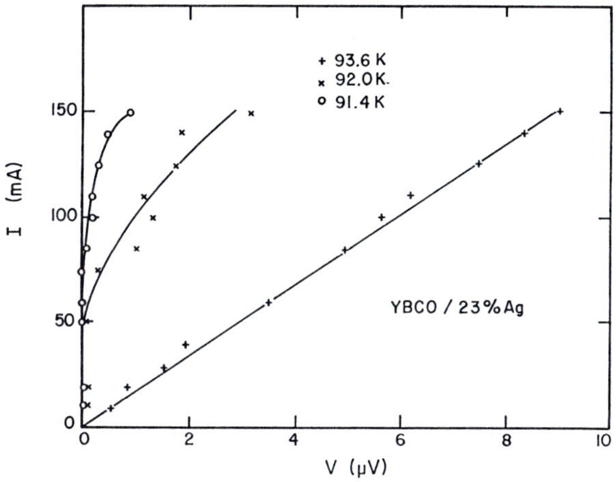

Figure 2. CVC of pure YBCO (above) and silver-coated (23%) YBCO (below). Note that the silver-coated CVC are essentially a magnification of the ones of pure YBCO. The lines are only guides for eyes (after Ref. [10]).

metallic junctions, avoiding any discrepancy, even when the authors state in contrast that the GB form SIS junctions [6].

In the case of samples with a 3-dimensional network of GB it is convenient to compare [10] the CVC of pure ceramic YBCO with the CVC of another one which has nonrandom silver-coated grains [11]. The former sample has only MJJ between grains, due to the presence of silver coating rather uniformly each grain. Thus, it is a control sample for determining the nature of the GB in the first sample of pure YBCO. Figure 2 shows the CVC of both samples for different temperatures close to T_c. It is remarkable that at T_c both CVC are linear (ohmic) and cross the origin, which is the typical normal metal behaviour. For temperatures below T_c the CVC of both samples exhibit an excess conductance, nonlinear at low voltages but constant at higher voltages, and increasing with the decreasing temperature, which is a signature of the AR mechanism, as we discussed above. This shows clearly that the GB present in the pure YBCO sample are, from the charge transport point of view, of the same character of the intergrain metal in the silver coated sample. Following the above criteria, this means that the GB are junction of the metallic kind, the normal state of the YBCO, and the dominant charge transport process is definitely the metallic conductance.

The comparison of the critical currents or the current values at the same voltage between both samples shows that the responses in the ceramic with silver coated grains are magnifications of the ones in pure YBCO, as we see in figure 2. This is in qualitative agreement with the model for critical current density in large and clean SNS junctions [12], which means that the length of the normal metal region is larger than the coherence length but smaller than the inelastic mean free path. This assumption is reasonable for high T_c materials, which have a very short coherence length [1]. The raise of the critical current density and the current response to the applied voltage is the result of the competition between the increasing of the effective length of the junction normal metal part roughly with the cubic root of the silver content and that of the average electronic density, which tends asymptotically to its silver value, more than two orders larger than the YBCO one [12]. The limit to such enhancement is the decrease of the bulk critical density with the silver content, due to the consequent reduction of the superconducting fraction in the cross section of the sample [10]. Thus, the enhancement of the critical current density with the silver content implies the assumption that the GB of pure YBCO sample are its metallic state.

In conclusion, the dominant charge transport process through GB in high-T_c superconductors has metallic weak link (nontunnelling) character, which means that it is a kind of metallic conductance with an additional component due to the Andreev scattering mechanism. This means that there are intrinsically *normal electron density of states* in YBCO ceramics even in the supercon- ducting state. This density of states is definitely located at the GB and possibly other parts connecting fully superconducting regions coupled by Josephson effect, as the twin planes and even the unit cell part between two sets of CuO_2 double planes [7].

References

[1] K.A. Müller and G. Deutscher, *Phys. Rev. Letts.* **59**, 1745 (1987).
[2] M. Tinkham, *Introduction to Superconductivity* (Robert E. Krieger Publishing Co., Malabar, FL, 1985), Chap. 6, p. 192.
[3] R. Kümmel, U. Gunsenheimer, and R. Nicolsky, *Phys. Rev.* **B42**, 3992 (1990), and references therein.
[4] J. Mannhart, P. Chaudhari, D. Dimos, C.C. Tsuei, and T.R. McGuire, *Phys. Rev. Letts.* **61**, 2476 (1988).
[5] Z. Ivanov and T. Cleason, *Physica* **B165-166**, 69 (1990).
[6] R. Gross, P. Chaudhari, D. Dimos, A. Gupta, and G. Koren, *Phys. Rev. Letts.* **64**, 228 (1990).
[7] R. Kleiner, F. Steinmeyer, G. Kunkel, and P. Müller, *Phys. Rev. Letts.* **68**, 2394 (1992).
[8] R. Nicolsky, *Cryogenics* **29**, 388 (1989).
[9] R. Nicolsky, *Physica* **C185-189**, 2611 (1991).
[10] R. Nicolsky, L. Ghivelder, P. Rodrigues Jr., P. Pureur, and S. Reich, to be published.
[11] S. Reich and I. Felner, *J. Appl. Phys.* **67**, 388 (1990).
[12] J. Bardeen and J.L. Johnson, *Phys. Rev.* **B5**, 72 (1972).

The Chemical Potential and Thermodynamic Properties of Narrow-Band Superconductors

D. van der Marel and G. Rietveld

Delft University of Technology, Department of Applied Physics, Lorentzweg 1, NL-2628 CJ Delft, The Netherlands

Abstract. We discuss some of the consequences for the thermodynamic properties if a superconductor has a non-neglegible ratio of T_c/T_F. Starting from the BCS expression we derive an analytic expression for the thermodynamic potential at finite temperature, which has the relevant physical properties. From there we derive the corresponding Helmholtz-Ginzburg-Landau free energy functional near the phase transition, and discuss the behaviour of the order parameter, the chemical potential, the specific heat and the expansivity near T_c.

1. Introduction

One of the features that distinguishes 'exotic' [1] from ordinary superconductors is a relatively large scale of the transition temperature compared to the (still larger) Fermi temperature. This feature is sometimes used as an argument in favour of a Bose-Einstein condensation picture of high temperature superconductivity. From an analysis of the BCS model in the low density limit, it has been shown [2], that if T_c/T_F is no longer small, the chemical potential is shifted at $T = 0$. At finite temperature the shift of the chemical potential can be approximated by the relation $\mu(T)/\mu_n \simeq 1-|\Delta(T)/2\mu_n|^2$, where $\Delta(T)$ is the temperature dependent BCS-gap [3]. At the superconducting transition the first derivative of the chemical potential has a jump, given by the relation $\Delta(d\mu/dT)_{T_c} \approx 2.4T_c/T_F$. A qualitatively similar behaviour of μ has also been predicted for a two-dimensional (2D) charged boson gas, which undergoes pair condensation due to an attractive interaction between the bosons [4]. In 'classical' weak coupling and Migdal-Eliashberg theory this effect is not considered, because $T_c \ll T_F$ is assumed. The jump in the specific heat at T_c is calculated as $T\partial S/\partial T$ at fixed μ in the standard BCS treatment.

The anomaly in μ does not lead to unusual behaviour of the other thermodynamic functions. It merely causes a small reduction of the jump in the specific heat and the thermal expansivity coefficient. Only if T_c/T_F is of order 1 or larger this reduction would become noticable. On the other hand, if the electronic pressure is somehow externally fixed, a jump in $d\mu/dT$ implies a a jump in entropy (with a corresponding portion of latent heat at the phase transition), because μ is the Gibbs free energy per electron. However, as long as it is justified to assume that the volume is essentially constant due to the elastic restoring forces of the crystal, the electronic pressure is a temperature dependent quantity and the entropy has to be calculated either from the Helmholtz free energy or from the thermodynamic potential. Due to the large value of the bulk modulus (of order 100 GPa) compared to the superconductivity induced changes of electronic pressure ($\leq$ 60 kPa in high T_c cuprates), the changes of the crystal volume are indeed very small.

Springer Series in Solid-State Sciences, Vol. 113 Electronic Properties of High-T_c Superconductors
Editors: H. Kuzmany, M. Mehring, J. Fink

2. General expressions for the thermodynamic potential and entropy of a BCS superconductor

We assume that the electrons interact with each other with an effective attraction V_{kq}, leading to a BCS-type superconducting state. The thermodynamic potential of a BCS superconductor is, after carrying out the Bogoliubov transformation [5]:

$$\begin{aligned}\Omega(\mu,T,V,\Delta) = & \sum_k \left[-2T\ln\left(1+e^{-E_k/T}\right)+\xi_k-E_k+\tfrac{\Delta_k^2}{E_k}\tanh\left(E_k/2T\right)\right] \\ & -\tfrac{1}{4}\sum_{kq}\left(\tfrac{\Delta_q}{E_q}\tanh\left(E_q/2T\right)\right)V_{kq}\left(\tfrac{\Delta_k}{E_k}\tanh\left(E_k/2T\right)\right) ,\end{aligned} \tag{1}$$

where $E_k = \sqrt{\xi_k^2+\Delta_k^2}$ are the quasi-particle energies and $\xi_k = \epsilon_k - \mu$ are the single electron energies relative to the Fermi energy. The BCS gap equation can be obtained from this functional by looking for the minimum with respect to Δ_k. An expression for the average number of electrons is found from the relation $N_e = -\partial\Omega/\partial\mu$

$$\begin{aligned} 2 &= gW\sum_k \frac{\tanh\left(E_k/2T\right)}{E_k} , \\ N_e &= \sum_k \left[1-\frac{\xi_k\tanh\left(E_k/2T\right)}{E_k}\right] . \end{aligned} \tag{2}$$

The only types of excitations considered are the quasi-particles, hence the (fermionic) quasi-particle occupation numbers determine the electronic entropy in the usual way for a fermion gas, namely

$$S = -\tfrac{\partial}{\partial T}\Omega(\mu,T)\,|_\mu = -\sum_k\left[(1-f(E_k))\ln(1-f(E_k))+f(E_k)\ln f(E_k)\right] . \tag{3}$$

The entropy depends on Δ and μ through the quasi-particle energies entering the Fermi occupation functions and through the integration boundaries. As these are analytical functions, and as we will see that Δ and μ have no discontinuity at T_c, also $S(T)$ is continuous at the phase transition. Hence the transition remains of the second order type.

3. Coupled gap equations of a layered superconducting electron gas

We assume that the electronic structure is represented by a stack of 2D layers, with a bandwidth $W = N_a/(V\rho)$, where V is the crystal volume, N_a is the number of atoms, and ρ is a constant density of states per unit volume. We assume that, in the same way as in a free electron model, ρ does not depend on V and N_a, and that the electrons have a k-independent non-retarded effective attractive interaction $(-gW)$, so that the gap-parameter Δ is also k-independent.
At $T = 0$ the thermodynamic potential is obtained by direct integration of Eq. 1. The summations over k can be replaced by integrals using the relation $\sum_k = V\rho\int_{-\mu}^{W-\mu} d\xi$

$$\Omega(\mu,0,V,\Delta) = -\rho V\left[\mu^2+\tfrac{\Delta^2}{2}\left(1+\tfrac{g}{2}\ln\tfrac{\Delta^2}{4W\mu}\left(\tfrac{2}{g}+\ln\tfrac{\Delta^2}{4W\mu}\right)\right)\right] . \tag{4}$$

We determine Δ at the minimum, and the condition for particle number conservation as in the previous section. We furthermore approximate terms of the form $\ln\frac{4(W-\mu)\mu}{\Delta^2}$ with $\ln\frac{4W\mu}{\Delta^2}$, and expand in leading orders of Δ^2. This way we find

$$\Delta^2 = 4W\mu \exp\left(-\tfrac{2}{g}\right) \quad . \tag{5}$$

From direct integration of Eq. 2b, and after inserting the expression for Δ we find that the number of electrons tends to increase upon opening of the superconducting gap:

$$N_e = 2V\rho\left(\mu + \tfrac{\Delta^2}{4\mu}\right) \quad . \tag{6}$$

As the average number of electrons in a solid is macroscopically conserved due to the long range Coulomb forces, we now use this as a constraint on the chemical potential. Defining the Fermi temperature through the relation $N_e = 2V\rho\mu_n$ we obtain for the chemical potential

$$\mu = \tfrac{\mu_n}{2}\left(1 + \sqrt{1 - \tfrac{\Delta^2}{\mu_n^2}}\right) \simeq \mu_n - \tfrac{\Delta^2}{4\mu_n} \quad . \tag{7}$$

Because the change in μ is due to an increase of the surface charge, it is exactly matched by a change of workfunction ($\delta\mu + \delta W = 0$). Changes in workfunction manifest themselves as a modified electric field directly outside the sample surface, which can be measured with a variety of experimental techniques. Although the derivation leading to Eq. 7 is only valid at $T = 0$, from numerical calculations [3] it can be shown that the change in chemical potential due to the opening of a gap is given by the same relation if we insert $\Delta(T)$ for Δ. In the normal state $\mu_n(T)$ also depends on temperature due to the gradual transition to a non-degenerate gas at high temperatures. From Eqs. 5 and 6 we see that at the minimum with respect to Δ we have $\ln\frac{\Delta^2}{4W\mu} = -2/g$. Hence the expression for the Helmholtz free energy ($F(N_e, V) = \Omega(\mu, V) + 2\rho V\mu_n\mu$) for $T = 0$ is *at its minimum* with respect to Δ

$$F_s - F_n = -\tfrac{\rho V\Delta^2}{2}\left[1 + \tfrac{\Delta^2}{8\mu_n^2}\right] \quad . \tag{8}$$

4. Thermodynamic potential at finite temperature

For $T \neq 0$ it is not possible to solve the integrals occurring in the thermodynamic potential (Eq. 1) in closed analytical form. Instead we introduce a temperature dependance in a similar way as in the Ginzburg-Landau free energy. We first simplify the thermodynamic potential by realizing that in Eq. 4 the factor $\frac{g}{2}\ln\frac{\Delta^2}{4W\mu}$ occuring in front of the last two terms in brackets is almost constant and equal to -1 near the minimum. We approximate it with the constant value -1.

The first term of Eq. 1 equals $-\gamma T^2/2$ in the normal state. In the superconducting state it is reduced due to the opening of a gap. Using a series expansion for small T and Δ the leading terms are $-(\gamma T^2/2)(1 + \lambda\Delta^2(W^{-2} + \mu^{-2}))$, where λ is a dimensionless constant. The term proportional to Δ^2 adds a small contribution to the entropy, which we will however neglect in the rest of this discussion.

In the numerator inside the logarithmic term we replace Δ^2 with $\Delta^2 + \beta^2T^2$. From the various possible modifications leading to a temperature dependance this is the simplest one that leads correctly to a second order transition, with approximately the right temperature dependance of Δ, as well as various other properties in qualitative agreement with numerical calculations [3].

We furthermore define $D \equiv 4W\exp(-2/g)$, and combine the sum of three terms within the logarithm. We therefore consider the following form of Ω:

$$\Omega_s(\mu, T, V, \Delta) - (\Omega_n + \rho V\mu_n^2) = \rho V\left[-\mu^2 + \tfrac{\Delta^2}{2}\ln\tfrac{\Delta^2 + \beta^2T^2}{eD\mu}\right] \quad . \tag{9}$$

As we will later be interested in the electronic pressure, it is important to note in this context, that D is a volume dependent function, whereas β is a constant number.
The gap equation is obtained as usual from the minimum with respect to Δ. The number of electrons is found from $-\partial\Omega/\partial\mu$, which provides the temperature dependance of μ due to the opening of a gap. These coupled equations are

$$\begin{aligned} \Delta^2 &= \mu D \exp\left[\frac{\beta^2 T^2}{\Delta^2+\beta^2 T^2}\right] - \beta^2 T^2 \quad , \\ \frac{N_e}{\rho V} &= 2\mu_n = 2\mu + \frac{\Delta^2}{2\mu} \quad . \end{aligned} \tag{10}$$

At $T = 0$ these expressions are seen to reduce to the result of the previous section. From the equation for Δ we see, that the critical temperature is

$$T_c = \beta^{-1}\sqrt{eD\mu_n} \quad . \tag{11}$$

In order to have a $2\Delta_0/T_c$-ratio of about 3.5, we need $\beta \simeq 2.9$. The critical temperature depends on volume (and therefore on pressure) via D and μ_n. The latter is proportional to V^{-1}, whereas the volume dependance of the former can have any sign and value depending on the details of the underlying model [10]. The pressure dependance can be written in the form

$$\frac{d\ln T_c}{dp} = -\frac{1}{2B} + \frac{1}{2}\frac{d\ln D}{dp} \quad , \tag{12}$$

where B is the bulkmodulus of the crystal. Near the critical temperature we can expand around $\Delta = 0$:

$$\begin{aligned} \Delta(T)^2 &= \frac{\beta^2(T_c^2 - T^2)}{2+eD/4\mu_n} \quad , \\ \mu &= \mu_n - \frac{\Delta(T)^2}{4\mu_n} + O(\Delta^4) \quad . \end{aligned} \tag{13}$$

5. Helmholtz free energy and thermodynamic properties

As we are interested in the thermodynamic properties of the system at constant particle number it is useful to write down the Helmholtz free energy. We can derive this quantity from the thermodynamic potential by means of a Legender transformation, *i.e.* by adding $\mu N_e = 2\mu\mu_n/\rho V$ and expressing all quantities which were previously a function of μ explicitly in the new variable N_e. For general values of Δ this requires the inversion of a rather formidable expression, but near T_c it is sufficient to make a Tayler series expansion of Δ, keeping only terms up to order Δ^4. The result is the following Ginzburg-Landau free energy functional

$$F_s(N_e, T, V, \Delta) - F_n = \rho V\left[\Delta^2 \ln\frac{T}{T_c} + \frac{\Delta^4}{2\beta^2 T_c^2}\left(1 + \frac{\beta^2 T_c^2}{8\mu_n^2}\right)\right] \quad , \tag{14}$$

where it is understood, that $\mu_n = N_e/(2\rho V)$ is an explicit function of N_e. The same applies to T_c, which is depens on N_e through μ_n and D as can be seen from Eq. 11. The logarithmic term $\ln(T/T_c)$ is a remnant of the logarithmic term in the expressions for the thermodynamic potential. As the series expansion in Δ is only valid near T_c we will replace it with $-(1 - T/T_c)$ in the remainder of this section.
The temperature dependance of the order parameter, as well as the behaviour of μ (using $\mu = \partial F/\partial N_e$) follow easily from the above Helmholtz free energy expression, and have exactly the same limiting behaviour near T_c as in the earlier expressions.

The entropy is calculated from Eq. 14 using $S = -(\partial F/\partial T)_{N_e,V,\Delta}$. (Alternatively one may use Eq. 9 with $S = -(\partial\Omega/\partial T)_{\mu,V,\Delta}$. The result is, of course, the same near the phase transition.)

$$S_s - S_n = \frac{-\rho V \Delta(T)^2}{T} \tag{15}$$

which is continuous at the critical temperature. From it we can now express the jump in the specific heat:

$$(c_n - c_s)\,|_{T=T_c} = -\frac{\rho V \beta^2 T_c}{1 + \frac{\beta^2 T_c^2}{8\mu_n^2}} \quad . \tag{16}$$

The term in the denominator as a reduction factor which is due to the coupling between the order parameter and μ.

The electronic pressure is obtained from the relation $p = -(\partial\Omega/\partial V)_{\mu,T}$ (using Eq. 9) while keeping μ and T fixed, where it is important that μ_n, T_c and D depend on volume. Near T_c the same result is obtained from differentiation of Eq. 14

$$\begin{aligned} p_s - p_n &= \rho\left[\mu^2 - \mu_n^2 + \tfrac{1}{2}\tfrac{\Delta^4}{\Delta^2+\beta^2T^2} + \tfrac{1}{2}\Delta^2\tfrac{d\ln D}{d\ln V}\right] \\ &= -B\rho\Delta(T)^2\tfrac{d\ln T_c}{dp} + O(\Delta^4) \quad , \end{aligned} \tag{17}$$

where in the last line we used Eq. 12.

So far we have left the elastic deformation energy of the crystal out of consideration. The bulk modulus relates changes in pressure to changes in volume: $\delta V = (B/V)\delta p$. This way we can now calculate the jump in expansivity ($\alpha \equiv d\ln V/dT$)

$$(\alpha_n - \alpha_s)\,|_{T=T_c} = -\frac{\rho\beta^2 T_c}{1 + \frac{\beta^2 T_c^2}{8\mu_n^2}}\frac{dT_c}{dp} \quad . \tag{18}$$

6. Discussion

The expansivity and specific heat jumps should obey the Ehrenfest relation [7]

$$\frac{dT_c}{dp} = VT_c\frac{\alpha_n - \alpha_s}{c_n - c_v} \tag{19}$$

which, comparing the expressions 16 and 18, is indeed satisfied. The corrections on the expansivity coefficient and the specific heat due to the coupling between the order parameter and the chemical potential are usually small: for the high T_c cuprates the ratio of T_c/T_F is about 6%, so that there is only a reduction of 0.1% of the specific heat jump. Vice versa, even if there is no direct coupling between the order parameter and the chemical potential, a jump in expansivity coefficient will contribute to the jump in $d\mu/dT$, because $\mu \propto V^{-1}$ in a layered 2D electron gas. The jump in expansivity of $YBa_2Cu_3O_7$ is about $-2 \cdot 10^{-7}K^{-1}$ [6], with a strong in-plane anisotropy and no contribution along the c-axis. The former could be related to the transfer of charge between planes and chains occuring at the onset of superconductivity as has been treated by Khomskii [8], the latter is consistent with the assumption of quasi-2D behaviour. As the effective Fermi temperature is about 1500 K we can estimate that due to the lattice anomaly there is a contribution to $(d\mu_s/dT - d\mu_n/dT)\,|_{T=T_c}$ of $3 \cdot 10^{-4}$. The observed effect is about 3 orders of magnitude larger [9], which implies that has a different origin. In particular the effect can be attributed to the coupling between ψ and μ assuming that T_c/T_F is about 0.06.

7. Conclusions

We generalized the Ginzburg-Landau free energy expression to incorporate the effect of the coupling of the order parameter to the chemical potential occurring in the BCS theory of a dilute interacting electron gas. We have shown that there is a jump in $d\mu/dT$ at the phase transition, and calculated the consequences of this effect for some of the other thermodynamic properties, in particular the specific heat and the expansivity parameter. The corrections do not change the nature of the transition, and they are small even in the range of parameters of high T_c cuprates with a relatively large T_c/T_F-ratio of about 0.06.

Acknowledgements

The authors like to thank G. M. Eliashberg for pointing out the importance of the relation between $\mu(T)$ and other thermodynamic properties. One of the authors (D.v.d.M.) gratefully acknowledges stimulating discussions on this subject with D. I. Khomskii, M. J. Rice, B. Batlogg, C. M. Varma, A. Kapitulnik, and I. Mazin.

References

[1] Y. J. Uemera *et al.*, Phys. Rev. Lett. **66**, 2665 (1991).

[2] D.M.Eagles, Phys. Rev. **186**, 456 (1969); A. J. Legget, in *Modern Trends in the Theory of Condensed Matter*, edited by A. Pekalski and J. Przystawa (Springer-Verlag, Berlin, 1980); P. Nozieres and S. Schmitt-Rink, J. Low Temp. Phys. **59**, 195 (1985); M. Randeria, J. M. Duan and L. Y. Shieh, Phys. Rev. Lett. **62**, 981 (1989).

[3] D. van der Marel, Physica C **165**, 35 (1990); D. van der Marel, in *Electronic properties of High-T_c Superconductors and Related Compounds*, p. 401, edited by J. Fink, Springer-Verlag, Berlin.

[4] M. J. Rice and Y. R. Wang, Phys. Rev. B **37**, 5893 (1988).

[5] G. Rickayzen, *Theory of Superconductivity*, edited by R.E.Marshak, (Interscience publishers, New York, 1965).

[6] C. Meingast, O. Kraut, T. Wolf, H. Wühl, A. Erb, and G. Müller-Vogt, Phys. Rev. Lett. **67**, 1634 (1991).

[7] D. Shoenberg, *Superconductivity* (Cambridge University Press, London, 1952).

[8] D. I. Khomskii and F. V. Kusmartsev, in *Physics and Materials Science of High Temperature Superconductors, II*, edited by R. Kossowsky, B. Raveau, D. Wohlleben, and S. K. Patapis, (Kluwer Academic Publishers, Dordrecht , 1992.)

[9] G. Rietveld, N. Y. Chen, and D. van der Marel, to be published (1992).

[10] We have defined D as $4W\exp(-2/g)$. If the bandwidth is proportional to $V^{-\nu}$ we have $d\ln D/dp = (\nu/B) - (2/g)(d\ln g/d\ln p)$, where B is the bulkmodulus. Especially the pressure dependance of g can have any sign depending on the details of the mechanism for superconductivity.

Nonequilibrium Properties of HTSC Under Microwave Irradiation

A.L. Solovyev[2], *V.M. Dmitriev*[1], *and A.B. Agafonov*[1]

[1]Institute for Low Temperature Physics and Engineering, Ukranian Academy of Sciences, Lenin ave. 47, 310164 Kharkov, Ukraine
[2]Present address: Max-Planck-Institut für Festkörperforschung, Heisenbergstr. 1, W-7000 Stuttgart 80, Fed. Rep. of Germany

Abstract. Measurements of the current-voltage characteristics of S-c-N Nb-TlBaCaCuO point contacts have been performed over the temperature range from 4,2K to 300K under applied microwave radiation at a frequency of about 12 GHz. Two types of the excess current dependence on the power P of the external radiation were found. In one case, excess current oscillates with P increase that is explained by the processes of Andreev reflection in S-c-N contacts. In the other case,the excess current is found to be stimulated by the radiation power. Obtained resultes indicate the complicated nature of the quasi-particle spectrum and transport properties of the new superconductors.

1. Results and Discussion

Performing the study of S-c-N point contacts between normal metals and HTSC Y 1:2:3 ceramics we have obtained the series of results indicating the presence of noticeable quantity of quasi--particles in these superconductors well below T_c. In this connection, the investigation of the nonlinear and nonequilibrium phenomena in the high-T_c superconductors is of a great interest.

Therefore, the current-voltage characteristics (IVC) of S-c-N point contacts between Nb needle and single-phase ceramic crystallite $Tl_2Ba_2CaCu_2O_x$ with $T_c \cong 100K$ have been studied as a function of temperature and applied microwave radiation. For these measurements, the contacts having metallic type IVC with large excess current I^{exc} and pronounced $dV/dI=R_d$ minimum at zero bias V=0 were chosen. Two types of I^{exc} behaviour were found. Nonmonotonous $I^{exc}(P)$ dependence was observed for the first type point contacts over the temperature range from T_c to 50K (Fig.1). The dots is the I^{exc} on $z \simeq \sqrt{P}$ dependence for T=55K and V=200mV (where $z = eV_\omega/\omega$). These results support the idea [1] that induced by Andreev reflection IVC nonlinearity mechanism is responsible for the existence of I^{exc} in S-c-N contacts at the bias $V \gg \Delta$, T. In this case the IVC affected by external radiation can be described by

$$I(P)=J_o^2(z)I_o^{exc}\mathrm{sign}V + V/R. \qquad (1)$$

Therefore, $I^{exc} = I(P)-V/R$ must oscillate with P increase following the law $J_o^2(z)$. This curve (Fig.1) fits well our data. We think this is the first experimental confirmation of the predicted for conventional superconductors [1] I^{exc} on P

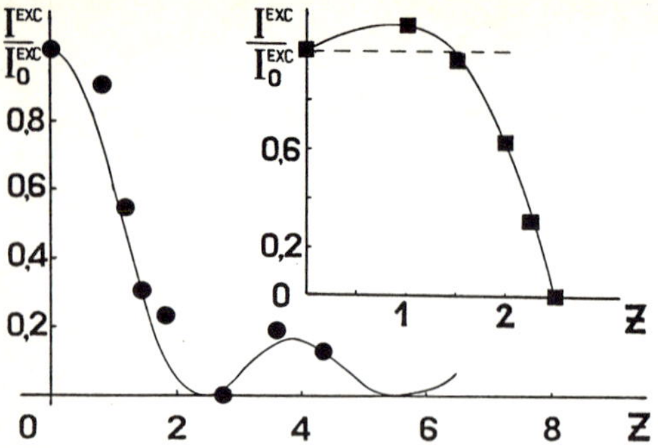

Fig.1 I^{exc} as a function of $z=eV_\omega/\omega \sim \sqrt{P}$ for the 1-st type contacts (dots). Solid line is the Bessel function $J_0^2(z)$. Squares - the analogous dependence for the 2-nd type contacts showing the I^{exc} stimulation effect. Solid line is guiding the eyes.

dependence in the S-c-N contacts. Thus, the induced by Andreev reflection non-Josephson mechanism of IVC nonlinearity at high biases can also exist in HTSC S-c-N contacts showing the presence of energy gap Δ in the excitation spectrum of quasi-particle current carriers. Besides, this mechanism may be used for detection and mixing of microwave signals as well.

Somewhat different $I^{exc}(P)$ behaviour was found for the second type contacts (insertion of Fig.1, squares connected by a solid curve, T=93 K, V=60 mV). We revealed stimulation of I^{exc}, i.e. of supercurrent which was observed earlier on Nb-Nb and Nb-Sn point contacts near T_c [2].

There are several physical mechanisms responsible for increasing of direct current through contact under applied rf radiation. First of all, we think this effect cannot be explained by classic detection because the IVC displacement at V=0 under microwave irradiation was not observed. In conventional superconductors such behaviour is usually connected with well-known superconductivity stimulation effects. If the current is homogeneously distributed in the superconductor Eliashberg mechanism acts [3]. In this case the microwave irradiation with frequency $\omega > \tau_\varepsilon^{-1}$ (where τ_ε is the electron-phonon inelastic relaxation time) stimulates the shift of superconductor distribution function "center of gravity" to higher energies. Such shift leads to energy gap increasing and, consequently, to increasing of superconductor critical parameters. In the structures with a pronounced spatial inhomogeneity of the order parameter, such as point contacts, the stimulation obeys the Aslamasov-Larkin [4] theory. This mechanism is due to energy diffusion of electrons, localized in the contact region, upward to energies mainly caused by the "vibration" of potential well. In the latter case, however, there should be two superconducting banks, while we deal with S-c-N contacts. Thus, there are several theoretical approaches to the rf power dependence of the critical current in superconductors, but to use them, more detailed information on the nature of the revealed effect should be necessary.

We would like to emphasize here, that we obtained our data well below T_c. Moreover, earlier we have found I^{exc} stimulation of the Nb-$YBa_2Cu_3O_x$ point contacts at T=5K. The observation of

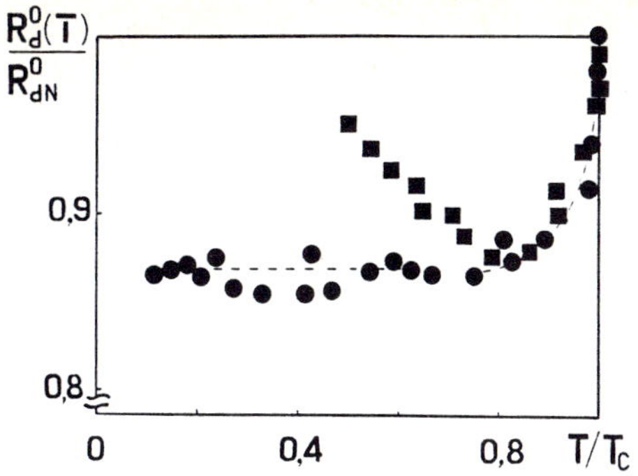

Fig.2. Differential resistance as a function of the reduced temperature. Dots - Nb-Y 1:2:3 contact; squares - Ta-Cu contact [7]

such effects associated with non-equilibrium processes in superconductor at temperatures $T<<T_c$ suggests that the quasi-particles in HTSC have a more complicated dynamics than in conventional superconductors.

Firstly, there should be mechanisms providing existence of non-freezing quasi-particles. This role can be played by electron scattering from uncompensated spin magnetic moments of Cu^{2+} localized in low-oxygen regions of HTSC, and by strong electron-phonon and electron-electron interaction [5]. The experimental results and the ideas presented here are consistent with our earlier data [6] on the temperature dependence of R_d^o=dV/dI of HTSC S-c-N point contacts at zero bias. There is a well-known fact that at $T<T_c$ the conductivity of S-c-N point contacts is due to quasi-particles, both with energy $E>\Delta$ and $E<\Delta$ [7]. In accordance with these ideas R_d^o of measured contacts drops sharply at $T<T_c$ (Fig.2,dots) at the expense of the appearance of the additional conductivity channel for quasi-particles with $E<\Delta$ due to Andreev reflection connected with energy gap increasing in superconductor with lowering T. Then the value of R_d^o practically does not change because of the energy gap saturation at low temperatures.In contrast with these results the zero-bias conductivity of the classical S-c-N contacts decreases [$R_d^o(T)$ rises] at $T/T_c<0,8$ (Fig.2, squares [7]) because of the freezing of quasi-particles with $E>\Delta$. Thus, our data did not display the increase of R_d^o and, consequently, the decrease of the number of the quasi-particles in high-T_c superconductors with lowering T.

Secondly, localization phenomena, which can make their contribution to transport properties of the contacts, are strong in HTSC [5]. Thus, in the case of weak localizations, the delocalization can take place due to external radiant energy and a total number of current carriers may increase affecting I^{exc} growth. Fig.3 shows $I^{exc}(T)$ dependence at P=0 (squares). Triangles denote $I^{exc}(T)$ of the 30x200 μm^2 microbridge cut out by laser scribing from the $YBa_2Cu_3O_x$ film on which only a common monotonous suppression of I^{exc} and I_c was observed under irradiation. In this case $I^{exc}(T)$, according to the theory [8] can be written as

$$I^{exc}(T) = \Delta/eR_N(\pi^2/4-1)\times th(eV/2kT) \qquad (2)$$

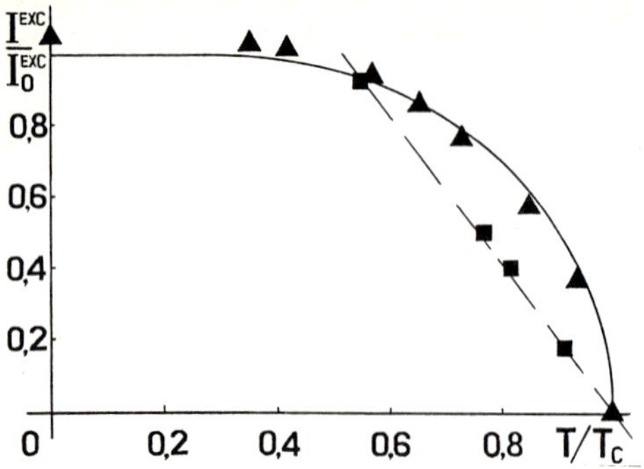

Fig.3. I^{exc} as a function of the reduced temperature. Squares - Nb - Tl 2:2:1:2 point contact; triangles - Y 1:2:3 thin film $30x200\mu m^2$ microbridge.

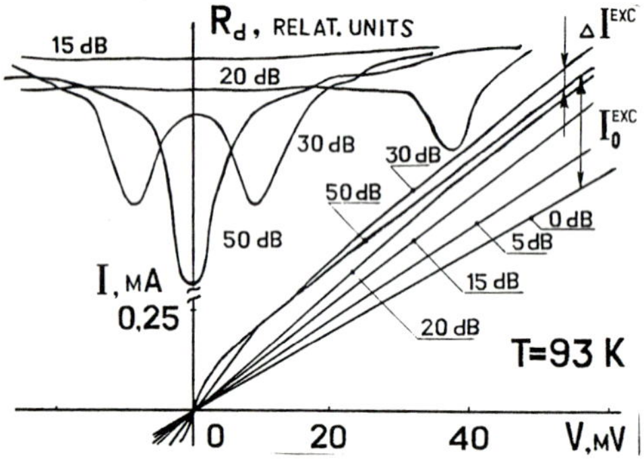

Fig.4. R_d=dV/dI and IVC vs T at different rf power levels $P(\alpha)$, (P_{max}=40mW). The waveguide attenuation α is denoted by dB. ΔI^{exc} and I_o^{exc} are the stimulated and undisturbed excess currents.

and follows $\Delta(T)$ dependence with a sufficient degree of accuracy (Fig.3, solid curve). In the first case, the dependence $I^{exc}(T)$ is practically linear indicating the lack of an excess current that agrees with statements of ref.5 about localization phenomena in HTSC.

Figure 4 shows the IVCs and their derivatives $dV/dI=R_d(V)$ of the second type contact measured as a function of rf power P.The unusual linearization of I-V characteristics at small biases under applied microwave radiation was found simultaneously with I^{exc} increasing. The obtained results demonstrate (Fig.4,α=30dB) that at voltages less than V_{min}=9mV IVC becomes linear and goes under the undisturbed curve (Fig.4, α = 50dB), giving the corresponding minima on $R_d(V)$ usually connected with the gap features $2\Delta/e$ of a superconductor. Assuming $\Delta(T=93K)$=9meV and follows the BCS theory we will get the value of $\Delta(0)$=20 meV, which is typical for HTSC. But this minimum swiftly shifts to higher V with increasing of P (V_{min}=37 mV at α=20 dB, Fig.4) that is difficult to connect with Δ increasing. We suppose this behaviour is due to expansion of linear part of I-V characteristic under microwave irradiation as it takes place in conventional long superconducting channel being in current resistive state [9]. The physical mechanism of this behaviour both in HTSC and in conventional superconductors was not explained yet. These results will be further developed in another papers.

References

1. A.F.Volkov, A.V.Sergeev: ZETF, **51**, 1716 (1981)
2. V.M.Dmitriev, E.V.Khristenko, S.Shapiro: Sbornik FKS, Instit. for Low Temp. Phys. Ukranian Acad. of Sciences, **28**, 3 (1973)
3. G.M.Eliashberg: Pis'ma V ZETF **11**, 186 (1970)
4. A.G.Aslamasov & A.I.Larkin: ZETF, **70**, 1349 (1976)
5. M.Yu.Kupriyanov, K.K.Likharev: UFN, **160**, 49 (1990)
6. V.M.Dmitriev, A.L.Solovyev: Fiz. Nizk.Temp. **16**, 650 (1990)
7. V.N.Gubankov, N.M.Margolin: Pis'ma v ZETF, **29**, 733 (1979)
8. S.N.Artemenko, A.F.Volkov, A.V.Zaitsev: ZETF, **76**, 1816 (1979)
9. V.M.Dmitriev, I.V.Zolochevsky, E.V.Khristenko: Fiz.Nizk.Temp. **12**, 643 (1986)

Hall Effect of Epitaxial $YBa_2Cu_3O_{7-x}$ and $Bi_2Sr_2CaCu_2O_y$ Films

R. Hopfengärtner[1], *M. Leghissa*[1], *G. Kreiselmeyer*[1], *B. Holzapfel*[1,2], *P. Schmitt*[1,2], *and G. Saemann-Ischenko*[1]

[1]Physikalisches Institut, Universität Erlangen, Erwin-Rommel-Str. 1, W-8520 Erlangen, Fed. Rep. of Germany

[2]Siemens AG, Zentrale Forschung und Entwicklung, W-8520 Erlangen, Fed. Rep. of Germany

Abstract: The Hall effect of epitaxial $YBa_2Cu_3O_{7-x}$ and $Bi_2Sr_2CaCu_2O_y$ films has been investigated experimentally and theoretically. In both compounds the normal state Hall coefficient R_H ($B \parallel$ c-axis) is positive and exhibits a strong temperature dependence, which is more pronounced in $YBa_2Cu_3O_{7-x}$ than in $Bi_2Sr_2CaCu_2O_y$. The Hall coefficient R^H_{xyz} in the normal phase has been calculated on the basis of a renormalized two-dimensional tight binding model using the relaxation time approximation. Strong correlation effects are accounted for via doping dependent hopping terms leading to band narrowing. The influence of the choice of the relaxation time on the Hall coefficient is explored. The calculations have been performed for a wide range of parameters and are compared to experimental data.

1. Introduction

Besides their striking superconducting properties copper oxide superconductors exhibit a variety of anomalous properties in the normal state. Among various other transport phenomena the Hall effect, which has triggered immense efforts of both experimental and theoretical investigations [1], provides valuable information about the electronic structure of the high-T_c superconductors (HTSC) in the normal phase. In this brief contribution we report on a comparative study of the Hall coefficient on epitaxial $YBa_2Cu_3O_{7-x}$ and $Bi_2Sr_2CaCu_2O_y$ films and its interpretation on the basis of a simple model.

2. Experiment and Discussion

The Hall effect measurements have been performed on epitaxial films of $YBa_2Cu_3O_{7-x}$ ($T_c \approx 90$ K) and $Bi_2Sr_2CaCu_2O_y$ ($T_c \approx 80$ K) prepared by pulsed laser ablation onto (100)-$SrTiO_3$ substrates. The details of the sample preparation are described in Refs. [2] and [3]. The measurements were carried out in magnetic fields up to 5 T by a standard dc-method for the configuration $B \parallel c$–axis ($j \parallel ab$–plane). Figure 1 displays the Hall coefficient R_H versus temperature of various $YBa_2Cu_3O_{7-x}$ (1:2:3) and $Bi_2Sr_2CaCu_2O_y$ (2:2:1:2) films. The Hall coefficient in the normal state in both compounds is holelike and exhibits a strong temperature dependence (more pronounced in 1:2:3 than in 2:2:1:2) with a maximum slightly above T_c. It is worth noting that the unusual temperature dependence of $R_H(T)$ as well as the complicated electronic structure of high-T_c superconductors does not allow a simple interpretation of the Hall coefficient in terms of the carrier concentration. In the phase transition $R_H(T)$ shows

Springer Series in Solid-State Sciences, Vol. 113 Electronic Properties of High-T_c Superconductors
Editors: H. Kuzmany, M. Mehring, J. Fink

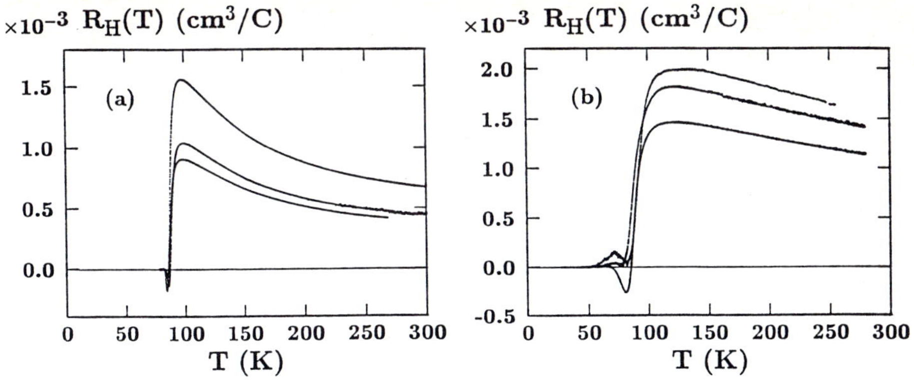

Figure 1: Hall coefficient versus temperature of several epitaxial $YBa_2Cu_3O_{7-x}$ (a) for $B = 5\,T$ and $Bi_2Sr_2CaCu_2O_y$ (b) films for $B = 5\,T$ (upper curve) and $B = 3\,T$ (two lower curves).

a peculiar behavior including a sign reversal. These overall features of R_H are in good agreement with reported data [1].

For the interpretation of the Hall coefficient $R_H(T)$ in the normal state, we propose for the electronic structure of the CuO_2 planes a two-dimensional tight binding model on a square lattice:

$$\epsilon(\vec{k}) = -2\tilde{t}(\cos(k_x a) + \cos(k_y a)) - 4\tilde{t}^* \cos(k_x a)\cos(k_y a), \tag{1}$$

where

$$\tilde{t} = t\delta, \quad \tilde{t}^* = t^*\delta \tag{2}$$

denote the renormalized nearest and next nearest neighbor hopping terms, δ the doping concentration (per site), and a the lattice constant. This band dispersion, which might be a reasonable starting point in the large doping regime of HTSC, accounts to some extent for strong correlation effects between the quasiparticles. The tight binding model describes an *effective* O $2p$ band which is located between the splitted lower and upper Cu $3d$ Hubbard sub-bands. Doped holes are created close to the top of the upper band edge. Assuming $B \parallel c$-axis and the weak field limit, we have calculated within the relaxation time approximation the anisotropic Hall tensor $R_H = R^H_{xyz} = \sigma_{xyz}/(\sigma_{xx}\sigma_{yy})$. The transport coefficients are given by [4]:

$$\sigma_{xx} = \sigma_{yy} = \frac{2e^2}{V}\sum_{\vec{k}}^{1.BZ} \tau(\vec{k})v_x^2(\vec{k})\left(-\frac{\partial f}{\partial\epsilon(\vec{k})}\right), \tag{3}$$

$$\sigma_{xyz} = -\frac{2e^3}{\hbar V}\sum_{\vec{k}}^{1.BZ} \tau^2(\vec{k})v_x(\vec{k})\left(v_x(\vec{k})\frac{\partial v_y(\vec{k})}{\partial k_y} - v_y(\vec{k})\frac{\partial v_y(\vec{k})}{\partial k_x}\right)\left(-\frac{\partial f}{\partial\epsilon(\vec{k})}\right), \tag{4}$$

where V is the normalization volume, $\tau(\vec{k})$ the relaxation time, $\hbar v_\alpha(\vec{k}) = \partial\epsilon/\partial k_\alpha$ ($\alpha = x, y$), and $f(\epsilon(\vec{k}))$ the Fermi distribution function. For the relaxation time, which in general might be a very complicated function of $\vec{k}$ and T, we have examined two simple approaches:

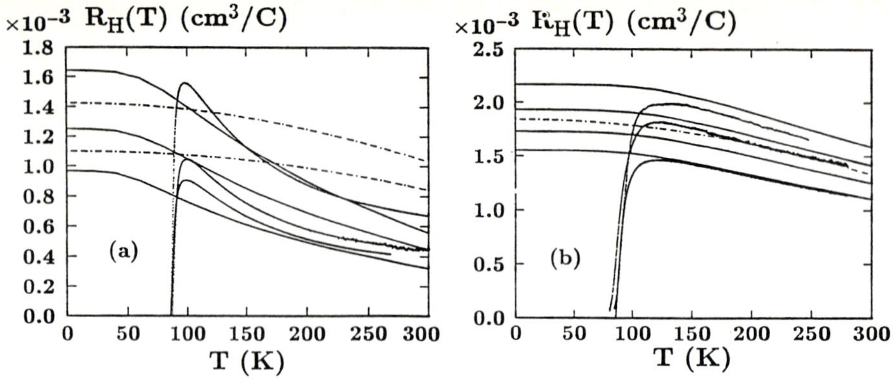

Figure 2: (a) Comparison between theory and R_H of 1:2:3. Solid lines are the predictions for the parameters $t = 0.40\,\text{eV}$, $t^* = 0.175\,\text{eV}$ and $\delta = 0.25, 0.3, 0.35$ (from top to bottom) assuming τ_l. The dash-dotted lines are the results for τ_0 and the parameters $t = 0.30\,\text{eV}$, $t^* = 0.075\,\text{eV}$ and $\delta = 0.3$ (upper curve) and $\delta = 0.35$ (lower curve). (b) Comparison of theory and data of 2:2:1:2. The solid curves are the results for the parameters $t = 0.45\,\text{eV}$, $t^* = 0.18\,\text{eV}$ and $\delta = 0.275, 0.3, 0.325, 0.35$ (from top to bottom) assuming τ_l, while the dash-dotted line is the result for $t = 0.3\,\text{eV}$, $t^* = 0.075\,\text{eV}$ and $\delta = 0.3$ taking τ_0.

$$\tau(\vec{k}) = \tau_0 = \tau(T, \delta) \tag{5}$$

and

$$\tau(\vec{k}) = \tau_l = \frac{l(T, \delta)}{\sqrt{v_x^2(\vec{k}) + v_y^2(\vec{k})}}. \tag{6}$$

The $\vec{k}$-independent relaxation time τ_0, which is often used for theoretical investigations of the Hall effect, has *no* influence on R_H. The calculations of R_H have been perfomed numerically for $t > 2 \mid t^* \mid$ taking into account the temperature dependence of the chemical potential.

In the following the unusual temperature dependence of the normal-state Hall coefficient of the 1:2:3 and 2:2:1:2 films is compared to the predictions of our calculations. Values for the doping concentration δ have been chosen to be close to $0.20 - 0.25$ per Cu site (and per sheet), which Shafer et al. [5] found for the $YBa_2Cu_3O_{7-x}$ ($T_c \approx 90\,\text{K}$) compound by iodometric titration. In the case of 2:2:1:2 we assumed similar values. The volume of the *model* unit cell entering in the calculations is $89\,\text{Å}^3$ for 1:2:3 and $115\,\text{Å}^3$ for 2:2:1:2. For t we take such values, which lead to a reasonable bandwidth $W = 8t\delta$ of $0.6 - 1.2\,\text{eV}$, and t^* has been choosen to fit the experimental Hall data as good as possible.

In Fig. 2 (a) and (b) we plot the experimental data of the 1:2:3 and 2:2:1:2 samples as well as the calculated Hall coefficient for fixed hopping terms varying the doping concentration. It should be noted that the temperature dependence of the calculated Hall coefficient comes only from the Fermi distribution function. Assuming the $\vec{k}$-dependent relaxation time τ_l we find a qualitatively good agreement between theory and $R_H(T)$ of $YBa_2Cu_3O_{7-x}$, while for τ_0 there is no agreement (opposite curvature of the graphs). In the case of the 2:2:1:2 samples it can be seen that for the chosen parameters the calculated normal-state Hall coefficient is in good quantitative agreement with experiment for both relaxation times.

At first glance it seems that our simple model for the electronic structure is capable to explain qualitatively the unusual temperature dependence of the 1:2:3 and 2:2:1:2 samples. However, the corresponding Fermi surfaces (small hole pockets, not shown here) are not consistent with experimental data [6]. A detailed discussion of this serious problem of our model as well as predictions of some other transport properties can be found in Ref. [7]. Concerning the unusual doping and temperature dependence of the Hall coefficient of HTSC several approaches have been made, including calculations on the basis of conventional band structure [8] and strongly correlated models e.g. Refs. [9] and [10]. But so far, no satisfactory explanation of the Hall coefficient, which is also compatible with the large Fermi surfaces observed in some of the cuprates, has been achieved.

3. Acknowlegments

We are grateful to D. Rainer and J. Heym, Universität Bayreuth, for many valueable discussions and stimulating support. This work was supported by the Bundesministerium für Forschung und Technologie.

References

[1] N. P. Ong, in: *Physical Properties of High-T_c Superconductors II*, ed. D. M. Ginzberg (World Scientific, Singapore, 1990) (and references therein).
[2] B. Roas, L. Schultz, and G. Endres, Appl. Phys. Lett. **53**, 1557 (1988).
[3] P. Schmitt, L. Schultz, and G. Saemann-Ischenko, Physica C **168**, 475 (1990).
[4] J. M. Ziman, *Electrons and Phonons*, (Oxford Univ. Press, New York, 1960).
[5] M. W. Shafer, T. Penney, B. L. Olson, R. L. Greene, and R. H. Koch, Phys. Rev. B **39**, 2914 (1989).
[6] J. C. Campuzano, G. Jennings, M. Faiz, L. Beaulaigue, B. W. Veal, J.Z. Liu, A. P. Paulikas, K. Vandervoort, H. Claus, P. S. List, A. J. Arko, and R. J. Bartlett, Phys. Rev. Lett. **64**, 2308 (1990).
[7] R. Hopfengärtner, G. Kreiselmeyer, M. Leghissa, B. Holzapfel, P. Schmitt, and G. Saemann-Ischenko, submitted to Phys. Rev. B.
[8] P. B. Allen, W. E. Pickett, and H. Krakauer, Phys. Rev. B **37**, 7482 (1987).
[9] H. Fukuyama and Y. Hasegawa, Physica B **148**, 204 (1987).
[10] S. A. Trugman, Phys. Rev. Lett. **65**, 500 (1990).

Anomalous Thermoelectric Power of the High-T_c Materials in Normal State: Both Copper Oxides and C_{60} Fullerene

Y.S. Song[1], *E.B. Park*[1], *Y.W. Park*[1], *S.K. Han*[2], *Y.C. Kim*[2], *and M.S. Jang*[2]

[1]Department of Physics, Seoul National University, Seoul 151–742, Korea
[2]Department of Physics, Pusan National University, Pusan 609–735, Korea

Abstract. We have measured the temperature dependence of thermoelectric power (TEP) and resistivity for the cuprate superconductors and the alkali metal doped bulk C_{60} fullerenes. The results for both high T_c materials are anomalous. The magnitude of TEP is small characteristic to that of the broad band metal. But the temperature dependent TEP of cuprate superconductors are semiconductor–like. To understand this somewhat controversial behavior, we propose the so called 'mixed state model' where the independent bound pairs and single–particle–like carriers coexist in the normal state, $T > T_c$. This mixed state model is compared with the local pair theory, as well as the marginal Fermi liquid theory. For the alkali metal doped bulk C_{60} fullerenes, the TEP shows two types of temperature dependences. One is very much anomalous with positive TEP values and the other is less anomalous in a sense that it is more or less simple metallic with negative TEP values. In both types, however, there exist electronic transitions in $70K < T < 200K$.

1. Introduction

The high T_c superconducting materials, both copper oxides and doped C_{60} fullerenes, have shown many anomalous features compared to the conventional BCS–type superconductors. One of the most pronounced anomalous data, perhaps, is the temperature dependences of thermoelectric power (TEP) [1,2]. In this paper, we will summarize the anomalous features of TEP data of both cuprate superconductors and the doped C_{60} fullerenes and propose a possible charge transfer mechanisms for each case. Moreover, a set of data on the pyrolyzed C_{60} samples is presented, which turns out very much similar with those of the positive TEP class of doped C_{60} fullerenes.

2. Experimental

Doping on C_{60}/ C_{70} fullerenes have been carried out in our laboratory and the details are published in reference [2]. One remark is that we have used the two zone heating method, as in the case of the graphite intercalation. This two zone heating method is particularly interesting. Because the heating of the C_{60}/C_{70} fullerenes in one side could create some kind of the amorphous fullerenes. Z. Iqbal et al. in Allied-Signal Inc. have pyrolyzed the C_{60}/C_{70} fullerenes at three different temperatures (T_p = 800K, 1000K and 1500K) for 16 hours in vacuum sealed tube and measured the X-ray diffraction patterns. It turns out that for T_p = 800K, the peaks corresponding to the C_{60}/C_{70} signal are still existing although the peaks are broadened. At T_p = 1000K, the original peaks of C_{60}/C_{70} have disappeared and very broad peaks corresponding to the amorphous nature of samples have appeared. But these broad peaks are different from those of the amorphous graphite. At T_p = 1500K, the X-ray diffraction patterns are very much similar to the peaks of the amorphous graphite [3]. We have chosen the T_p = 1000K sample and measured the TEP and resistivity as a function of temperature.

Springer Series in Solid-State Sciences, Vol. 113 Electronic Properties of High-T_c Superconductors
Editors: H. Kuzmany, M. Mehring, J. Fink

3. Results and Discussions

3.1 Cuprate superconductors

We have reported [1] the anomalous TEP of Y-Ba-Cu-O(YBCO), substituted YBCO such as $CaBaACu_3O_y$ with A = Y or Lanthanide, Bi-Sr-Ca-Cu-O(BSCCO) single crystals and Tl-Ca-Ba-Cu-O(TCBCO). All these results are not consistent with the simple metallic picture. The magnitude of TEP at room temperature for the cuprate superconductors are very small characteristic to that of broad band metals. But the temperature dependence is semiconductor–like. That is, the TEP increases upon cooling. Besides, the sign of TEP is quite complicate, so that it is not consistent with the expected values from the point of the doping. To understand these anomalous features of TEP, we have proposed the "mixed-state model" to fit our TEP data of TCBCO, YBCO, substituted YBCO, BSCCO single crystals. The model is based on the assumption of the strong Coulomb correlation in this system. In the normal state, i.e., for $T > T_c$, there exist two types of independent carriers. One is the single particle like carrier and the other is the bound pair. The bound pairs are not correlated each other, so that it is an independent bound pair. To exist such a bound pair in real space, the high Coulomb correlation is essential. At this moment, it is not clear whether it is the negative U type attraction or the antiferromagnetic type short range interaction which causes the formation of a bound pair. Intuitively, the existence of such bound pairs in the normal state is plausible because of the short coherence length of Cooper pair in the superconducting state. The idea is that as T becomes higher than T_c, the paired electrons do not change to the normal electrons completely. Instead, the pair-pair correlation vanishes at $T \geq T_c$ but the individual bound pairs remain uncorrelated each other. These bound pairs change to normal electrons as temperature becomes higher. The temperature dependence of the number of bound pairs turns out slightly different from TCBCO and other cuprate superconductors when we fit the data. The "mixed-state" means the coexistence of the bound pairs and the single particles in the normal state. The concept is somewhat similar to the two fluid model of Gorter-Casimir for the superconducting state (which is in the same frame of the BCS type superconductors) except that we are dealing with the normal state properties, i.e., for $T > T_c$. But if the origin of the bound pairs are the negative U attraction, then it is similar to the local pair theory of superconductors. In fact, Elishberg et al. had proposed [4] the mixed state of the local pairs and the single particle band carriers to explain the linear temperature dependence of resistivity for the cuprate superconductors in early days. Another interesting point is that the coexistence of the bound pairs and single particle like charge carriers are similar to the mixture of the charged bosons and fermions in the normal state. In this sense, the marginal Fermi liquid theory proposed by Varma et al. [5] might have some relationship with our mixed–state model. At this moment, we must admit that our mixed–state model is only a phenomenological model which could fit some of the anomalous TEP results of cuprate superconductors. But we have to extend our model to fit all the rest of the unusal phenomena of cuprate superconductors. Furthermore, the model itself should be well established in the firm theoretical frame.

3.2 C_{60} fullerene

Figure 1 shows the temperature dependence of resistivity and TEP for the pyrolyzed C_{60}/C_{70}. The pyrolysis of C_{60}/C_{70} mixture is done at T_p = 1000K for 16 hours. Being discussed in the previous section, the sample pyrolyzed at T_p = 1000 K, which is used in the resistivity and TEP measurements shown in fig. 1, is amorphous fullerene in a sense that the XRD pattern is in between the fullerene and the amorphous graphite.

Both resistivity and TEP have been measured from room temperature to 5K. The room temperature conductivity is high, σ_{RT} = 80 S/cm, even without doping. The weak temperature dependent resistivity is observed with $\rho(5K)/\rho(RT) \simeq 1.4$. The slope of resistivity versus temperature, $d\rho(T)/dT$, changes at $T \simeq 50K$, but there is no noticable electronic transition in $\rho(T)$ data. On the other hand, TEP data shows big electronic transition. The sign of TEP is positive

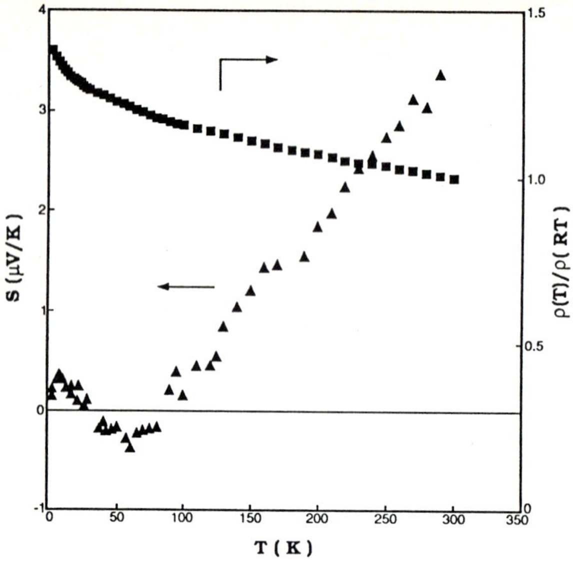

Figure 1. Temperature dependence of resistivity(■) and thermoelectric power(▲) of the pyrolyzed C_{60}/C_{70} fullerene

and the room temperature value is quite small, $S_{RT} \simeq +3.5\ \mu V/K$. Quasi-linear temperature dependence with a small knee at T $\simeq$ 180K is observed. The small magnitude as well as the linear temperature dependence of TEP is characteristic to that of the diffusive simple metals. At T $\simeq$ 100K, the TEP crosses zero. Below T =100 K, it remains negative until it changes the sign to positive at T $\simeq$ 30K. The absolute value of TEP for 5K $<$ T $<$ 100K is less than 0.3 μV/K.

Figure 2 shows the TEP of potassium doped C_{60}/C_{70} fullerenes. The doping conditions for all samples shown in fig.2 are identical to that described in reference [2]. However, the resistivity and the TEP of each sample are quite different as shown in the figure.

The large temperature independent TEP of sample 1(△) shown in fig.2 can be analyzed using the Heikes formula.

$$S = \frac{k_B}{e} \ln \frac{1-\rho}{\rho} \quad , \tag{1}$$

where ρ is the ratio of the number of charge carriers to the number of available sites. For $S_{RT} \simeq 100\mu V/K$, ρ can be calculated as $\rho \simeq 0.25$. This means that the potassium concentration x $\simeq 0.25$ in K_xC_{60}. The temperature independent TEP of sample 1 is well known for the molecular solid, where it can be understood as a result of the mobility activated hopping conduction [6]. The quasi–linear temperature dependences shown in sample 2 and 4 in fig.2 can be analyzed using the diffusive TEP formular for normal metals.

$$S(T) = \frac{\pi^2}{3}\frac{k_B}{e} k_B T \eta(E_F) \quad , \tag{2}$$

where $\eta(E_F)$ is the density of state at the Fermi level. From the slope of the linear temperature dependence of sample 2, one can estimate that $\eta(E_F) \simeq 20$ states/eV $\cdot$ C_{60} consistent with the value measured by the photoemission method [7]. Here we assumed three potassium atoms per each C_{60}, i.e., the composition of sample to be K_3C_{60}. Similarly, for sample 4, $\eta(E_F) \simeq$ 5 states/eV$\cdot$ C_{60}, which is about factor of four smaller. The TEP of sample 3 is somewhat peculiar. It is in between the TEP of sample 2 and sample 4, which is presumably due to the

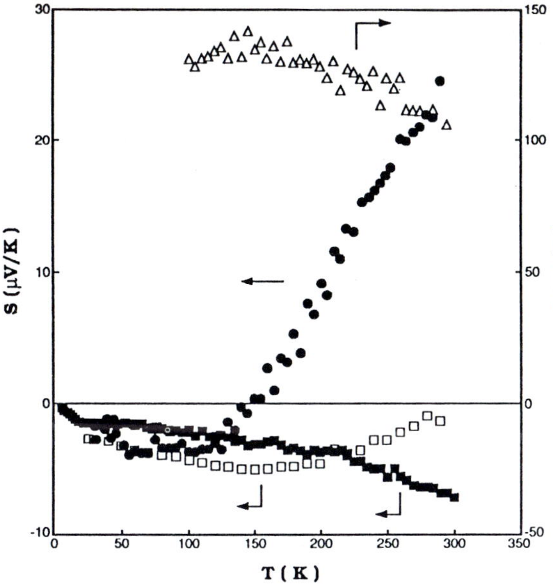

Figure 2. Temperature dependence of thermoelectric power of K_xC_{60}; Sample 1 (△), Sample 2 (•), Sample 3(□) and Sample 4 (■)

intermediate doping concentration between the two samples. The origin of this kind behavior might be due to the phase separation of the two phases, one is the positive TEP phase and the other is the negative TEP phase. Unfortunately, we have not succeeded in measuring the composition of x in K_xC_{60} of each sample by chemical analyses. The TEP data of sample 2 shown in fig.2 and the TEP data of pyrolyzed C_{60} shown in fig.1 are very much akin with each other in their temperature dependences, although the room temperature value is different for one order of magnitude. From the X-ray diffraction result, it was determined that the structure of the pyrolyzed C_{60} is amorphous fullerenes [3]. Thus, the anomalous TEP data (sample 2 in fig.2) suggest that our potassium doped C_{60} also has amorphous-like structure. When we dope alkali metal to C_{60} fullerene, we used the two zone heating method [2]. Our sample zone is heated up to 210°C very slowly. The C_{60} fullerene could have pyrolyzed during the slow heating process.

In summary, we have shown the anomalous TEP results for both cuprate superconductors and the doped C_{60}/C_{70} fullerenes as well as the pyrolyzed C_{60}/C_{70} fullerene. Although all the data are consistently reproducible, there are a lot more to be done to understand the charge trasport mechanisms in these unusual solids.

Acknowledgements

This work is supported by the Ministry of Science and Technology (MOST) and the Korea Science and Engineering Foundation (KOSEF), Korea.

References

[1] Y. S. Song, Y. S. Choi, Y. W. Park, M. S. Jang, S. K. Han, *J. Moscow Phys. Soc.* 1, 293 (1991); *Physica C* 185–189, 1341 (1991)
[2] E. B. Park, J. W. Shim, H. Park, Y. W. Park,*Synth. Met.* 44, 363 (1991); E. B. Park, J. W. Shim, H. Park, Y. W. Park, K. B. Lee, H. S. Kim, Z. Iqbal, R. H. Baughman, *Physica C* 185–189, 409 (1991)
[3] Z. Iqbal, R. H. Baughman, *to be published*
[4] G. M. Eliashberg, *Pisma Zh. Eksp. Teor. Fiz.* 46, 94 (1987)
[5] C. M. Varma, P. B. Littlewood, S. Schmitt–Rink, E. Abrahams and A. E. Ruckenstein, *Phys. Rev. Lett.* 63, 1996 (1989)
[6] Y. W. Park, A. J. Heeger, M. A. Druy, A. G. MacDiarmid, *J. Chem. Phys.* 73, 946 (1980); Y. W. Park, *Synth. Met.* 45, 173 (1991)
[7] C. T. Chen, L. H. Tjeng, P. Rudolf, G. Meigs, J. E. Rowe, J. Chen, J. P. McCauley Jr, A. B. Smith III, A. R. McGhie, W. J. Romanow, E. W. Plummer, *Nature* 352, 603 (1991)

On the Valency of Pr in $(Y_{1-x}Pr_x)Ba_2Cu_3O_7$

G. Schaudy[1], *T. Holubar*[1], *M. Forsthuber*[1], *G. Hilscher*[1], *E. Holland-Moritz*[2], *V. Nekvasil*[3], *and P. Rogl*[4]

[1]Institut für Experimentalphysik, TU Wien, A-1040 Wien, Austria
[2]Universität zu Köln, Zülpicher Str. 77, W-5000 Köln, Fed. Rep. of Germany
[3]Institut of Physics, Cukrovanicka 10, CS-16200 Praha 6, Czechoslovakia
[4]Institut für Physikalische Chemie, Universität Wien, A-1090 Wien, Austria

Abstract: We present specific heat measurements of $(Y,Pr)Ba_2Cu_3O_7$ in external fields up to 11 T. The results are analysed in terms of crystalline electric field (CF) effects and indicate that in these systems Pr appears to be trivalent rather than tetravalent.

Among the family of superconducting $RBa_2Cu_3O_7$ compounds (R = Rare Earth and Y except Ce, and Yb) that form the orthorhombic *Pmmm* structure, PrBCO is an exception since PrBCO is insulating and orders antiferromagnetically (AF). To investigate the effect of Y/Pr substitution upon superconductivity the phase diagram was determined which shows a gradual reduction of superconductivity until antiferromagnetism occurs for both the Cu- and Pr sublattices for $x>0.55$ [1]. In order to obtain information about the valency of Pr several experiments have been performed (see e.g. Ghamaty et al. [2] and Fink et al. [3]). However, the valency of Pr (either +3 or +4) is still a matter of debate.

Shown in Fig.1 is the specific heat of $PrBaCuO_{7-\delta}$ for $\delta \cong 1$ and 0. For both the orthorhombic (δ = 1) and the tetragonal compound (δ = 0) the anomaly at the antiferromagnetic ordering temperature of Pr is only slightly shifted to lower temperatures with rising external fields and appears to be suppressed almost at 11 T. In contrast to the Cp measurements, the shift of the anomaly at T_n is hardly observable in the susceptibility measurements up to 5T which indicates that either the AF order is not of a simple mean-field type or an appreciable anisotropy is present.

The entropy associated with the AF order yields important information about the valency of Pr as long as the phonon contribution can be subtracted from the total heat capacity with reasonable accuracy. This is a point to which we come back later. The crystal field calculation by Nekvasil [4] using the superposition model predicts details of the structure of the CF spectra. Accordingly the groundstate of the Kramers ion Pr^{+4} is a doublet whereas for Pr^{+3} the ground state is a quasitriplet corresponding to an entropy gain of S = Rln2 or Rln3, respectively, above T_n.

To avoid complications due to the AF order of the Pr sublattice we substituted Pr by Y and applied external fields up to 11T; thus via the Zeeman splitting of the ground state we try to elucidate of whether Pr is either tri- or tetravalent. For the heat capacity of $Y_{1-x}Pr_xBa_2Cu_3O_7$ (x=0.2 and 0.6) in external fields, displayed in Fig.2, we obtain reasonable

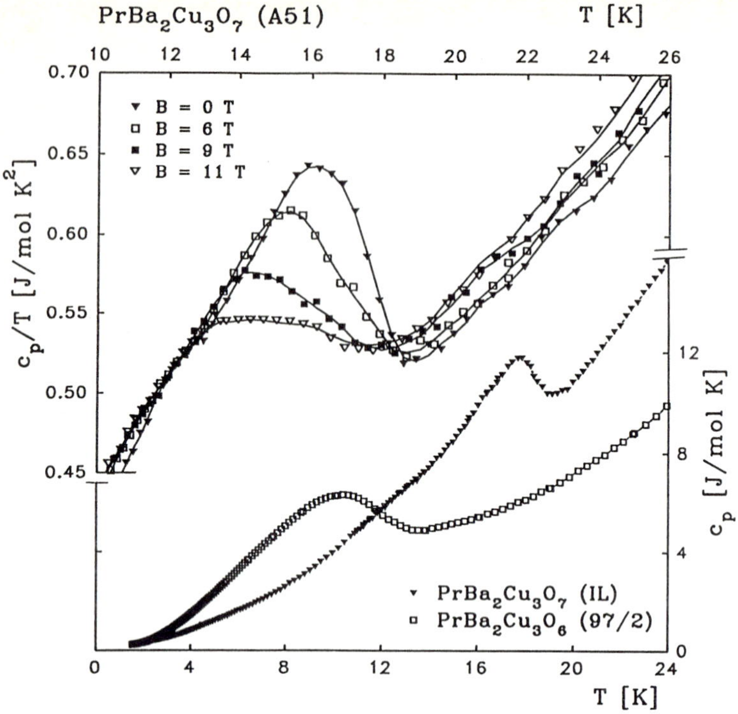

Fig.1. Specific heat of $PrBa_2Cu_3O_7$ and $PrBa_2Cu_3O_6$ as a function of temperature. The effect of external fields fields upon T_n is shown for $PrBa_2Cu_3O_7$ in the upper part in a C_p/T representation. A similar effect of the external field is observed for the O6 compound.

quantitative agreement between the experimental data and the calculated specific heat under the following conditions:
For the background heat capacity we use the experimental $C_p(T)$ data of YBCO assuming identical phonon contributions to C_p for $x \neq 0$ and $x = 0$. Although we measured the heat capacitity of YBCO and PrBCO up to room temperature, we failed to determine an accurate lattice heat capacity for PrBCO since the Debye approximation is only valid at low temperatures and Einstein frequencies give rise to a rather significant deviation from the Debye function in the intermediate temperature range. The use of the phonon contribution of YBCO for PrBCO appears to be a rather crude approximation, which hampers an unambigous determination of the entropy associated with the magnetic order. Nevertheless, an estimation of the entropy corresponding to the quasitriplet groundstate of Pr^{+3}, for which we used Pr/Y diluted samples (with x=0.2 and x=0.6) at 11T, yields an entropy gain of 0.85ln3 ± 10% up to 60 K for both samples (x=0.2 and 0.6)

To determine the CF contribution of Pr^{+3} to the heat capacity, we use the complete set of CF parameters obtained by fitting the CF spectra to the inelastic neutron scattering data [5]. The calculation including the J

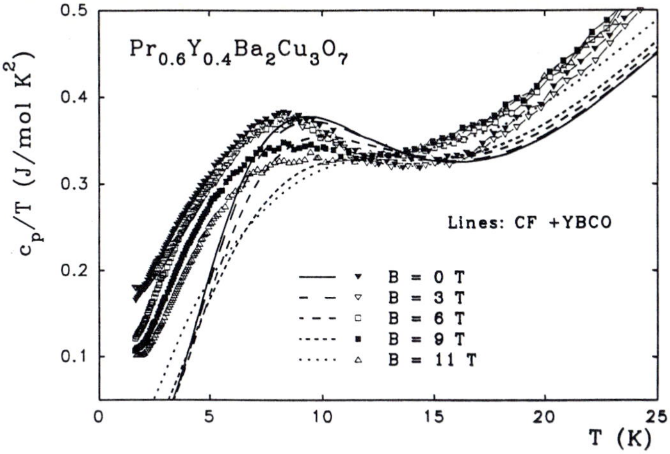

Fig.2. Experimental and calculated specific heat of $Pr_{0.6}Y_{0.4}Ba_2Cu_3O_7$ for various external fields as labeled.

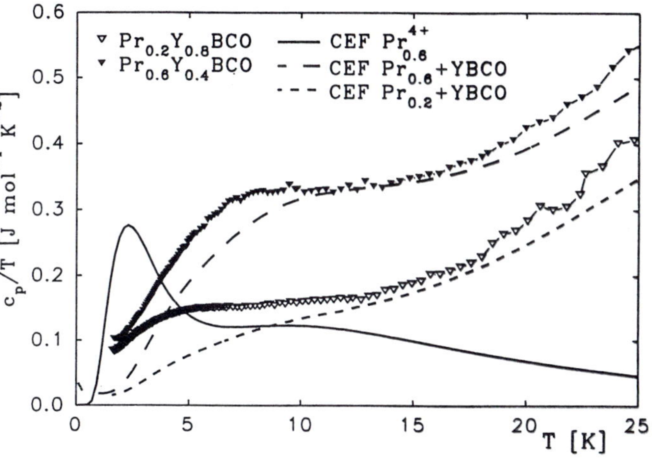

Fig.3. Comparison of the experimental specific heat of $(Pr_xY_{1-x})Ba_2Cu_3O_7$ (x =0.2 and 0.6) at 11T with the calculated CF contribution to Cp (for Pr^{+3}) plus Cp of YBCO. Full line: CF contribution to Cp only for Pr^{+4}.

mixing of the three lowest multiplets as well as intermediate coupling wavefunctions of the free ion predicts a well isolated quasitriplet ground state with Γ_4 as the lowest level [5]. In the present work, both the susceptibility and the specific heat were calculated according to the Pr^{+3} CF level scheme as derived from inelastic neutron scattering without any further adjustment. A comparison of the calculated and experimental specific heat for x=0.2 and 0.6 at 11T is displayed in fig.3, where we also included the corresponding heat capacity contribution of Pr^{+4} for x = 0.6 at 11T. Under the assumption that Pr is tetravalent in this compounds the the

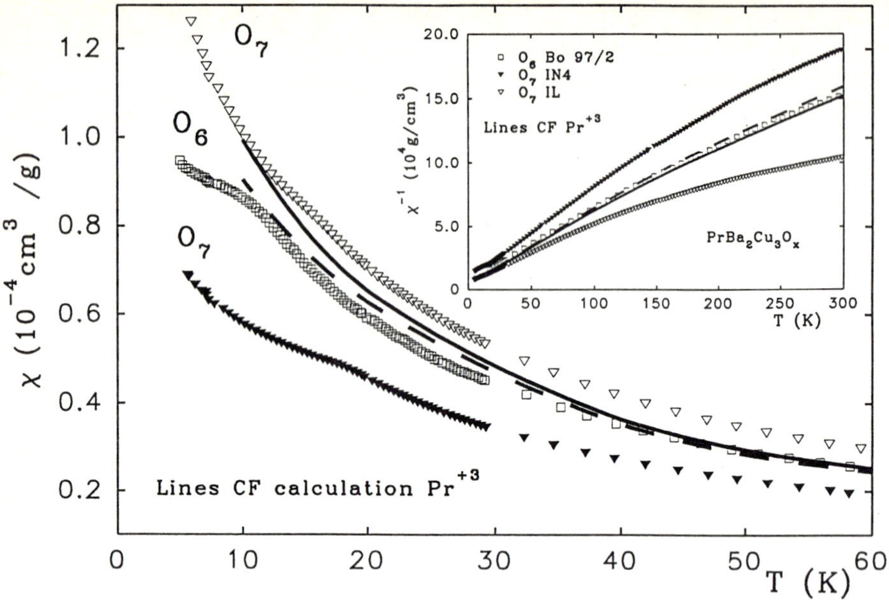

Fig.4. Comparison of the calculated (lines: O7—, O6– – –) and experimental dsusceptibility of PrBa2Cu3O7 (▽,▼) and PrBa2Cu3O6 (□). Two PrBa2Cu3O7 samples are displayed which are representative for the susceptibility data in the literature.

external field should split the doublet ground state of the Kramers ion (Pr^{+4}) giving rise to a pronounced Schottky anomaly which, however, is not observed in the experiment.

We note that the experimental Cp data of fig.3 are the same as in ref. [6] where the CF calculation has been performed in terms of the Stevens notation without J mixing. The inclusion of J mixing significantly improves the agreement between the experiment and the calculation in fig.3. Nevertheless we still find a deviation between the experimental and calculated data below 11K. A plot of this difference ΔCp as a function of lnT yields a bell-shaped curve. Its maximum is shifted to higher temperatures with rising external fields whereby the height of the maximum remains unchanged for both the superconducting (x=0.2) and the semiconducting compound (x=0.6). This behavior is reminiscent to the specific heat of magnetic clusters which might be created by Y/Pr substitution and contribute to the suppression of superconductivity.

According to the analysis of the inelastic neutron scattering data of the fully oxidized (O7) and the oxygen deficient (O6) sample, the oxygen deficiency appears to have only a minor influence upon the CF parameters Bmn and therefore upon the splitting of the quasitriplet ground state [5]. Consequently the calculated susceptibilities of both compounds are, as shown in fig.4, rather similar to each other. The agreement between the calculated and experimental susceptibility for the O_6 compounds above T_n seems satisfactory. In the literature a broad scatter of the the susceptibility data of $PrBa_2Cu_3O_7$ exsists (and we measured also various O_7 samples of different laboratories), therefore we plot the susceptibility of two representative O_7 compounds together with the calculated $\chi(T)$ for comparison. In this context we believe that the O_7 sample labeled as IL with the lower susceptibility contains fewer impurities than the other one, labeled as IN since the latter exhibits a field dependend susceptibility below and above T_n which is not the case for the former. Despite the experimental uncertainty this comparison in fig.4 also supports that Pr can be considered as trivalent. However, susceptibility measurements of a single crystal would be very helpful for a further CF analysis.

Contrary to our interpretation, Ghamaty et al. [2] recently discussed the zero field heat capacity data of this series in terms of a S= 1/2 Kondo effect. This implies a tetravalent Pr with an $^2F_{5/2}$ ground multiplet where the grond state is a Kramers doublet. As stated above, this doublet would be splitted by external fields giving rise to a significant Schottky anomaly at 11T with Cp/T peak values nearly three times larger than the experimental values for x =0.6. This, however, is not found in the experiment (see fig.3). The interpretation of Ghamaty et al. [2] yields impressive agreement beween their model calculation in terms of a Kondo effect and the zero field $C_p(T)$ data up to 10K. However, the comparison of the susceptibility and the high field specific heat data with our results from the CF calculation (fig.2 - 4) strongly indicates that the ground state of Pr in these systems is a quasitriplet rather than a doublet. This means that Pr is mainly in trivalent state which is in full agreement with recent inelastic neutron experiments [5] and electron loss spectroscopy [3].

Acknowledgement

This work was supported by the Austrian Science Fondation Fonds under project #7918 and #7620.

References

[1] I.Felner, U.Yaron, I.Nowik, E.R. Bauminger, Y.Wolfus, E.R. Yacoby, G.Hilscher and N. Pillmayr, Phys. Rev.B 40 (1989) 6739; G.Hilscher et al. J.Magn.Magn.Mat. 90&91 (1990) 628

[2] S.Ghamaty, B.W.Lee, J.J. Neumeier, G.Nieva and M.B.Maple, Phys.Rev. B 43 (1991) 5430; G.Nieva, S.Ghamaty, B.W.Lee, M.B.Maple, and I.K.Schuller, Phys. Rev. B 44 (1992) 6999

[3] J.Fink, N.Nücker, H.Romberg, M.Alexander, M.B.Maple, J.J.Neumeier and J.W.Allen, Phys.Rev. B 42 (1990) 4823

[4] V.Nekvasil, J. de Physique 49 (1988) C8-2177

[5] V.Nekvasil, E.Holland-Moritz, H.-D.Jostarndt, U.Walter and G.Hilscher, J.Magn.Magn. Mat. (1992), in press
[6] G.Schaudy, T.Holubar, N.Pillmayr, G.Leitenbauer, G.Hilscher, P.Rogl and A.Hanninger, J.Magn. Magn. Mat. (1992) in press.

Anisotropy of Transport Properties of HTSC Monocrystals

V. Efimov

Max-Planck-Institut für Festkörperforschung,
Heisenbergstr. 1, W-7000 Stuttgart 80, Fed. Rep. of Germany and
Institute of Solid State Physics, Chenogolovka,
142432 Moscow District, Russia

Investigation of the thermal conductivity, $\kappa(T)$, of high temperature superconductors (HTSC) is particularly useful in probe scattering processes, in both the normal state above T_c and the superconducting state below T_c. In particular, studying the anisotropy of κ in superconductors reveals the electron-phonon coupling and carrier scattering mechanisms. This work reports measurements of thermal and electrical conductivity in $YBa_2Cu_3O_{7-y}$ and $Bi_2Sr_2CaCu_2O_{8-x}$ single crystals. Measurement were made in the *ab*-plane and along the *c*-axis of all samples. Single crystals of $YBa_2Cu_3O_{7-y}$ were prepared at the Institute of Solid State Physics in Chernogolovka, and $Bi_2Sr_2CaCu_2O_{8-x}$ crystals were grown in Moscow Institute of Steel and Alloys. Further characteristics of the investigated samples are tabulated in Tab.1.

Table 1. Characteristics of investigated monocrystals.

Material and Abbreviation Sample №	Size mm^3	T_c K	ΔT K	ρ_{300} $\mu\Omega$*cm	$d\rho/dT$ $\mu\Omega$*cm/K
YBCO-21	1.70*0.94*0.030	92.5	0.5K	208	0.77
YBCO-25	1.65*1.00*0.135	92.5	2 K	428	1.51
BSCCO-3	2.30*1.20*0.020	82	4 K	-	-
BSCCO-4	2.00*0.59*0.050	86	1.5 K	417	0.99
BSCCO-6	0.96*0.58*0.016	89	3.5 K	756	1.53

The measurements were made using standard experimental methods. For example, the electrical resistivity was measured using a conventional four-wire configuration. Silver paint was used used to insure good contact between the sample and the connected copper wire (diameter 0.05 mm). The thermal conductivity was measured using a classical steady-state technique in a liquid helium cryostat. The plate-like samples were glued to a heat sink on one end, while a heater (≈ 300 Ω) was attached to the opposite end. The temperature gradient across the sample, ΔT_s, was determined by means of differentially space constantan-chromel thermocouple junctions (diameter ⌀ =10 μm). The overall temperature of the sample was monitored with a similar thermocouple oriented with one leg attached to the sample, and the other to the cold plate which enclosed a calibrated germanium and platinum resistance thermometer. The limited temperature resolution of the constantan-chromel thermocouples restricted the studied temperature range at low temperatures to a minimum ≈ 10 K. The absolute error of the thermal conductivity measurement was potentially large because of the uncertainties in the effective sample geometry, which in our investigation was on the order of 30% for thinner samples. The reproducibility of the measurements were within 2-5%, and the error in the ratio κ/σ was ≈ 10%.

Results and Discussion

In Fig.1, we show the electrical resistivity as a function of temperature for speciments investigated. The resistivity ratios $RR=(\rho_c/\rho_{ab})$ of sample Y-25 were $RR(300\ K) \approx 20$ and $RR(100\ K) \approx 55$. Figures 2 and 3, show the temperature dependence of the in-plane and out-of-plane thermal conductivity of our samples.

The most pronounced properties in thermal conductivity HTSC monocrystals are:

1. The anisotropy in κ is less for the Y compound (for Y-25 from $\kappa_{ab}/\kappa_c \approx 3.4$ at 150 K to ≈6 at 10 K), and more for Bi materials (Bi-3 $\kappa_{ab}/\kappa_c \approx 5.1$ at 150 K and 100 K, to ≈ 7.5 at 50 K; for Bi-4 $\kappa_{ab}/\kappa_c \approx$ 8.6-->11 at 20 K; for Bi-6 $\kappa_{ab}/\kappa_c \sim$100-->220 at 10 K).
2. The *ab*-plane conductivity is found to be 5-10 times large than in the corresponding ceramics.
3. The maximum of $\kappa_{ab}(T)$ for all samples occurs near $T_c/4$ which is in the lower temperature than in ceramic HTSC materials where $T_{max} \approx T_c/2$.
4. We note the monotonic decrease of $\kappa_c(T)$ as a function of temperature, in the *c*-direction. From highest investigated temperature, $\kappa(T)$ monotonic ally decreases without any peculiarities near T_c.The out-of-plane conductivity does not show

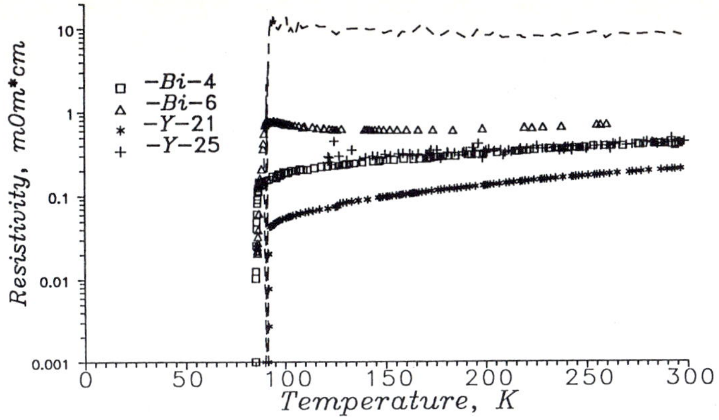

Fig.1. Temperature dependence of the resistivity of the investigated HTSC monocrystals. The measurements were carried out in the *ab*-plane. The dashed line is results of the measurement of the resistivity in the *c*-direction.

a behavior correlated to the upturn of the κ_{ab}(T) curve (in *ab*-plane) below T_c.

Resistivity was measured, and using the Wiedemann-Franz law we separated the free-electron contribution to κ(T) by describing the total κ as the sum of thermal phonon and electron conductivities:

$$\kappa = \kappa_{ph} + \kappa_e$$

The electronic contribution in the *ab*-plane contributed up to 50% or more of the total (sample Y-21). κ_e/κ ~10% for Y-25, κ_e/κ ~13% for Bi-4 and κ_e/κ ≈2.4-3.5% for Bi-6. In the *c*-direction, throughout the normal state temperature range, κ_c was dominated by phonons carrying the thermal energy. The heat flow coupled with electron system in sample Y-25 was only a few percent of the total ($\kappa_e/\kappa \approx 1\%$).

For an estimation of the phonon-electron interaction we separated the phonon thermal conductivity from electronic. For thermal resistivity *W* we expressed interaction between phonons and any kind of scatterers as

$$W_p = 1/\kappa_p \approx W_{pp} + W_{pd} + W_{pe}$$

where as W_i denoted the thermal resistivity of phonon-phonon, phonon-defect and phonon-electron scattering respectively. At low temperature (8-20 K) thermal conductivity decreased li-

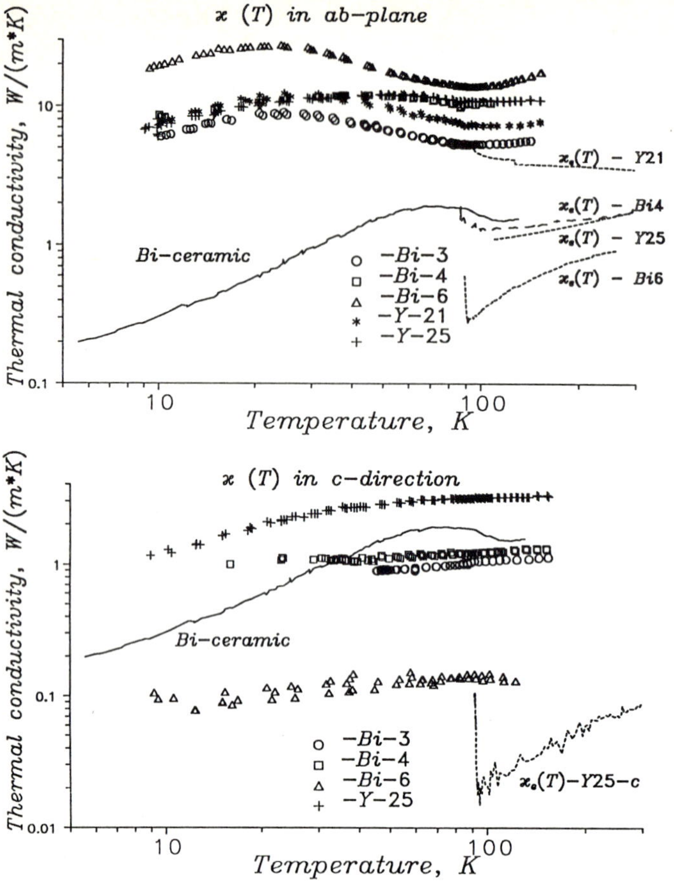

Fig.2 and 3. Temperature dependence of the thermal conductivity in the *ab*-plane and *c*-direction. The dashed lines are calculated the electronic part κ_e of the thermal conductivity. The solid line is a - typical curve of the thermal conductivity for Bi ceramic sample (Reference [3]).

nearly with T. We subtracted low temperature behavior ($W_{LT} \sim T^{-1}$) from common thermal resistivity (without further examination of its nature). These estimation value gave us upper limit of phonon-electron interaction $W_{pe} \approx$ 0.05-0.15 K*m/W, which led to typical relaxation times of phonon-electron interaction in HTSC $\tau_{pe} \approx 3\text{-}9 * 10^{-12}$ s at $T \approx T_c$ (sound velocity $v_s \approx 4000$ m/s [1] and for specific heat $C_p \approx 1 J/(cm^3 K^2)$ [2]). This value was about 10 times higher than the corresponding values calculated for ceramic samples [3].

For a quantitative explanation of the difference in the absolute values of thermal conductivity in the *ab*-plane and *c*-direction we suggest a reduction of relaxation time τ_{ph} in *c*-direction. This may be only a change of matrix of phonon scattering on any centers or the appearence of a new dominant scattering mechanism, or only an increasing contribution of this onteraction in common of interaction processes .

Our investigation of thermal conductivity of HTSC monocrystals showed ahsignificant anisotropy in κ, $3<\kappa_{ab}/\kappa_c<20$.

Typical phonon relaxation time on electrons is $\tau_{pe} \approx 3-9 * 10^{-12}$ s at $T \approx T_c$ in HTSC monocrystals.

For relaxation time of phonon interaction we may write the ratio $(\tau_e/\tau_{ph})_{ab} >\approx 10*(\tau_e/\tau_{ph})_c$.

Comparison thermal conductivities withween monocrystals and ceramics show that simple average ($\kappa_{cer} \approx 2/3\kappa_{ab} + 1/3\kappa_c$) doesn't give absolute values of thermal conductivity of ceramics, we must take into account scattering phonons on intercrystalline boundaries.

1.T.I.Kim, J.Kowalewski, W.Assmus et al-Z.Phys.B, 1990, 78, 207
2.S.B.Ota, V.S.Sastry, E.Gmelin et al - Phys.Rev.B, 1991, 43, 4
3.V.Efimov, L.P.Mezhov-Deglin, S.A. Shevchenko et al. - Сверхпроводимость (USSR, Superconductivity) 1991, 4, 6, 1114

Part IV

High-Energy Spectroscopies

On the Surface-Derived State of Cleaved $YBa_2Cu_3O_{7-\delta}$ Single Crystals

R. Manzke[1], *S. Harm*[1], *G. Mante*[1], *J. Fink*[2], *M. Knupfer*[2], *and M. Skibowski*[1]

[1]Institut für Experimentalphysik, Universität Kiel, Olshausenstraße 40, W-2300 Kiel, Fed. Rep. of Germany
[2]Kernforschungszentrum Karlsruhe, Institut für Nukleare Festkörperphysik, Postfach 3640, W-7500 Karlsruhe, Fed. Rep. of Germany

Abstract. Angle–resolved photoemission experiments on the cleaved surface of $YBa_2Cu_3O_{7-\delta}$ single crystals revealed an intrinsic surface–derived electronic state around the X and Y point of the Brillouin zone with 0.92 eV binding energy. A surface electronic structure different to the bulk can be of basic importance for the surface superconductivity of this high–T_c cuprate. Here we briefly review recent experimental results and present new hydrogen adsorption experiments, demonstrating the surface character of the 0.92 eV state.

1. Introduction

Angle–resolved photoemission spectroscopy (ARPES) performed with high energy and momentum resolution on single–crystalline high–T_c superconductor surfaces has provided valuable experimental information on the electronic structure in both their normal and superconducting state. Most of the results concerning the origin of the electronic states, in particular of that at E_F, their binding energies and dispersions, the Fermi surface in the normal state, and the opening of the superconducting gap for $T < T_c$ were obtained on the system $Bi_2Sr_2CaCu_2O_{8+\delta}$ [1]. For $YBa_2Cu_3O_{7-\delta}$ it is a puzzeling problem, why no superconducting gap could be detected by ARPES. Early photoemission measurements could not even observe a Fermi edge in this material. Arko et al. [2] have shown that the $YBa_2Cu_3O_{7-\delta}$–surface is not stable in vacuum at room temperature but that the surface remains stable if the sample is cleaved and kept at very low temperatures. Under these conditions a Fermi edge is observed for certain k values, determining parts of the Fermi surface, but no superconducting gap has been realized [3, 4, 5, 6]. Since ARPES is a very surface sensitive spectroscopic technique with a probing depth of about 5–30 Å depending on the kinetic energy of the photoelectrons the question has to be posed, how far the electronic structure derived from the surface of superconductors is representative for the bulk properties.

Because of the quasi two dimensional character of $Bi_2Sr_2CaCu_2O_{8+\delta}$ chemically stable surfaces can be prepared by cleavage between the adjacent Bi–O layers. These layers are only weakly bonded by van der Waals–like forces with almost no valence charge between them and the creation of a surface represents no strong disturbance to the bulk electronic structure. This, and the observation that besides the Cu–O planes, common to all cuprate superconductors, it contains of metallic [1] and below T_c even superconducting Bi–O layers [7, 8] make $Bi_2Sr_2CaCu_2O_{8+\delta}$ appear somewhat extraordinary among the high-T_c cuprates. Thus, for $Bi_2Sr_2CaCu_2O_{8+\delta}$ there exists up to now no evidence for surface effects.

For the high-T_c compound $YBa_2Cu_3O_{7-\delta}$ the situation is rather different. Here the formation of a surface inevitably requires breaking of strong ionic or covalent bonds between the layers. In particular, cleavage between the Ba–O and Cu–O planes obtained by cleavages from the top of the sample, the charge transfer in the bulk from the CuO_3 chains to the CuO_2 planes may lead to a rearrangement of electronic charge and thus to changes of the electronic structure at the surface compared to that of the bulk. Such surface effects have been first proposed by Calandra et al. [9, 10], finding distinct modifications of the surface-derived density of states with respect to the bulk. The present contribution adresses the experimental evidence for surface effects on $YBa_2Cu_3O_{6.8}$, obtained from recent high-resolution angle-resolved photoemission studies [4, 11], and new hydrogen adsorption experiments.

2. Experimental

In the hydrogen adsoption experiments we used similar $YBa_2Cu_3O_{7-\delta}$ ($\delta = 0.2$) single crystals as in the previous studies [4, 11]. The preparation of the samples with a sharp transition temperature of 1.5 K between 88.5–89.5 K is described elsewhere [4]. The samples were attached to the cold finger of a cryostat by a conducting glue and were cleaved in ultra–high vacuum (base preassure in the low 10^{-10} mbar range) after they were cooled down to less than 20 K. In order to reduce water and other rest gas contaminants with high sticking coefficients at these low temperatures from the sample surface, in addition to the ion pump, a refrigerator-cooled cryopump was used.

The photoemission spectra were taken with HeI radiation ($h\nu = 21.22$ eV) by means of a spherical analyzer mounted on a two-axes goniometer. The energy resolution was 25 meV, the angle resolution better than 0.5°. In order to avoid oxygen loss from the surface the sample temperature was kept below 20 K for all experiments. The quality was judged by the strength of the Fermi edge for certain emission angles, the absence of the notorious 9 eV peak, which is related to oxygen depletion in the surface region [12] and becoming visible after heating the sample to above 100 K, and the intensity and sharpness of the surface peak at 0.92 eV binding energy which will be discussed in detail below. Molecular hydrogen of high purity is adsorbed on the surface via an ultra–high vacuum valve from a bakable reservoir.

Results and Discussion

During systematic ARPES studies of the Fermi surface and of occupied dispersive bulk–derived bands close to E_F of $YBa_2Cu_3O_{6.8}$ we have observed a sharp and intense peak around the X(Y)–point of the Brillouin zone [4]. In Fig. 1 typical energy distribution curves for this peak are shown between 0.5 and 1.5 eV taken along the Γ–X,Y direction at emission angles corresponding to wavevectors $k_{\|}$ around the Brillouin zone boundary. Such a spectra series is representative for this material and in agreement with previous [4, 5, 6] and very recent [14] data on twinned and untwinned samples from different laboratories. Besides several dispersing emission maxima close to E_F, which have been discussed in detail with respect to the bulk band structure calculated within the local density approximation [4], the pronounced maximum (assigend S) with dispersion parallel to the surface, $k_{\|}$, around the X(Y)–point is discussed in detail in ref. [11]. Its intensity is strongest at the X(Y)–point, decreasing dramatically away from X(Y), and vanishing at a distance of about 1/3 of the Brillouin zone extension. Within this regime the $k_{\|}$ dispersion is about 70 meV, shown together with the most prominent bulk band at E_F (for details see ref. [4]) in Fig. 2. The binding energy of S is 0.92 eV at X(Y).

The extraordinary low value of the intrinsic linewidth of S of about 100 meV (FWHM) made this peak to one of the sharpest emissions observed in high–T_c materials so far. Such a small band width is reminiscent of widths found

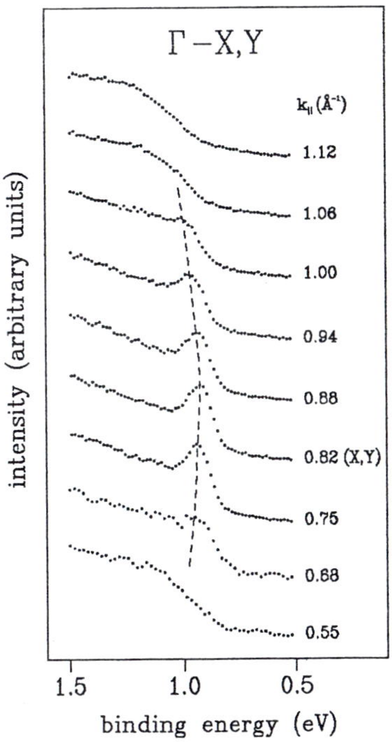

Figure 1:
Angle resolved photoemission spectra of a $YBa_2Cu_3O_{6.8}$ twinned single crystal taken with 21.22 eV photon energy along the Γ–X,Y direction in the first and second Brillouin zone at $T < 20$ K.

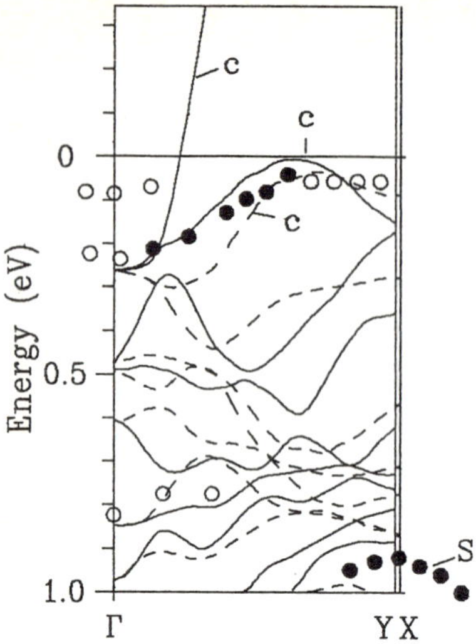

Figure 2:
Comparison of the ARPES results of $YBa_2Cu_3O_{6.8}$ *with a LDA band structure [13]. Solid and dashed lines represent theoretical bands along the Γ–X and Γ–Y direction, resp., and c assigns Cu–O chain bands. Full circles denote pronounced ARPES peaks, open circles weaker structures and shoulders. Note the* $k_{\parallel}$*–dispersion of the surface band S from the series of Fig. 1 around the X(Y) point.*

for surface states in metals, e.g. Cu metal. Because of these properties and the fact that band S has no direct equivalent in the bulk band structure it is attributed to a surface derived state [11]. The observation of $k_{\parallel}$ dispersion rules out an assignment to a localized defect state, but supports an interpretation as an intrinsic surface band, which is located in a gap of the projected bulk band structure near the X(Y)–point (due to a surface state) and merges into the bulk band region becoming a surface resonance away from it.

Further evidence for the surface nature of band S is given by the absence of $k_{\perp}$ dispersion proved by photon energy dependent measurements. Thus S is localized perpendicular to the c–axis as is characteristic for a surface state. In addition, band S reveals a strong sensitivity to adsorbates. In ref. [11] we described contamination experiments. Because the sample temperature was below 20 K during the measurement, the sticking coefficient of residual molecules in the chamber hitting the surface approches unity. Hence, after about 6 hours the intensity of band S appeared to be strongly reduced and after about 13 hours it was completely suppressed. All the other peaks in the spectra due to emissions from bulk–like states are not affected.

Although it is well known that in contamination experiments from the residual gas at low temperatures mostly water adsorbs on the surface, a more reliable prove of the surface sensitivity may be achived by using only one adsorbate. In Fig. 3 we show a spectra series obtained with hydrogen. The spectrum on the bottom is an example for a fresh surface recorded within 20 minutes after cleavage. Besides the intense surface–derived state at 0.92 eV binding energy lying on a broad emission onset of bulk bands the spectrum consists of broad emission starting at the Fermi energy (0 eV binding energy). After an amount of 0.02 L hydrogen the intensity of the surface peak is already decreased and after 0.5 L the intensity has decreased dramatically. The uppermost spectrum

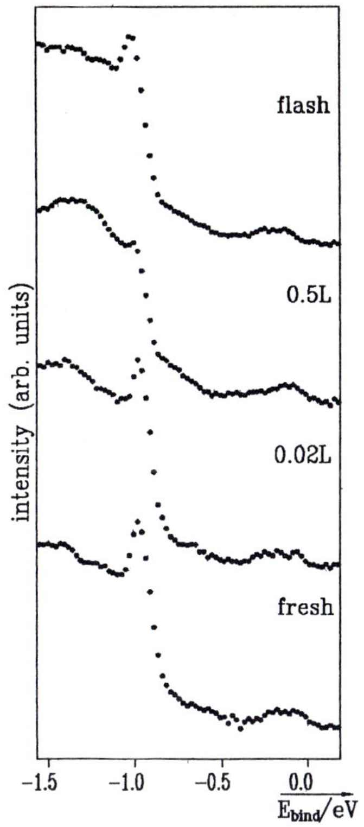

Figure 3:
Sensitivity of the surface band S on hydrogen adsorption given in Langmuirs. The spectra have been taken at the X(Y) point of the Brillouin zone with 21.22 eV photon energy (overall energy resolution of 25 meV, $T < 20$ K) and are normalized by constant photon flux. The measuring time for the whole series was about 1 hour.

was recorded shortly after the 0.5 L one, but with the sample having been heated to 50 K for a few minutes (flashing) and cooled to below 20 K again. By this procedure it became possible to desorb most of the hydrogen from the surface, controlled by a mass analyzer, the surface peak is found to be almost totally recovered. Note that, similar to the previous contamination experiments, all additional emission is not affected by the adsorbed hydrogen. It is interesting to mention further that after the flashing procedure the intensity of the surface peak starts to decrease again and reveals a suppression similar to the 0.5 L spectrum after about 1 hour. With a next flashing treatment one is able to recover it again, and so on. This behaviour points to hydrogen diffusion out of the sample which has been absorbed in the bulk of the $YBa_2Cu_3O_{6.8}$ crystal during the adsorption.

The appearence of a surface derived state indicates a redistribution of charge in the surface. This can be explained by the fact that cleavage of $YBa_2Cu_3O_{7-\delta}$ requires the breaking of strong bonds between the layers. In particular, for a Ba–O(4) termination with a Cu(1)–O(1) sublayer, which is the only non–polar one, marked changes have been theoretically proposed by Calandra et al. [9, 10] in the surface density of states in comparison to the bulk. X–ray photoemission [15] and photoemission experiments in the constant–final–state mode [16] show shifted components of the Ba core levels, which are interpreted to represent a Ba surface species. From our photoemission investigations we would conclude that the cleavage plane consists of Ba–O(4) and Cu(2)-O(2,3) domains. This seems to be the easy cleavage plane of $YBa_2Cu_3O_{6.8}$. On the other hand, it should be mentioned here that, besides the normally obtained cleavages between adjacent Ba-O and Cu-O planes, there seems to be also some probability to cleave the crystals between the Cu-O planes separated by the yttrium layer [14]. For this surface Ratz et al. [14] observe that the surface-derived band at about 1 eV binding energy is absent in the spectra and the emission onset at the Fermi level is shifted compared to the Fermi-Dirac edge of a normal metal, what may be a hint of the superconducting gap.

In summary, the observation of a surface-derived band on the Ba-O(4)/Cu(2)-O(2,3) face ('normal' cleavage plane) of $YBa_2Cu_3O_{6.8}$, indicating a rearrangement of electronic charge at the surface probably explains why in this compound no superconducting gap could be detected by photoemission (or scanning tunneling spectroscopy, STS) so far. The very recent evidence for the possibility of a second cleavage plane in this compound reported in ref. [14] is interesting and needs further experimental work, but also shows that spectroscopic experiments on $YBa_2Cu_3O_{7-\delta}$ are much more complicated than on the previously studied $Bi_2Sr_2CaCu_2O_{8+\delta}$ system. On the other hand, Fermi edges and dispersing bands have been detected on surfaces where the 0.9 eV surface peak was realized. Hence, a mapping of bulk derived bands by ARPES remains to be a meaningful experiment.

Acknowledgement

This work is supported by the *Bundesministerium für Forschung und Technologie* (project no. 05401 AAI).

References

[1] see e.g. G. Mante, R. Claessen, T. Buslaps, S. Harm, R. Manzke, M. Skibowski, J. Fink, Z. Phys. B **80**, 181 (1990) and references therein

[2] A.J. Arko, R.S. List, Z. Fisk, S.-W. Cheong, J.D. Tompson, J.A. O'Rourke, C.G. Olson, A.-B. Yang, T.W. Pi, J.E. Schirber, and N.D. Shin, J. Magn. Mater. Lett. **75**, L1 (1988)

[3] J.C. Campuzano, G. Jennings, M. Faiz, L. Beaulaigue, B.W. Veal, J.Z. Liu, A.P. Paulikas, K. Vandervoort, H. Claus, R.S. List, A.J. Arko, R.J. Bartlett, Phys. Rev. Lett. **64**, 2309 (1990)

[4] G. Mante, R. Claessen, A. Huß, R. Manzke, M. Skibowski, Th. Wolf, M. Knupfer, J. Fink, Phys. Rev. B **44**, 9500 (1991)

[5] R. Liu, B.W. Veal, A.P. Paulikas, J.W. Downey, H. Shi, C.G. Olson, C. Gu, A.J. Arko, J.J. Joyce, Phys. Rev. B **45**, 5614 (1992)

[6] J.G. Tobin, C.G. Olson, C. Gu, J.Z. Liu, F.R. Solal, M.J. Fluss, R.H. Howell, J.C. O'Brien, H.B. Radonski, P.A. Sterne, Phys. Rev. B **45**, 5563 (1992)

[7] B.O. Wells, Z.-X. Shen, D.S. Dessau, W.E. Spicer, C.G. Olson, D.B. Mitzi, A. Kapitulnik, R.S. List, A.J. Arko, Phys. Rev. Lett. **65**, 3056 (1990)
[8] Chen Wang, B. Giambattista, C.G. Slough, R.V. Coleman, M.A. Subramanian, Phys. Rev. B **42**, 8890 (1990)
[9] C. Calandra, F. Manghi, T. Minerva, G. Goldoni, Europhys. Lett. **8**, 791 (1989)
[10] C. Calandra, T. Minerva, Z. Phys. B - Condensed Matter **77**, 357 (1989)
[11] R. Claessen, G. Mante, A. Huß, R. Manzke, M. Skibowski, Th. Wolf, J. Fink, Phys. Rev. B (Rapid Commun.) **66**, 2399 (1991)
[12] A.J. Arko, R.S. List, R.J. Bartlett, S.-W. Cheong, Z. Fisk, J.D. Tompson, C.G. Olson, A.-B. Yang, R. Liu, C. Gu, B.W. Veal, J.Z. Liu, H.P. Paulikas, K. Vandervoort, H. Claus, J.C. Campuzano, J.E. Schirber, N.D. Shin, Phys. Rev. B **40**, 2268 (1989)
[13] W.E. Pickett, R.E. Cohen, H. Krakauer, Phys. Rev. B **42**, 8764 (1990)
[14] S. Ratz, N. Schroeder, R. Böttner, E. Dietz, U. Gerhardt, and Th. Wolf, preprint (1992)
[15] D.E. Fowler, C.R. Brundle, J. Lerczak, F. Holzberg, J. Electron. Spectr. Rel. Phen. **52**, 323 (1990) and references therein
[16] R. Liu, C.G. Olson, A.-B. Yang, C. Gu, D.W, Lynch, A.J. Arko, R.S. List, R.J. Bartlett, B.W. Veal, J.Z. Liu, A.P. Paulikas, K. Vandervoort, Phys. Rev. B **40**, 2650 (1989)

Investigation of the Electronic Structure of High-Temperature Superconductors by Polarized X-Ray Absorption Spectroscopy

N. Nücker[1], E. Pellegrin[1], G. Roth[1], C. Politis[1], J. Fink[1], M. Domke[2], M. Gutierez[2], Z.W. Hu[2], S. Molodsov[2], E. Navas[2], O. Strebel[2], G. Kaindl[2], A.Krol[3], J.L. Peng[4], Z.Y. Li[4], R.L. Greene[4], S. Uchida[5], H. Takagi[5], Y. Tokura[5], J. Markl[6], M. Klauda[6], G. Saemann-Ischenko[6], D. Hahn[7], T. Zetterer[7], H.H. Otto[7], and K.F. Renk[7]

[1]Kernforschungszentrum Karlsruhe, Institut für Nukleare Festkörperphysik, Postfach 3640, W-7500 Karlsruhe, Fed. Rep. of Germany
[2]Institut für Experimentalphysik, Freie Universität Berlin, W-1000 Berlin, Fed. Rep. of Germany
[3]Department of Physics, SUNY at Buffalo, NY 14260, USA
[4]Department of Physics, University of Maryland, College Parc, MD 20742, USA
[5]Engineering Research Institute, University of Tokyo, Hongo 7-3-1, Bunkyo-ku, Tokyo 113, Japan
[6]Physikalisches Institut Universität Erlangen, W-8520 Erlangen, Fed. Rep. of Germany
[7]Universität Regensburg, W-8400 Regensburg, Fed. Rep. of Germany

Abstract. The electronic structure of high-temperature superconductors near the Fermi level which is of primary interest for the understanding of the mechanism of superconductivity, is not yet well understood. Most theoretical investigations deal with $Cu3d_{x-y}$ and $O2p_{x,y}$ orbitals at E_F, but whether or not $O2p_z$ and $Cu3d_{3z-r}$ orbitals contribute to states at E_F is still under discussion. The contribution of states with out-of-plane orbital character has been investigated by polarized x-ray absorption spectroscopy (XAS) on HTSC single crystals. For $La_{2-x}Sr_xCuO_4$ a small contribution from $O2p_z$ orbitals (8% of holes in O2p valence band states) was observed which increased to about 13% on 30% Sr doping. In n-type doped HTSC there is no clear evidence for $O2p_z$ orbitals at E_F, but states are observed slightly above E_F with $O2p_z$ character depending on the doping and annealing conditions. An observed admixture of Cu $3d_{3z-r}$ states to the predominant $3d_{x-}$ hole states at E_F of a few percent did not significantly exceed the expermental error limits.

1. Indroduction

The commonly accepted picture for the electronic structure of CuOplanes in La_2CuO_4 as derived from cluster calculations gives a lower occupied Cu 3d band, the lower Hubbard band, and an occupied O2p band separated by

Springer Series in Solid-State Sciences, Vol. 113 Electronic Properties of High-T_c Superconductors
Editors: H. Kuzmany, M. Mehring, J. Fink

a charge transfer gap from the unoccupied upper Hubbard band. On p-type doping, states with $Cu3d_{x^2-y^2}$-$O2p_{x,y}\sigma$ symmetry having strong Zhang-Rice singlet [1] character form in the gap. These states may be related to superconductivity. This picture satisfactorly describes the observed O1s absorption edges for LaSrCuO. Upon Sr doping O2p hole states at the top of the valence band are formed and the transfer of spectroscopic weight from the upper Hubbard band to states at E are observed as measured by Romberg *et al.* [2] and Chen *et al.* [3]. According to Khomskii *et al.* [4], upon p-type doping the cuprates the energy of the $3d_{x^2-y^2}$ states are lowered, while states with $3d_{3z^2-r^2}$ orbital character crosses E_F. Maekawa *et al.* [5] point out that the increase of apical $O2p_z$ states to the in-plane holes may destabilize the Zhang-Rice singlets and thus may destroy superconductivity. On the other hand, electron-phonon Jahn-Teller interactions involving the apical oxygen was at the origin of the search for the cuprate superconductors [6]. In the d-d model of Weber [7] holes in the O2p band pair mainly via virtual excitations of d-d transitions on Cu sites. Kamimura *et al.* [8] have proposed a spin-polaron model with high-spin hybrides of $Cu3d_{3z^2-r^2}$ and $O2p_z$ orbitals for p-type doped cuprates and of $Cu3d_{x^2-y^2}$ and Cu4s orbitals for n-type doped cuprates. Experimental investigations of the symmetry and orbital character of the states near to the Fermi level are very valuable as they allow discrimination between different models.

2. Experimental

$La_{2-x}Sr_xCuO_4$ crystals used in this investigations were large enough to cut a,c-oriented surfaces. The other cuprate samples studied were thin single crystalline platelets with a,b oriented surfaces. The crystals were glued to Pt-covered sample holders and clean, flat and mirror-like surface were produced using an ultramicrotome with a diamond knife. Finally, they were mounted on a manipulator which can be rotated around the horizontal and the vertical axes to adjust the crystal axis under investigation so as to be parallel to the electrical field vector of the incident light. Bulk sensitive, polarized XAS measurements were performed at the SX700/II monochromator at BESSY using a Germanium fluorescence detector. The energy calibration and resolution were monitored with the help of a low-pressure Ne gas cell. The energy resolution used was 340 meV (780 meV) for most O1s (Cu2p) investigations. The O1s absorption measurements were corrected for the intensity variation of the photon beam as a function of energy with the help of a normalizing spectrum derived from total electron yield measurements of a clean Au surface. Self absorption corrections had to be applied to the Cu2p absorption data considering the different experimental geometries.

3. Results

Fig.1 shows the fluorescence yield spectra of $La_{2-x}Sr_xCuO_4$ for x = 0, 0.1 ± 0.01, 0.15 ± 0.01, and 0.3 ± 0.02 for the polarization vector **E** of the incident synchrotron light perpendicular and parallel to the crystallographic c-axis. For **E**⊥**c** and x = 0 there is a peak at 530.2 eV assigned to transitions to $O2p_{x,y}$ states hybridized with $Cu3d_{x-y}$ states in the conduction band (i.e., the upper Hubbard band). This is followed by a steep rise at 531 eV due to transitions into unoccupied $O2p_{x,y}$ states hybridized to La4f and 5d states. For x > 0 a new peak due to hole states in the valence band (E ~ 529 eV) and a transfer of spectral weight from the conduction band to valence band states is observed. These results agree with previous investigations on polycrystalline samples [2,3] and with theoretical investigations [9,10]. For **E** ‖ **c** the spectral weight below 531 eV is strongly reduced, but shows a similar x-dependence. A chemical shift of 0.3 eV is observed for the absorption threshold energies between the **E** ‖ **c** and **E** ⊥ **c** spectra. This indicates that the absorption edges originate from different O sites, that for **E** ⊥ **c** from the in-plane O sites and that for **E** ‖ **c** from the apical oxygen sites. From an analysis of the pre-peak at 529 eV we infer an O2p character relative to the total number of O2p holes induced by doping of 9%, 7%, and 13% for samples with x = 0.1, 0.15, and 0.3, respectively. The absence of Op_z holes in $Bi_2Sr_2CaCu_2O_8$ (T_c =85 K) [11] and the lower T_c < 40 K for $La_{2-x}Sr_xCuO_4$ samples with about 8% of apex holes may be taken as an argument for the destabilization of the Zhang-Rice singlet due to holes on the apical oxygen.

In contrast to the O1s spectra of $La_{2-x}Sr_xCuO_4$, those of the n-type doped $(Nd, Sm)_{2-x}Ce_xCuO_{4-\delta}$ show no unoccupied states in the valence

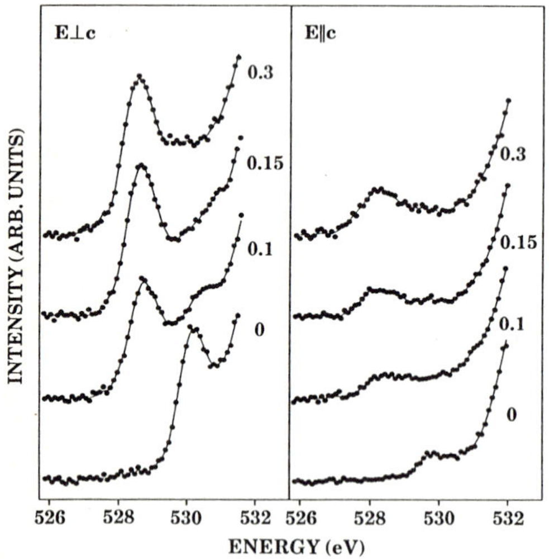

Fig.1: O1s x-ray absorption spectra of $La_{2-x}Sr_xCuO_4$ for x = 0, 0.1, 0.15, and 0.3 measured for polarizations **E** ⊥ **c** and **E** ‖ **c**.

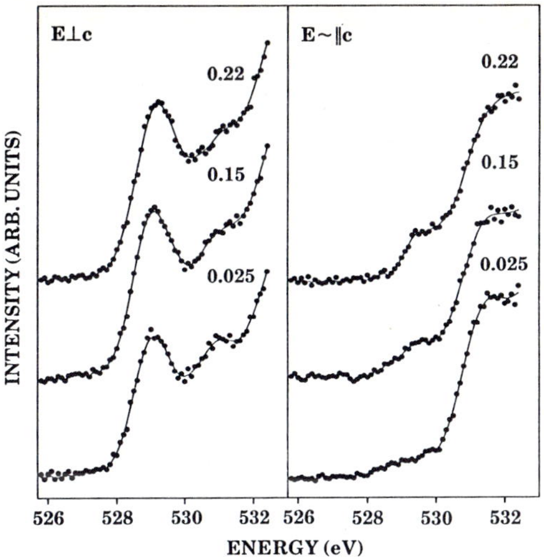

Fig.2: O1s x-ray absorption spectra of $Nd_{2-x}Ce_xCuO_{4-\delta}$ for x = 0.025, 0.15 and 0.3 measured for polarizations **E** ⊥ **c** and **E** ∥ **c**.

band. The relative intensity of the conduction band states for in plane (E⊥c) excitations does not change significantly with Ce doping. Despite the absence of apical oxygen sites there is some absorption observed for **E** ∥ **c** in the energy range of the conduction band (528-530.5 eV) even for the undoped samples. In $Nd_{2-x}Ce_xCuO_4$ (Fig.2), the absorption for **E** ∥ **c** seems to increase proportional to the doping concentration x. Hence, the observed $O2p_z$ states could be assigned to hybridization of O2p states with Ce4f and Ce5d states. Ce5d states are predicted by band structure calculations [12] to be close to the Fermi level. On the other hand, investigations on $Sm_2CuO_{4-\delta}$ (Fig.3) show that a similar increase in the **E** ∥ **c** absorption can be observed on reducing an undoped crystal. The similarity of the spectra for undoped, annealed and for x = 0.15 doped $Sm_{2-x}Ce_xCuO_4$ indicate that similar defect states at ~529.5 eV can be induced by oxygen defect states produced in a reducing atmosphere.

In Fig.4 we show the Cu2p absorption edges of SmCeCuO for **E** ⊥ **c** and **E** ∥ **c**. For **E** ⊥ **c** the transition into empty $Cu3d_{x^2y^2}$ states is observed and assigned to the upper Hubbard band. For **E** ∥ **c** a strongly reduced peak is obseved at the same energy. This transition is commonly assigned to $Cu3d_{3z^2r^2}$ states. In Table I the ratio of $Cu3d_{3z^2r^2}$ to Cu3d (total) holes are given for cuprates from the present XAS investigations. These values represent upper limits, since systematic errors as misorientation of the whole crystal or local misorientation and non-perfect polarization of the photon beam will result in the inclusion of part of the $3d_{x^2-y^2}$ spectrum in the **E** ∥ **c**-spectrum.

In Fig.4, above 932 eV, a clear edge is observed for **E** ∥ **c**. In the undoped as prepared sample the edge appears at ~935.2 eV, while it is

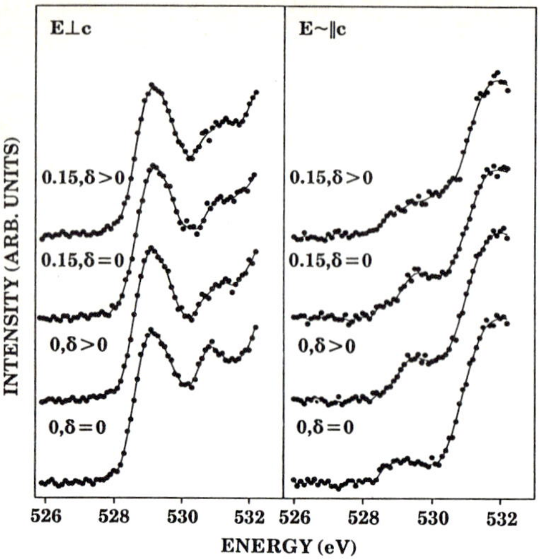

Fig.3: Polarized O1s x-ray absorption spectra of $Sm_{2-x}Ce_xCuO_{4-\delta}$ for x=0 and x=0.15. Samples with $\delta>0$ were annealed in argon.

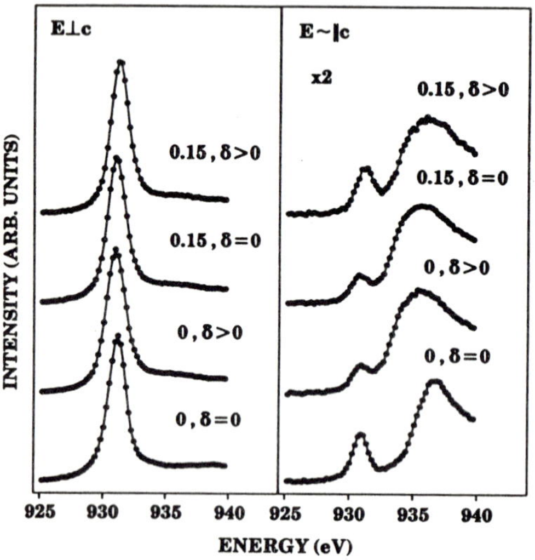

Fig.4: Cu2p absorption spectra of $Sm_{2-x}Ce_xCuO_{4-\delta}$ with x=0 and x=0.15, samples with $\delta>0$ were annealed in argon. The spectra are not corrected for self-absorption, which would enhance the **E ⊥ c** spectrum by a factor of 2.8 in the maximum.

shifted by ~2eV to lower energy upon reduction and/or doping. These edges may be assigned to $Cu3d_{z^2}$ character probably hybridized with a broad Cu4s band. This would indicate that the Cu4s band would be shifted towards the Fermi level upon reducing and/or doping. The additional intensity formed upon doping or annealing as observed in the O1s

Table I: Experimental radio R = holes $3d_{3z^2-r^2}$/holes in 3d
(a = annealed in argon; g.a.: c in grazing angle; a,c: a,c-plane)

sample	x	R(%)	geom.
$Ca_{1-x}Sr_xCuO_2$	0.14	1	g.a.
$La_{2-x}Sr_xCuO_4$	0.0	1	a,c
	0.1	4	a,c
	0.15	2	a,c
	0.3	4	a,c
$Tl_2Ba_2CaCu_2O_8$		1	g.a.
$Sm_{2-x}Ce_xCuO_{4-\delta}$	0	3	g.a.
	0, a	1	g.a.
	0.15	2	g.a.
	0.15, a	3	g.a.
$Nd_{2-x}Ce_xCuO_{4-\delta}$	0	1	g.a.
	0.15, a	1	g.a.
	0.22, a	1	g.a.

absorption edges for **E** ∥ **c** (Figs.2 and 3) may be related to this shift of the Cu4s band to lower energies.

4. Conclusions

Common to most actual models for the high temperature superconductors, the states near E_F have dominant in-plane character. The contribution of $Cu3d_{3z^2-r^2}$ to 3d states in the upper Hubbard band is small or zero. In $La_{2-x}Sr_xCuO_4$, about 8% of holes on oxygen sites have O2p character. At x = 0.3 this number is slightly increased to 13%. These results are in qualitative agreement with those reported by Chen *et al.* [13]. For the n-type doped T' phase cuprates there are O2p states in the energy range of the upper Hubbard band close to E independent of doping. At slightly higher energy additional O2p states are formed upon doping.

References

[1] F.C. Zhang and T.M. Rice, *Phys. Rev.* B **37** (1988) 3759

[2] H. Romberg, M. Alexander, N. Nücker, P. Adelmann, and J. Fink, *Phys. Rev.* B **42** (1990) 8768

[3] C.T. Chen, F. Sette, Y. Ma, M.S. Hybertsen, E.B. Stechel, W.M.C. Foulkes, M. Schlüter, S.-W. Cheong, A.S. Cooper, L.W. Rupp, jr., B. Batlogg, Y.L. Soo, Z.H. Ming, A. Krol, and Y.H. Kao, *Phys. Rev. Lett,* **66** (1991) 104
[4] D.I. Khomskii and E.I. Neimark, *Physica* C **173** (1991) 342
[5] S. Maekawa, Y. Ohta, and T. Tohyama, *Springer Series in Solid-State Sciences*, **106** (1992) 29
[6] J.G. Bednortz and K.A. Müller, *Z. Phys.* B **64** (1986) 189
[7] W. Weber, *Z. Phys.* B **70** (1988) 323
[8] H. Kamimura, M. Eto, S. Matsumo, and H. Ushio, *Comments on Condensed Matter Phys.* **15** (1992)
[9] M.S. Hybertsen and M. Schlüter, to be published in: *New Horizons in Low Dimensional Electron Systems*, ed. H. Aoki et al., Kluwer Academic Publ.
[10] H. Eskes, M.B.J. Meinders, and G.A. Sawatzky, *Phys. Rev. Lett.* **67** (1991) 1035
[11] N. Nücker, H.Romberg, X.X.Xi, J.Fink, B.Gegenheimer, and Z.X. Zhao,*Phys.Rev.* **B** 39 (1989) 6619
[12] Z. Szoetk, G.Y. Guo, and W.M. Temmerman, *Physica* C **175** (1991) 1
[13] C.T. Chen, L.H. Tjeng, J. Kwo, H.L. Kao, P. Rudolf, F. Sette, and R.M. Fleming, *Phys. Rev. Lett.* **86** (1992) 2543

Unusual Temperature-Dependent Behavior of the $Bi_2Sr_2CaCu_2O_{8+\delta}$ Energy Gap

C.T. Simmons, S. Molodtsov, G. Stadermann, C. Laubschat, and G. Kaindl

Institut für Experimentalphysik, Freie Universität Berlin,
Arnimallee 14, W-1000 Berlin 33, Fed. Rep. of Germany

Abstract. The electronic structure close to the Fermi level of $Bi_2Sr_2CaCu_2O_{8+\delta}$ was studied in the superconducting state by high resolution angle-integrated, resonant photoemission spectroscopy as a function of temperature and submonolayer Au coverage. In addition to the opening of an energy gap below T_c, described by a reduced gap parameter $2\Delta(20K)/k_BT_c \approx 8$, a relatively sharp density of states feature is discovered within the gap. Resonant enhancement at a photon energy of 18 eV indicates that this feature is oxygen-derived. Its relative spectral weight decreases with temperature, and also under submonolayer gold coverage. This suggests that it either originates from oxygen atoms in the Bi-O planes exposed at the cleaved (001) surface, or possibly the 'apex' oxygen atoms situated immediately below.

1. Introduction

An important issue in current thinking about high-T_c superconductivity is the attempt to uncover its underlying electronic pairing mechanism. For this reason, the observation of deviations from the usual BCS behaviour is of special interest, since these provide important clues for identifying the sought mechanism.

Analogous to what has been observed in ac-conductivity measurements and infrared spectroscopy,[1] we present angle-integrated photoemission evidence in favor of electronic states effectively filling in the gap upon warming towards T_c. A resonance effect strongly indicates the oxygen 2p-derived nature of this feature, while submonolayer gold deposition depresses this signal and suggests that it originates either from oxygen in the Bi-O planes exposed at the cleaved (001) surface, or else the 'apex' oxygen atoms, which lie in direct neighborhood to the superconducting Cu-O plane.

2. Experimental

Our experiment was carried out at the 3m-NIM 1 beamline at the Berliner Elektronenspeicherring für Synchrotronstrahlung (BESSY), employing a commercial angle-integrating electron spectromenter system (Leybold EA-11, acceptance angle $\pm$ 14°) in order to simultaneously monitor changes in as large a portion of the total density of states as possible. In order to gain signal intensity, the total system resolution was set to 40 meV (FWHM). The as grown $Bi_2Sr_2CaCu_2O_{8+\delta}$ crystals were single phase, with a sharp superconducting transition at 85 K, as measured with x-ray diffraction and low-field magnetic susceptibility. All PE spectra were taken directly after cleaving under vacuum, in the low 10^{-10} Torr range, at the temperature of measurement. In all cases, the Fermi edge of bulk Au in thermal contact with the sample was monitored for reference. Identical results were obtained with samples made at the St. Petersburg State University and in our own group.[2]

The spectra were least-squares fitted by superposing a BCS-like density of states resulting from a constant density in the normal state, with the trailing edge of the weakest-bound valence-band peak, the latter also being multiplied by a BCS density function; in addition, a narrow Lorentzian-shaped peak P in the gap had to be added. The resulting curve was multiplied by a Fermi distribution function and convoluted by a Gaussian to simulate instrumental broadening. The solid curves represent the results. It must be noted that using the BCS function here must be regarded as qualitative, since angle-resolved photoemission results have shown an appreciable deviation from the expected shape, notably at aprox. 75 meV binding energy.[3] This however, does not detract from the basic phenomenon reported here: filling-in of the superconducting gap.

3. Results and Discussion

Figure 1 shows selected valence-band PE spectra at hv = 18 eV, the energy of the oxygen 2s-2p resonance. Consistently good fits could only be obtained when peak P was included. At 20 K the valence-band edge is moved farthest away from E_F, due to the formation of an energy gap. This gap decreases only slightly with increasing temperature, while P's weight increases dramatically. Above 80 K, peak P is so intense that we can no longer discern the energy gap.

Figure 2 demonstrates the removal of the resonant enhancement of feature P when the photon energy is shifted away from the oxygen 2s-2p resonance. This is strong evidence for the oxygen-derived nature of this intragap electron density. The gap parameter is the same for both spectra (20 $\pm$ 3 meV). Note that the valence-band peak, whose tail is visible here, is known to resonate also at hv = 18 eV.

In order to learn more about the origin of peak P, we further studied its intensity as a function of gold coverage in the submonolayer range. Au was chosen because of its very little chemical reaction with the cleaved (001) superconductor surface. Fig. 3 displays PE spectra taken at 63 K from surfaces with three different coverages Θ. A decrease of peak P's relative spectral weight under Au coverage is clearly observed, while the gap remains constant. One can expect that changes induced by an almost inert overlayer will predominantly effect the surface. This means that the electron density P inside the gap must originate either directly from oxygen in the Bi-O planes exposed at the cleaved (001) surface, or possibly the 'apex' oxygen atoms, which lie immediately below and directly above the superconducting Cu-O plane. The bottom data of Fig. 3 show the relative intensity

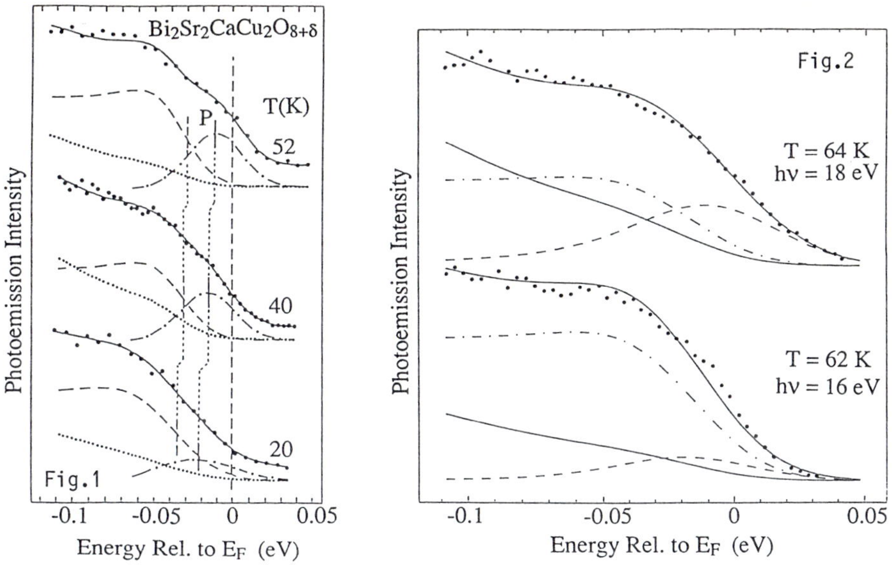

Figure 1. Some high-resolution valence-band PE spectra at hν = 18 eV, the energy of the oxygen 2s-2p resonance.

Figure 2. Spectra taken both on and off the O 2s-2p resonance at approx. 63 K. The gap parameter is the same for both ($\Delta = 20 \pm 3$ meV). Note that the valence-band peak whose tail is visible here, is known also to resonate at hν = 18 eV.

of P with Au coverage at 63 K. The presumed asymptotic saturation indicates the intrinsic bulk nature of P, against just a surface state, since the residual portion of P coming from deeper layers should remain unaffected.

There remains the question, why angle-resolved photoemission work has so far not reported seeing this intragap intensity. For this there are several reasons. The first is that almost all PES studies of the superconducting state have been conducted at temperatures around 20 K, at which this feature is so much reduced that, for our experiment, it is no more compelling in the data analysis. The second is the resonance at hν = 18 eV, a photon energy not used these works. Third is the nature of angle-resolved work, where workers so far have restricted themselves to directions of high symmetry (Γ-M and Γ-X,Y), and so missed this interesting feature, which must lie somewhere else in the Brillouin zone.

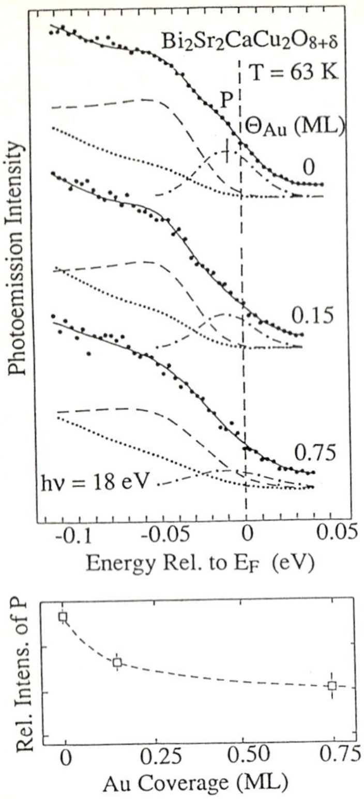

Figure 3. Top: T= 63 K spectra for a clean surface and two coverages of gold. Bottom: relative intensity of peak P.

References

[1] see e.g. R.T. Collins, Z. Schlesinger, F. Holtzberg, C. Feild, U. Welp, G.W. Crabtree, J.Z. Liu, and Y. Fang, Phys. Rev. B **43**, 8701 (1991)

[2] S.V. Moshkin, M.A. Kuzmina, M.U. Vlasov, O.F. Vyvenko, Inst. of Geology and Institute of Physics, St. Petersburg State University, 198904 St. Petersburg, Russia

[3] Y. Hwu, L. Lozzi, M. Marsi, S. La Rosa, M. Winkur, P. Davis, M. Onellion, H. Berger, F. Gozzo, F. L. Lévy, G. Margaritondo, Phys. Rev. Lett. **67**, 2573 (1991)
D.S. Dessau, B.O. Wells, Z.-X. Shen, W.E. Spicer, A.J. Arko, R.S. List, D.B. Mitzi, and A. Kapitulnik, Phys. Rev. Lett. **66**, 2160 (1991)

Metal and Semiconductor Overlayers on $Bi_2Sr_2CaCu_2O_{8+\delta}$

R. Seemann[1], *A. Sewing*[1], *R. Sporken*[2], *J. Ghijsen*[2], *and R.L. Johnson*[1]

[1]II. Institut für Experimentalphysik, Universität Hamburg, Luruper Chaussee 149, W-2000 Hamburg 50, Fed. Rep. of Germany

[2]L.I.S.E., rue de Bruxelles 61, B-5000 Namur, Belgium

We have studied the electronic properties of interfaces formed by Al, Au, Bi, CdTe, Cu, Ge, Pb and Sn with cleaved single crystals and with epitaxial thin films of $Bi_2Sr_2CaCu_2O_{8+\delta}$ using angle-integrated photoemission spectroscopy with synchrotron radiation. Measurements were performed over a wide range of photon energies, from 16 eV to 160 eV, yielding valence band, core level and resonant photoemission spectra which, in combination, provided detailed information about the interfaces. The resonant photoemission spectra give clear evidence of changes in the electronic structure associated with the CuO_2-planes of the superconductor as a function of adsorbate film thickness. All the materials deposited on the superconductor induce some changes in the weakly-bound electronic states arising from the CuO_2-planes. Al, Cu, Ge and Sn form strongly reactive interfaces, whereas Bi, CdTe and Au are less reactive. Pb is an intermediate case since it forms a monolayer of insulating PbO at the interface. The system CdTe/$Bi_2Sr_2CaCu_2O_{8+\delta}$ is an interesting example of a less reactive interface between a semiconductor and a superconductor. In this paper we focus on Au overlayers, which are suitable for use as metallic contacts in devices.

Interfaces between semiconductors or metals and copper-oxide-based high-temperature superconductors have attracted attention because the materials compatibility issues have to be thoroughly explored and optimized if these superconductors are to be integrated with other materials in devices. Although the Au/$Bi_2Sr_2CaCu_2O_{8+\delta}$ interface has been extensively studied it is still the subject of controversy [1-6]. Our results show that Au deposited at room temperature on $Bi_2Sr_2CaCu_2O_{8+\delta}$ forms a reactive interface.

Evidence of the disruption of the $Bi_2Sr_2CaCu_2O_{8+\delta}(001)$ surface due to Au-deposition is provided by the Bi $5d_{3/2}$ and $5d_{5/2}$ core level spectra shown in Fig. 1. As expected the intensity of the Bi 5d core levels decreases with increasing gold coverage, but at a coverage of 86 Å a small peak at lower binding energy due to released metallic Bi can be seen. The density of states at the Fermi edge ($E_B = 0$ eV), consisting of states from

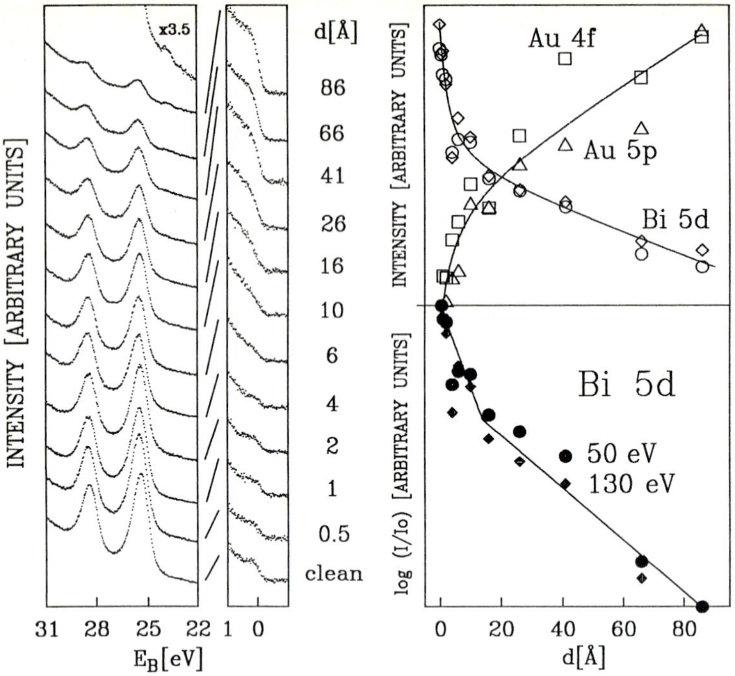

Fig. 1: *The Bi 5d core levels and the Fermi edge were measured for different Au coverages at 50 eV photon energy; the intensity of the core levels is plotted on the right-hand side.*

the CuO_2 and BiO planes, is suppressed at intermediate Au-coverages and increases again at higher coverages because gold itself has a large density of states at E_F.

Weaver et al.[5, 6] showed using scanning tunneling microscopy (STM) that submonolayer deposit of Au at 300 K produce ~25 Å diameter clusters that form rows along the b-axis. These clusters result from conversion of the terminating BiO surface layer into a Bi_2O_3-like structure which is energetically more favourable and the activation energy is probably provided by Au–Au bonding or clustering.

The model proposed by Weaver et al. is supported by our photoemission results. The suppression of the density of states at the Fermi edge for intermediate coverages shows that the metallicity of the surface BiO plane is destroyed and it is likely that parts of the surface become insulating as expected for the formation of Bi_2O_3–clusters. The two slopes in the attenuation curves in the lower part of the right hand side in Fig. 1 show clearly that the sticking coefficient changes for different gold depositions; for coverages up to 3 Å it is larger than for coverages of more than

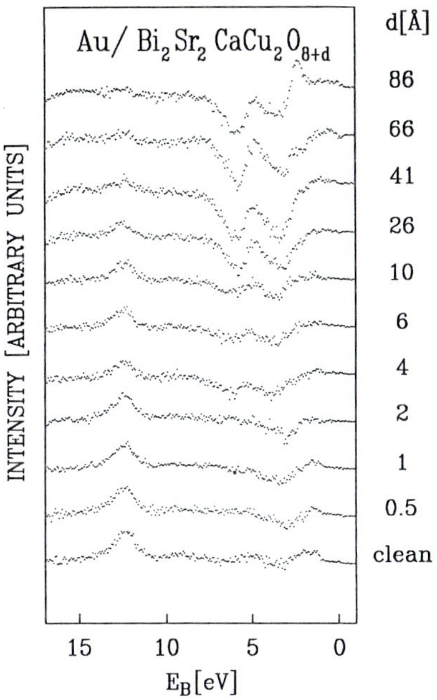

Fig. 2: *Difference spectra obtained by subtracting the off-resonance spectra ($\hbar\omega = 70$ eV) from the Cu 3p-3d resonantly enhanced spectra ($\hbar\omega = 75$ eV) for different Au-coverages.*

3 Å. The first slope can be explained by the formation of Bi_2O_3-clusters up to a Au coverage of 3 Å and the second slope is due to layer growth of the gold on the reacted surface.

The 200 meV shift of the Bi 5d core levels to higher binding energies observed in the photoemission spectra for small Au coverages shown in Fig. 1 can also be explained by a higher oxidation state of Bi which would normally cause a shift to higher binding energies. It should be mentioned that local charging effects can be excluded, because otherwise it would not have been possible to perform STM measurements on this surface.

There are two ways of converting the BiO plane into Bi_2O_3 clusters; one involves the addition of oxygen ($2BiO + O \rightarrow Bi_2O_3$) and the other separation into Bi and Bi_2O_3 ($3BiO \rightarrow Bi + Bi_2O_3$). The photoemission results in Fig. 1 show that Bi segregation occurs, but the amount of segregated Bi is only about 1 %. Hence, insufficient oxygen for complete Bi_2O_3 formation is provided by this reaction and the additional oxygen has to be provided by the superconductor. The question that arises is therefore from which layers in the superconductor is the oxygen removed? Photoemission measurements of the Sr 4p and O 2s core levels show that some oxygen is released from the SrO layer, but the amount does not correspond to what would be needed to convert the first BiO layer into Bi_2O_3-clusters. In Fig. 2, the Cu 3p-3d resonant photoemission spectra demonstrate that the CuO_2 layer also suffers oxygen depletion.

The Cu 3p-3d resonance is particularly important in the cuprate superconductors because the spectra are sensitive to changes in the electronic structure associated with the CuO_2-planes. Difference spectra obtained by subtracting spectra measured off-resonance ($\hbar\omega = 70$ eV) from those measured on-resonance ($\hbar\omega = 76$ eV) are shown in Fig. 2. There are three distinct features in the difference spectra from the freshly cleaved sample: the structure at 12.7 eV binding energy associated with the singlet final state of CuO, the antiresonance of the valence band and a small resonance near the Fermi edge. The antiresonance, which delicately reflects any small changes of the chemical state of the CuO_2-planes, remains almost linebreak[2] unaltered for low coverages. At higher Au-coverages the structures arising from the Au 5d core levels become more predominant. The intensity of the structure at 12.7 eV binding energy decreases not as much as would be expected for Au-coverages up to 2 Å and changes significantly for coverages above 2 Å. This effect can be explained in terms of modified Auger matrix elements for the super-Coster-Kronig transition, that reflect changes of the hybridization between Cu 3d and O 2p orbitals in the CuO_2-planes [7]. These changes are probably due to oxygen diffusing out from the CuO_2 planes. This clearly indicates that gold modifies the electronic structure of at least the first CuO_2-plane. It can be concluded that the interface of Au/$Bi_2Sr_2CaCu_2O_{8+\delta}$ formed at room temperature is reactive and the electronic structure of at least the first CuO_2- and SrO-layer is modified and the surface BiO-layer is converted into Bi_2O_3-like clusters.

References

[1] B. O. Wells et al., Phys. Rev. Lett. **65**, 3056 (1990).

[2] T. Takahashi and H. Katayama-Yoshida, Phys. Rev. Lett. **68**, 416 (1992).

[3] B. O. Wells et al., Phys. Rev. Lett. **68**, 417 (1992).

[4] Y. Hwu et al., Appl. Phys. Lett. **59**, 979 (1991).

[5] J. H. Weaver, in *Interfaces in Superconducting Systems*, ed.: S. L. Shinde (Springer-Verlag 1992).

[6] Y. S. Luo, Y.-N. Yang, and J. H. Weaver, Phys. Rev. **B**, (1992), submitted.

[7] R. Seemann and R. L. Johnson, to be published.

Electronic Properties of T^*-$Nd_{1.4}Ce_{0.2}Sr_{0.4}CuO_{4-\delta}$

M. Klauda[1], *P. Lunz*[1], *J. Markl*[1], *G. Saemann-Ischenko*[2], *R. Seemann*[2], *and R.L. Johnson*[2]

[1]Physikalisches Institut der Universität Erlangen,
Erwin-Rommel-Str. 1, W-8520 Erlangen, Fed. Rep. of Germany
[2]II. Institut für Experimentalphysik, Universität Hamburg,
Luruper Chaussee 149, W-2000 Hamburg 50, Fed. Rep. of Germany

Abstract Investigations on the electronic structure of T^*–type $Nd_{1.4}Ce_{0.2}Sr_{0.4}CuO_{4-\delta}$ by means of photoelectron spectroscopy are presented and compared with results for electron doped compounds of the T'–structure. Concerning the Cu–O–layers we find slightly altered Cu–O–hybridization and –charge transfer energy, which can be explained by the different surrounding of copper in both compounds. Also the electronic properties of the rare earth layers exhibit small but distinct differences in both systems which also can be related to different structural properties.

1. Introduction

Superconductivity in the $Nd_{1.4}Ce_{0.2}Sr_{0.4}CuO_{4-\delta}$–system was discovered in 1988 by Akimitsu et al. [1]. Neutron refinements [2] confirmed its "T^*–structure" to be a hybrid of the well known T– (La_2CuO_4–) and T'– (Nd_2CuO_4–) structures. Thus instead of CuO_4–plates (as in T') or CuO_6–octahedrons (as in T), Cu in the T^*–compounds has an pyramidal surrounding of 5 O–ions. Hall–effect measurements revealed a positive sign of majority charge carriers [3] for this compound, which therefore stands at the borderline to n–type superconductivity within the family of the closely related T–, T^*– and T'–systems. Furthermore due to the simplicity of its crystal structure it can be considered as model compound for other HTSC containing CuO_5–pyramides (like i.e. $Bi_2Sr_2CaCu_2O_{8+\delta}$). We therefore think investigations on the electronic structure of T^* to be of particular interest.

2. Experimental

Samples were prepared by a standard solid state reaction technique, described in detail elsewhere [4]. The samples had a T_c of 25 K and a Meißner fraction of 26% of the ideal value.
For photoemission experiments surface quality of the samples was checked by the E_B = 932 eV–shoulder of the O1s–peak for core level spectroscopy and the 9.5 eV–feature of the valence band spectra, respectively, which are both due to chemisorbed oxygen on the surface. Both features were minimized by scraping the samples under UHV. Both core level– and valence band–spectra show degradation of the surface in UHV at room temperature within few hours, as was also observed for other HTSC [5].

3. Results and discussion

Cu–O–layers. A rough estimate of a first important electronic parameter of the Cu–O–layers, namely the hole–hole–correlation energy at the copper site U_{dd}, can be given by a

Springer Series in Solid-State Sciences, Vol. 113 Electronic Properties of High-T_c Superconductors
Editors: H. Kuzmany, M. Mehring, J. Fink

Table 1: Values for Cu–O–hybridization V and –charge–transfer–energy Δ obtained by a Single–Impurity Anderson model ($U_{dc} = 8.1\,eV$).

	Nd_2CuO_4	$Nd_{1.4}Ce_{0.2}Sr_{0.4}CuO_{4-\delta}$	$Bi_2Sr_2CaCu_2O_{8-\delta}$	
I_m/I_s	3.1	2.6	2.2	
ΔE (eV)	8.6	8.6	8.7	
V (eV)	4.1	3.2	2.2	W =
Δ (eV)	3.4	2.45	1.45	2.0 eV
V (eV)	4.1	3.2	2.2	W =
Δ (eV)	3.75	2.8	1.95	3.0 eV

comparison of the two–hole binding energies of the Cu *Lvv*–Auger feature and of the self convolution of the XPS–valence band [6]. From this we estimate an U_{dd} of approximately 7.2 eV for $Nd_{1.4}Ce_{0.2}Sr_{0.4}CuO_{4-\delta}$.

The mean Cu–O–hybridization V and –charge transfer energy Δ were determined by evaluating the $Cu2p_{3/2}$–core level spectra by using a Single Impurity Anderson Model [7]. For divalent copper compounds the $Cu2p_{3/2}$–spectra consist of a main peak at about 933 eV and a broad satellite feature around 941 eV. Whereas the main line is mainly due to a $|d^{10}\,\underline{L}\,\underline{c}\rangle$–configuration in the final state (charge transfer of one O2p–electron to the Cu), the broad satellite has its main origin in $|d^9\,\underline{c}\rangle$–final states [8]. $\underline{L}$ and $\underline{c}$ denote holes in the ligand O2p–orbitals and in the Cu2p–core levels, respectively. From the spectra one extracts the main line to satellite intensity ratio I_m/I_s and the peak separation ΔE. Within the above mentioned model one obtains for a constant value of the Cu2p-hole–Cu3d–interaction of $U_{dc} = 8.1\,eV$ for different oxygen bandwidths W the results for V and Δ given in table 1.

For the Cu–O–hybridization one observes an increasing value going from T′–compounds over T*–systems to $Bi_2Sr_2CaCu_2O_{8-\delta}$. Since in the p–doped systems one has a very remote apical oxygen with CuO–bond lengths of 2.23 Å and 3.31 Å for $Nd_{1.4}Ce_{0.2}Sr_{0.4}CuO_{4-\delta}$ and $Bi_2Sr_2CaCu_2O_{8-\delta}$, respectively, the *mean* CuO–hybridization is reduced for those systems compared to Nd_2CuO_4. The smaller value of $\Delta = \varepsilon_d - \varepsilon_p + U_{dd}$ for p–doped systems we attribute to a smaller value of U_{dd} for those compounds: Cu3d–holes may delocalize on 5 instead of 4 ligand oxygen, leading to a reduced Coulomb interaction.

The difference in U_{dd} between p– and n–doped systems can be checked more directly by considering the valence band spectra in the Cu3p→3d–resonance at a photon energy of $\hbar\omega = 74\,eV$. At this energy the emission of the features with Cu $3d^8$–final states at binding energies of 12.5 eV (singlet states) and 10 eV (triplet states) is resonantely enhanced. The energy speration of the Cu3d–singlet–feature and the main valence band around 4 eV gives an estimate for the Coulomb repulsion U_{dd} of two holes (d^8–final state) at the copper site [7,9]. As can be seen from Figure 1, the $|d^8\rangle$–peak is shifted to lower binding energies for the p–doped T* compounds by about 0.5 eV, reflecting the same trend for U_{dd} as concluded from the Cu2p–core level spectra.

Rare–Earth–Layers. Figure 2 shows the **Nd3d–spectra** of $Nd_{1.4}Ce_{0.2}Sr_{0.4}CuO_{4-\delta}$ and Nd_2CuO_4. Besides the main line at $E_B = 1004\,eV$, for Nd3d–spectra of trivalent Nd–compounds ($n_f = 3$) there are two satellite lines at binding energies of 1000 eV and 1008 eV, which are due to $4f^2$– and $4f^4$–configurations in the final state. Evaluation was done within a simple two dimensional CI–model, similar to the analysis of Ikeda et al. [10] in the limit of zero O2p–bandwidth. With a 4f–core hole interaction $U_{fc} = 12.7\,eV$ one obtains for the Nd–O–hybridization values of 1.49 eV and 1.47 eV for Nd_2CuO_4 and

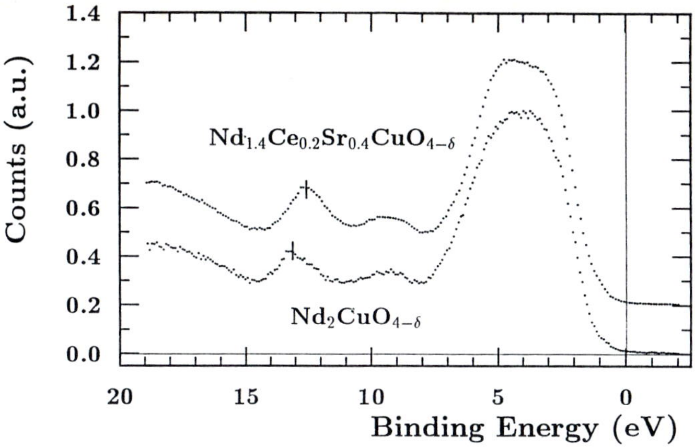

Figure 1: Valence band spectra of Nd_2CuO_4 and $Nd_{1.4}Ce_{0.2}Sr_{0.4}CuO_{4-\delta}$ at $\hbar\omega = 74\,eV$.

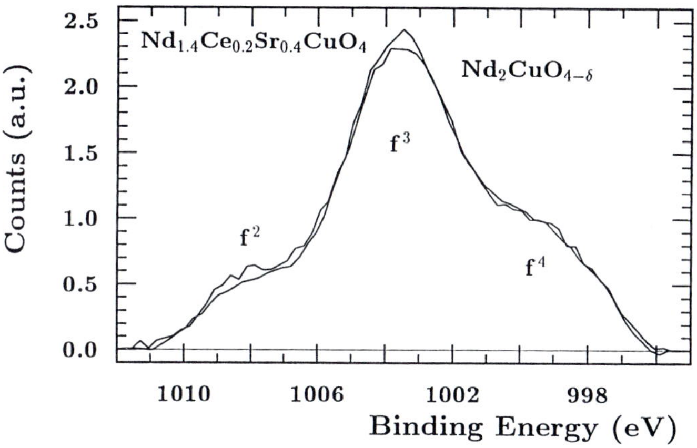

Figure 2: $Nd3d_{3/2}$–spectra of $Nd_{1.4}Ce_{0.2}Sr_{0.4}CuO_{4-\delta}$ and of Nd_2CuO_4. Spectra are normalized on the $4\,f^4$–satellite.

$Nd_{1.4}Ce_{0.2}Sr_{0.4}CuO_{4-\delta}$, respectively. The Nd–O–charge transfer energy can be obtained to be 9.65 eV and 9.58 eV for T′ and T*–systems, respectively. A similar trend in the charge transfer energy can also be seen from the partial Nd4f–valence band spectra, which are presented elsewhere [11]. The larger mean Nd–O–distance in the $Nd_{1.4}Ce_{0.2}Sr_{0.4}CuO_{4-\delta}$–system [4] together with the completely different surrounding of Nd in the T–type part of the T*–structure should be able to explain the observed differences.

From an analysis of the **Ce3d–spectra** one can confirm Ce also in T*–systems to be tetravalent ($n_f = 0.5$). Thus, the T′–type (Nd,Ce)–layers of the system closely resemble to those of n–doped HTSC, whereas the majority charge carriers seem to be due to the divalent Sr–dopants in the T–type (Nd,Sr)–sheets.

4. Acknowledgement

We gratefully acknowledge Prof. L. Ley for helpful discussions and the Bundesminister für Forschung und Technologie for financial support.

References

[1] J.Akimitsu, S.Suzuki, M.Watanabe, H.Sawa, Jpn.J.Appl.Phys. **27**, L1859 (1988).

[2] F.Izumi, E.Takayama–Muromachi, A.Fujimori, T.Kamiyama, H.Asano, J.Akimitsu, H.Sawa, Physica C **158**, 440 (1989).

[3] M.Kosuge, S.Ikegawa, N.Koshizuka, S.Tanaka, Physica C **176**, 373, (1991).

[4] M.Klauda, P.Lunz, J.Markl, J.P.Ströbel, C.Fink, G.Saemann–Ischenko, Physica C **191**, 137 (1992).

[5] A.Grassmann, J.P.Ströbel, M.Klauda, J.Schlötterer, G.Saemann–Ischenko, Europhys.Lett. **9**, 827 (1989).

[6] E.Antonides, E.C.Janse, G.A.Sawatzky, Phys.Rev.B **15**, 1669 (1977).

[7] J.Zaanen, C.Westra, G.A.Sawatzky, Phys.Rev.B **33**, 8060 (1986).

[8] G.van der Laan, C.Westra, C.Haas, G.A.Sawatzky, Phys.Rev.B **23**, 1439 (1981).

[9] J.Ghijsen, L.H.Tjeng, J.van Elp, H.Eskes, J.Westerink, G.A.Sawatzky, M.T.Czyzyk, Phys.Rev.B **38**, 11322 (1988).

[10] T.Ikeda, K.Okada, H.Ogasawara, A.Kotani, J.Phys.Soc.Jpn. **59**, 622 (1990).

[11] M.Klauda, P.Lunz, J.Markl, G.Saemann–Ischenko, R.Seemann, R.L.Johnson, to be published.

Part V

Hyperfine Interactions, Magnetic Properties

Introduction to the Nuclear Magnetic Resonance (NMR) in High-T_c Superconductors

M. Mehring

2. Physikalisches Institut, Universität Stuttgart,
W-7000 Stuttgart 80, Fed. Rep. of Germany

Abstract. In this tutorial lecture I want to introduce the non-NMR expert to the physics and terminology of NMR and its application to high-temperature superconductors. An introduction is given to the basic principles of NMR, the experimental technique as well as the important parameters relevant for superconductors like Knight shift (K_s) and nuclear spin relaxation (T_1,T_2). Special emphasis is placed on the connection of these parameters with the charge and spin dynamic in high-temperature superconductors. It will be demonstrated that NMR experiments have revealed some important information on the anti-ferromagnetic correlation and on Fermi-like quasiparticles in this class of materials. This lecture serves as an introduction to the following NMR presentations.

1. Introduction

Nuclear magnetic resonance (NMR) and nuclear quadrupole resonance (NQR) have played a decisive role in solid state physics in general[1] and in superconductors in particular. One of the prominent features in BCS type superconductors was the observation of the Hebel-Slichter peak[2] in the relaxation rate $1/T_1$ which appeared around T_c and was taken as an indication of the "coherence factor", an important ingredient in the BCS theory. Another important aspect in classical superconductors was the determination of the temperature dependence of the paramagnetic susceptibility in the superconducting state by NMR via the Knight shift, leading to a strong support for s-wave pairing. In fact the two parameters mentioned, namely Knight shift (K_s), where the subscript s stands for the spin-dependent part, and the spin-lattice relaxation time T_1 turn out to be also the most important parameters in the NMR spectroscopy of high-temperature superconductors as I want to demonstrate below. For reviews on the subject see [3,4].

For introductory purposes I mention a few facts about NMR and NQR[1]. If the nuclear spin under consideration has spin $I > 1/2$ and has a quadrupole moment (Q) and in addition its local surrounding is lower than cubic or tetrahedral symmetry an electric field gradient splits the energy levels of the nucleus. In the case of $I=3/2$ the $\pm$ 3/2 levels are separated from the $\pm 1/2$ levels by the quadrupole frequency ν_Q. Irradiation with radio-frequency fields at this frequency causes transitions which can be detected in a coil surrounding the sample.

To be more specific we consider the ^{63}Cu nucleus ($I=3/2$) in $YBa_2Cu_3O_{6+\delta}$ (abbreviated $YBCO_{6+\delta}$). There are two different Cu-sites, namely in the Cu-O-Cu chains (labelled Cu(1)) and in the CuO_2 planes (labelled Cu(2)). Both show a large quadrupole splitting of about 22 MHz for Cu(1) and about 32 MHz for Cu(2)[3, 4, 5]. Other quadrupole interactions of e.g. ^{17}O and ^{137}Ba have also been measured in the YBCO systems(see e.g. Brinkmann and Berthier in this volume). From these measurements one obtains the electric field gradient (EFG) for the particular nuclear site, which is an important parameter for the electronic structure of cuprate superconductors.

It is important to note that the values for the EFG calculated by Schwarz and co-workers and others [6] within LDA approximation for all different sites in the YBCO unit cell agree quite nicely with the experimentally observed data, besides the Cu(2) position which is off. As Schwarz pointed out, however, a slight charge redistribution in the copper d_{z^2}-orbital could rectify this deficiency. This sheds some light on the contribution of this orbital to the conduction band.

In NMR an external magnetic field B_0 is applied in the z-direction. This splits all Kramers doubletts which were still degenerate in the NQR situation. The splitting is called Zeeman splitting and it separates the spin levels by the Larmor frequency $\nu_0 = \gamma_n B_0$, where γ_n is the nuclear gyromagnetic ratio. With fields between 1-10 Tesla this corresponds to frequencies in the range of 10 - 300 MHz. If $I=1/2$ (e.g. in ^{89}Y) only one transition, i.e. a single NMR line occurs. If $I>1/2$ as is the case for $^{63}Cu(I=3/2)$ or $^{17}O(I=5/2)$ a total of 2I lines occur according to all possible $\Delta m = \pm 1$ transitions. Whereas the "central" transition (-1/2 - +1/2) is affected by quadrupole interaction only in second order, first order quadrupole interaction determines the splitting and broadening of the other transitions. If one wants to determine the Knight shift, to be discussed below, one restricts oneself to the observation of the central transition, where magnetic interactions are dominant.

Both NMR and NQR allow to measure the spin-lattice relaxation time T_1 and spin-spin relaxation time T_2. The experimental techniques involved require radio-frequency pulses applied on-resonance to the nuclear spin system. The recovery of the z-magnetization (population difference) is observed in a typical T_1 measurement, whereas the decay of the x,y-magnetization as observed in a spin-echo experiment leads to T_2. Both quantities give information on the fluctuations of the local magnetic or in the case of quadrupole moment also of the electrical fields.

2. Hyperfine Interaction and Knight shift

In Fig.1 I have scetched the important atoms in and near the CuO_2 plane of cuprate superconductors. These are besides Cu(2) and O(2,3) also Y or Tl(2) between two CuO_2 planes and Cu(1) or Tl(1) in the intermediate chain or plane. The arrows mark the different hyperfine contributions (A,B,C,D,E) to different nuclear sites deriving from electron spins in the copper-oxygen hybrid orbitals[7]. Due to the itinerant nature of the electron spins these hyperfine interactions cause a shift of the resonance line which is called the Knight shift K_s.

There are of course other contributions to the lineshift of an NMR line which we label chemical shift δ_c, because they originate from orbital contributions which depend on the bonding orbitals. The total shift can therefore be expressed as

$$\delta(T) = \delta_c + K_s(T) + (1-N)\, M(T)/B_0 \quad , \tag{1}$$

where I have added the additional shift due to the magnetization M(T) including also the demagnetizing factor N of the sample. The magnetization can usually be neglected in the normal state but has to be taken into account in the superconducting state. In singlett pairing superconductivity it is expected that the Knight shift vanishes at T=0, neglecting here pair breaking effects. This allows to separate the Knight shift from the chemical shift.

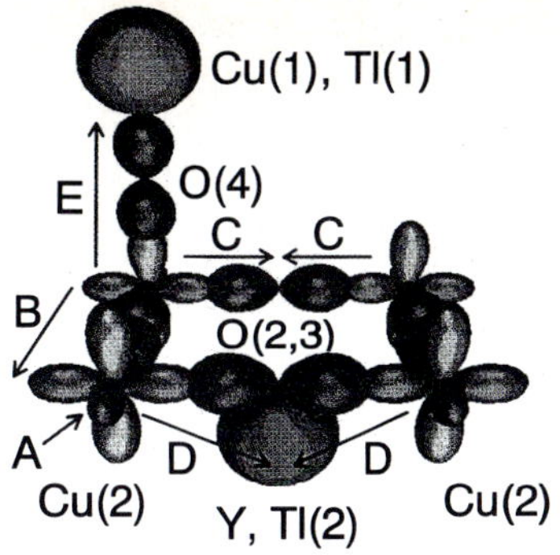

Fig.1 Atomic orbitals and nuclear sites in and off the CuO_2 plane including the hyperfine alphabet with arrows indicating the transferred hyperfine interaction.

It has been demonstrated by comparing Knight shift data of $^{63}Cu(2)$, $^{17}O(2,3)$ and ^{89}Y that all scale with the same spin susceptibility, leading to a single spin fluid model. In such a single spin fluid model[8, 9, 10, 11] the Knight shift is connected with the spin susceptibility by

$$K_S = \frac{\sum A_j}{g\,\mu_B}\,\chi_S = \sum_j a_j\,\chi_S \qquad (2a)$$

$$\text{with} \quad \chi_S = g^2\,\mu_B{}^2\,\chi(q=0)\;, \qquad (2b)$$

where $A_j(a_j)$ is the z-component of the hyperfine tensor and χ_s is the electron spin susceptibility per CuO_2 unit. For comparison with theoretical calculations I have introduced the reduced spin susceptibility at wavevector q=0 according to Eq.(2b). Once the hyperfine interaction is known the Knight shift is a direct measure of the paramagnetic susceptibility χ (q=0)and vice versa[12, 13, 17]. As an example of such such an evaluation I have plotted in Fig.2 the paramagnetic susceptibility of $YBa_2Cu_4O_8$ (124)(T_c=82K) as obtained from $^{63}Cu(2)$ data by Brinkmann [5]. Note that there is a strong temperature dependence in the normal state, typical for underdoped YBCO. A similar behaviour is observed for $YBCO_{6.6}$ (T_c=60K), however, with smaller values of $\chi(0)$[8, 11]. In contrast, the $\chi(0)$ values of $YBCO_7$(T_c=92K) are larger and are almost temperature independent. In a one electron model $\chi(0) = D(E_F)/4$, where $D(E_F)$ is the density of states per CuO_2 unit and spin. It is interesting to note that the value obtained for $YBCO_7$ corresponds to $D(E_F) = 3.3\ eV^{-1}$ which is rather close to the value 2.5 eV^{-1} obtained from LDA bandstructure calculations. The decreased susceptibility in the less doped samples can be readily interpreted as a reduction in the density of states. The temperature dependence, however, is not comptible with Pauli susceptibility and has its origin in the unusual properties of this spin fluid. In fact the curve drawn through the points is a fit to $\chi(0)=\chi_0[1\text{-}\tanh^2(\Delta/2T)]$ where Δ is the "spin gap" energy as proposed by Tranquada[18]. It results in Δ=233K and $\chi(0) = 0.64\ eV^{-1}$ for this particular system.

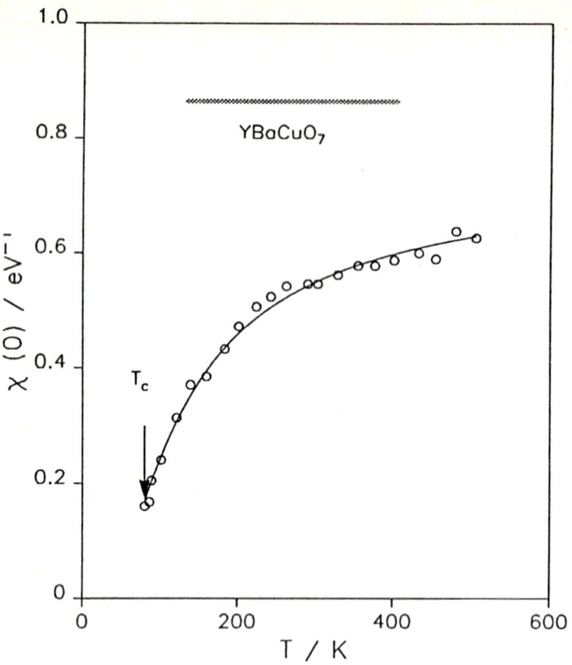

Fig.2 Static susceptibility of YBCO(124) derived from Knight shift data [5](see text).

3. Spin-Lattice Relaxation and Antiferromagnetic Correlations.

Adopting the Moriya expression for the spin-lattice relaxation rate in metals to the specific hyperfine couplings in cuprate superconductors one arrives at[9, 10]

$$\frac{1}{T_1} = \hbar\, k_B\, T\, \gamma_n{}^2\, (A_{iso}(q=0))^2\; I_K \tag{3a}$$

$$\text{with} \quad I_K = \sum_q F(q)\, \frac{\mathrm{Im}\,\chi^{+-}(q,\omega_0)}{\hbar\,\omega_0} \tag{3b}$$

$$\text{and} \quad F(q) = \frac{A(q)\, A(-q)}{(A_{iso}(q))^2} \quad , \tag{3c}$$

$$\text{where} \quad A(q) = \sum_j A_j \exp(-i\mathbf{q}\, \mathbf{r}_j) \quad . \tag{3d}$$

$A_{iso}(q=0) = \sum A_{jiso}$ is the total isotropic hyperfine interaction constant, T is the temperature and Im χ^{+-} (q, ω_0) is the imaginary part of the dynamic susceptibility χ^{+-} (q, ω) at some characteristic frequency ω_0 which is usually considered to be the nuclear Larmor frequency. It is important to realise that the formfactor F(q) is a weighting factor in q-space which can filter certain parts of q-space. As an example let us consider the $^{17}O(2,3)$ relaxation. Its formfactor can be expressed as $F(q) = \cos^2(q_x/2)$ if the Cu-O-Cu bond direction is along x and besides a constant factor which is given by the ratio of the hyperfine interaction perpendicular to the magnetic field and the isotropic hyperfine interaction. Note that $q_x = \pi$ and vice versa $q_y=\pi$ give vanishing contribution to the ^{17}O(2,3) relaxation, i.e. it is "blind" to the antiferromagnetic fluctuations[13, 17]. In contrast ^{63}Cu(2) has a more complex formfactor, which has particularly strong weight at $Q=(\pi,\pi)$ if the magnetic field is applied perpendicular to the c-axis[8, 11, 15, 16, 19]. If the dynamic susceptibility $\chi(q,\omega)$ is separated into the two parts $\chi(q,\omega) = \chi_{QP}(q,\omega) + \chi_{AF}(q,\omega)$ as proposed by Millis, Monien and Pines[9], where χ_{QP} is the quasiparticle contribution centered around $q=(0,0)$ and χ_{AF} represents the antiferromagnetic correlations centered around $Q=(\pi,\pi)$. From the foregoing it is evident that ^{17}O(2,3) relaxation picks out the χ_{QP} contribution, whereas ^{63}Cu(2) relaxation is dominated by χ_{AF}. Their relaxation behaviour is indeed observed to be very distinct. In order to supply parameters which characterize these different contributions I separate I_K according to Eq.(3b) into [20]

$$I_K = F(0)\, I_0 + F(Q)\, I_Q = \frac{1}{\hbar\, k_B\, T_1 T\, \gamma_n^2\, (A_{iso}(q=0))^2} , \qquad (4a)$$

where the sum $$I_{0,Q} = \sum_q \frac{\mathrm{Im}\, \chi^{+-}(q,\omega_0)}{\hbar\, \omega_0} \qquad (4b)$$

is restricted to $0 \leq q_x < \pi/2$; $0 \leq q_y < \pi/2$ in the case of I_0, whereas for I_Q it is restricted to $\pi/2 < q_x \leq \pi$; $\pi/2 < q_y \leq \pi$. Altough the detailed features of the q-dependance of the formfactors is still contained in the quantities I_0 (quasiparticle spectral density:QSD) and I_Q (antiferromagnetic spectral density:ASD), this dependence is weak and will not be considered in the following where the gross features of these fluctuations will be discussed. It is one of the major goals of spin lattice relaxation measurements to determine I_0 and I_Q.

Particularly interesting is the temperature dependence of I_Q which is shown in Fig.3 in the case of $YBa_2Cu_4O_8$(124) which has $T_c=82K$ and is considered an underdoped sample. The data were taken from Brinkmann[5] and using the standard set of hyperfine interactions[9, 20]. Similar features have been observed some time ago in oxygen depleted $YBa_2Cu_3O_{6+\delta}$ samples [13, 15]. It was argued that the characteristik peak at $T^* > T_c$ is connected with a "spin gap" opening above T_c. This has independently been observed in neutron scattering [21] and a comparison between NMR and neutron scattering results is made by Berthier in this volume. Rossat-Mignod [21] gives a detailed account on this also in this volume. See also [22]. The solid curve in Fig.3 is given by $T^{-1.5} * [1-\tanh^2(\Delta/2T)]$ as discussed in section 2, with $\Delta=280K$ here. A more realistic form would include $\Delta=\Delta_0[(T^*-T)/T^*]^{1/2}$ or another temperature dependence, which will be discussed elsewhere[20]. In Fig.3 I have also marked the I_Q values of $YBCO_7$($T_c=92K$) and $YBCO_{6.6}$($T_c=60K$) at 200K. It appears that samples with larger I_Q, i.e. larger antiferromagnetic fluctuations have lower T_c. This is a preliminary analysis which is based on certain assumptions about the hyperfine interactions in these samples. It still has to be

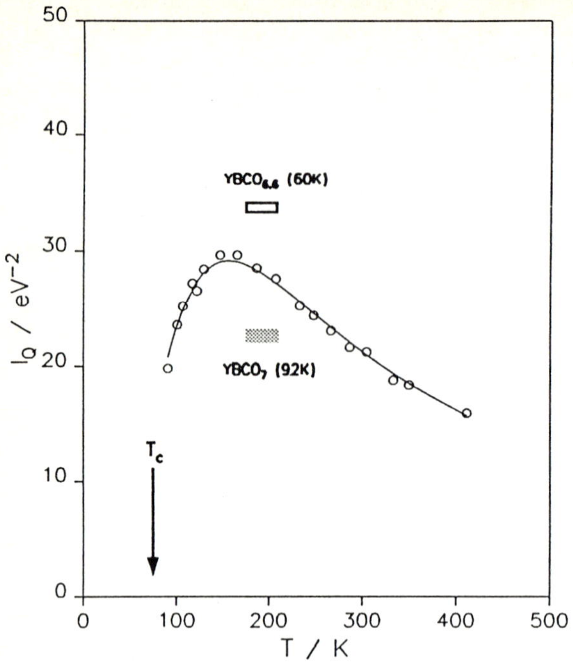

Fig.3 Antiferromagnetic spectral density I_Q of YBCO(124)[5] showing spin gap behaviour.

proven that these assumptions hold. A more detailed discussion on Knight shifts and spin lattice relaxation in cuprate superconductors can be found in [20].

Acknowledgements. I gratefully acknowledge financial support from the Bundesminister für Forschung und Technologie as well as from the Land Baden Württemberg.

References

1. C. P. Slichter, Principles of Magnetic Resonance (Springer, Berlin, 1989), 3rd ed.
2. L. C. Hebel and C. P. Slichter, Phys. Rev. 107, 901 (1957); and Phys. Rev. 113, 1504 (1959).
3. C. H. Pennington and C. P. Slichter in Physical Properties of High Temperature Superconductors II, D. M. Ginsberg, ed. (World Scientific, New Jersey, 1990).
4. R. E. Walstedt and W. W. Warren, Jr., Science 248, 1082 (1990).
5. H. Zimmerman , M.Mali , J.Roos , D.Brinkmann , J.Karpinski, E.Kaldis and S.Rusiecki, Physica C 159, 681, (1989); H.Zimmerman, M.Mali, I.Mangelschots, J.Roos, L.Paul, D.Brinkmann, J.Karpinski, S.Rusiecki and E.Kaldis, J. Less-Common Metals, 164/5, 138 (1990).
6. K.Schwarz, C.Ambrosch-Draxl, H.Blaha, Phys. Rev. B42, 2051 (1990); J.Yu, A.J.Freeman, R.Podloucky, P.Herzig, P.Weinberger, Phys. Rev. B43, 532 (1991).
7. F. Mila and T. M. Rice, Phys. Rev. B 40, 11382 (1989).
8. S. E. Barrett, D. J. Durand, C. H. Pennington, C. P. Slichter, T. A. Friedmann, J. P. Rice, and D. M. Ginsberg. Phys. Rev. B 41, 6283-6296 (1990);S. E. Barrett, J. A. Martindale, D. J. Durand, C. H. Pennington, C. P. Slichter, T. A. Friedmann, J. P. Rice, and D. M. Ginsberg, Phys. Rev. Lett. 66, 108-111 (1991).

9. A.J. Millis, H. Monien, D. Pines, Phys.Rev.B 42, 167 (1990);H. Monien,D. Pines, M. Takigawa, Phys.Rev.B 43, 258 (1991)
10. N. Bulut and D. J. Scalapino, Phys. Rev. Lett. 67, 2898 (1991).
11 M. Takigawa, A.P. Reyes, P.C. Hammel, J.D. Tompson, R.H. Heffner, Z. Fisk, K.C. Ott, Phys.Rev.B43, 247 (1991); P.C. Hammel, M. Takigawa, R.H. Heffner, Z. Fisk, K.C. Ott, Phys.Rev. Lett. 63, 1992 (1989);
12. H. Alloul, P. Mendels , G. Collin and P. Monod, Phys. Rev. Lett. 61, 746 (1988);H. Alloul, P. Mendels, H. Casalta, J.F. Marucco and J. Arabski, J. of Less Common Metals,164/5, 1022 (1990)
13. M. Horvatic, P. Ségransan, C. Berthier , Y. Berthier , P. Butaud, J.Y. Henry, M. Couach and J.P. Chaminade , Phys.Rev B39, 7332 (1989); M. Horvatic´, P. Butaud, P. Segransan, Y. Berthier, C. Berthier , J.Y. Henry and M. Couach: Physica C166, 151 (1990).
14. Y. Yoshinari,H. Yasuoka, Y. Ueda, K. Koga, K. Kosuge, J.Phys.Soc. Jpn. 59, 3698 (1990)
15. W. W. Warren, R. E. Walstedt, G.F. Brennert, R.J. Cava, R. Tycko, R.F. Bell and G. Dabbagh Phys.: Rev. Lett. 62, 1193 (1989)
16. C.H. Pennington, D.J. Durand, C.P. Slichter, J.P. Rice, E.D. Bukowski, D.M. Ginsberg, Phys.Rev. B39, 274 (1989); ibidem p. 2902.
17. Y. Kitaoka, Y. Berthier, P. Butaud, M. Horvatic´, P. Ségransan, C. Berthier, H. Katayama-Yoshida, Y. Okabe,T. Takahashi, Physica C162/4, 265 (1990).
18. J. M. Tranquada,in Miami Workshop on Electronic Structure and Mechanisms for HighTemperature Superconductivity, January 3-9 1991 (eds. J.Ashkenazi and G. Vezzoli, Plenum, New York, 1992).
19. M. Mali, I. Mangelschots, H. Zimmermann and D. Brinkmann, Physica C 175, 581 (1991).
20. M.Mehring, Appl. Magn. Res.1992 (in press)
21. J. Rossat-Mignod, L.P. Regnault, C. Vettier, P. Burlet, J.Y. Henry and G. Lapertod, Physica B169, 58 (1991);J. Rossat-Mignod, L.P. Regnault, C. Vettier, P. Bourges, P. Burlet, J. Bossy, J.Y. Henry and G. Lapertod, Physica C185/9, 86 (1991)
22. P. Bourges, P. M. Gehring, B. Hennion, A. H. Moudden, J.M. Tranquada, G. Shirane, S. Shamoto, and M. Sato, Phys.
Rev. B43, 8690 (1991).

Probing the Electronic Structure of Y–Ba–Cu–O Superconductors by Cu, O and Ba NQR and NMR

D. Brinkmann

Physik-Institut, Universität Zürich,
Schönberggasse 9, CH-8001 Zürich, Switzerland

Abstract. We summarize some results of recent copper, oxygen and barium NQR/NMR studies of various Y-Ba-Cu-O compounds. We will deal with: electric field gradients in 1-2-3-7 and 1-2-4-8; ^{17}O Knight shift and relaxation in 1-2-4-8 (evidence for single spin fluid); thermally activated Ba relaxation process in 1-2-4-8; evidence for inter-planar coupling in the "superstructure" 2-4-7-15.

1. Introduction

The power of the NMR/NQR spectroscopies is that they may probe directly substances on an *atomic* level. By using different isotopes, various aspects of the electronic properties may be investigated. We will summarize some results of recent studies of some Y-Ba-Cu-O compounds, in particular the $YBa_2Cu_4O_8$ (1-2-4-8) structure which has become a "playground" for our research because of its stoichiometry and its thermal stability and homogeneity. Some new data for the "superstructure" compound $Y_2Ba_4Cu_7O_{15-y}$ (2-4-7-15) will be presented; some remarks will concern the electric field gradients in 1-2-4-8 and $YBa_2Cu_3O_7$.

The 1-2-4-8 samples have been prepared in collaboration with the group of Prof. E. Kaldis of the ETH-Zürich; Prof. A. Yakubovskii (Kurchatov Institute, Moscow) has been involved in the Ba studies. The 2-4-7-15 work is a collaboration with the group of Prof. J. Muller (University of Geneva).

2. Electric field gradients in 1-2-3-7 and 1-2-4-8

The electric field gradient (EFG) at a nuclear site is an important property of a solid since it depends sensitively on the charge distribution around the nucleus in question. Blaha et al. [1] have developed a first principles method to compute EFG's from a full potential linearized augmented plane wave (LAPW) band structure calculation. The good agreement with experimental values for 1-2-3-7, 1-2-3-6 and 1-2-3-6.5 (except for the planar Cu2 site) was already discussed in [2].

Springer Series in Solid-State Sciences, Vol. 113 **Electronic Properties of High-T_c Superconductors**
Editors: H. Kuzmany, M. Mehring, J. Fink

In the past, we have determined experimentally the Cu EFG's in 1-2-3-7 [3,4] and 1-2-4-8 [5,6]. Recently, we have obtained the EFG's for all four O sites [7] and the Ba site [8] in 1-2-4-8 which agree quite well with the theoretical values [1]. Together with the recent experimental result for the Ba site in 1-2-3-7 [9], it is now established that the LAPW method within the local density approximation adequately describes the charge distributions for Cu1, all O and Ba sites in 1-2-3-7 and 1-2-4-8. However, for the Cu2 site the theoretical values are too low. In 1-2-4-8 the experimental value is three times larger than the theoretical result. The origin of this discrepancy probably is that the local density approximation not fully accounts for exchange-correlation effects [2].

3. Oxygen Knight shift and relaxation in 1-2-4-8

We will start with a discussion of new ^{17}O NMR shift measurements [7] which yield access to susceptibilities on a microscopic scale.

The magnetic shift K_i is the sum of two contributions: $K_i(T) = K_i^{orb} + K_i^{spin}(T)$ where K^{orb} is the orbital or chemical shift generally being temperature independent, and $K^{spin}(T)$ is the spin or Knight shift. As in 1-2-3-6.63 [10], all components of K diminish significantly with decreasing temperature in the normal state. Both systems show even remarkable quantitative similarities as their K values only differ within 10 % in the measured temperature range, thus revealing again (in accord with our copper shift data [11]) the equivalence between these compounds, *i.e.* their low-doping character. However, there is a big difference between the plane oxygen K data in 1-2-4-8 and those in 1-2-3-7 where all K components are larger and show no temperature dependence in the normal state.

With the help of K_α^{orb} values from 1-2-3-6.63 and 1-2-3-7 we calculate K_α^{spin} of the plane O sites in 1-2-4-8. K^{spin} arises from the spin density in the 2s and 2p states. The separate contributions of the 2p and 2s states are obtained from the axial spin part $K_{ax}^{spin} = (1/3)(K_{\|}^{spin} - K_{\perp}^{spin})$ and from the isotropic part $K_{iso}^{spin} = (1/3)(K_{\|}^{spin} + K_{\perp}^{spin} + K_c^{spin})$. Here, K_c denotes the component perpendicular to the CuO_2 planes ($B_0 \parallel c$) and $K_{\|}$ and $K_\perp$ the in–plane components where B_0 is parallel and perpendicular to the CuO–bond axis, respectively.

Evaluation for 100 K yielded the remarkable result that all components of K^{spin} are larger in 1-2-3-7, whereas in 1-2-3-6.63 and 1-2-4-8 the same K^{spin} values are found within the experimental error. This again is evidence for the different doping. Fig. 1 shows the important result that various components of K^{spin} at the Cu and O sites have a common temperature dependence. In 1-2-3-7, 1-2-3-6.63 and 1-2-4-8 the same $K_{ax}^{spin}/{}^{63}K_{ab}^{spin}$–ratio has been found, which is moreover independent of temperature because K_{ax}^{spin} and ${}^{63}K_{ab}^{spin}$ follow the same temperature

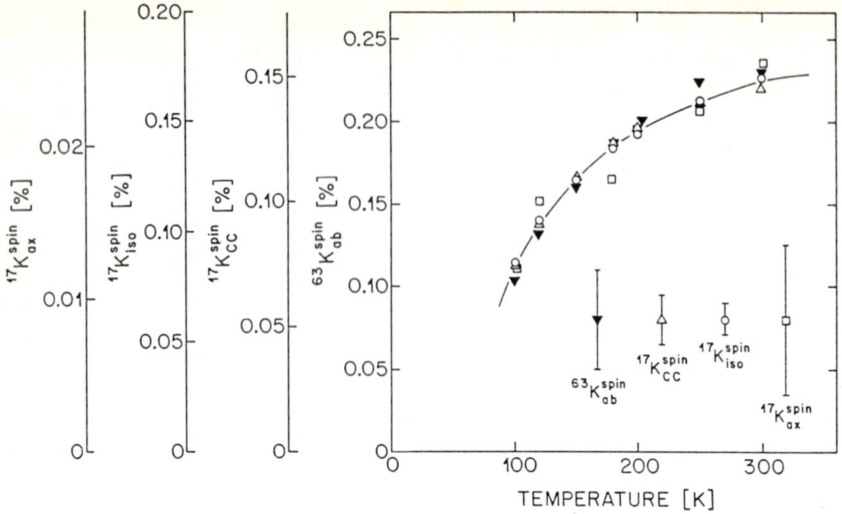

Fig. 1. Temperature dependence of various magnetic shift components of ^{17}O and ^{63}Cu in 1-2-4-8 [7].

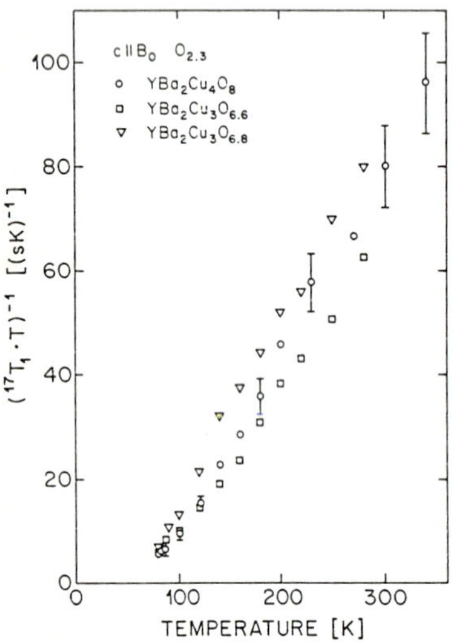

Fig. 2. Temperature dependence of the ^{17}O $1/T_1T$ for planar oxygen sites O2 and O3 in 1-2-4-8 [12]. The 1-2-3-6.6 and 1-2-3-6.8 data are from [13].

behavior. According to Cu NMR experiments, $^{63}K_{ab}^{spin}$ is directly proportional to the spin susceptibility χ_{3d} [6,11] which implies that the ratio χ_{2p}/χ_{3d} is independent of hole content and temperature. This requires that, provided there exists a hole spin susceptibility, χ_{hole}^{spin} and χ_{3d}^{spin}

should have the same dependence on hole concentration and temperature. In other words: the spin of the oxygen hole forms one single entity with the Cu $3d$ spin system, the system behaves as a single spin fluid.

We have measured the ^{17}O spin-lattice relaxation rate so far for the planar oxygen sites above T_c [12]. Fig. 2 shows the plot of $1/T_1T$ versus temperature, the data are intermediate to those of 1-2-3-6.6 and 1-2-3-6.8 [13]. Usually, the Cu and O relaxation in the normal state are treated within the framework of wave-vector (q) dependent fluctuating hyperfine fields and of the imaginary part of the dynamical spin susceptibility. For the planar oxygen sites the anti-ferromagnetic fluctuations (which are "seen" by the Cu nuclei) cancel. Thus the dominant contribution to $1/T_1T$ will be due to spin fluctuations around $q \approx 0$. Whether $1/T_1T$ is proportional to the *static* susceptibility at the oxygen sites - as suggested by a comparison of the three data sets of Fig. 2 - remains to be proven.

4. Barium NQR in 1-2-4-8

Because Ba is located close to the apex oxygen O1, Ba NQR/NMR should shed additional light on the role the oxygen ions are playing for the superconductivity mechanism. In addition, the Ba site NMR/NQR properties are valuable informations with respect to the problem of the Ca substitution [14]. So far we have measured the temperature dependence of the NQR frequency, ν_Q, of the NQR spin-lattice relaxation time, T_1, and of the spin-spin relaxation time, T_2 [8].

Surprisingly, the temperature dependence of ν_Q can be described by $\nu_Q(T) = \nu_Q(0) - AT^{3/2}$ where A is a constant. This relation has been found to be applicable to non-cubic metals and it has been explained on the basis of conduction electron screening of the lattice potential [15]. Interesting enough, we found that the Ba $\nu_Q(T)$ data in 1-2-3-7 [9] can be described by the same A value as in 1-2-4-8. Does this point to a metallic behavior in the Ba sublattice?

A very unexpected result is the temperature dependence of the Ba spin-lattice relaxation in 1-2-4-8. Fig. 3 shows $1/T_1$ of the two Ba isotopes ^{137}Ba and ^{135}Ba in 1-2-4-8. While preliminary data indicated a maximum in the rate, the new data clearly show a power law behavior. The underlying relaxation mechanism is mainly quadrupolar as revealed by the ratio of the rates for the two isotopes. The fit to the data yields $1/T_1 \propto T^{2.1}$. This comes very close to the T^2 behavior for relaxation via the two-phonon Raman process. In other words: the anti-ferromagnetic fluctuations as seen by Cu and very weakly by O nuclei seem to be very small or negligible at the Ba site. This contrasts with the 1-2-3-7 compound where at 300 K the ^{137}Ba relaxation rate becomes flat [9].

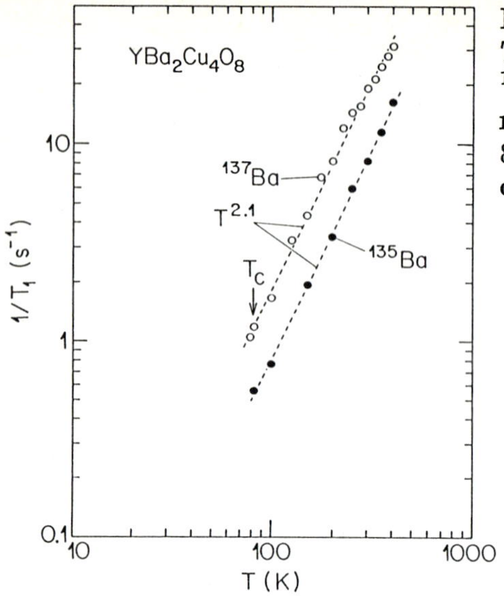

Fig. 3. Temperature dependence of ^{137}Ba and ^{135}Ba spin-lattice relaxation rate $1/T_1$ in 1-2-4-8 [8]. The dashed lines are fits of a power law to the data.

5. Cu NQR in 2-4-7-15

The 2-4-7-15 compound can be considered as a natural superlattice made by an ordered sequence of 1-2-3-7 and 1-2-4-8 unit cells in a 1:1 ratio. The central question here is: why can a T_c of 92 K be obtained which is significantly higher than the $T_c = 82$ K of the 1-2-4-8 structure?

So far our Cu NQR studies have revealed two very surprising facts [16]. First, between 100 and 300 K, the Cu2 NQR frequencies $\nu_Q(T)$ of the 1-2-3-7 and the 1-2-4-8 block in the 2-4-7-15 structure differ only slightly from those of the "pure" structures 1-2-3-7 and 1-2-4-8, respectively. This means that the charge transfer between the 1-2-3-7 and 1-2-4-8 layers is negligible and the increase of T_c cannot be explained by a simple enhancement of charge carriers. The second fact is that the Cu2 relaxation rates of the two different structure blocks in 2-4-7-15 are *proportional* to each other, at least between 100 and 300 K - in contrast to the rates in the "pure" structures. This implies the presence of a *common* spin dynamics in the different layers of the 2-4-7-15 structure and hence a coupling of these layers.

References

1. P. Blaha, K. Schwarz, P. Herzig; Phys. Rev. Lett. 54 (1985) 1192.
2. K. Schwarz, C. Ambrosch-Draxl, P. Blaha; Phys. Rev. B 42 (1990) 2051.

3. M. Mali, D. Brinkmann, L. Pauli, J. Roos, H. Zimmermann, J. Hulliger; Physics Letters A 124 (1987) 112.
4. D. Brinkmann; Z. Naturforsch. 45a (1990) 393.
5. H. Zimmermann, M. Mali, D. Brinkmann, J. Karpinski, E. Kaldis, S. Rusiecki; Physica C 159 (1989) 681.
6. H. Zimmermann, Ph.D. Thesis, University of Zürich (1991).
7. I. Mangelschots, M. Mali, J. Roos, D. Brinkmann, S. Rusiecki, J. Karpinski, E. Kaldis; Physica C 194 (1992), in press.
8. A. Lombardi, M. Mali, J. Roos, D. Brinkmann, A. Yakubovskii; to be published.
9. A. Yakubovskii, A. Egorov and H. Lütgemeier; submitted to Applied Magnetic Resonance.
10. M. Takigawa, A.P. Reyes, P.C. Hammel, J.D. Thompson, R.F. Heffner, Z. Fisk and K.C. Ott; Phys. Rev. B 43 (1991) 247.
11. H. Zimmermann, M. Mali, I. Mangelschots, J. Roos, L. Pauli, D. Brinkmann, J. Karpinski, S. Rusiecki and E. Kaldis; J. Less-Common Metals 164&165 (1990) 138.
12. I. Mangelschots, M. Mali, J. Roos, D. Brinkmann; to be published.
13. Y. Yoshinari, H. Yasuoka, Y. Ueda, K. Koga and K. Kosuge; J. Phys. Soc. Japan 59 (1990) 3698.
14. I. Mangelschots, M. Mali, J. Roos, H. Zimmermann, D. Brinkmann, S. Rusiecki, J. Karpinski, E. Kaldis and E. Jilek; Physica C 172 (1990) 57.
15. Nishiyama et al.; Phys. Rev. Lett. 37 (1976) 357.
16. R. Stern, M. Mali, J. Roos, D. Brinkmann, J. Muller and Th. Graf; to be published.

NMR Investigation of Low-Energy Excitations in $YBa_2Cu_3O_{6+x}$ Single Crystals

T. Auler[1], *C. Berthier*[1], *Y. Berthier*[1], *P. Butaud*[1;*], *W.G. Clark*[1;**], *J.A. Gillet*[1], *M. Horvatić*[1;***], *P. Ségransan*[1], *and J.Y. Henry*[2]

[1]Laboratoire de Spectrométrie Physique (UA 08 CNRS), Université Joseph Fourier Grenoble I, B.P. 87, F-38402 Saint-Martin d'Hères, France

[2]C.E.N. Grenoble, DRF/SPh-MDN, 85 X, F-38041 Grenoble Cedex, France

*Present address: C.R.T.B.T., CNRS, 166X, F-38042 Grenoble-Cedex, France

**Present address: Department of Physics, University of California, Los Angeles, CA 90024, USA

***Present address: Institute of Physics of the University, P.O. Box 304, 41001 Zagreb, Croatia

Abstract. ^{17}O and ^{63}Cu NMR results obtained in three single crystals of $YBa_2Cu_3O_{6+x}$, show that the static spin susceptibility and $(T_1T)^{-1}$ for Cu(2) and O(2,3) have completely different temperature dependence according to the regime - overdoped for $x > 0.94$, underdoped for $x < 0.94$. In the overdoped regime a Fermi liquid description seems to be correct, while in the underdoped regime a pseudo-gap in the magnetic excitations opens well above T_c, supporting the phase diagram based on the spin-charge separation. We also show that both neutron inelastic scattering results and Cu(2) and O(2,3) NSLRR results can be explained using the same $\chi''(q, \omega)$.

1. Introduction

The possibility of describing the whole phase diagram, from antiferromagnetism to superconductivity, by simply changing the oxygen concentration in the CuO chains [1] has promoted $YBa_2Cu_3O_{6+x}$ to a model system for high T_c superconducting oxides. Recently, a careful analysis of the phase diagram of $YBa_2Cu_3O_{6+x}$ by Graf et al. [2] has revealed that close to the maximum concentration of oxygen, one moves from an underdoped regime with a maximum value of $T_c = 94$ K for $x = 0.94$, to an overdoped regime for $0.94 < x < 1$ with T_c decreasing down to 92 K. Indeed, a drastic difference in the temperature (T) dependence of the Cu(2) Nuclear Spin-Lattice Relaxation Rate (NSLRR) between $YBa_2Cu_3O_7$ and $YBa_2Cu_3O_{6.9}$ has already been pointed out by et Horvatić al. [3]: in the stoichiometric compound, the NSLRR divided by temperature $^{63}(T_1T)^{-1}$ continuously increases when T decreases from 300 K to T_c, and then drops abruptly, whereas in $YBa_2Cu_3O_{6.9}$ the $^{63}(T_1T)^{-1}$ passes through a maximum around $T^* = 130$ K, well above T_c. However, this difference was attributed to the disorder present in the substoichiometric phase, and its consequence on the conductivity along the c-axis. Later, $^{63}(T_1T)^{-1}$ data in $YBa_2Cu_4O_8$ [4] revealed the same behaviour as for $YBa_2Cu_3O_{6.9}$, i.e., a maximum well above T_c, although the former is an ordered and stoichiometric compound, thus indicating that this behaviour is related rather to the hole concentration in the CuO_2 planes. Theoretically, it has been predicted by Suzumura et al. [5] and Nagaosa and Lee [6] in the framework of the spin-charge separation [7] that the normal state in the underdoped and overdoped regime should be quite different. For hole concentrations δ smaller than δ_c (which corresponds to the maximum of T_c), when lowering T, the system should first cross-over from a "strange metal", in which holons and spinons are decoupled, into an RVB state, and then undergo a Bose condensation at $T = T_c$. For overdoped

Springer Series in Solid-State Sciences, Vol. 113 Electronic Properties of High-T_c Superconductors
Editors: H. Kuzmany, M. Mehring, J. Fink

compounds ($\delta > \delta_c$), there is a transition line below which holons condense to give a Fermi liquid, before undergoing a BCS type transition at T_c.

In this paper, we compare the NMR properties - T dependence of the spin susceptibility and of the NSLRR for Cu(2) and O(2,3) sites - in $YBa_2Cu_3O_{6+x}$ single crystals of compositions belonging either to the overdoped or to the underdoped regime. The general features are in fair agreement with the phase diagram mentioned above; we also show that they are not restricted to the 123 system, but extend to other high T_c materials, and thus put severe constraints to any comprehensive microscopic theory of these compounds.

2. Results and discussion

NMR measurements were carried out on three "porous" single crystals [8] corresponding to the following compositions: $YBa_{1.92}Sr_{0.08}Cu_3O_7$ (Sample 1, T_c = 89 K), $YBa_{1.93}Sr_{0.07}Cu_3O_{6.92}$ (Sample 2, T_c = 91 K) and $YBa_2Cu_3O_{6.52}$ (Sample 3, T_c = 59 K). Sample 1 and 3 were enriched in ^{17}O, whereas Sample 2 is a piece of the single crystal used for neutron experiments by Rossat-Mignod et al. [9,10]. As will be discussed below, Sample 1 and 2 belong respectively to the overdoped and underdoped regime of the so called "90 K" phase. We first compare the Cu(2) $(T_1T)^{-1}$ in the three samples, which are plotted in Fig. 1. (We also include the data from a $YBa_2Cu_3O_7$ oriented powder sample, obtained by grinding porous single crystals, with a T_c of 92 K [3]). There are two clearly distinct behaviours:
– for the two O_7 samples (T_c = 92 and 89 K), $^{63}(T_1T)^{-1}$ continuously increases when T decreases from 300 K to T_c, and then drops abruptly, while
– for Samples 2 (T_c = 91 K) and 3 (T_c = 59 K), $^{63}(T_1T)^{-1}$ passes through a maximum around T^* = 130 K, irrespective of T_c. Such behaviour was first reported by Horvatić et al. [11], and Warren et al. [12] for the 60 K phase.

These results are now fully corroborated by neutron inelastic scattering; in the case of Sample 2, the T dependence of $^{63}(T_1T)^{-1}$ and that of $\chi''(Q_{AF}, \hbar\omega = 10\text{ meV})$ [10] as given by neutron inelastic scattering are quite similar (Fig.2).

Remembering that $(T_1T)^{-1} \propto \sum_q |A_q|^2\chi''(q,\omega_n)/\omega_n$, this means that the Cu(2) NSLRR is dominated by the contribution of the enhanced antiferromagnetic fluctuations (AFF) to $\chi''(q,\omega)$. Neutron data [9,10] indicate that the decrease of $^{63}(T_1T)^{-1}$ below $T^* \approx 130$ K is due to the opening of a pseudo-gap in the magnetic excitations, i.e., due to a transfer from low energy to high energy in the spectral weight of the magnetic excitations. The maximum of $(T_1T)^{-1}$ above T_c is a common feature in all underdoped compounds: $YBa_2Cu_4O_8$ [4], as grown $Bi_{2x}Sr_2CaCu_2O_8$ [13], and also $La_{2-x}Sr_xCuO_4$ [14] where $^{63}(T_1T)^{-1}$ seems to have a maximum around 50 K. On the contrary, in overdoped compounds: $YBa_2Cu_3O_7$, annealed $Bi_2Sr_2CaCu_2O_8$ [13] and $Tl_2Sr_2CaCu_2O_8$ [15] there is no maximum above T_c, i.e., the gap for

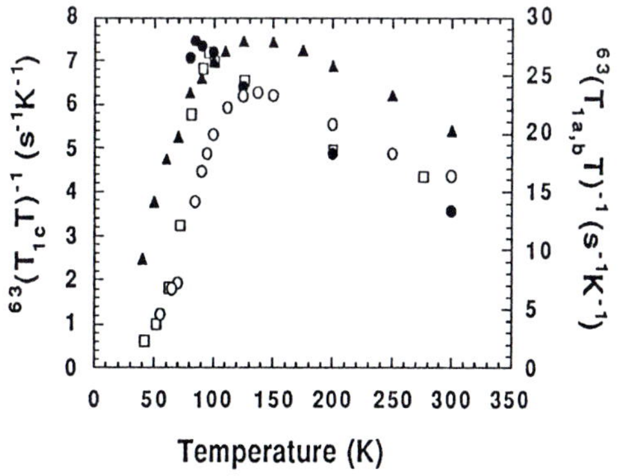

FIG. 1 Temperature dependence of $^{63}(T_1T)^{-1}$ in:
a) overdoped regime:
❑ $YBa_2Cu_3O_7$ (oriented powder, H_0 // c-axis, data from Ref. [3]); and ● $YBa_{1.92}Sr_{0.08}Cu_3O_7$ (single crystal, H_0 // a,b plane), and in
b) underdoped regime:
❍ $YBa_{1.93}Sr_{0.07}Cu_3O_{6.92}$ and ▲ $YBa_2Cu_3O_{6.52}$ (single crystals, H_0 // c-axis).

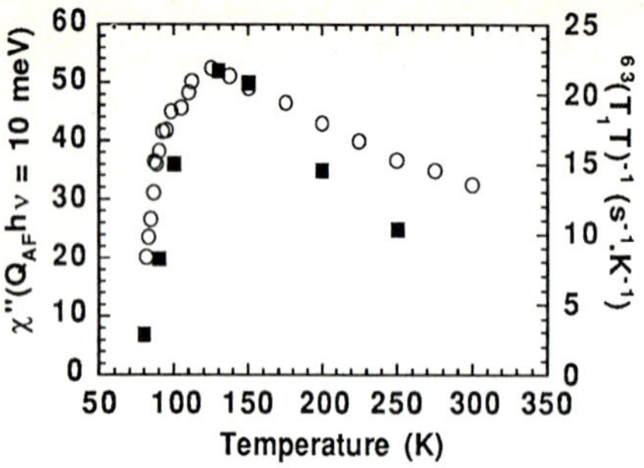

FIG. 2 Comparison of $^{63}(T_1T)^{-1}$ (○) and $\chi''(Q_{AF}, \hbar\omega = 10$ meV) (■) measured by NMR [24] and inelastic neutron scattering [10] in the same $YBa_{1.93}Sr_{0.07}Cu_3O_{6.92}$ single crystals.

the spin and charge excitations opens at the same temperature. This has recently been confirmed by neutron inelastic scattering in a $YBa_{1.93}Sr_{0.07}Cu_3O_7$ single crystal, a composition very close to our Sample 1 [16].

As regards the NMR of O(2,3) nuclei, we first consider the T dependence of the spin susceptibility. It is now fairly well established in $YBa_2Cu_3O_{6+x}$ that all nuclei of the CuO_2-Y-CuO_2 sandwich probe a unique static spin susceptibility $\chi_S(T)$, which has the same T dependence as the macroscopic susceptibility [17-21]. The $\chi_S(T)$ is directly related to the spin part of the Magnetic Hyperfine Shift (MHS) tensor $^{17}\mathbf{K}$ experienced by the O(2,3) nuclei: $^{17}K_{\alpha\alpha} \propto {}^{17}C_{\alpha\alpha}\,\chi_S$, where α refers to the principal axes of the MHS and Electric Field Gradient tensors (i.e., X parallel to the c-axis, Y perpendicular and Z parallel to the Cu-O-Cu bond in the ab plane,) and $^{17}C_{\alpha\alpha}$ is the hyperfine field. Fig. 3a shows the $^{17}O(2,3)$ MHS results in Sample 1. Note that $K_{\alpha\alpha}$ increases slightly with decreasing T, which means that the spin susceptibility is not flat, but slightly increases as already noticed in Cu(2) [22] and Y [23] MHS. This appears to be the signature of slightly overdoped samples, which is the case of pure $YBa_2Cu_3O_7$ [2]. In contrast, the MHS of Sample 3 shown in Fig. 3b exhibits a strong T dependence as already reported in "60 K phase" samples [18,20,21,25]. The relationship between K_{ZZ} and K_{YY} is linear [21] as expected for one spin degree of freedom. In the overdoped phase (Sample 1) the slight increase of χ_S when T decreases from 300 K to T_c is compatible with the Pauli susceptibility of a Fermi liquid in a narrow band metal. In the underdoped regime (Sample 3) $\chi_S(T)$ decreases continuously with T; no definite theory is available yet to explain this behavior, except recent quantum dynamical Monte-Carlo calculations [26]. However, in the scenario proposed by Nagaosa and Lee [6], this should be due to pairing of spinons. Experimentally, it is obviously related to the opening of a pseudo-gap.

Fig. 4a shows the T dependence of the NSLRR for O(2,3) nuclei in Sample 1 for the three orientations of the applied external magnetic field H_0 [27]. The most striking feature of these data is that $^{17}(T_1T)^{-1}$ also continuously increases on decreasing T from 350 K down to T_c [21,27], although this increase is much less pronounced than that for the Cu(2) $^{63}(T_1T)^{-1}$ (As for the MHS, the increase is more pronounced when H_0 is in the a,b plane.). Note that in $YBa_2Cu_3O_7$ only T independent behaviour has been reported so far [20,28] corresponding to c-axis component of NSLRR measured on oriented powders.

The behaviour of $^{17}(T_1T)^{-1}$ in $YBa_2Cu_3O_{6.52}$ is quite different, as shown in Fig. 4b. It continuously decreases with T, and at T_c only a small change in the slope can be noticed. Plotting $^{17}(T_1T)^{-1}$ versus K_{ZZ} demonstrates that for H_0 // Y the $^{17}(T_1T)^{-1}$ is accurately proportional to the spin part of the MHS [21]. Similar results have been reported in the 60 K phase for H_0 // X (c-axis) [18,20]. However, if we now turn to the data measured with H_0 // Z, such a relationship no longer holds, which has the important consequence that the NLSRR anisotropy is now T dependent [21], in contrast to the behaviour observed in $YBa_{1.92}Sr_{0.08}Cu_3O_7$ [21,27]. Such a T dependence of the NSLRR anisotropy for H_0 in the a,b plane was first reported by Barriquand et al. [29] in a $YBa_2Cu_3O_{6.5}$ single crystal.

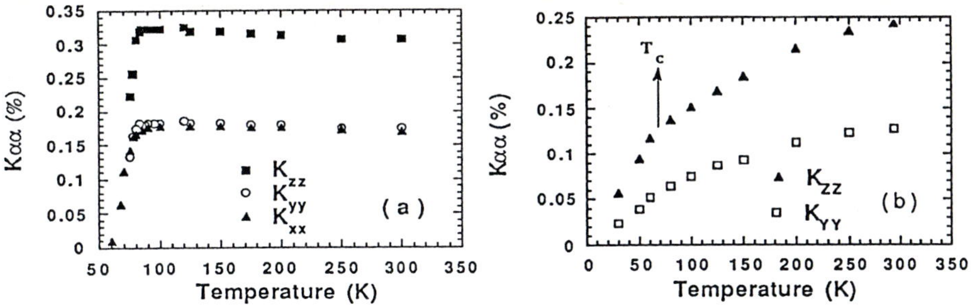

FIG. 3 Temperature dependence of the principal components of the MHS tensor for O(2,3) sites in a)$YBa_{1.92}Sr_{0.08}Cu_3O_7$ and b) $YBa_2Cu_3O_{6.52}$.

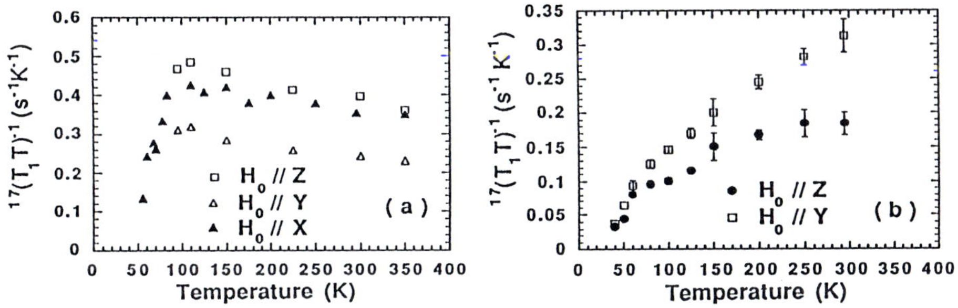

FIG. 4 Temperature dependence of $^{17}(T_1T)^{-1}$ for O(2,3) sites a) in $YBa_{1.92}Sr_{0.08}Cu_3O_7$ and b) in $YBa_2Cu_3O_{6.52}$.

It is now widely recognized that the different T dependences of the NSLRR for Cu(2) and O(2,3) result from the filtering of the AFF at the O(2,3) site, because of its symmetric position between its two Cu(2) first neighbors [28]:

$$^{17}(T_1T)^{-1} \propto \sum_q {}^{17}C^2[1 + 1/2(\cos q_a a + \cos q_b b)]\chi''(q,\omega_n)/\omega_n \ .$$

Since in substoichiometric samples $^{17}(T_{1\alpha}T)^{-1}$ (α=X,Y) depends linearly on $\chi_S(T)$ [18,21], a decomposition of the dynamic susceptibility has been proposed [30]: $\chi''(q,\omega) = \pi\chi_S(T)/\Gamma + \chi''_{AF}(q,\omega)$ [31]. Because of the filtering form factor, the contribution of $\chi''_{AF}(q,\omega)$ which is peaked around **Q** = (π/a, π/a) vanishes, and $^{17}(T_1T)^{-1} \propto \chi_S(T)$.

We now turn to the results in the overdoped regime. Both $^{17}K_{\alpha\alpha}$ and $^{17}(T_1T)^{-1}$ increase when T decreases, and we see in Fig. 5a that $(K_{spin}T_1T\ )^{-1}$ slightly increases rather than staying constant. One possible explanation for this behaviour is that the filtering of the AFF is no longer as perfect as in the substoichiometric compounds, due to a shortening of the AF correlation length. Another possibility is a Fermi liquid like behavior: $\chi_S^2 T_1 T$ = const. Indeed, it can be seen in Fig. 5b that the Korringa law is well obeyed in the whole T range above T_c, where $(T_1T)^{-1}$ varies by ≈30 %. Since it is hard to believe that the agreement with the Korringa law is an accident, this renders the first explanation unlikely and strongly supports the phase diagram based on the spin-charge separation.

We now turn to the comparison of the NMR data with the neutron results and, for the sake of clarity, we shall limit ourself to the case of the 60 K phase. Starting from the Mila-Rice Hamiltonian to describe the coupling between the electronic and the nuclear spins, and taking the appropriate hyperfine coupling constants and form factors for Cu and O, the ratio R = $^{63}(T_1T)^{-1}$ / $^{17}(T_1T)^{-1}$ depends only on the functional form of $\chi''(q,\omega_n)/\omega_n$. Neutron experiments tell us that the characteristic energy $\hbar\omega_{AF}$ of the AFF is of the order of 25 meV,

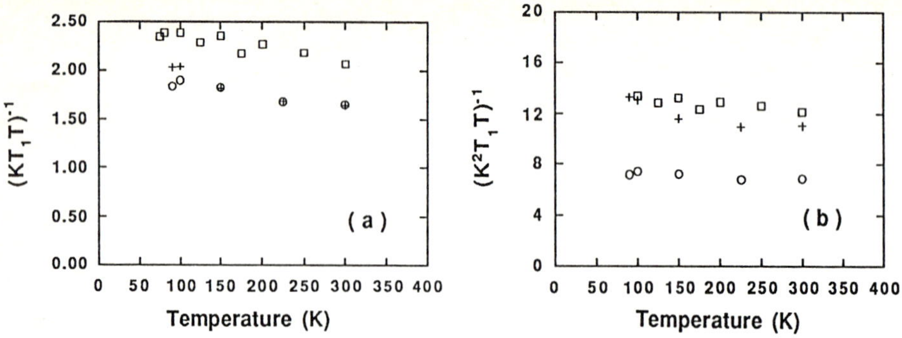

FIG. 5 Temperature dependence of $(K^{\alpha}_{spin}T_1T)^{-1}$ with a) $\alpha = 1$ and b) $\alpha = 2$ in $YBa_{1.92}Sr_{0.08}Cu_3O_7$. Different symbols correspond to $(K^{\alpha}_{XX}T_{1X}T)^{-1}$ (❑), $(K^{\alpha}_{YY}T_{1Z}T)^{-1}$ (+) and $(K^{\alpha}_{ZZ}T_{1Y}T)^{-1}$ (O).The Korringa law K^2T_1T = const. is more appropriate to describe the data.

and the width in q space of $\chi''_{AF}(q,\omega)$ is temperature independent and amounts to 0.1 - 0.14 in reduced lattice units along the *(h,h)* direction of the Brillouin zone in two dimensions. The shape, however, is not accurately determined. On the other hand, in all NMR experiments on samples belonging to the 60 K phase $^{17}(T_1T)^{-1}$ was found accurately proportionnal to $\chi_S(T)$, which implies that the AFF contribution to the O(2,3) NSLRR is negligible, and thus imposes a severe constraint on the q dependence of the $\chi''(q,\omega_n)/\omega_n$. We have calculated the ratio R for various forms of $\chi''_{AF}(q,\omega)$, including the squared Lorentzian proposed by Millis, Monien and Pines [30], and verified whether the contribution of $\chi''_{AF}(q,\omega)$ to $^{17}(T_1T)^{-1}$ is small enough to fall within the experimental uncertainty. Fitting the shape of $\chi''_{AF}(q,\omega)$ observed by neutron spectroscopy to a squared Lorentzian centered at $\mathbf{Q} = (\pi/a, \pi/a)$ provides a contribution which is definitely too large. We found [32] that the only way to reconcile NMR and neutron data is to fit the experimental $\chi''_{AF}(q,\omega)$ to a Gaussian or, even better, to the sum of four Gaussians centered on $\mathbf{Q}^i_{AF}$ equal to (1/2 ± , 1/2) and (1/2, 1/2 ± δ), as proposed by Tranquada et al. to explain the q-dependence of $\chi''(\mathbf{q},\omega)$ of their neutron data in $YBa_2Cu_3O_{6.5}$ [33]. In the latter case, the total width at mid-height of the $\chi''_{AF}(q,\omega)$ is mostly determined by the incommensurability δ, whereas the AF correlation length ξ is rather related to the steepness of the sides of the AAF peak.

3. Conclusion

In conclusion, we have shown in $YBa_2Cu_3O_{6+x}$ that depending on the hole concentration in the CuO_2 plane, the low energy excitations around $\mathbf{Q} = (\pi/a, \pi/a)$ and $\mathbf{q} = 0$, as well as the static susceptibility, exhibit drastically different behaviours; in the underdoped regime ($x < 0.94$) the decrease of the static susceptibility $\chi_S(T)$, the opening of a pseudo-gap in the spin excitations at T^* well above T_c, the proportionality between $^{17}(T_1T)^{-1}$ and $\chi_S(T)$, and the T dependence of the O(2,3) NSLRR above T_c are signatures of a strange metal. In the overdoped regime ($x > 0.94$) the gap for spin and charge excitations opens at the same temperature T_c, and despite a T dependence of $^{17}(T_1T)^{-1}$, a Korringa behaviour is recovered, as in a normal Fermi liquid. The cross-over between the two regimes occurs just *within* the so-called "90 K plateau" in $YBa_2Cu_3O_{6+x}$. Such different behaviours for underdoped and overdoped compounds can also be recognized in other compounds, e.g., in $YBa_2Cu_4O_8$ [4] and $Bi_2Sr_2CaCu_2O_8$ [13]. These features strongly support the phase diagram based on the spin-charge separation [5,6] and put severe constraints on any theoretical microscopic description of the normal state of the cuprate oxides.

This work was supported by the Direction des Recherches et des Etudes Techniques (contract DRET N° 89/045) and by the Ministère de la Recherche et de la Technologie (contract MRT N° 90.A.0579).

References

[1] R. J. Cava, B. Battlog, M. Rabe, E. A. Rietman, P. K. Gallagher and L. W. Rupp Jr., Physica C **156**, 523 (1988)

[2] T. Graf, G. Triscone, and J. Muller, J. Less-Common Met., **159**, 349 (1990)

[3] M. Horvatić, P. Butaud, P. Ségransan, Y. Berthier, C.Berthier, J. Y. Henry and M. Couach, Physica C **166**, 151 (1990)

[4] H. Zimmermann, M. Mali, I. Mangelschots, J. Roos, L. Paul, D. Brinkmann, J. Karpinski, S. Rusiecki and E. Kaldis, J. Less-Common Met. **164&165**, 138 (1990)

[5] Y. Suzumura, Y. Hasegawa and H. Fukuyama, J. Phys. Soc. Jpn. **57**, 2768 (1988); H. Fukuyama, unpublished

[6] N. Nagaosa and P. A. Lee, Phys. Rev. Lett. **64**, 2450 (1990); Phys. Rev. B **43**, 1223 (1991); *ibid.* **45**, 966, (1992)

[7] P. W. Anderson, Science **235**, 1196 (1987)

[8] J. Y. Henry, unpublished

[9] J. Rossat-Mignod, L. P. Regnault, C. Vettier, P. Bourges, P. Burlet, J. Bossy, J. Y. Henry and G.Lapertod, Physica B **169**, 58 (1991)

[10] J. Rossat-Mignod, L. P. Regnault, C. Vettier, P. Bourges, P. Burlet, J. Bossy, J. Y. Henry and G.Lapertod, Physica C **185-189**, 86 (1991)

[11] M. Horvatić, P.Ségransan, C. Berthier, Y.Berthier, P. Butaud, J. Y. Henry, M. Couach and J. P. Chaminade, Phys. Rev. B **39**, 7332 (1989)

[12] W. W. Warren, R. E.Walstedt, G. F. Brennert, R. J. Cava, R. Tycko, R. F. Bell and G. Dabbagh, Phys. Rev. Lett. **62**, 1193 (1989)

[13] R. E. Walstedt, R. F. Bell and D. B. Mitzi, Phys. Rev. B **44**, 7760 (1991)

[14] S. Oshugi, Y. Kitaoka, K. Ishida and K. Asayama, J. Phys. Soc. Jpn., **60**, 2351 (1991)

[15] F. Hentsch, N. Winzek, M. Mehring, Hj. Mattausch, A. Simon, and R. Kremer, Physica C **165**, 485 (1990)

[16] J. Rossat-Mignod, L. P. Regnault, P. Bourges, C. Vettier, P. Burlet and J. Y. Henry, This Conference

[17] H. Alloul, P. Mendels, G. Collin and P. Monod, Phys. Rev. Lett. **61**, 746 (1988)

[18] M. Takigawa, A. P. Reyes, P. C. Hammel, J. D. Tompson, R. H. Heffner, Z. Fisk and K. C. Ott, Phys. Rev. B **43**, 247 (1991)

[19] T. Shimizu, H. Yasuoka, T. Tsuda, K. Koga and Y. Ueda, Bull. Mag. Res., **12**, 39 (1990)

[20] Y. Yoshinari, H. Yasuoka, Y. Ueda, K. Koga, K. Kosuge, J. Phys. Soc. Jpn. **59**, 3698 (1990)

[21] M. Horvatić , C. Berthier, Y. Berthier, P. Butaud, W. G. Clark, J. A. Gillet, P. Ségransan and J. Y. Henry, Physica C **185-189**, 1139 (1991)

[22] R. E. Walstedt , R. F. Bell, L. F. Schneemeyer, J. V. Waszcak and G. P. Espinosa, unpublished

[23] G. Balakrishnan, R. Dupree, I. Farnan, D. McK. Paul and M. E. J. Smith Phys. C **21**, L847 (1988)

[24] C. Berthier, Y. Berthier, P. Butaud, W. G.Clark, J. A. Gillet,M. Horvatić, P. Ségransan and J. Y. Henry, Physica C **185-189**, 1141 (1991)

[25] P. Butaud, M. Horvatić, Y. Berthier, P. Ségransan, Y. Kitaoka, C. Berthier and H Katayama-Yoshida, Physica C **166**, 301 (1990)
[26] G. Dopf, A. Mutsamura, W. Hanke, Phys. Rev. Lett. **68**, 353 (1992)
[27] M. Horvatić, Thesis, Zagreb (1991)
[28] P. C. Hammel, M. Takigawa, R. H. Heffner, Z. Fisk, K. C.Ott, Phys. Rev. Lett. **63**, 1992 (1989)
[29] F. Barriquand, P. Odier, D. Jérome, Physica C **177**, 230 (1991)
[30] A. J. Millis, H. Monien, D. Pines, Phys. Rev. B **42**, 167 (1990); H. Monien, D. Pines, M. Takigawa, Phys. Rev. B **43**, 258 (1991)
[31] Note that in a usual Fermi-Liquid description, $\hbar\Gamma \propto N(E_F)^{-1}$ and should vary as $\chi_S(T)^{-1}$, while here Γ is constant
[32] C. Berthier, Y. Berthier, P. Butaud, W. G. Clark, J. A. Gillet, M. Horvatić, P. Ségransan and J. Y. Henry, to appear in Appl. Mag. Res., Special issue
[33] J. M. Tranquada, P. M. Gehring, G. Shirane, S. Shamoto and M. Sato, unpublished

Vortex Lattice and Vortex Motion in $YBa_2Cu_3O_{7-\delta}$ and $YBa_2Cu_4O_8$ Superconductors from ^{89}Y NMR

P. Carretta and M. Corti

Dipartimento di Fisica “A. Volta”, Sezione INFN and
Unitá GNSM-INFM University of Pavia, I-27100 Pavia, Italy

Abstract. The analysis of the second moment of the field distribution inside the vortex lattice at low temperatures and its temperature dependence are discussed in the light of new relevant data from ^{89}Y NMR experiments in samples of $YBa_2Cu_3O_{7-\delta}$ (Y123) and $YBa_2Cu_4O_8$ (Y124) families.

1. Introduction.

Since the early days after the discovery of high T_c superconductors (HT_cSC) the study of the vortex lattice (VL) has provided relevant information both on macroscopic and microscopic aspects of these new materials. In particular, the analysis at low temperatures of the second moment of the field distribution inside the VL ($< \Delta B^2 >$) in different samples showed that T_c and $< \Delta B^2 >$ are related and a linear dependence of T_c on $\frac{n}{m_{ab}}$ was inferred for the low doped samples [1], being n the superconducting carriers density and m_{ab} the inplane effective mass. Moreover, the observed temperature dependence of $< \Delta B^2 >$ appeared to be consistent with a two-fluid model [2].

In this manuscript we discuss critically the approach used to analyse these results in view of new relevant data from ^{89}Y NMR and μ^+SR [3-7]: i) a remarkable difference between the values of $< \Delta B^2 >_{T\to 0}$ that we have derived through ^{89}Y NMR [3,4] and those obtained by Uemura et al. [1] through μ^+SR is observed; ii) both our ^{89}Y NMR measurements and recent μ^+SR experiments [7] evidence the onset of motional narrowing phenomena related to the motion of vortex lines. The comprehension both of the vortex motion and of the origin of the differences observed between ^{89}Y NMR and μ^+SR is crucial for any further understanding of microscopic aspects of HT_cSC.

2. Low temperatures. Rigid vortex lattice.

We will first discuss the VL at low temperatures , where it may be considered rigid provided that the characteristic correlation time τ_c of vortex motion is longer than the characteristic time scale of the microscopic probe, namely for NMR or μ^+SR $(< \Delta B^2 >^{\frac{1}{2}} \gamma)^{-1}$ (γ is the gyromagnetic ratio of the microscopic probe). Being $\gamma_\mu \gg \gamma_{89}$ the above condition is more easily suited in μ^+SR experiments.

In the low temperature limit due to the strongly type-II character of HT_cSC, namely $\xi(0) \ll d \ll \lambda(0)$ (d is the intervortex separation, ξ and λ are the coherence and penetration lengths respectively), London approximation appears suitable to describe the field distribution inside the VL, and in view of the high anisotropy of these new materials ($m_c > 25m_{ab}$), a simple relation holds between the second moment of the field distribution inside the VL of a powder sample and λ_{ab} ($\vec{B} \parallel \vec{c}$) in the clean limit [8]:

$$< \Delta B^2 >= k\frac{\Phi_o^2}{\lambda_{ab}^4} \propto (\frac{n}{m_{ab}})^2. \quad (1)$$

with $k = 0.00162$.

The London approximation is appropriate to describe a homogeneous superconductor with no reliable variations of the order parameter. However, in HT_cSC at low temperatures the coherence length along the c axis is shorter than the separation s between CuO_2 layers and therefore, the intralayer region becomes "less superconductive" and creates an intrinsic pinning center which distorts the ideal VL field distribution predicted by London approximation. Although such an effect is known from the study of the VL in superconductor-insulator superlattices [9] the problem of how $< \Delta B^2 >$ is affected by these distortions in a powder sample has not been solved yet. Anyway, in principle, $< \Delta B^2 >$ should depend also on the magnitude of the ratio ξ_c/s.

Experimentally $< \Delta B^2 >$ can be derived both from the full width at half intensity of the ^{89}Y NMR line, $\Delta\nu \simeq 2.36 < \Delta B^2 >^{\frac{1}{2}}$, or from the muon depolarization rate $\sigma = 2\pi\gamma_\mu < \Delta B^2 >^{\frac{1}{2}} /\sqrt{2}$; in the case of Gaussian lines. In Fig. 1 we show the general trend of $< \Delta B^2 >^{\frac{1}{2}}_{T\to 0}$ as derived by Uemura et al. from μ^+SR in different HT_cSC [1] compared to the values we have derived through ^{89}Y NMR in Y123 and Y124 powder samples, where T_c was varied

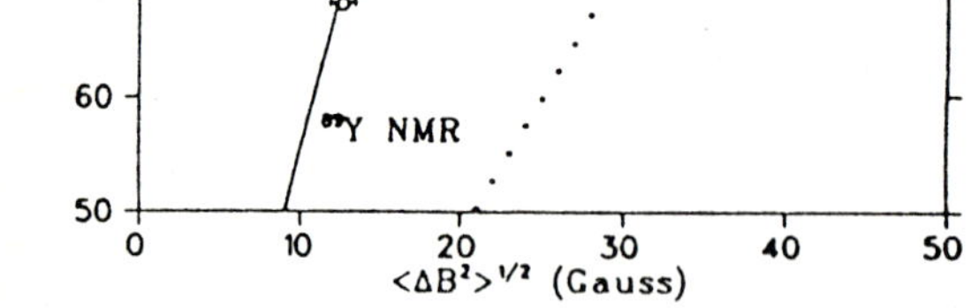

Fig. 1 Dependence of T_c from $< \Delta B^2 >^{\frac{1}{2}}$ for $T\to 0$, as obtained from the ^{89}Y NMR linewidth. Circles give the data extracted from our measurements in Y124 samples [4], while triangles refer to the values derived from ^{89}Y NMR in Y123 samples [3,5,6]. The solid line is the best fit line according to the linear relation $T_c = \alpha < \Delta B^2 >^{\frac{1}{2}}$ with $\alpha = 5.55$ K/Gauss. From Ref. [1] one would derive $\alpha_\mu = 2.4$ K/Gauss (dotted line).

either by deoxigenating the sample or by Ca doping. The general trend of the data is similar, T_c increases as $< \Delta B^2 >^{\frac{1}{2}}_{T\to 0}$ increases for the low doped samples and then reaches a plató; it is not well estabilished, however, if only n is varying while T_c is increasing or if m_{ab} and ξ_c are also varying. As can be observed from the figure there is a remarkable difference between the absolute values of $< \Delta B^2 >$ that we have derived from ^{89}Y NMR measurements and those derived from Ref. [1]. Up to now only two tentative explanation, both based on the effect of pinning centers on the VL, can be given. μ^+SR experiments are usually performed in fields of a few KGauss, much smallers than NMR ones; under this condition the number of vortex lines per grain can be comparable to the number of pinning centers and a stronger distortion of the VL is expected with respect to the case of NMR experiments where the higher number of unpinned vortex lines gives rise to a more regular VL with a smaller $< \Delta B^2 >$. The second possible explanation: Uemura's and most μ^+SR experiments have been performed on sintered samples where grain boundaries act as efficient pinning centers distorting the VL and increasing $< \Delta B^2 >$; this explanation seems to be supported by recent μ^+SR experiments in $Bi_2Sr_2CaCu_2O_x$ single crystals [7] where a much smaller value for the second moment of the field distribution was derived with respect to a nominally equivalent sintered sample.

3. T→ T_c. Vortex motion.

At higher temperatures the thermal activation of vortex motion shortens τ_c and when $\tau_c < (< \Delta B^2 >^{\frac{1}{2}} \gamma)^{-1}$ a narrowing of ^{89}Y NMR line with respect to the rigid lattice behaviour is observed (Fig. 2). Two narrowing regimes are evidenced: one at low temperatures where $\Delta\nu$ decreases sharply with increasing temperature and another one at higher temperatures where the linewidth decreases more smoothly. The analysis of the temperature dependence of $\Delta\nu$(T) in the context of intermediate narrowing conditions [10] shows that the low temperature behaviour is consistent with an activated vortex motion ($\tau_c = \tau_o e^{(U/T)}$), while the high temperature one with a non-activated motion [3,4].

The crossover from one regime to the other can be attributed to the breaking of vortex lines in 2D pancake-like vortexes once their electromagnetic and Josephhson coupling has been overcome by thermal fluctuations [11]. When the 2D vortexes are still coupled forming a vortex line the pinning centers are very efficient since they can pin the whole vortex line, while when they are decoupled the pinning center is able to pin only the 2D vortex in the same plane leading to an effectively non-activated vortex motion. Such a decoupling has been also observed through resistivity measurements in superconductor-insulator superlattices when an external magnetic field was applied [12]. The crossover temperature is directly related to the coupling between CuO_2 layers, and we observed through ^{89}Y NMR that this temperature increases as T_c increases [4], showing that in a certain family of HT_cSC the coupling between

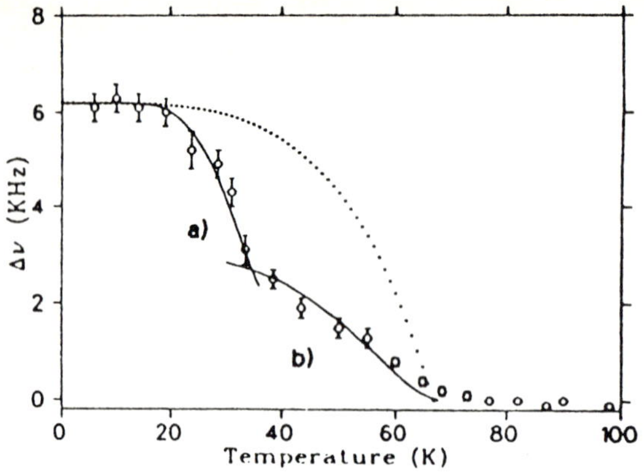

Fig. 2 Temperature dependence of the extrabroadening of the ^{89}Y NMR line below $T_c = 68$ K for an $YBa_2Cu_4O_{7.9}$ sample (a constant value of $\Delta\nu =$ 1.1 KHz, the linewidth measured above T_c, has been subtracted) The dotted line shows the expected behaviour for $\Delta\nu$ according to the two-fluid model in the absence of vortex motion. The solid line *a*) shows the behaviour of the linewidth in the low temperature thermally activated regime for a temperature dependence of the correlation time given by $\tau_c = e^{\frac{145}{T}}\mu s$. The solid line *b*) shows the behaviour in the high temperature melted regime with $\tau_c = 35\mu s$.

different CuO_2 layers is stronger for the materials with higher T_c. We remark that this crossover temperature is different from the measured irreversibility temperature [4,12].

In the activated regime the effective potential U is related not only to the pinning potential but also to the anisotropy of the superconductor; infact, being ^{89}Y nuclei able to probe the fluctuation of vortex lines at different wave vectors they are sensible also to their tilting motion, which is more relevant in more anisotropic superconductors. The effective activation potential U is temperature dependent, however, since no appropriate description of its temperature behaviour far from the critical region is available we assumed, for simplicity, a temperature independent U. From ^{89}Y NMR measurements in different Y124 powder samples we observed that U increases as T_c increases, probably not only due to a variation of the pinning potential but also because of a decrese of the anisotropy with a correspondent increase of the tilt modulus.

4. Conclusion.

For what concernes the extracted values of the second moment of the field distribution inside the VL there is still some controversy, probably arising from distortions in the VL introduced by pinning centers, especially at low fields; therefore, the presence of a universal T_c vs. $< \Delta B^2 >^{\frac{1}{2}}_{T\to 0}$ line [1] is still an open question, especially in the light of these new results. Furthermore, a more appropriate theory to describe inhomogeneous superconductors should be used to derive informations on microscopic aspects of these HT_cSC.

As regards the temperature dependence of $< \Delta B^2 >$ it was observed that its behaviour is strongly influenced by vortex motion especially at high temperatures. The effect of vortex motion on the temperature dependence of $< \Delta B^2 >$ has been detected both by our ^{89}Y NMR measurements and, in more anisotropic HT_cSC, also by μ^+SR [7]; its analysis points out the existance of different regimes for the motion of vortex lines, activated and non-activated, and their study gives relevant information on how the anisotropy of HT_cSC vary while T_c changes.

5. References.

[1] Y. J. Uemura et al., Phys. Rev. Lett. 62, 2317 (1989)
[2] B. Pümpin et al., Phys. Rev. B 42, 8019 (1991)
[3] P. Carretta and M. Corti, Phys. Rev. Lett. 68, 1236 (1992)
[4] P. Carretta, accepted for pubblication in Phys. Rev. B, March (1992)
[5] H. B. Brom and H. Alloul, Physica C 177, 297 (1991)
[6] S. E. Barrett et al., Phys. Rev. B 41, 6283 (1990)
[7] D. R. Harshman et al., Phys. Rev. Lett. 67, 3152 (1991)
[8] W. Badford and J. M. F. Gunn, Physica C 156, 515 (1988); E. H. Brandt, Phys. Rev. B 37, 2349 (1988)
[9] K. E. Gray and D. H. Kim, Physica C 180, 139 (1991)
[10] A. Abragam, "The Principles of Nuclear Magnetism" (Clarendon Press, Oxford 1961), p. 439
[11] J. R. Clem, Phys. Rev. B 43, 7837 (1991)
[12] W. R. White et al., Phys. Rev. Lett. 66, 2826 (1991); O. Brunner et al., Phys. Rev. Lett. 67, 1354 (1991)

Neutron Scattering Investigation of the Spin Dynamics in the High-Temperature Superconducting System $YBa_2Cu_3O_{6+x}$

J. Rossat-Mignod[1;2], *L.P. Regnault*[1], *P. Bourges*[2], *C. Vettier*[3], *P. Burlet*[1], *and J.Y. Henry*[1]

[1]Centre d'Etudes Nucléaires de Grenoble, DRFMC/MDN, 85 X, F-38041 Grenoble Cedex, France

[2]Laboratoire Léon Brillouin, CEA-CNRS, CE Saclay, F-91191 Gif-sur-Yvette Cedex, France

[3]European Synchrotron Research Facility, B.P. 220, F-38043 Grenoble Cedex, France

Abstract. We report on inelastic neutron scattering experiments carried out on single-crystals of the $YBa_2Cu_3O_{6+x}$ system. The spin dynamics has been successfully investigated as a function of temperature in the metallic state over the whole doping range from the weakly doped (x = 0.45, 0.51) to the heavily doped (x = 0.69, 0.92) and the overdoped (x = 1) regimes. Dynamical AF-correlations remain in the metallic state but the in-plane correlation length decreases with doping whereas the AF-coupling between the two Cu(2) layers is not affected, excepted in the overdoped regime.

At low temperatures, in any superconducting samples, an energy gap has been discovered in the spin excitation spectrum, with a value $E_G/kT_C \simeq 3.5$) which becomes weaker close to the I-M transition. Moreover, in the heavily doped regime, a pseudo gap persists above T_C.

A quite unusual T-dependence of the spin excitation spectrum was found, especially in the weakly doped regime.

1. Introduction

Since the discovery of superconductivity in copper oxide materials by J.G. Bednorz and K.A. Muller [1] a huge amount of experimental and theoretical works has been reported [2]. However there is not yet a well accepted understanding of their unusual physical properties in the normal state and the origin of the physical mechanism involved in the Cooper pair formation is still controversial.

With the advances in single crystal growth careful and quantitative experimental works on well characterized high quality materials are becoming available [3] and are establishing on firm grounds that cuprate oxydes are not "classical" metals but they must be considered as strongly correlated electronic systems.

Macroscopic measurements of transport (resistivity, Hall effect, thermoelectric power), magnetic (susceptibility, magnetization) and thermodynamical (specific heat) properties were fundamental in establishing the unusual properties of these materials. However microscopic measurements were of crucial importance to get more insight in the physics of these high-T_C materials.

Springer Series in Solid-State Sciences, Vol. 113 Electronic Properties of High-T_c Superconductors
Editors: H. Kuzmany, M. Mehring, J. Fink

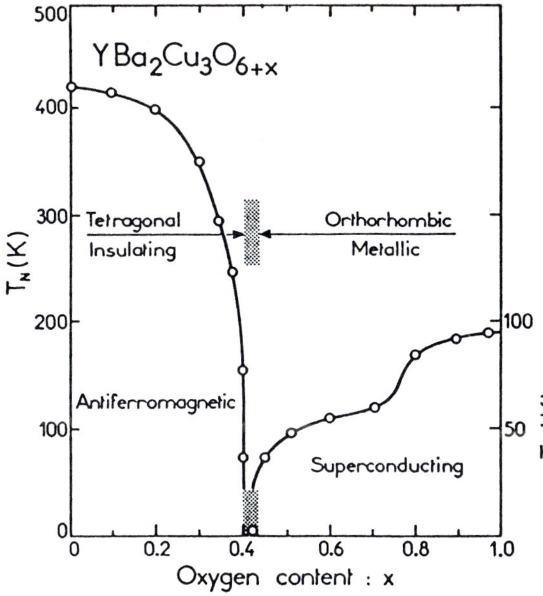

Fig. 1. Phase diagram of the $YBa_2Cu_3O_{6+x}$ system as a function of the oxygen content.

In particular, nuclear magnetic resonance (NMR) and inelastic neutron scattering (INS) experiments, by establishing the existence of spin excitations, have provided master piece informations which prove the strongly correlated nature of the CuO_2 electronic planes. They are actually complementary techniques, NMR is probing locally with high accuracy the zero-frequency spin fluctuation spectrum at different sites (Cu, O, Y,...), whereas INS gives informations on both spatial and temporal spin fluctuations over the whole crystal. Neutron scattering actually is the unique probe to get both the wave vector and the energy dependences of the spin excitation spectrum, i.e. the imaginary part of the dynamical spin susceptibility $\chi(\vec{q},\hbar\omega)$.

As far as INS measurements are concerned, an important activity started, since the discovery of high-T_c materials, in Europe, US and Japan but it is during these last two years that very important results were obtained in the metallic and superconducting state as the evidence of a spin gap in the $YBa_2Cu_3O_{6+x}$ system [4] and the existence of incommensurate peaks in the $La_{2-x}(Ba,Sr)_xO_4$ system [5] at low temperatures.

Our group has focused his interest, from the beginning, on the $YBa_2Cu_3O_{6+x}$ system because of its versatile character and the possibility of growing a large single crystal (~ 0.3 cm^3) of sufficiently good quality for INS measurements in which the oxygen content can be changed from O_6 to O_7 with good accuracy and homogeneity.

During the last five years a continuous investigation has been carried out from the antiferromagnetic (AF), to the metallic and superconducting states [4,6-10]. The phase diagram has been determined, see Fig.1, and six characteristic regimes can be defined. For each of them a systematic study of the spin dynamics has now been performed, successively with increasing difficulty, in the pured (x = 0.15) and doped (x = 0.37) AF-states, the weakly doped metallic state (x = 0.45 and 0.51), the heavily doped metallic state exhibiting superconductivity below T_c = 60 K (x = 0.69) and T_c = 90 K (x = 0.92), and the overdoped metallic state (x = 1).

In this paper we shall concentrate mainly on the most recent results obtained in the weakly and heavily doped metallic states (x = 0.51, 0.69, 0.92) and new results in the overdoped state (x = 1) will be reported here for the first time.

We have to mention that similar experiments have been carried out by the Brookhaven group in the weakly doped states and a detailed study has been reported recently by Tranquada et al. [11] on a sample with x = 0.6.

2. Experimental

Recent neutron scattering experiments on single crystals were performed on the three-axis spectrometer 2T at the Laboratoire Léon Brillouin. This high flux spectrometer, operated by the Karlsruhe neutron scattering group, is equipped with both a vertically and horizontally focusing monochromator and analyser. The gain in intensity is quite important in our case because the q-width of the resolution function is smaller that the intrinsic physical q-width.

The single crystal sample (~ 0.30 cm^3) was kept inside an aluminium box and orientated with the [110] and [001] axes within the horizontal scattering plane. The single crystal, grown by a special technique, has a mosaic spread $\eta \simeq 1°$ and a porous morphology allowing to change easily the oxygen content from x = 0 to x = 1 with good accuracy and homogeneity (~ 1%). However, recently, we realized that the sample contains some Sr because the purchased BaO materials had not the required purity, but contained about 3% Sr. Therefore the exact chemical formula of the single crystal is $Y(Ba_{0.965}Sr_{0.035})_2Cu_3O_{6+x}$. The main effect of Sr-substitution is to depress slightly T_c, as an example from 93 K to 91 K for x = 0.92.

3. The Weakly Doped Metallic State (x = 0.51)

For an oxygen content larger that $x_c \simeq 0.40$, an insulating metal (I-M) transition takes place because of a sudden transfer of a large amount of p-holes (~ 10 %) from Cu(1) into Cu(2) planes. This sudden transfer occurs because of some oxygen ordering yielding the formation of long Cu-O chains inducing then a tetratogonal-orthorhombic phase transition. Experiments, carried out on samples with oxygen contents x = 0.45 and 0.51, have already been reported [4,7,8]. While no 3d-AF ordering survives to such a p-hole doping, AF-dynamical correlations persist in the metallic state and the spin excitation spectrum exhibits an energy gap (E_G = 3 and 4 meV, respectively) in the superconducting state ($T_c \simeq 37$ K and 47 K, respectively).

More accurate measurements have been performed again on a newly prepared sample with about the same oxygen content x = 0.51. The magnetic scattering consists in a broad spectrum in energy (see Fig.2), weakly temperature dependent, which is concentrated, in q-space, along the 2d-AF rods, as can be seen in Fig. 3 and 4 showing q-scans across and along the rod, respectively. The magnetic contribution can accurately be determined due to a good knowledge of the background contribution,

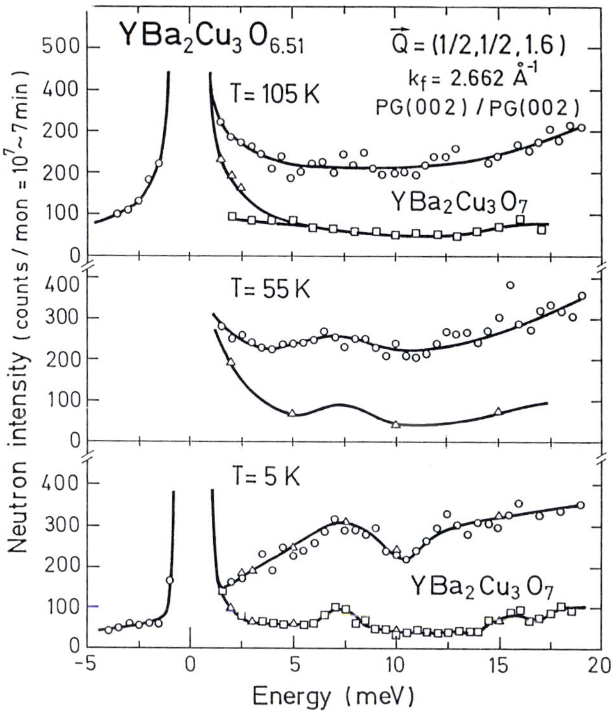

Fig. 2. Low energy scans performed at $\vec{Q}$ = (1/2, 1/2, 1.6) for $YBa_2Cu_3O_{6.51}$ as a function of temperature. The background is well determined by the scattering measured on the fully oxygenated sample $YBa_2Cu_3O_7$ (□) and by q-scans (Δ).

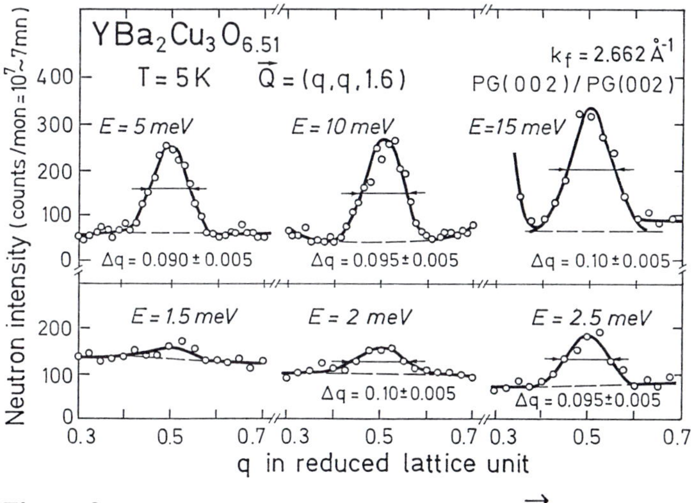

Fig. 3. Q-scans across the 2d-magnetic rod at $\vec{Q}$ = (1/2, 1/2, 1.6) and different energies for $YBa_2Cu_3O_{6.51}$ in the superconducting state (T = 5 K).

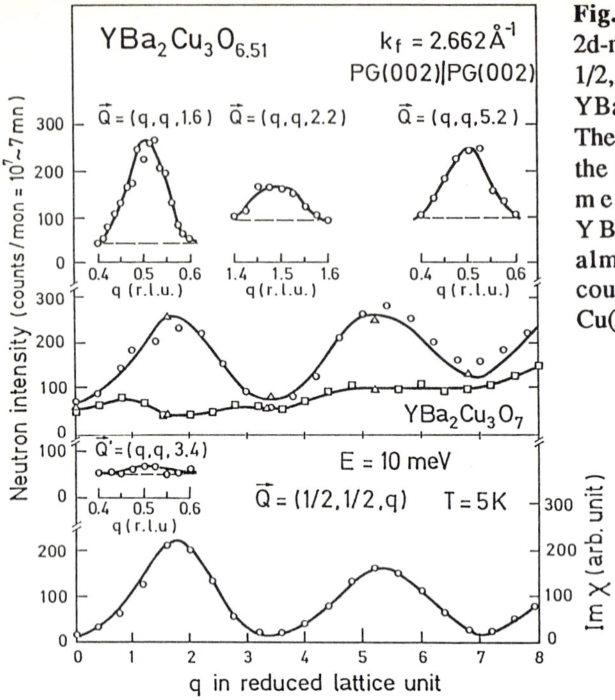

Fig. 4. Q-scans along the 2d-magnetic rod, $\vec{Q} = (1/2, 1/2, q)$, at $\hbar\omega = 10$ meV for $YBa_2Cu_3O_{6.51}$ at T = 5 K. The careful determination of the background value, from measurements on $YBa_2Cu_3O_7$ yields an almost complete AF-coupling between the two Cu(2) layers.

obtained from both the above q-scans and the same measurements on the same single crystal, but fully oxygenated (x = 1), which exhibits no magnetic scattering in this energy range.

Q-scans along the (110) direction yield a q-width, $\Delta q = 0.10 \pm 0.01$ r.l.u., from which a correlation length $\xi_{AF}/a \simeq 2.2$ can be deduced. It must be emphasized that this q-width is energy-independent and temperature-independent up to room temperature. Moreover the line shape is not of lorentzian type but rather of gaussian type which makes the determination of the correlation length less accurate.

Actually the physical quantity of interest we can extract from the measured magnetic cross section is the imaginary part of the dynamical susceptibility $\chi(\vec{Q},\hbar\omega)$ according to the following expressions :

$$\frac{d^2\sigma(\vec{Q},\hbar\omega)}{d\Omega\, d\hbar\omega} \propto \sum_{\alpha=x,y,z} (1 - \hat{Q}_\alpha^2)\, S^{\alpha\alpha}(\vec{Q},\hbar\omega) \quad ,$$

where the dynamical structure factor $S^{\alpha\alpha}(\vec{Q},\hbar\omega)$ is the Fourier transform of the correlation function of the spin components S^α with

$$S^{\alpha\alpha}(\vec{Q},\hbar\omega) = \frac{1}{\pi}\,\frac{1}{1-\exp(-\hbar\omega/kT)}\ \mathrm{Im}\,\{\chi^{\alpha\alpha}(\vec{Q},\hbar\omega)\} \quad .$$

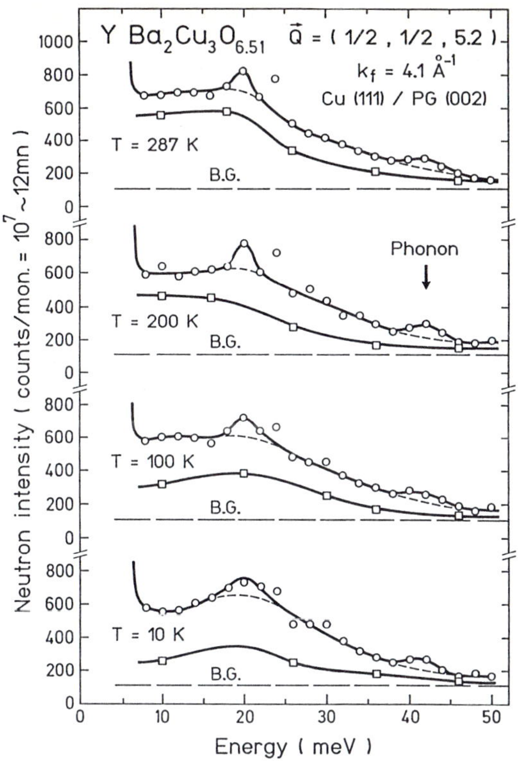

Fig.5. High energy scans performed at $\vec{Q}$ = (1/2, 1/2, 5.2) for $YBa_2Cu_3O_{6.51}$ as a function of temperature. Above the background (BG) the nuclear contributions is indicated (□).

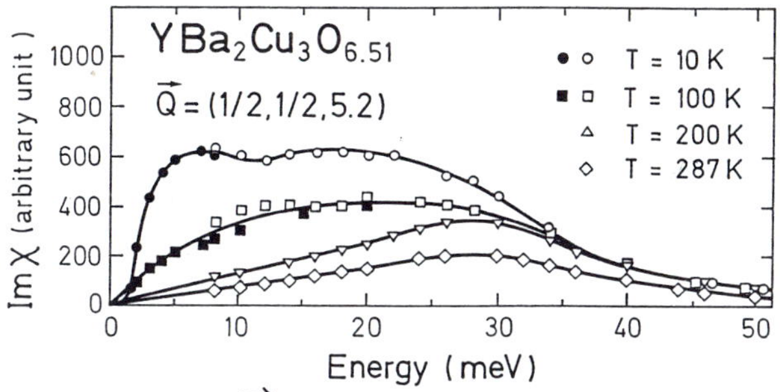

Fig. 6. Im{$\chi(\vec{q}, \hbar\omega)$} as a function of the energy for $YBa_2Cu_3O_{6.51}$ and increasing temperature.

From the above data and the high energy scans, reported in Fig.5, we have determined the energy and temperature dependences of Im $\chi(\vec{Q}, \hbar\omega)$ as shown in Fig.6.

At low temperatures, Imχ exhibits a broad maximum as a function of energy. Imχ is almost constant from 5 to 20 meV and falls off at high energies much faster than a simple lorentzian function, the scattering above 50 meV being quite small even after a q-integration.

By increasing the temperature the low energy part of the spectrum is strongly depressed in a non trivial manner, a simple $h\omega/kT$ law is not obeyed. From 200 K to 287 K, the maximum of $\mathrm{Im}\chi$ is temperature independent, yielding a quasi-particule characteristic energy $\Gamma_\omega \simeq 28$ meV, at room temperature. Surprisingly, above 150 K a Curie-Weiss type of law was found for the temperature behaviour :

$$\mathrm{Im}\chi = \mathrm{Im}\chi_o/(1+\alpha(T-\theta_p)) \quad ,$$

where $\mathrm{Im}\chi_o$ is the $T = 0$ value and with the following values : $\theta_p = 117$ K and $1/\alpha = c(h\omega)^{3/2}$ ($1/\alpha = 23.5$ K at 10 meV).

In the superconducting state, the low energy part of the spectrum (see Fig. 4,6) clearly shows the opening of an energy gap in the spin excitation spectrum. The spin gap, surprisingly, has a quite small value of the order of kT_c which appears to be a characteristic feature on approaching the I-M transition.

In conclusion, in the weakly doped regime, the spin excitation spectrum is not that expected for a disordered AF-system but it reflects the behaviour of the quasi-particles which undergo a superconducting transition at low temperature with a quite small spin gap value. The small value of the characteristic energy ($\simeq 28$ meV) results certainly in many body effects due to strong correlations.

4. The T_c = 60 K Superconducting Phase (x = 0.69)

As the results have already been reported elsewhere [4,9,10] we shall briefly summarize them.

A sample with an oxygen content $x = 0.69$ ($T_c = 59$ K), at the end of the $T_c = 60$ K plateau, has been investigated. The obtained low energy spectra as a function of temperature are reported in Fig. 7 in the form of $\mathrm{Im}\chi$. The broad energy spectrum yields a characteristic energy $\Gamma_\omega \simeq 28$ meV quite similar to the previous case. However, at low temperature, the low energy spin excitation spectrum is not enhanced, as previously but strongly suppressed by the appearance of an energy gap with a much larger value, $E_G = 16 \pm 1$ meV, in comparison with kT_c ($E_G/kT_c \simeq 3.2$). No magnetic scattering can be measured below an energy transfer of 10 meV.

An other quite important difference is that $\mathrm{Im}\chi$ recovers a linear energy dependence, at small energies, only above $T^* \simeq 160$ K. This unusual behaviour is illustrated in the insert of Fig. 7 which shows the temperature dependence of the slope of $\mathrm{Im}\chi$. This result establishes that a pseudo-gap in the spin excitation spectrum starts to develop well above T_c and so gives an explanation for the unusual temperature dependence of $1/T_1T$ as measured by NMR [12,13,14]. It is actually a behaviour typical for the heavily doped regime.

The data obtained by Tranquada et al. [11] on a sample with $x = 0.6$ are actually intermediated between the results reported above for samples with $x = 0.5$ and $x = 0.69$, especially concerning the spin gap value which is reported to be about 10 meV.

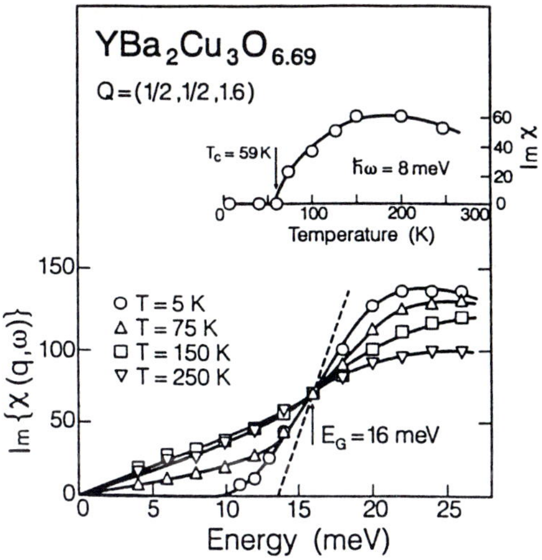

Fig. 7. Low energy part of the spin excitation spectrum of $Im\{\chi(\vec{q},h\omega)\}$ for $YBa_2Cu_3O_{6.69}$ below (T = 5 K) and above (T = 75, 150, 250 K) the superconducting transition (T_C = 59 K). An energy gap (E_G= 16 meV) clearly persists above T_C.

5. The Heavily Doped Metallic State (x = 0.92)

A sample with an oxygen content x = 0.92 has been successfully investigated a year ago [9,10] and the results were presented for the first time at the high-T_C Conference in Kanazawa. This oxygen content was chosen to get the highest T_C value (T_C = 91 K, a value slightly smaller than 93 K because of the small Sr content) but with still an unusual temperature dependence of $1/T_1T$, a behaviour not found by NMR in fully oxygenated samples [13], as we shall see in next section. Energy scans, performed at increasing temperatures (see Fig.8) exhibit a rather complex lineshape. However q-scans, across (Fig. 9) or along (Fig. 10) the (1/2 1/2 l) rod, clearly show evidence for a magnetic scattering contribution and allow us to define the nuclear contribution. The latter one can be explained by assuming three contributions on top of a flat background : a contamination from the (006) Bragg peak at 24 meV, a peaked contribution at 20 meV and a broad response well accounted for by a damped harmonic oscillator ($h\omega_0$ = 21.5 meV, Γ_ω = 26 meV) which may arise from tunneling fluctuations of apical oxygen atoms. Knowing the nuclear contribution, the magnetic one can now be determined at any temperatures (see Fig.7). The obtained results are reported in Fig.11 in the form of Imχ. Several unusual features have to be underligned.

At T = 5 K, there is no measurable scattering below 25 meV giving evidence for a sharp energy gap in the spin excitation spectrum at E_G = 28 ± 1 meV. More surprising is the sharp drop of the spectrum above 45 meV and the existence of a strong enhancement of the spectrum around 41 meV which resultes from a narrowing of the q-width : 0.18 r.l.u. instead of 0.27 r.l.u. (see Fig. 9). This enhancement

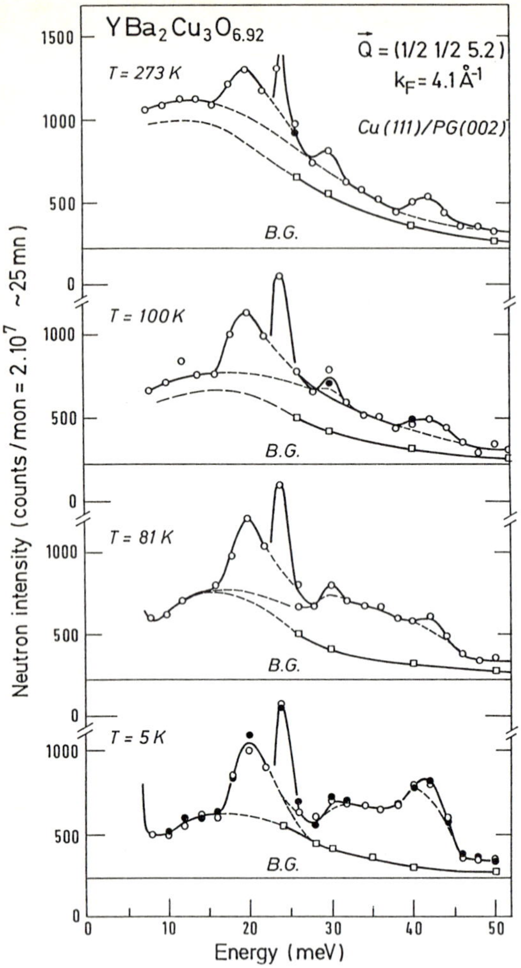

Fig. 8. Energy scans performed at $\vec{Q}$ = (1/2, 1/2, 5.2) for $YBa_2Cu_3O_{6.92}$ as a function of temperature. Above the background (BG) the nuclear contributions is indicated (❐) together with a spurious contribution arising from the (006) Bragg peak.

already desappears at T = 81 K, i.e. below T_C = 91 K, and correlatively some excitations appear in the gap. It must be emphasized that the spin excitation gap is not decreasing with temperature as expected in the classical BCS theory.

An other astonishing result is the strong intensity modulation found in a q-scan performed along the AF-rod (Fig.10) because it establishes that the AF-coupling between the two Cu(2) layers remains almost unaffected while the in-plane correlation length is very short ($\xi/a = 0.84 \pm 0.04$). This may indicate that a strong coupling exists in addition of the AF-one which is at most one order of magnitude smaller than the in-plane AF-coupling.

At higher temperatures, the magnetic scattering is strongly depressed. However it must be noticed that the characteristic energy scale $\Gamma_\omega = 30 \pm 2$ meV does not change with temperature, nor does the AF-correlation length which is now quite short ($\Delta q = 0.27 \pm 0.02$ r.l.u., $\xi/a = 0.84 \pm 0.04$).

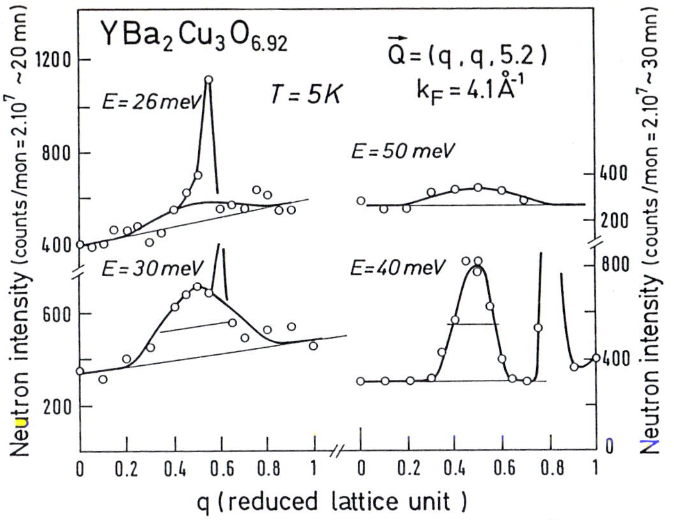

Fig. 9. Q-scans across the 2d-magnetic rod at ($\vec{Q}$ = (1/2, 1/2, 5.2) and different energies for $YBa_2Cu_3O_{6.92}$ in the superconducting state (T_c = 91 K).

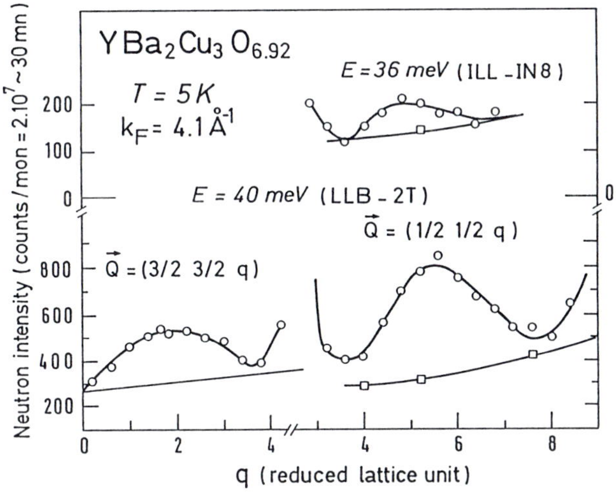

Fig. 10. Q-scans along the 2d-magnetic rod for $YBa_2Cu_3O_{6.92}$ (T = 5 K) showing the almost complete AF-coupling between the two Cu(2) layers.

As in the 60 K-superconducting phase, $\text{Im}\chi$ recovers a linear energy dependence only well above T_c. Actually the slope $\text{Im}\chi/\hbar\omega$ (see Fig. 12) starts to decrease below $T^* \simeq$ 120-130 K in excellent agreement with $1/T_1T$ NMR measurements performed on the same sample [13]. Therefore a pseudo-gap is also opening in the 90 K-phase with x = 0.92 but at a smaller temperature than for the 60 K-phase, a behaviour typical of the heavily doped regime.

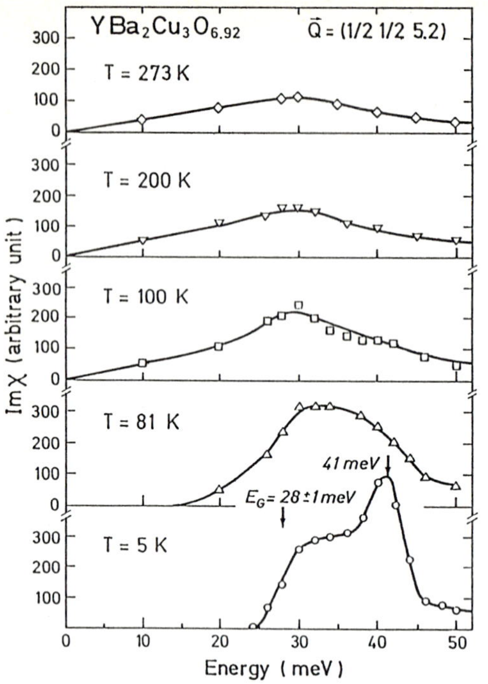

Fig. 11. $Im\{\chi(\vec{Q},\hbar\omega)\}$ as a function of the energy for $YBa_2Cu_3O_{6.92}$ and increasing temperatures below and above $T_c = 91$ K. An energy gap ($E_G = 28$ meV) is clearly seen together with a strong enhancement at $\hbar\omega$ = 41 meV at low temperatures.

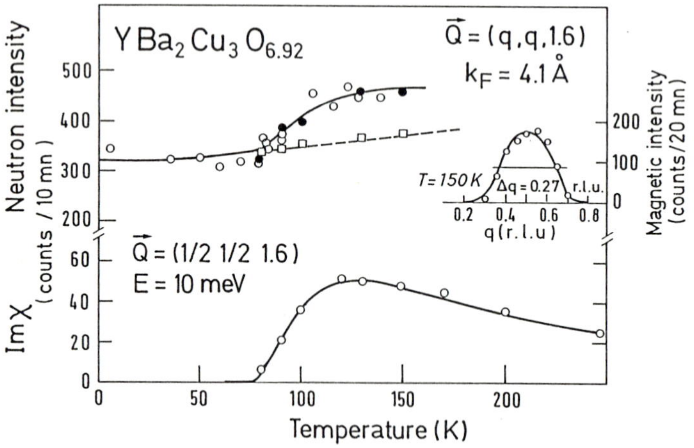

Fig. 12. $Im\chi$ at $\hbar\omega$ = 10 meV and $\vec{Q}$ = (1/2, 1/2, 1.6) as a function of temperature for $YBa_2Cu_3O_{6.92}$. In this 90 K-superconductor a pseudo-gap opens for $T^* \simeq$ 120-130 K, i.e. well above T_c.

6. The Overdoped Metallic State (x = 1)

In order to understand why $1/T_1T$ NMR measurements show a pseudo-gap effect for a sample with x = 0.92 and no pseudo gap effect for a fully oxygenated sample (x = 1) [13], a INS experiment has been performed, quite recently, on such a sample and results are reported here for the first time. Actually a careful investigation of the phase diagram between x = 0.9 and 1 has shown [15] that $YBa_2Cu_3O_7$ is already an overdoped sample because T_c is smaller by a couple of degrees than the optimum value found around x = 0.94. Moreover in O_7 the conductivity along the c-axis has been found of metallic type ($\rho_c \propto T$) [16].

Experiments were more difficult because the magnetic scattering continues to decrease. However at high energies a magnetic scattering has clearly been identified (see Fig. 13). The q-width along [110] has increased by about 10 % in comparison with x = 0.92 ($\Delta q = 0.30 \pm 0.02$ r.l.u., $\xi/a \simeq 0.76 \pm 0.04$) . Moreover an important difference exists in the AF-coupling between the two Cu(2) layers which is now much weaker. The temperature dependence of the spin excitation spectrum is reported in fig. 14 in the form of Imχ.

At low temperatures the shape in energy of Imχ has changed. A sharp gap is also observed but with a slighthly smaller value : $E_G \simeq 26 \pm 1$ meV. More important at high energies the spectrum drops sharply, no measurable scattering is found at 50 meV (see Fig. 15). This sharp decrease is even more pronounced at higher temperatures than at low temperatures because at low temperature it is compensated by a strong enhancement around 40 meV due to a narrowing of the q-width ($\Delta q = 0.20$ instead of 0.30 r.l.u.). This result is quite similar to that observed in the sample with x = 0.92. In fig. 15 we have reported the temperature dependence of this enhanced scattering at $\hbar\omega = 36$ meV. Actually it starts to decrease around 60 K and

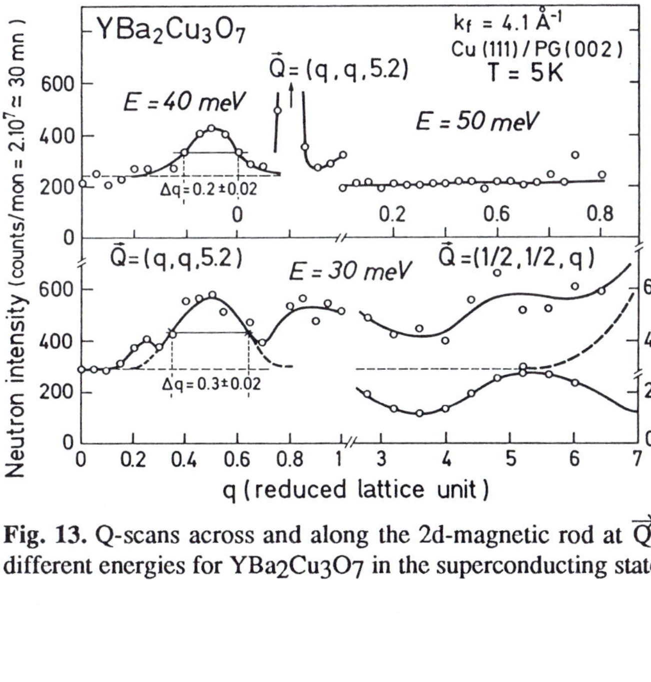

Fig. 13. Q-scans across and along the 2d-magnetic rod at $\vec{Q}$ = (1/2, 1/2, 5.2) and different energies for $YBa_2Cu_3O_7$ in the superconducting state (T_c = 89 K).

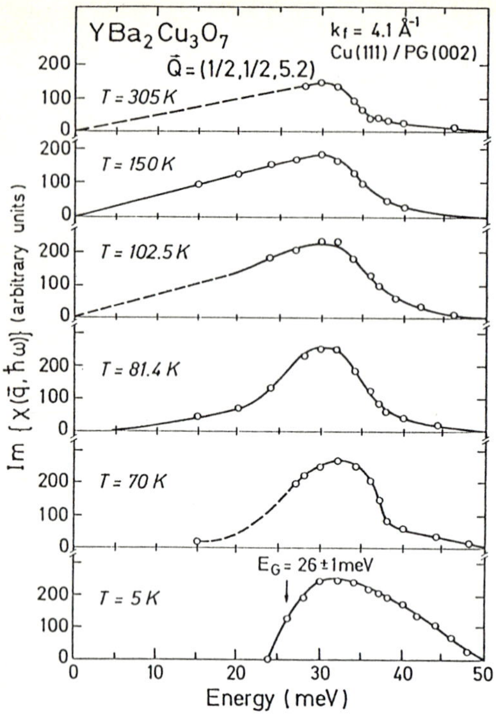

Fig. 14. $Im\{\chi(\vec{Q},h\omega)\}$ as a function of the energy for $YBa_2Cu_3O_7$, above and below T_C = 89 K. An energy gap (E_G = 26 ± 1 meV) is clearly seen together with a strong enhancement at $h\omega \simeq 40$ meV at low temperatures.

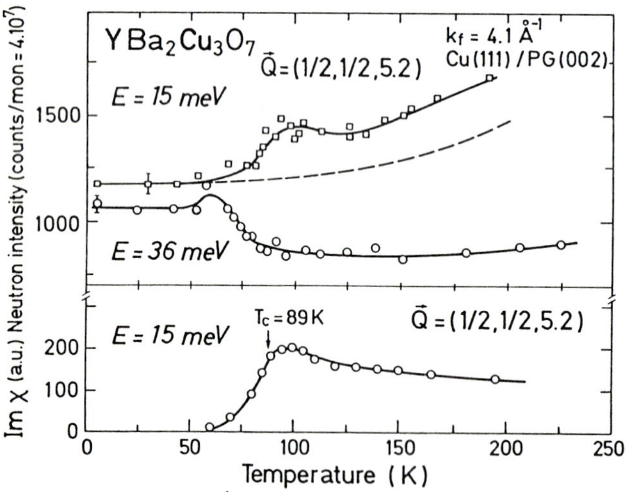

Fig. 15. Imχ at $\vec{Q}$ = (1/2, 1/2, 5.2) for two typical energy transfers : $\hbar\omega$ = 15 meV showing the filling of the spin gap and the absence of pseudo-gap opening above T_C, and $h\omega$ = 36 meV showing the corallated disappearence of the strong enhancement at $h\omega$ = 40 meV.

vanishes completely around T_C = 89 K. Correlated to the suppression of this enhancement, excitations appear in the gap as shown by the temperature dependence of Imχ at E = 15 meV (see Fig. 15). More interesting is the fact that Imχ at 15 meV starts to decrease only around T_C in excellent agreement with NMR measurements. These results lead to the important conclusion that, in overdoped samples, the gap in the spin excitation spectrum opens around T_C and not above as for the 90 K-underdoped samples. This behaviour is one of the main characteristic of the overdoped regime together with a sharper decrease of the spectrum at high energies and a weaker AF-coupling between the two Cu(2) layers.

7. Conclusion

The spin excitation spectrum has been found and investigated as a function of temperature in the metallic state over the whole damping range. Dynamical AF-correlations have always been observed, the q-width (correlation length) is increasing (decreasing) with doping and mimics the T_C behaviour. However the characteristic energy of spin fluctuations ($\Gamma_\omega \simeq$ 30 meV) is almost not depend on doping and indeed has a quite small value compared with J and E. Another characteristic of the spectrum is its gaussian-shape in q-space and its rapid drops at high energies, especially for x = 1.

In metallic samples, a gap in the spin excitation spectrum has been found for any doping. However, at low doping, the gap is much weaker compared with kT_C. The dependence of the energy gap value as a function of T_C is given in Fig. 16. At large doping a ratio $E_G/kT_C \simeq 3.5$ is reached. However the spin gap value remains much smaller than the charge gap value $2\Delta/kT_C$ which ranges from 5, in Raman spectroscopy, to 7-8 in point contact spectroscopy or photo-emission measurements. Moreover, for the 90 K-superconducting states (x = 0.92 and 1) a strong enhancement of the energy spectrum was found at low temperatures around 41 meV. The spin gap energy does not depend on temperature as expected from a BCS theory,

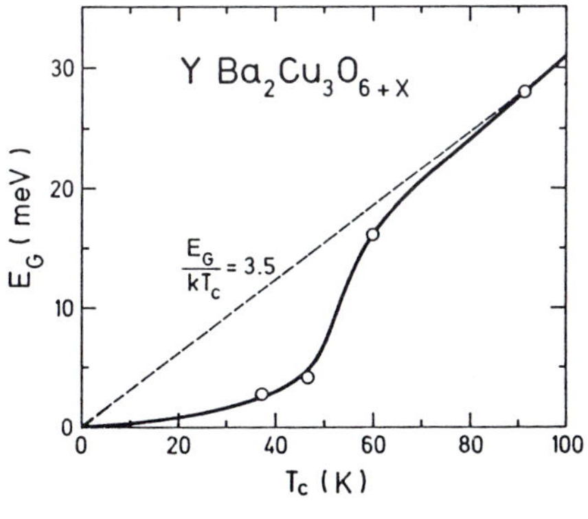

Fig. 16. Value of the spin excitation energy gap as a function of the superconducting transition temperature for the system $YBa_2Cu_3O_{6+x}$.

indeed the gap is filled up with increasing temperatures. In the heavily doped regime a pseudo-gap already develops below a temperature T much larger than T_C, but not in the overdoped regime for which it is the main characteristic.

We hope that these neutron scattering experiments will bring valuable informations for building a reliable theory of high-T_C materials. Certainly these results have raised many questions and more detailed second generation experiments have to be envisages and will be carried out in a near future.

Acknowledgments

We acknowledge stimulating discussions with D. Grempel, M. Lavagna and S.V. Maleyev. The collaboration with the NMR group of C. Berthier throughout the course of this work has been quite fruitful.

References

[1] J.G. Bednorz and K.A. Muller, Z. Phys. B **64**, 189 (1986).

[2] See Proceedings of International Conferences on High Temperature Superconductors : Interlaken, Standford, Kanazawa.

[3] B. Batlogg, Summary of Kanazawa Conference, Physica C **185-189** (1991) and Proceeding of Toshiba International School of Superconductivity, Kyoto, Eds. S. Maekawa and M. Sato, Springer Verlag (1991).

[4] J. Rossat-Mignod, L.P. Regnault, C. Vettier, P. Burlet, J.Y. Henry, G. Lapertot, Physica B **169**, 58 (1991).

[5] S-W. Cheong, G. Aeppli, T.E. Mason, H. Mook, S.M. Hayden, P.C. Canfield, Z. Fisk, K.N. Clausen, J.L. Martinez, Phys. Rev. Lett. **67**, 1791 (1991).

[6] J. Rossat-Mignod, et al, J. Phys. France **49**, C8-2119 (1988).

[7] J. Rossat-Mignod, L.P. Regnault, M.J. Jurgens, P. Burlet, J.Y. Henry, G. Lapertot, in "Dynamics of Magnetic Fluctuations in High T_C Materials", Eds. G. Rieter, P. Horsh and G. Psaltakis, Plenum Press (1990).

[8] J. Rossat-Mignod, L.P. Regnault, M.J. Jurgens, C. Vettier, P. Burlet, J.Y. Henry, G. Lapertot, Physica B **163**, 4 (1990).

[9] J. Rossat-Mignod, L.P. Regnault, C. Vettier, P. Bourges, P. Burlet, J. Bossy, J.Y. Henry, G. Lapertot, Physica C **185-189**, 86 (1991).

[10]J. Rossat-Mignod, L.P. Regnault, C. Vettier, P. Bourges, P. Burlet, J. Bossy, J.Y. Henry, G. Lapertot, Proceeding of ICNS'91, Oxford, Physica B (1992).

[11]J.M. Tranquada, P.M. Gehring, G. Shirane, S. Shamoto, M. Sato, Preprint.

[12]Y. Kitaoka, K. Ishida, S. Ohsugi, K. Fujiwara, K. Asayama, Physica C **185-189**, 98 (1991).

[13]C. Berthier, Y. Berthier, P. Butaud, W.G. Clark, J.A. Gillet, M. Horvatic, P. Segransan, J.Y. Henry, Physica C **185-189**, 1141 (1991).

[14]M. Takigawa, A.P. Reyes, P.C. Hammel, J.D. Thompson, R.H. Heffner, Z. Fisk., K.C. Ott, Phys. Rev. B **43**, 247 (1991).

[15]T. Graf, G. Triscone and J. Muller, J. Less-Common Met., **159**, 349 (1990) ; J.Y. Genoux, T. Graf, A. Junod, D. Sanchez, G. Triscone and J. Muller, Physica **177**, 315 (1991).

[16]C. Ayache, Private communication.

^{205}Tl NMR in the High-T_c Superconductor $Tl_2Ba_2CaCu_2O_{8-\delta}$

N. Winzek[1], *J. Groß*[1], *P. Gergen*[1], *Hj. Mattausch*[2], *R. Kremer*[2], *A. Simon*[2], *and M. Mehring*[1]

[1]II. Physikalisches Institut, Universität Stuttgart, Pfaffenwaldring 57, W-7000 Stuttgart 80, Fed. Rep. of Germany
[2]Max-Planck-Institut für Festkörperforschung, Heisenbergstr. 1, W-7000 Stuttgart 80, Fed. Rep. of Germany

1. Abstract

We report on the NMR Knight shift of ^{205}Tl in $Tl_2Ba_2CaCu_2O_{8-\delta}$ for different δ. Due to the variation of the oxygen content T_C ranges from 85K up to 101K. The ^{205}Tl spectra consist of two lines. The main line arises from Tl(1) in the TlO-layer whereas the defect line belongs to Tl(2) in the Ca-layers. The temperature dependence of the line shift of this defect line is strongly related to the oxygen content of the sample. Since the line shift of the defect line is dominated by a negative Knight shift, this Knight shift should be very sensitive to a change of the hole concentration in the CuO_2-layers.

2. Experimental

All samples were initially prepared under the same conditions as described earlier [1], [2]. This was necessary to make sure that there is no change of the amount of Tl in the Ca-layers. The variation of the oxygen content was controlled by different heat treatment of the samples in Ar-atmosphere. By heating the samples up to 200°C and 600°C for two hours, T_c decreased from 101K (sample 1) to 99K (sample 2) and 85K (sample 3). The NMR measurements were carried out using a home built pulsed NMR spectrometer operating at 105MHz at a field of 4.26T. The spectra were obtained by taking a two pulse sequence (Hahn - Echo - sequence, $(\pi/2)_x - \tau - (\pi)_x)$) with different pulse spacings to excite a spin echo and taking the Fourier transform of the second half of the echo. As reference we used a solution of $TlNO_3$ with the ^{205}Tl Larmor frequency of $\nu = 104.699$MHz.

3. Results

In analyzing the spectra we were mainly interested in the temperature dependent behavior of the line shift and relaxation rate of the defect line Tl(2). At low temperatures the lines of Tl(1) and Tl(2) overlap and therefore it is difficult to separate the two different lines to get the exact shift values. There are two possibilities to overcome this problem. On one hand one can use single crystals, where the broadening of the lines due to the chemical shift anisotropy is removed. Since we have powdered samples we made use of the fact that T_2 of Tl(1) and Tl(2) is different. $T_2 = 32\,\mu s$ for Tl(1) and around $100\,\mu s$ for Tl(2). By using short pulse spacings of $\tau = 25\mu s$ we observe spectral contributions of both lines but for long pulse spacings of $\tau = 100\,\mu s$ the Tl(1) part in the spectrum vanishes and only the Tl(2) part is observable. So it is possible even for powdered samples to measure the line shift and the relaxation rate down to low temperatures.

Springer Series in Solid-State Sciences, Vol. 113 Electronic Properties of High-T_c Superconductors
Editors: H. Kuzmany, M. Mehring, J. Fink

4. Discussion

Since it is necessary to separate the various contributions to the line shift of Tl(2) one has to measure the total line shift down to low temperatures. The various contributions to the total line shift are:

- δ_{Ch}, the chemical shift. δ_{Ch} is due to the atomic surrounding of the nucleus and is temperature independent.
- δ_M, which arises from demagnetization in the superconducting state.
- K_S, the spin dependent part of the Knight shift. K_S vanishes for T = 0K because of the pairing mechanism.
- K_{orb}, the orbital part of the Knight shift. K_{orb} is temperature independent like the chemical shift.

The total line shift was corrected for δ_M for low temperatures to obtain the pure spin dependent part of the Knight shift.

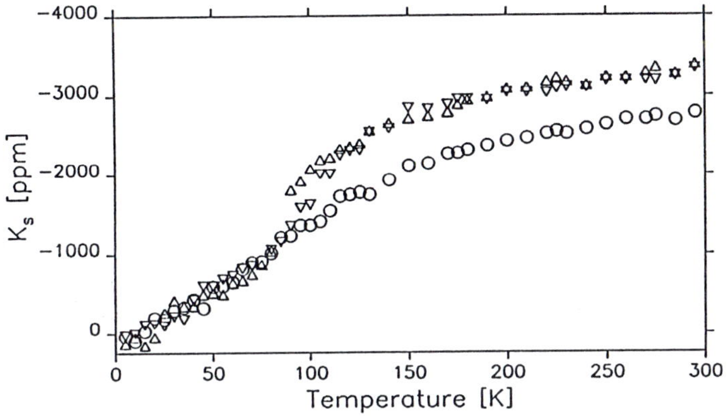

Fig.1: *Temperature dependence of the Knight shift of Tl(2) for the sample 1* (△), sample 2 (▽) and sample 3 (○)

Knight shift K_S for different samples at room temperature:

	T_c	K_S(295K)
sample 1	101 K	-3362ppm
sample 2	99 K	-3352ppm
sample 3	85 K	-2779ppm
single crystal	101 K	-3615ppm, -3502ppm

The temperature dependence in the line shift of Tl(2) for sample 2 and sample 3 are in good agreement with measurements on a single crystal (T_c = 101K) [3]. This dependence for different oxygen content shows the same feature as in the NMR experiments on ^{89}Y [4]. This is not surprising in the sense that both nuclei are located at the same lattice site and both have spin I = 1/2. Like in the Y case we observe a monotonic decrease of the Knight shift with decreasing temperature already above T_c for oxygen depleted samples. This behavior is characteristic for the temperature dependence of the spin susceptiblity in oxygen depleted samples.

The spin dependent part of the Knight shift K_S is connected to the spin susceptibility via the hyperfine coupling constant A.

$$K_S = \frac{A}{g\mu_B}\frac{\chi^{mole}}{N_A} \quad .$$

By measuring the spin susceptibility the hyperfine coupling constant could be determined like in $YBa_2Cu_3O_{7-\delta}$ [4] or like in $La_{1.85}Sr_{0.15}Cu_2O_4$ [5]. We measured the susceptibility but in our samples a Curie contribution was observed which overlayed the part of the Pauli spin susceptibility therefore A was estimated using consistency arguments to A = -52 T or -260 kOe/μ_B [6]. We analyse our data according to the two quantities S_K and M_K as defined in [7]

$$K_S^2\, T_1\, T\, C_0\, S_K = 1 \qquad \text{with} \qquad S_K = \frac{1}{T_1 T K_S^2 C_0} \quad ,$$

$$K_S\, A\, C_1\, T_1\, T\, M_K = 1 \qquad \text{with} \qquad M_K = \frac{1}{T_1 T K_S A C_1} \quad .$$

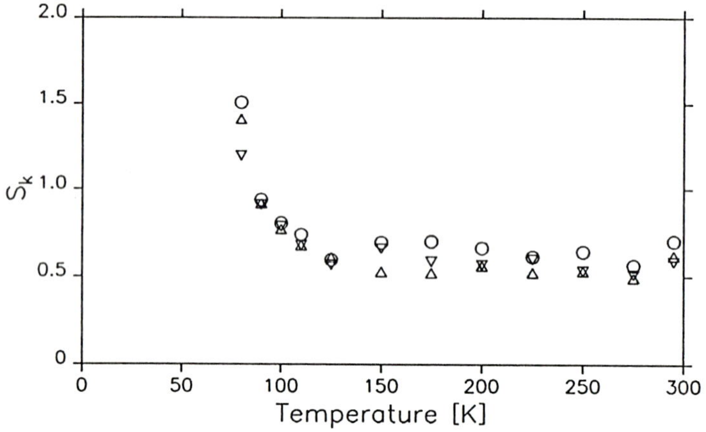

Fig.2: *S_K vs. temperature of Tl(2) for sample 1* (△), sample 2 (▽) and sample 3 (○)

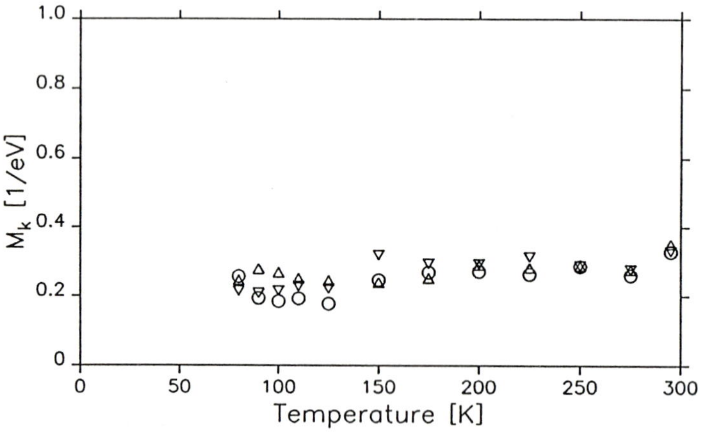

Fig.3: *M_K vs. temperature of Tl(2) for sample 1* (△), sample 2 (▽) and sample 3 (○)

5. Conclusion

The ^{205}Tl NMR of Tl(2) shows similar behavior as ^{17}O and ^{89}Y NMR in YBCO. The temperature dependence of the line shift above T_c is due to the paramagnetic susceptibility and is correlated to the total hole concentration in the CuO_2-layers which we have varied in our experiments by removing oxygen from the sample. M_K is a measure of energy scale for the quasiparticles in the CuO_2-layer [7].

References

[1] N. Winzek, F. Hentsch, M. Mehring, Hj. Mattausch, R. Kremer and A. Simon, *Physica* **C 168** (1990) 327

[2] F. Hentsch, N. Winzek, M. Mehring, Hj. Mattausch and A. Simon, *Physica* **C 165** (1990) 485

[3] J. C. Jol, D. Reefman, H. B. Brom, T. Zetterer, D. Hahn, H. H. Otto and K. F. Renk, *Physica* **C 175** (1991) 12

[4] H. Alloul, T. Ohno and P. Mendels, *Phys. Rev. Lett.* **63** (1989) 1700

[5] K. Ishida, Y. Kitaoka, G. Zheng and K. Asayama, *J. Phys. Soc. Jpn.* **60** (1991) 3516

[6] M. Mehring, to be published in *J. Appl. Magn. Res.*

[7] M. Mehring, in Extended Abstracts of *10th Specialized Colloque AMPERE on NMR/NQR in High - T_c Superconductors Zürich*, August 26 - 30, 1991, 26

Effects of Ni to Cu Substitution in La_2CuO_4 from ^{139}La NQR and Relaxation

A. Rigamonti[1], *J. Choisnet*[2], *M. Corti*[1], *K.O. Khutsishvili*[3], and *T. Rega*[4]

[1]Department of Physics "A. Volta", Sezione INFN and Unita INFM, Via Bassi n. 6, Pavia, Italy
[2]Laboratoire de Cristallochimie, Université d'Orleans, France
[3]State University, Tbilisi, Georgia
[4]ISRIM, Terni, Italy

Abstract. ^{139}La NQR and relaxation measurements in $La_2Cu_{1-x}Ni_xO_4$ for x ranging from zero to one aimed at learning about the effects on the spin excitation and correlation properties of the substitution of Cu^{2+} S=1/2 ions by Ni^{2+} S=1, are presented. The hyperfine magnetic fields and the electric field gradients at the Lantanum site are evaluated and the x dependence of the Neel temperature is obtained, for x up to 0.2. From the NQR relaxation rate driven by the spin dynamics it is shown how the substitution changes the spin fluctuations spectrum, while the hyperfine field and the electric field gradient remain practically the same. These effects are discussed in terms of the role of the S=1 Ni spin in affecting the correlation length with the consequence of inducing spin excitations in the low frequency range.

1. Introduction

In the attempt to elucidate the mechanisms of high T_c superconductivity a line of investigation is to study the effects of substitutions, by incorporating diamagnetic or magnetic ions into the magnetic lattice of the Cu^{2+} spins. A fruitful tool to investigate the magnetic properties in cuprates has been NQR-NMR spectra and relaxation. The spectra yield information on the electric field gradients (EFG) and on the hyperfine magnetic fields, while the relaxation rates lead to the correlated spin dynamics. In this paper we present ^{139}La NQR spectra and relaxation measurements in $La_2Cu_{1-x}Ni_xO_4$, for x ranging from zero to one and in the temperature range 4-350 K, aimed at learning about the Cu^{2+} magnetic correlation and fluctuations upon substitution of S=1 Ni^{2+} ions for S=1/2 Cu^{2+}.

2. Experimental Results

Previous NQR and relaxation measurements in La_2CuO_4 and in Sr- doped La_2CuO_4 around the Neel temperature T_N yielded information on the hyperfine field and on the role of the charge defects on the spin dynamics /1/. In La_2NiO_{4-y} La NQR spectra were detected /2/ over a wide frequency range, with a structure dependent on the oxygen stoichiometry. A quadrupole frequency ν_Q ranging from 1.8 MHz (for y=0.022) to 2.7 MHz (for y>0.06) was deduced, while the internal magnetic field at the La site was estimated H_i=19.3 and 17.8 kGauss, respectively. A quantitative explanation for the strong differences with respect to La_2CuO_4 (where ν_Q =6.4 MHz and H_i=1kGauss) was not given.

The ^{139}La NQR lines in $La_2Cu_{1-x}Ni_xO_4$ have been recorded mostly from the envelope of the echo signals. In Fig.1 the resonance frequencies for the (5/2-7/2) line are shown. For x<0.05 and T<100 the lines corresponding to the (1/2-3/2) transitions were observable and allowed an estimate of the splitting due to H_i more precise with respect to the (5/2-7/2) line. For x=0.01 and x=0.02 the splittings confirm that H_i is practically the same as for x=0. For T>100 K and for x> 0.05 the (1/2-3/2) lines were not observable. Above that temperature and for x=0.2 only the frequency correspondent to the center of the (5/2-7/2) line

Springer Series in Solid-State Sciences, Vol. 113 **Electronic Properties of High-T_c Superconductors**
Editors: H. Kuzmany, M. Mehring, J. Fink

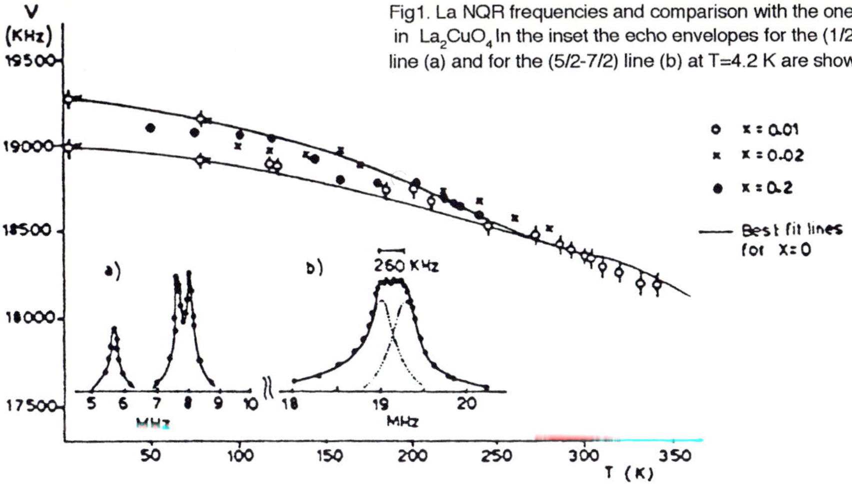

Fig1. La NQR frequencies and comparison with the ones in La_2CuO_4 In the inset the echo envelopes for the (1/2-3/2) line (a) and for the (5/2-7/2) line (b) at T=4.2 K are shown.

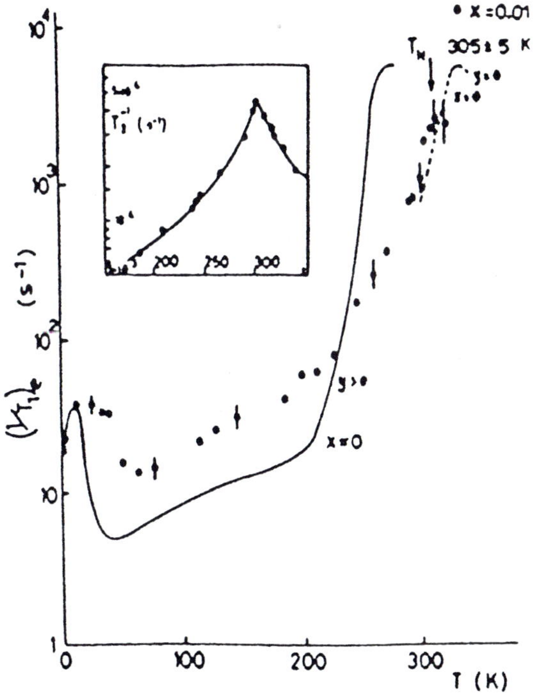

Fig.2 Effective relaxation rate for x=0.01 and comparison with the one in La_2CuO_4. In the inset the spin-spin relaxation rate is reported.

is reported in Fig. 1 .For x>0.5 the NQR frequency falls around 19.8 MHz , with a marked line broadening. Above 200 K the signal was practically undetectable, for x>0.5.

The ^{139}La NQR relaxation rates have been estimated from the recovery of the echo signal following the saturation of the (5/2-7/2) line.In Fig.2 the relaxation rate for the sample at x=0.01 is shown.Since one can expect that the magnetic and the quadrupolar relaxation mechanisms are both present, the data refer to the inverse time at which the recovery plot reduces to 1/e. For magnetic relaxation one has $(T_1)_e^{-1} = 21\ W_m$, while for the quadrupole

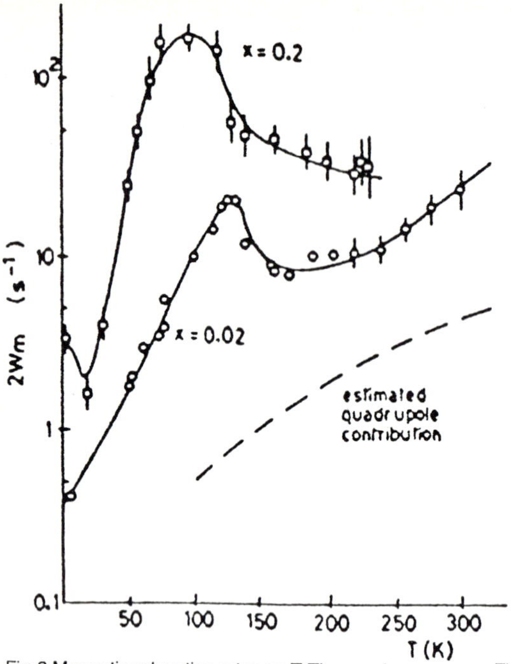

Fig.3 Magnetic relaxation rates vs T.The quadrupolar contribution (dotted line) has been estimated as in Ref. 1

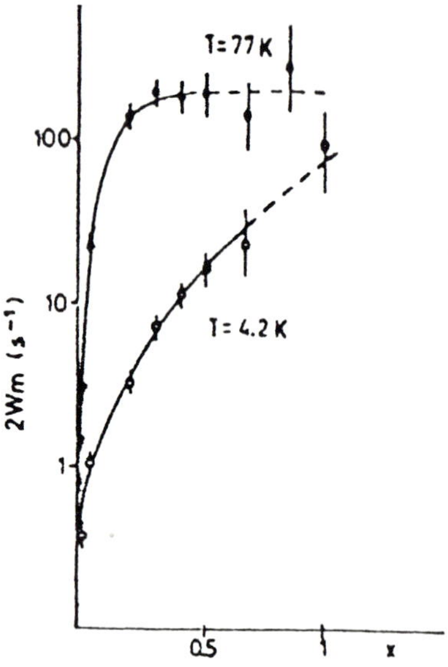

Fig. 4 X-dependence of the magnetic relaxation rate

mechanism $(T_1)_e^{-1} = 3.3\,W_q$, W_m and W_q being the correspondent relaxation transition probabilities.For $T < 150$ K in the sample at $x < 0.02$ and over all the explored temperature range for the samples at larger x, the magnetic relaxation mechanism is dominant.In Figure 3 the temperature behavior of $2W_m$ is shown for x=0.02 and x=0.2.In Figure 4 the x dependence of the magnetic relaxation rate at 4.2 K and at 77 K is reported.

3. Analysis of the Data and Discussion

For $x \lesssim 0.2$ the effect of the substitution is mainly to cause a distribution of EFG's without significative modification of ν_Q,which appears close to the one in pure La_2CuO_4 .This conclusion is consistent with the findings for x=0.15 at 1.3 K /3/.Also H_i appears slightly affected by the Ni to Cu substitution. For $x > 0.3$ the broadening of the lines,due to the distribution of EFG, and possibly of H_i ,prevents reliable estimates. The large broadening appears to persist also for $x \rightarrow 1$ and one should conclude that ν_Q is around the value in La_2CuO_4 also for large Ni contents. The discrepancy with the results for La_2NiO_{4-y} /2/could be due to different oxygen stoichiometry, with the related effects on T_N and H_i. To discuss the behavior of the relaxation rates we will mostly refer to a range of x where our results indicate that the EFG's and H_i are close to the values in La_2CuO_4.

The temperature at which the maximum in the relaxation rates is observed (Fig.s 2 and 3) marks the transition to the antiferromagnetic (AF) phase.From our results the quantity $A = (-1/T_N)(dT_N/dx)$ for $x \rightarrow 0$, which can be taken as a measure of the effect of doping with the "anomalous" spin over the lattice of the Cu^{2+},is about 5, a value close to the one in Zn-doped La_2CuO_4 /4/.

For the ^{139}La NQR magnetic mechanism the relaxation rate can be written /1/

$$2W_m = \gamma^2 \Sigma_q H_q^2 : S_q^2 / \Gamma_q \quad , \tag{1}$$

where H_q is the Fourier transform of the lattice functions (dipolar or transferred hyperfine interactions) relating the field **h**(t) at the La site to the Cu^{2+} spin **S** and S_q^2 is the mean square amplitude of the collective fluctuations measured at $\omega=\omega_Q$, while Γ_q is its decay rate. The form factor H_q in Eq.1 usually can be expanded around the value correspondent to the critical wavevector $\mathbf{q}=\mathbf{q}_{AF}$ describing the magnetic ordered lattice below T_N and Eq. 1) can be rewritten

$$2W_m = \gamma^2 H_i^2 \Sigma_q S_q^2 / \Gamma_q \qquad \text{with } H_i = 1 \text{ k Gauss} \quad . \tag{2}$$

In conventional paramagnets S_q^2 and Γ_q can be related to the magnetic correlation length ξ and to the exchange frequency by resorting to scale arguments. Thus the temperature dependence of ξ can be extracted and ,in general, for $T \gg T_N$, $\xi(T)$ follows the behavior theoretically expected for 2D Heisenberg models, including a reduction from quantum fluctuations . For T close to to T_N a crossover in the spin and/or in the lattice dimensions drives the transition to the AF state.

In the presence of charge defects, as in $La_{2-x}Sr_xCuO_4$, relevant modifications have been shown to occur /1,5/: the effective correlation length is the average distance among defects; the spin fluctuations are no longer thermally driven by a function simply related to $\xi(T)$; the q-dependence of S_q^2 and Γ_q is also unusual. In particular Γ_q appear to decrease, as indicated by the enhancement of the NQR relaxation rate , while the static correlation length , as observed from neutron, stays constant / 6 /.The spectrum of the spin excitations is also drastically different from the one in conventional AF's. Infact, for $T \ll T_N$ where only the magnon spectrum of quasi-resonant character should be present, in doped cuprates one detects a strong low- frequency component of diffusive type, hardly detectable from neutron scattering.

The behavior of W_m can be discussed in the light of the above mentioned aspects. For a probe in the rf range the most effective component should be the one at the lowest frequency and one can expect this being Γ_{SF} corresponding to $\mathbf{q}=\mathbf{q}_{AF}$ .The small value of ξ and its weak temperature dependence imply that $\Gamma_q = \Gamma_{SF}$ and since $\Sigma_q S_q^2$ is the effective spin (measured at $\omega=\omega_Q$) we write Eq. 2) in the form

$$2W_m = \gamma^2 H_i^2 S_{eff}^2 / \Gamma_{SF} \quad . \tag{3}$$

It should be noted that when a gap is opened in the spin fluctuation spectrum, then S_{eff} is decreased.In our case ,for small x,S_{eff} should not change much.

By using Eq. 3 and the data reported in Fig. 4, one can extract the x dependence of Γ_{SF} (see Fig. 5). The dramatic decrease of Γ_{SF} with x corresponds to the increase of the low-frequency spectral density $J(\omega \to 0)$. While in the case of x=0, in the AF phase the relaxation mechanism is mostly due to magnons scattering and $J(\omega \to 0)$ is negligible, when Ni substitutes Cu we derive

$$J(\omega \to 0) = J^o e^{x/x^*} \qquad \text{for } x<0.1, \tag{4}$$

with $x^* = 1.5\ 10^{-2}$ and $J^o \simeq 10^{-13}\ \mathrm{rad}^{-1}\ \mathrm{s}$. Equivalently, in terms of $A = -\Gamma^{-1}_{SF}(d\Gamma_{SF}/dx)$, one obtains the value $A = 50 \mp 5$, much larger than the correspondent factor for $T_N(x)$.
Further work on the charge and spin substitutional effects in AF's and in superconducting systems is under way.

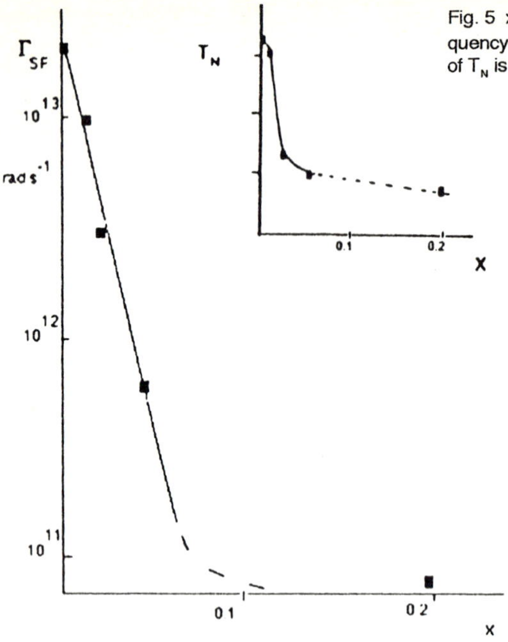

Fig. 5 x-dependence of the spin-fluctuaton fre - quency at T=77 K. In the inset the x-dependence of T_N is shown.

Acknowledgments Fruitful discussions with F. Borsa and with J. Murgich are gratefully acknowledged. Thanks are due to M. Acquarone for sharing his thorough work on the substitutional effects in high T_C superconductors.The research has been carried out with the support by National Research Council of Italy (CNR) under the "Progetto Finalizzato Superconductive and Cryogenic Technologies"

References

1) F.Borsa,M.Corti,T.Rega and A. Rigamonti,Nuovo Cimento 11, 1785 (1989); A. Rigamonti, F.Borsa,M.Corti,J.Ziolo and F. Waldner,in "Early and Recent Aspects of Superconductivity" Eds. J.G. Bednorz and K.A. Muller,(Springer Verlag 1990) p.441

2)S.Wada,T.Kobayashi,M.Kaburagi,K.Shibutani and R.Ogawa, J.Phys.Soc.Japan 58,2658 (1989); ----Physica B 165,1313 (1990)

3)Z.Tan,J.I.Budnick,Y.D.Zhang and B.Chamberland, Physica C 156,137 (1988)

4)R.L. Lichti,C.Boekema,J.C.Lam,D.W.Cooke,S.F.J.Cox,S.T.Ting and J.E.Crow, Physica C 180,358 (1991)

5)J.H. Cho,F.Borsa,D.C. Johnston and D.R.Torgeson, to be published

6)B.Keimer,R.J.Birgenau,A.Cassanho,Y.Endoh,R.W.Erwin,M.AKastner and G.Shirane Phys.Rev.Lett. 67,1930 (1991)

^{1}H-NMR in $YBa_2Cu_3O_{7-\delta}H_x$

J. Groß and M. Mehring

II. Physikalisches Institut, Universität Stuttgart,
Pfaffenwaldring 57, W-7000 Stuttgart 80, Fed. Rep. of Germany

1. Abstract

We report on ^{1}H-NMR experiments on protonated samples of $YBa_2Cu_3O_{7-\delta}$. Our spectra show a seperation of the sample into an antiferromagnetic (afm) phase with high ^{1}H-concentration and a metallic resp. superconducting (sc) phase with a low ^{1}H-concentration. Cooling experiments suggest that the phase separation already takes place during the protonation process. Investigation of ^{1}H-NMR signals in our unprotonated samples show a high proton background (about 0.25 ^{1}H's per unit cell) already present in the as-received starting materials (commercially available). Comparison of the linewidth of the afm spectra with model calculations lead us to the conclusion that the protons in the afm phase are located within 1.5 Å above or below the Cu-chain layer.

2. Introduction

^{1}H-NMR-experiments have been performed on our homebuilt 330 MHz spectrometer. Subspectra have been recorded at different carrier frequencies to cover the large spectral range of our signals. The spectra presented here are a superposition of many subspectra, obtained by spin-echo spectroscopy including Fourier-transform. Phasing of the individual subspectra has been carried out with great care.

Both an antiferromagnetically ordered phase and a superconducting phase give rise to characteristic NMR-lineshapes. Very simple theories for either case are presented below.

Protons located in the antiferromagnetic (afm) or metallic / superconducting (sc) phase show pronounced differences in the longitudinal and transverse relaxation times. Therefore spectra of either part can be separated by choosing appropriate parameters of the pulse-echo-experiment.

3. Superconducting state - vortex lattice

High-T_c superconductors (HTSC) are known to be of extreme type II. In the superconducting state a (Abrikosov) vortex lattice is formed. This leads to a distribution of local fields, which is in case of extreme type II superconductors well described by the London-theory, where the penetration depth λ is the central parameter determining the distribution of local fields. As HTSC are highly anisotropic, the Abrikosov lattice is not regular triangular as in the isotropic case, but sheared triangular. The corresponding London-theory involves an anisotropic penetration depth, the principal components being λ_{ab} (current in the plane) and λ_c (current perpendicular to the plane) [1]. The distribution of local magnetic fields can be computed as a solution of this anisotropic London theory. The orientational angle θ between the crystal unique axis and the external field enters the calculation as a parameter. To obtain an estimate for the NMR lineshape in a powder

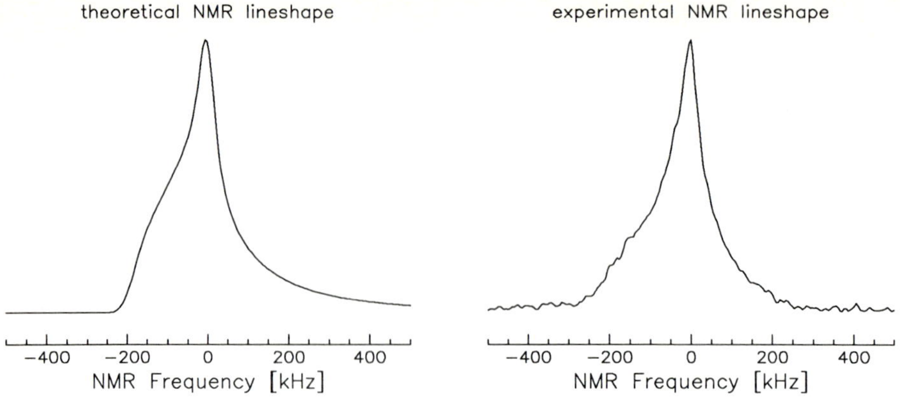

Fig. 1: *Comparison of theoretical and experimental lineshape in the superconducting state. The theoretical lineshape is plotted for* $\lambda_{ab} = 135\,\mathrm{nm}$ *and* $\lambda_c = 660\,\mathrm{nm}$. *Experimental data have been taken at 40 K*

sample, the above calculation was carried out for many θ's with the results summed up to give a powder average. Fig.1 compares this theoretical lineshape with an experimental spectrum on $YBa_2Cu_3O_{6.95}H_{0.6}$.

The ratio λ_c/λ_{ab} corresponds to the square root of the anisotropy parameter, which can be determined fairly accurate from torque magnetization measurements [2], therefore there is only one "unknown" component of λ to be measured. As the NMR linewidth depends very sensitively on λ (the linewidth varies as λ^{-2}), NMR in principle provides a precise way to measure λ. However, as the proton concentration in the sample increases, the density of superconducting carriers n_s decreases and therefore λ increases, as $\lambda^{-2} \sim n_s$ (see also e.g [3]). In order to obtain values for the unprotonated $YBa_2Cu_3O_7$ material, one must examine the linewidth for vanishing ^1H concentration. As already mentioned, our investigations so far suffered from the high protonic background in our samples. We will therefore not quote absolute values for λ.

4. Antiferromagnetic state - sum of localized magnetic moments

Although the detailed magnetic structure of the afm phase is known to be highly complex, especially in high magnetic fields (see e.g. Ref.[4]) , we have made a very simple approximation, which nevertheless should not be too far off as long as

- there is a unique place for protons in the unit cell,
- the afm order of the Cu(2) spins is not affected by the external field and
- the interaction between the proton nuclear spin and the Cu(2) electron spin is predominantly magnetic dipole interaction.

In this case, at any position in the unit cell the sum of all dipolar fields of the Cu(2) magnetic moments can be calculated. This field adds to the external field to give the "true" local field.

In the case of powder samples again a powder average has to be performed, because the additional dipolar sum field $\vec{B}_{dip}$ is fixed with the crystal lattice. For the above mentioned case of undisturbed afm order the resulting lineshape turns out to be of rectangular shape as displayed in Fig. 2.

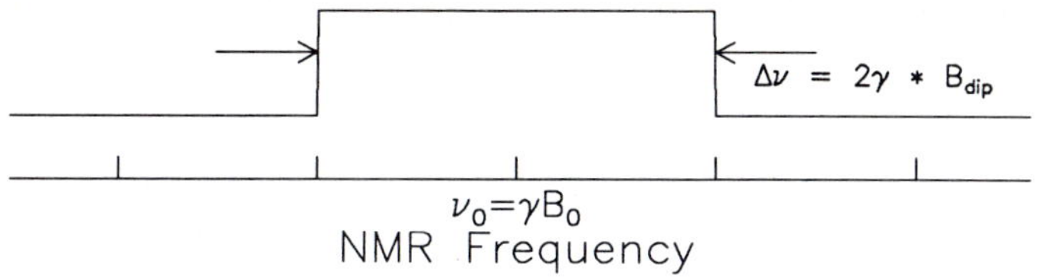

Fig. 2: *Theoretical NMR-powder-spectrum for an undisturbed antiferromagnet with pure dipolar interaction*

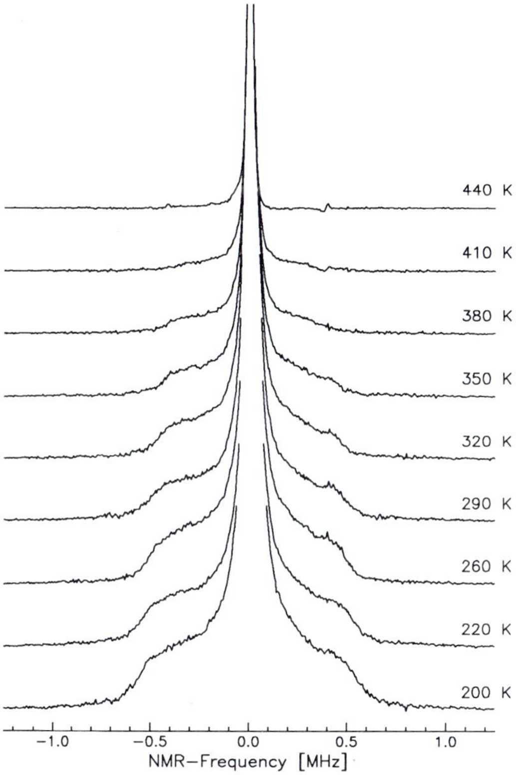

Fig. 3: *NMR spectra of the antiferromagnetic phase at high temperatures. Note the vanishing of the broad afm spectra at* $\approx 400\,K$

The above considerations, however, are only valid in the case of a static antiferromagnet with infinite correlation length. The real physical situation in our samples is supposed to differ from this idealized situation in space (finite correlation length) as well as in time (finite correlation time for each electron spin, dependent on temperature), therefore giving rise to dynamical line-narrowing effects, which increase with increasing temperature. This can be seen in Figure 3, where spectra of $YBa_2Cu_3O_{6.95}H_{0.8}$ are plotted for various temperatures up to the Neel-temperature of the afm compound $YBa_2Cu_3O_6$.

As the spectra show, at least part of the sample probes an afm order with the same Neel-temperature as $YBCO_6$, although the starting material was $YBCO_7$. Therefore protonation appears to be able to change the electronic structure of the $YBCO_7$ compound to that of the $YBCO_6$ compound.

5. Antiferromagnetic field strength at the ^1H location

As already mentioned, the width of the rectangular spectrum in the afm state contains information on the sum-field of the Cu(2) magnetic dipoles at the proton site. As is known from neutron scattering results [5] one Cu(2) spin posesses a moment of $\approx 0.65\mu_B$. We have calculated the dipolar sum-field for an antiferromagnetically ordered arrangement of Cu(2) spins at any site in the unit cell and have compared the results with the measured field of $\sim$ 120 G. It turned out, that for all places except for the close vicinity to the CuO-chain layer, the resulting afm sum-fields are much larger than our experimental values.

6. Phase separation - slow and fast cooling

One of our pertinent questions was, how the separation into a proton rich afm and a proton poor sc phase takes place. This phenomenon has also been observed in low doped samples of La(Sr)CuO as described in [6] and could be attributed to diffusive motion of protons and / or large ferromagnetic clusters in the sample. If this would be the case in our samples, there should be a marked dependence of our spectra on the cooling rate as reported by Kremer et al.[6]. We took spectra at liquid nitrogen temperature with a slow cooling rate of several hours from room temperature and fast coooling in a few seconds. Our spectra showed no difference. Therefore we conclude, that in our samples the separation into two different phases already takes place at room temperature or above and is established already during the protonation process.

The financial support by the Bundesministerium für Forschung und Technologie is gratefully acknowledged.

References

[1] S. L. Thieman et al. *Phys. Rev.* **B 39** 11409, (1989)
[2] D. E. Farrell et al. *Phys. Rev. Lett.* **61** 2805, (1988)
[3] H. Glückler at al. *Europhys. Lett.* **15** 355, (1991)
[4] T.Thio et al. *Phys. Rev.* **B 41** 231, (1990)
[5] J. M. Tranquada et al. *Phys. Rev.* **B 38** 2477, (1988)
[6] R. .K. Kremer et al. *Z. Phys.* **B 86** 319,, (1992)

Probing the Flux Distribution of Thin Films by Surface Spin Probes

O. Dobbert[1], *M. Rübsam*[1], *J. Geerk*[2], *and K.-P. Dinse*[1]

[1]Physics Institute, University Dortmund, P.O. Box 500 500, W-4600 Dortmund 50, Fed. Rep. of Germany

[2]Kernforschungszentrum Karlsruhe, Institut für Nukleare Festkörperphysik, Postfach 3640, W-7500 Karlsruhe, Fed. Rep. of Germany

Abstract. By evaluating EPR line narrowing for a spin probe with fast spin diffusion, evidence for a dominant contribution of magnetic field gradients was found for a GdBCO thin film. A fit leads to a typical structure d = 3 μm, much larger than the lattice constant of the ideal vortex state.

1. Introduction

The variance of the magnetic field distribution in the mixed state of a type II superconductor can only be related to the penetration depth λ if an ideal flux lattice is realized in the sample. By well known bulk methods like μSR[1–3] and NMR[4], results for λ(t) have been derived. Obviously it would be of interest to probe the local field variation with increased spectral resolution and in addition to derive a method which can also probe the anticipated flux lattice of thin film samples. The first aim can be reached by using paramagnetic spins as probes for the surface field variation, as suggested by Rakvin et al.[5]. In addition, EPR as surface method gives the possibility to vary the distance to the sample to search for additional field inhomogeneities, as was shown by Bontemps et al.[6] for a ceramic sample of YBCO. In this case, the grain stucture was found to be responsible for the spatial distribution of the field inhomogeneities at the surface.

We present here a new method which allows us to investigate quantitativly a spatial flux distribution at the surface of thin films. As an advantage of the EPR technique one is not restricted to the use of immobile spin probes as in μSR and NMR but one can also use systems with well defined spatial diffusion characteristics. For instance, organic 1-dimensional conductors are known[7] to exhibit extremely fast spin diffusion of up to D = 1 cm^2/s , thus probing "macroscopic" distances on the length scale of several hundred vortex lattice constants (d ≈ 70 nm at .3 T) on the time scale of a few μs, defined by the line width of the EPR line. It is the purpose of this contribution to give evidence for the lenght scale of the local field variation for epitactic GdBCO thin films using a surface spin probe with temperature-controlled fast spin diffusion.

2. Method and Materials

The EPR data were taken with a home-built pulsed EPR machine[8] . The GdBCO film was grown on $LaAlO_3$. A thin crystal of the $(Perylenyl)_2X$ charge transfer complex of size 10x500 x2000 μm^3 was attached to the film surface, so that the diffusion of the electrons take place along one direction in the a,b-plane.

3. Results and Discussion

In a simple model the field variation along one dimension due to the Abrikosov flux lattice or any other structural inhomogeneity is approximated by a cosine function

$$h(z) = h_0 \cos (2\pi z/d), \qquad (1)$$

where d denotes the typical scale length of the field variation. The diffusion of the electrons along the z-axis is described by the Green's function

$$G(z,t) = \frac{1}{(4\pi D t)^{1/2}} \cdot \exp(-z^2 / 4\pi D t) \qquad (2)$$

with D the diffusion constant of the electrons. Due to dephasing the number of the electrons involved in the Echo-experiment decreases exponentially with T_2, the spin dephasing time. The time average of the Green's function with exponential weighting leads to

$$\langle G(z,t) \rangle = \int_0^\infty G(z,t) \cdot \exp(-t/T_2)\, dt$$

$$= \frac{1}{2\sqrt{D T_2}} \cdot \exp(-z/\sqrt{D T_2}) \cdot \qquad (3)$$

The precession frequencies ω_i of the electrons are characterized by the fields at the surface of the Gd-film if the thickness of the attached crystal is comparabel to the modulation length. The variance σ of the resulting resonance frequencies in the static limit is reduced by the 1-dimensional diffusion. Its value is calculated as

$$\langle \Delta\omega^2 \rangle^{1/2} = \sigma^{1/2} \cdot \frac{d}{[d^2 + 4\pi^2 D(T)\ T_2(T)]^{1/2}} \qquad (4)$$

when assuming a homogeneous distribution of spins at the time of the microwave pulse. The static value is taken as proportional to $(1-(T/T_c)^4)^2$.

The linewidth of the 1-d charge transfer complex is measured attached to the Gd film as well as on a diamagnetic sample holder. Fig. 1 shows the flux distribution-induced linewidth, which

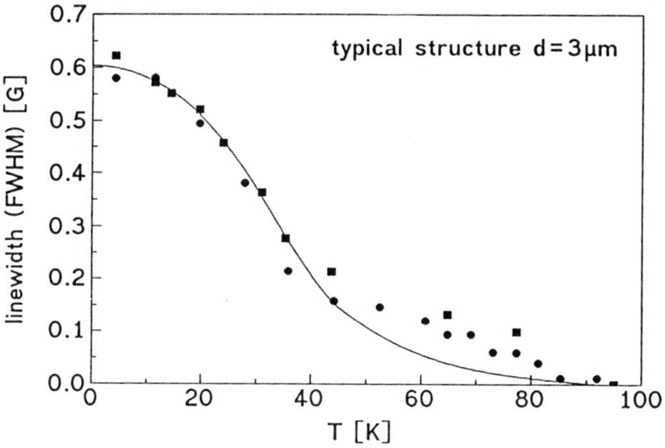

Figure 1
Temperature dependence of the flux distribution-induced linewidth of the 1-d conductor $(Perylenyl)_2X$ on a GdBCO film

is obtained after a quadratic deconvolution of the data. In contrast to the $(1-t^4)$ behaviour expected for the static limit, the deconvoluted line broadening shows a steep increase at 40 K. This can be explained when considering that at this temperature the mean displacement of spins is comparable to the characteristic length d of the spatially modulated flux. The knowledge of the diffusion constant is a prerequisit for the fit of the data. Its temperature dependence was determined via pulsed EPR measuring echoes in a field gradient. The existence of the lower limit is due to intra-chain hopping of the electrons. For the fit in fig. 1 the temperature dependence is approximated by the function

$$D(T)=1.5/(\exp\{(80-T/K)/8\}+1)+0.0024\ \mathrm{cm}^2/\mathrm{s} \qquad (5)$$

The temperature dependence of $T_2(T)$ is revealed by measuring the linewidth of Pe_2 on a diamagnetic sample holder. The solid line showes a fit with eq. 4 . The best fit leads to a typical modulation wavelength d = 3 μm, much larger than the ideal flux lattice constant of 0.07 μm at 0.3 T. We therefore conclude that the dominant contribution of the field inhomogeneity even under field-cooled conditions is not due to the vortex lattice for this system but is tentatively attributed to growth inhomogeneities of the film. Its not surprising that we could not record a noticeable effect of the vortex lattice. Because of the finite thickness Δ of the crystal, the flux inhomogeneity which decays exponentially on a length scale of the order d, is averaged accordingly. Therefore the vortex-induced contribution to σ is unobservable because $\Delta \gg 70$ nm, and the crystal acts like a filter discriminating against short modulation lengths.

In summary, the experiments presented here are an analogon to the flux melting experiments in Bi-samples with μSR[9]. In our case the spin is mobile and the flux lattice is localized, in the latter case it is vice versa.

Acknowledgement

This work is supported by the Bundesministerium für Forschung und Technologie under Contract No. 13N5724 5. The $(Pe)_2X$ sample was kindly provided by D. Schweitzer (Stuttgart).

References

1. D.R. Harshman et al., Phys. Rev. B36 (1987) 2386
2. Y.J. Uemura et al., Phys. Rev. B39 (1988) 909
3. B. Pümpin et al., Phys. Rev. B42 (1990) 8019
4. M. Mehring, F. Hentsch, H. Mattausch, and A. Simon, Z. Phys. B77 (1989) 355
5. B. Rakvin, M. Pozek, and A. Dulcic, Solid State Commun. 72 (1989) 199
6. N. Bontemps, D. Davidov, P. Monod and R. Even, Phys. Rev. B43 (1991) 11512
7. O. Dobbert, T. Prisner, K.P. Dinse, D. Schweitzer, and H.J. Keller, Solid State Commun. 61 (1987) 499
8. G. Kroll, M. Plüschau, K.P. Dinse, and H. van Willigen, J. Chem.Phys. 93 (1990) 8709
9. D. R. Harshman, R. N. Kleiman, M. Inui, G. P. Espinosa, D. B. Mitzi, A. Kapitulnik, T. Pfiz, and D. Ll. Williams, Phys. Rev. Lett. 67 (1991) 3152

Part VI

Optical Spectroscopy, Raman Scattering

Possible Origins of the Continuum in the Cu-O Plane-Polarized Raman Spectra of Copper-Oxide Superconductors

D. Reznik[1], *S.L. Cooper*[1], *M.V. Klein*[1], *W.C. Lee*[1], *D.M. Ginsberg*[1], *and S.-W. Cheong*[2]

[1]Science and Technology Center for Superconductivity, Department of Physics, University of Illinois, Urbana, IL 61801, USA

[2]AT&T Bell Laboratories, Murray Hill, NJ 07974, USA

Abstract. We found strong evidence against scattering by conduction electrons as an origin of the plane-polarized continua in copper oxides: in 1-2-3 and in 2-1-4 materials the a-axis polarized continuum does not change much with doping (a continuum in the insulating phases is just as strong as in the superconductors), though the electronic states do, and a-b anisotropy is greater in the T_c=66K than in the T_c=90K YBCO single crystals, though there should be more chain states in the higher T_c crystals. Hot luminescence or scattering of electrons into localized states are possible alternatives to the conduction electron picture. We also report anomalous temperature dependence of the insulating phase continuum.

1. Introduction

The Cu-O plane-polarized Raman scattering continuum observed in high temperature superconductors is one of the anomalous properties of the normal state of these materials and has been the focus of theoretical and experimental research. [1-8] Several theories have been proposed recently to explain the properties of the continuum. [5-8] We studied the doping, polarization, temperature, and laser frequency dependence of the continuum in YBCO to narrow down possible microscopic origins of the continuum.

2. Experimental

The sample preparation is described elsewhere. [9] Measurements at 300K were made with the sample in air. Laser power was 15mW; spot size ~ 40 μm. Measurements reported in section 4 were made with a sample in an optical helium cryostat; laser spot size was ~ 80 μm. Spectra were measured with a Spex "Triplemate" Raman Spectrometer equipped with a 516X516 CCD Camera detector. Chromatic aberration did not cause intensity loss from defocusing at large frequency shifts because we underfilled the entrance slit of the spectrometer with the laser spot image.

Spectra were corrected for the frequency-dependent efficiency of the spectrometer and detector as well as for the optical absorption, transmission and refraction at the sample-air interface. The optical constants were obtained from polarized IR reflectivity and ellipsometry measurements. [10] Intensity in all the figures is proportional to the energy cross section ($d\sigma/d\omega$) per unit volume.

The reason for the differences between the spectra presented in this paper and the previously published ones is that we neglected to make a correction for the sample and polarization dependence of the refractive index in our previous publications. [11,12] These differences do not change the qualitative picture discussed in Ref. 11, 12.

3. Room temperature results

The laser wavelength dependences of the XX and YY continua in $YBa_2Cu_3O_7$ are shown in Fig. 1. [Notation: XY means that incident photons are polarized along X, scattered along Y; X is parallel to the a-axis, Y is the b-axis (Cu-O chain)]. Assignments of the phonon peaks have been made elsewhere. [13] The XX and YY continua are nearly flat at the 4579Å incident laser wavelength, and decrease with Raman shift at the longer laser wavelengths.

XX, YY, and XY Raman spectra of untwinned $YBa_2Cu_3O_X$ single crystals were compared at different x at the 4579Å laser wavelength. Fig. 2 shows the spectra of an "as grown" insulating single crystal, an untwinned T_c=66K single crystal and an untwinned T_c=90K single crystal. The results have been confirmed on other samples.

In addition to the two-magnon scattering, [1,4] a strong background continuum extending above 10000 cm^{-1} was also present in the insulating sample (also see Ref. 20). The two magnon scattering disappears with doping, but the continuum in XX geometry remains unchanged. The X-Y anisotropy is significantly greater in the oxygen deficient (T_c=66K) sample than in the fully oxygenated (T_c=90K) sample.

It is difficult to identify the microscopic origin the continuum because the scattering vertex is not known. The spectral lineshape clearly does not fit any conventional electron-hole scattering models. [14] However, the experimental data can be fit reasonably well, if the imaginary part of the electron self energy $\Sigma(q,\omega)$ is assumed to vary linearly with ω. [3,6]. Since a similar frequency dependence of $Im\Sigma(q,\omega)$ has also been observed in the IR conductivity [10,15,18], many theories of the Raman continuum assume that it is caused by the scattering by the conduction electrons, seen by infrared (IR) conductivity measurements. [5-8] If so, the doping and polarization dependence of the continuum and the IR conductivity should be similar.

However, this is not the case. The XX room temperature continuum in YBCO as well as in Ce doped T' materials [16] and in $La_{2-x}Sr_xCuO_4$ [17, Fig. 2] does not change much with doping, but the IR conductivity has a strong doping dependence. [10,15,18] Chain IR conductivity in YBCO is greater in T_c=90K samples than in the T_c=66K samples, [10,15] but the opposite is true for the Raman continuum.

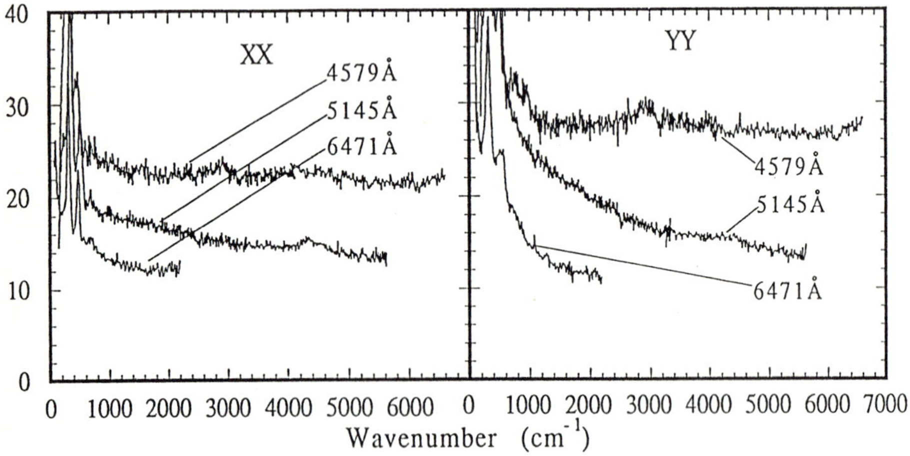

1. Raman continuum in $YBa_2Cu_3O_7$ in XX and YY geometry at different laser wavelengths. Resolution ~ 50 cm^{-1}. Intensity units are the same.

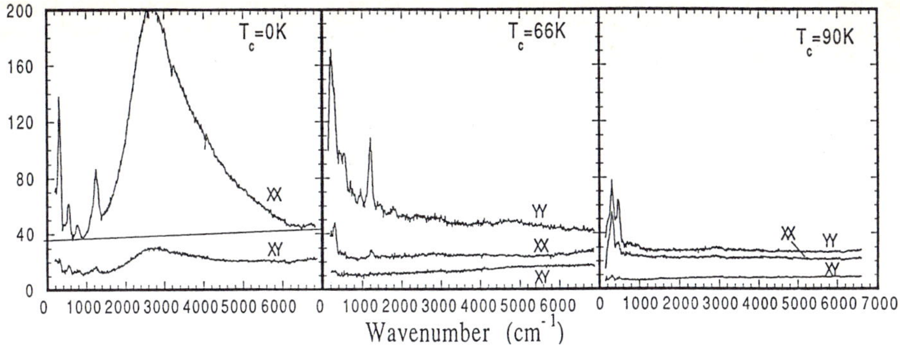

2. The continuum in the insulating, T_c=66K and T_c=90K single crystals. Resolution ~ 50 cm^{-1}. Intensity units for are the same as in Fig. 1. The horizontal line in the T_c=0K graph is a guide for the eye representing the background continuum.

Even if the Raman spectra reveal an electronic channel of a different symmetry than that of the IR spectra [14], we should still see zero scattering below the charge transfer gap in the insulators, and an increase in XX and YY scattering as the carrier concentration increases with doping. The only way to reconcile the conduction electron picture with the experimental results is to assume that in the 1-2-3 as well as in the 2-1-4 systems the doping variation of the scattering vertex accounts for all the experimentally observed inconsistencies, which is an unlikely coincidence.

Though the microscopic mechanism is far from clear, possible alternatives to the conduction electron picture as a cause of the bulk of the intensity of the plane-polarized continuum (to be investigated further) are summarized below.

Localized states have been observed in the IR conductivity spectra of the undoped samples as a weak (in comparison with the free electron conductivity) rising background at the energies below the charge transfer gap. If light couples strongly to these states during scattering and not to the conduction electrons, they could be responsible for the continuum. This mechanism is consistent with a stronger chain continuum in the T_c=66K than in the T_c=90K YBCO samples, because oxygen vacancies in the oxygen deficient samples could create localized states. If these states are intrinsic to the copper oxygen planes as well as to the chains, they might not be strongly affected by doping. However, the impurity IR conductivity is a factor of two stronger in the undoped YBCO than in Sm_2CuO_4 between 3000 and 10000 cm^{-1}, [19] but the Raman continuum has the same intensity in the same energy region [20], which appears to be inconsistent with the model.

Hot luminescence is very similar to resonant Raman scattering. During both processes an electron absorbs an incident photon and gets excited into an unoccupied band, where it exchanges energy with some excitations and then relaxes to the ground state emitting the scattered photon before reaching the bottom of the band. The difference is that during resonant Raman scattering the excitations that scatter the electron are well defined (e.g. an electron-hole pair, a phonon, two phonons, etc.) but during hot luminescence they are impossible to identify. Unlike resonant Raman scattering hot luminescence is not expected to preserve a well defined lineshape when the laser energy is changed and its temperature dependence is not expected to follow the Bose factor, which is consistent with experimental results (see Fig. 3, Ref. 3).

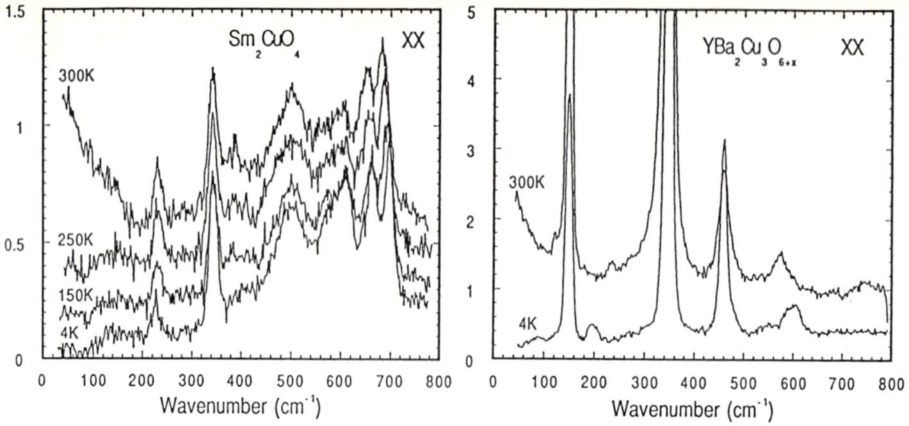

3. Raman spectra of Sm_2CuO_4 and $YBa_2Cu_3O_{6.1}$. Intensity units are the same (different from Figs. 1,2).

4. Temperature dependendence of the continuum in undoped phases

Temperature dependence of the continuum in the "as grown" $YBa_2Cu_3O_{6+\delta}$ and Sm_2CuO_4 shown in Fig. 3 is anomalous. Instead of scaling with the Bose factor, the continuum "freezes out": the intensity decreases significantly throughout the energy interval as the temperature is lowered. Similarity between the 2-1-4 and 1-2-3 behavior indicates that it is probably intrinsic to the undoped phases. Origin of this behavior is not understood. Preliminary results indicate that the freezing out in YBCO stops occuring before the metal insulator transition as doping is increased .

Rise of the room temperature spectra as $\omega \rightarrow 0$ is indicative of a quasielastic peak, which disappears at lower temperatures. We are currently investigating a possibility of scattering by thermally excited electrons as a possible cause of the quasielastic peak, because resistivity of these materials at T=300K, [21] is metallic-like.

5. Conclusion

Doping dependence of the plane polarized continua in 1-2-3 and 2-1-4 materials is quite different from the doping dependence of the IR conductivity and is not consistent with the scattering by the conduction electrons. Localized states or hot luminescence are possible alternatives to the conduction electron picture. Low energy continuum in the undoped phases has an anomalous temperature dependence.

6. Acknowledgement

The authors are grateful to S.L. Cooper and A.L. Kotz for providing their data on optical constants before publication. D.R. would also like to thank S.L. Cooper, R. Liu, for helpful discussions. This project received support from the NSF under contract DMR90-17156 and through the NSF funded Science and Technology Center for Superconductivity under DMR88-09854.

7. References

1 S. Sugai, Y. Entomoto, and T.Murakami, Solid State Comm. **72**, 1193 (1989).
2 T. Staufer, R. Hackl, and P. Muller, Solid State Comm. **75**, 975 (1990).
3 F. Slakey, M.V. Klein, D. Reznik, J.P. Rice, D.M. Ginsberg, A.P. Paulikas, J.W. Downey, B.W. Veal, Proc. SPIE **1336**, 86 (1990).
4 K.B. Lyons, P.A. Fleury, R.R. Singh, P.E. Sulewski, Proc. SPIE **1336**, 66 (1990).
5 C.M. Varma, P.B. Littlewood, S. Smitt-Rink, E. Abrams, and A.E. Ruckenstein, Phys. Rev. Lett. **63**, 1996 (1989).
6 A. Virosztek, and J. Ruvalds, Phys. Rev. B **45**, 347 (1992).
7 P.W. Anderson, Physica C **185-189**, 11 (1991).
8 B.S. Shastry, and B. I. Shraiman, Phys. Rev. Lett. **65** (1990).
9 J.P. Rice, and D.M. Ginsberg, J. Cryst. Growth **109**, 432 (1991); W.C. Lee and D.M. Ginsberg, Phys. Rev. B **44**, 2815 (1991); G.H. Kwei, S-W. Cheong, Z. Fisk, F.H. Garzon, J.A. Goldstone, and J.D. Thompson, Phys. Rev. B **40**, 9370 (1989).
10 S.L. Cooper, A.L. Kotz, M.A. Karlow, M.V. Klein, W.C. Lee, J. Giapintzakis, and D.M. Ginsberg. Phys. Rev. B **45**, 2549 (1992).
11 D. Reznik, A.L. Kotz, S.L. Cooper, M.V. Klein, W.C. Lee, and D.M. Ginsberg, Physica C **185-189**, 1029 (1991).
12 D. Reznik, A.L. Kotz, S.L. Cooper, M.V. Klein, W.C. Lee, and D.M. Ginsberg, Proc. Int. Workshop on Electronic properties and Mechanisms of High T_C Superconductivity (IWEPM). To be published (Elsevier).
13 K.F. McCarty, J.Z. Liu, R.N. Shelton, H.B. Radousky, Phys. Rev. B **41**, 8792 (1990).
14 M.V. Klein, Light Scattering in Solids 1, ed. by M. Cardona, Ch. 4 (Springer, 1983); M. Cardona and A. Zawadowski, Phys. Rev. B **42** 10732 (1990).
15 Z. Schlesinger, R.T. Collins, F.Holtzberg, C. Feild, S.H. Blanton, U. Welp, G.W. Grabtree, Y. Fang, Phys. Rev. Lett. **65**, 801 (1990).
16 S. Sugai, Springer Series in Material Science, **11**, 207 (1989) (editors H. Kamimura and A. Oshiyama)
17 I. Tomeno, M. Yoshida, K. Ikeda, K. Tai, K. Takamuku, N. Koshizuka, S. Tanaka, K. Oka, and H. Unoki, Phys. Rev. B **43**, 3009 (1991).
18 S. Uchida, T.Ido, H. Takagi, T. Arima, Y Tokura, S Tajima, Phys. Rev. B **43**, 7942 (1991).
19 S.L. Cooper et al., unpublished.
20 D. Reznik, M.V. Klein, W.C. Lee, D.M. Ginsberg, S-W. Cheong, submitted to Phys. Rev. B.
21 Y. Iye, Physical Properties of High Temperature Superconductors III, ed. by D.M. Ginsberg, Ch. 4 (World-Scentific 1992).

Phonon Self-Energy Effects in $YBa_2Cu_3O_{7-\delta}$ Below T_c: The Role of Oxygen Disorder

V.G. Hadjiev, C. Thomsen, and M. Cardona

Max-Planck-Institut für Festkörperforschung,
Heisenbergstr. 1, W-7000 Stuttgart 80, Fed. Rep. of Germany

Abstract. We discuss the discrepancies in the published literature concerning the gap value for $2\Delta/kT_c$ as deduced from the superconductivity-induced phonon self-energy changes. In particular, using the established correlation between the appearance of the Raman forbidden chain-related lines at 232 and 598 cm^{-1} and the phonon self-energy changes of the 340 cm^{-1} B_{1g}-like mode below T_c we demonstrate the effect of even slight oxygen disorder on the phonon self-energy below T_c in pure crystals.

1. Introduction

Andreev reflection experiments have shown the superconducting pairing of quasi-particles with opposite momentum in high-T_c superconductors [1]. Thus the determination of the superconducting order parameter Δ (the binding energy of the pair) or the gap ratio $2\Delta/kT_c$ (the strength of the coupling) is of primary interest. Among the spectroscopic methods for the gap determination, a recent development [2–4] exploits the superconductivity-induced changes in the self-energy Σ of $k = 0$ optical phonons via electron-phonon coupling. The self-energy effects for a given coupling constant are expected to be strongest when a phonon energy is in resonance with the gap (or one of several possible gaps [5]). The most drastic changes in the phonon self-energy due to superconductivity have been observed for the 340 cm^{-1} B_{1g}-like mode in $YBa_2Cu_3O_{7-\delta}$ [6,7] implying that the phonon energy is close to a gap (henceforth called "the" gap). Below T_c, all experiments reported up to now have indicated anomalous softening ($Re(\Sigma)$) of this mode, when the sample becomes superconducting [6]. However, discrepancies exist in the literature concerning the changes in the linewidth ($-Im(\Sigma)$) of the 340 cm^{-1} Raman line. In a series of experiments, a tremendous broadening of the 340 cm^{-1} line has been observed below T_c for polycrystalline samples [4,8], thin films [9], twinned [7,10] and untwinned [11–13] crystals while in other studies [14–17] just the opposite behavior for films, twinned and untwinned single crystals was seen: a moderate sharpening of this line. These results lead to different values of $2\Delta/kT_c$ provided the model [2] is used, namely 5 [4] and 6.8 – 7.7 [15,16] for polycrystalline and single crystal samples, respectively. The influence of impurities on the gap value determined this way has been studied in [9,10]. Here, we demonstrate the effect of even slight oxygen disorder on the phonon self-effects below T_c.

Springer Series in Solid-State Sciences, Vol. 113 Electronic Properties of High-T_c Superconductors
Editors: H. Kuzmany, M. Mehring, J. Fink

2. Correlation between the appearance of the symmetry forbidden Raman peaks and the phonon self-energy effects

The phononic Raman scattering from $YBa_2Cu_3O_{7-\delta}$ has been extensively studied. All the Raman lines predicted by the group-theoretical analysis have been identified and assigned to certain atom vibrations in accordance with lattice dynamical calculations [18]. Under some circumstances (defects, resonant excitations) the samples of $YBa_2Cu_3O_{7-\delta}$ feature extra (nominally forbidden by symmetry) peaks like those shown in Fig. 1. The most striking feature of the $Z(YY)\bar{Z}$ polarized spectra shown in Fig. 1 is that, although all samples have almost equal oxygen content as indicated by the frequency of the O4 peak, some of them are characterized by the appearance of two additional peaks at 232 and 598 cm^{-1}. These particular peaks: (i) are seen only under light polarized along Y, i.e along the CuO chains, (ii) They are resonant enhanced with maximum intensity near 2.2 eV [19], (iii) Below 100 K, they can be optically bleached if the illumination photon energy exceeds 2.2 eV [19].

Our observations can be summarized as follows: (i) No extra peaks under resonance ~2.21 eV were observed for the *heavily twinned* area HT-B (see the text under Fig. 1) and the *untwinned strip near this area* UT/HT-B, both *near*

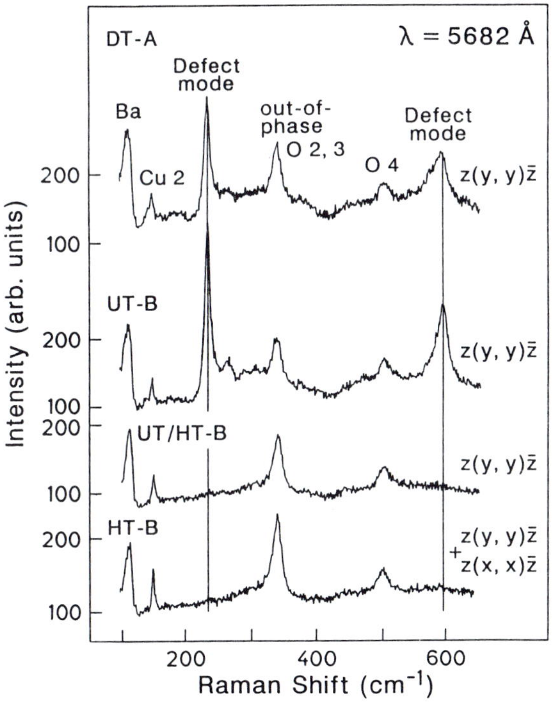

Fig. 1 Polarized Raman spectra of different samples: DT-A - detwinned area in the A-crystal (ZrO_2 crucible); UT-B - large untwinned area, HT-B - heavily twinned area, and UT/HT-B untwinned area neighboring the heavy twinned one, all in the B-crystal (SnO_2 crucible).

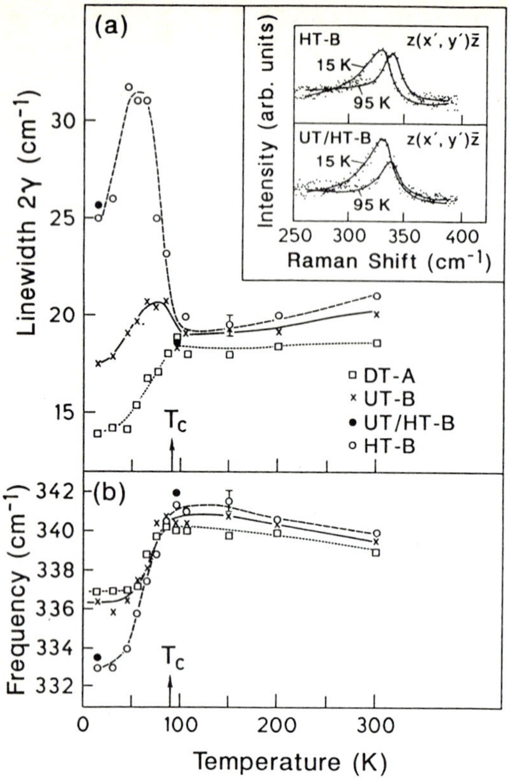

Fig. 2 Temperature dependence of the linewidths (a) and frequencies of the 340 cm^{-1} phonon for different samples measured in B_{1g}–$Z(X'Y')\bar{Z}$ geometry. The inset shows that the effect of broadening of the line is equally strong for twinned and untwinned areas.

the edge of the single crystal B. The same result was obtained for an undoped pellet (ii) The two peaks are characteristic of the detwinned area DT-A and the large untwinned area UT-B in the B-crystal, as well as for Au-doped ceramic pellets. (iii) For some single crystal samples the strength of the extra peaks is uniform over the crystal surface, whereas for others it varies.

From the unique polarization properties of the 232 and 598 cm^{-1} modes, it follows that they stem from orthorhombic structural elements, i.e. from the *CuO* chains. These modes have been also seen in oxygen deficient $YBa_2Cu_3O_{6.4}$ [20]. On the other hand, no sign of these modes has been observed in tetragonal $YBa_2Cu_3O_{6.1}$ [20,21]. Consistent with these findings, we conclude that the two modes arise from forbidden vibrations of the chain atoms becoming Raman active via the introduction of defects in the chains [22].

The dependence of linewidth and frequency of the 340 cm^{-1} phonon on temperature is given in Fig. 2 (for the samples specified in Fig. 1). The data presented in Fig. 2 were deduced by fitting the 340 cm^{-1} peak intensity distribution to a Fano-type line shape [4]. All the samples show a softening of the 340 cm^{-1} mode below T_c (Fig. 2b), as expected for superconducting crystals, although the degree of the softening varies. The temperature dependence of the phonon linewidth is, however, very intriguing: the samples featuring the absence of the extra peaks at 232 and 598 cm^{-1} exhibit the tremendous broadening of the 340 cm^{-1} line below T_c reported for ceramic samples [4], while a sharpening is seen for those which have pronounced additional peaks. Note that the softening correlates with the broadening/sharpening: it is larger for samples exhibiting broadening.

From the results in Figs. 1 and 2, for the *impurity-free crystals* we find a definite correlation between the appearance of the two extra Raman peaks at 232 and 598 cm^{-1} and the change of temperature dependence of the 340 cm^{-1} phonon linewidth below T_c .

3. Discussion and conclusions

The effect of disorder may find the same explanation as the one given in [9]. The oxygen disorder, similarly to the introduction of impurities, may smear the gap anisotropy, thus leading to an increase in the minimal gap to which the Raman modes have been proposed to couple [9]. On the other hand, model [2] gives a precursor of this process. With increasing concentration of nonmagnetic impurities or oxygen disorder, the impurity scattering rate increases as well (the mean free path of the carriers decreases). As a result the phonon energy resonance with the gap becomes less pronounced [2], in agreement with the experiment (Fig. 2).

In addition, it is important to note that the phonon self-energy changes scale with the electron-phonon coupling constant. The relatively large value of the coupling constant (λ_{340}=0.02) of the 340 cm^{-1} mode comes mostly from the *buckling* of the CuO_2 planes [3]. The introduction of vacancies into the CuO chains leads to local smearing of the buckling [23] and, in turn, this may reduce the coupling constant such that the self-energy effects predicted in [2] become smaller. The change in the coupling constant may not have a remarkable influence on superconductivity but rather makes the Raman phonons under consideration less sensitive to superconductivity. This would explain a decrease in softening and broadening (Fig. 2), but not a switch from broadening to narrowing.

Acknowledgments. We thank A. Erb, G. Müller-Vogt and M.R. Koblischka who supplied us with the samples and H. Hirt, M. Siemers and P. Wurster for the expert technical help. One of us (V.G.H.) acknowledges also support by the Alexander von Humboldt Foundation (Bonn, Federal Republic of Germany).

References

[1] P.G.M. van Bentum *et al.*, Physica C **153-155**, 1718 (1987).
[2] R. Zeyher and G. Zwicknagl, Z.Phys.B – Condensed Matter **78**, 175 (1990).
[3] C. Thomsen *et al.*, Solid State Commun. **75**, 219 (1990).
[4] B. Friedl, C. Thomsen, and M. Cardona, Phys. Rev. Lett. **65**, 915 (1990).
[5] A.A. Abrikosov, Physica C **182**, 191 (1991).
[6] R.M. Macfarlane, H. Rosen and H. Seki, Solid State Commun. **63**, 813 (1987).
[7] S.L. Cooper *et al.*, Phys.Rev. B **37**, 5920 (1988).
[8] M. Kranz *et al.*, Phys. Rev. B **38**, 4992 (1988).
[9] C. Thomsen *et al.*, Solid State Commun. **78**, 727 (1991).
[10] E. Altendorf *et al.*, Physica C **185-189**, 1375 (1991).
[11] S.L. Cooper *et al.*, Phys. Rev. B **38**, 11934 (1988).
[12] V.G. Hadjiev *et al.*, Solid State Commun. **80**, 643 (1991).
[13] E. Altendorf *et al.*, Phys. Rev. B **45**, 000 (1992).
[14] R. Feile *et al.*, Z. Phys. B - Condensed Matter **73**, 155 (1988).
[15] F.K. McCarty *et al.*, Phys. Rev. B **43**, 13751 (1991).
[16] F.K. McCarty *et al.*, Solid State Commun. **79**, 359 (1991).
[17] E. Altendorf *et al.*, Physica C **175**, 47 (1991).
[18] C. Thomsen and M. Cardona, in *Physical Properties of High-Temperature Superconductors I*, Ed. D.M. Ginsberg (World Scientific, Singapore 1989), p.409.
[19] D.R. Wake *et al.*, Phys. Rev. Lett. **67**, 3728 (1991).
[20] V.G. Hadjiev, C. Thomsen and M. Cardona, to be published.
[21] E.T. Heyen, J.Kircher, and M.Cardona, to be published.
[22] R. Liu *et al.*, Phys. Rev. B **37**, 7971 (1988).
[23] J.D. Jorgensen *et al.*, Physica C **185-189**, 184 (1991).

Normal-State Conductivity of Cuprate Superconductors: One-Component and Two-Component Viewpoints

Z. Schlesinger[1], *L.D. Rotter*[1], *R.T. Collins*[1], *F. Holtzberg*[1], *C. Feild*[1], *U. Welp*[2], *G.W. Crabtree*[2], *J.Z. Liu*[2;*], *Y. Fang*[2], and *K.G. Vandervoort*[2]

[1]IBM T.J. Watson Research Center,
P.O. Box 218, Yorktown Heights, NY 10598, USA
[2]Materials Science Division, Argonne National Lab., Argonne, IL 60439, USA
*Present address: Physics Department, University of California,
Davis, CA 95616, USA

Abstract. We discuss the evolution of our understanding of the normal state infrared conductivity of cuprate superconductors. The discussion begins with results from polycrystalline samples and continues up to the recent work on single domain (untwinned) crystals. The issue of whether the conductivity at low frequency (i.e. $\omega \lesssim 1000\ cm^{-1}$) should be described with one (intraband) component, or with two (intraband + interband) components is central to the discussion.

One of the persistent issues in the study of high T_c (cuprate) superconductors has been the question of how to interpret the normal state infrared conductivity. A key question is whether the conductivity in the far-infrared is predominantly intraband, or whether a more complex picture involving both intraband and interband excitations is needed. This issue is relevant to our understanding of the basic nature of the cuprates since in the former case novel aspects of the infrared conductivity are associated with unusual intraband dynamics (of the same carriers which become superconducting below T_c); while in the latter case the existence of very low energy interband or excitonic transitions is implied. Either result is potentially quite significant, since, for example, putative low energy excitons have been discussed as possible pair-mediating excitations, while, on the other hand, the former interpretation provides part of the experimental basis for the view that the normal state *intraband* transport is quite unlike that of ordinary (Fermi liquid) metals. Here I will review the history and origins of this issue, and the current status of the data. More general reviews of infrared and optical properties by the same authors as this paper have been presented elsewhere(1,2).

In the insulating cuprates there is a charge transfer excitation with a threshold of about 1.5 eV(3). Here we will focus on the conductivity which develops below this charge transfer threshold, as a result of adding additional holes to the CuO_2 planes. For a simple Drude metal, this low frequency conductivity is associated with transitions within the conduction band (intraband conductivity) which are made allowed by scattering processes. This intraband conductivity reaches a value equal to the d.c. conductivity as $\omega \to 0$, and falls like $1/\omega^2$ through most of the infrared region(2,4). At some frequency usually above about 1 eV, there is an onset of interband conductivity, i.e. absorption of light associated with electronic transitions between two different bands. In the cuprates one finds, surprisingly, that the normal state conductivity does not follow the simple $1/\omega^2$ form in any frequency range. Understanding this behavior is the subject of this paper. Our discussion will be divided into two parts. The main part deals with the normal state of high Meissner fraction, high T_c superconductors, e.g. $YBa_2Cu_3O_{7-x}$ and $Bi_2Sr_2CaCu_2O_{8-y}$ with $T_c \gtrsim 50$ K, and $La_{2-x}Sr_xCuO_4$ with $x \sim 0.15$. A very short second part mentions briefly the issue of the lightly doped region, where the samples are not such good superconductors and are close to a metal-insulator transition.

Early attempts to study the infrared behavior of the conductivity began with measurements of *polycrystalline samples* of $La_{1.85}Sr_{.15}CuO_4$ and $YBa_2Cu_3O_7$. From these measurements an infrared conductivity with a small narrow peak at $\omega = 0$, and had a large, broad maximum in the vicinity of about 3000 cm^{-1} ($\sim$0.4 eV) was inferred, as sketched in figure 1. Such spectra are strongly indicative of a *two component* conductivity, with the lower peak associated with the dynamics of free carriers (intraband excitations) and the upper peak associated with some sort of interband excitations. The report of such spectra, with a strong interband transition well below the charge transfer threshold of the insulator, was quite startling. There are, however, problems with studying polycrystalline cuprates associated with the fact that in these measurements reflectivities from highly conducting a-b plane faces and from the nearly insulating c-axis direction are mixed together in an uncontrolled manner(5-7). According to Schlesinger, Collins et al.(5) and Orenstein and Rapkine(6), the mixture itself is responsible for the strong peak in $\sigma_1(\omega)$ at $\sim$4000 cm^{-1}, which is not really representative of an intrinsic conductivity for any spatial direction. Ultimately the huge in-plane/out-of-plane anisotropy makes it nearly impossible to learn anything about the intrinsic normal state conductivities of cuprates from the study of polycrystalline material, and therefore researchers moved as quickly as possible to the study of crystals.

Early infrared results from crystals were obtained on $La_{1.85}Sr_{.15}CuO_4$ by Tajima et al.(8). Additionally, a significant part of the next generation of infrared experiments involved work on twinned $YBa_2Cu_3O_{7-x}$ crystals(9-15). For both $La_{1.85}Sr_{.15}CuO_4$ and the $T_c \simeq 92$ K twinned crystals, the conductivity decreases monotonically with frequency(8,9). This prompted Schlesinger et al.(9) to attempt to fit the room temperature conductivity with a simple Drude form using a very large scattering rate, however, this approach was not fruitful. As pointed out by Kamaras et al.(7), such a large scattering rate is essentially unphysical since it corresponds to an unreasonably short mean free path. Even in the limited frequency range of this original data(9) (1,000 to 13,000 cm^{-1}), the measured conductivity falls more slowly than the fitted Drude form. Extensions

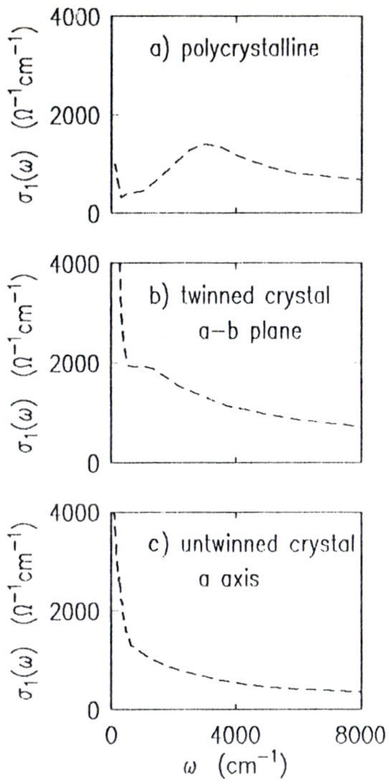

FIGURE 1
Normal state conductivity of various forms of $YBa_2Cu_3O_{7-x}$ as derived from infrared reflectivity measurements. The data in (a) are representative of results from polycrystalline material (circa 1987, see ref 5-7 and references therein). (b) shows the normal state conductivity of twinned(15) $YBa_2Cu_3O_{7-x}$ ($T_c \simeq 80$ K) (circa 1988), and (c) shows the $\hat{a}$ axis conductivity from a similar ($T_c \simeq 80$ K) untwinned crystal (18) (circa 1991). This progression illustrates the development of our understanding of the intrinsic normal state conductivity of $YBa_2Cu_3O_{7-x}$.

of the data to lower frequency and temperature(11-13) accentuate this inconsistency, and show quite convincingly that the data does not follow a simple (i.e., fixed scattering rate) Drude form.

Data from twinned $YBa_2Cu_3O_{7-x}$ crystals with a somewhat reduced oxygen content(10), tend to exhibit a "bump" in the normal state conductivity at about 1500 cm^{-1}, as shown in fig 1b for a crystal with $T_c \simeq 80$ K. While the magnitude and frequency of the bump are smaller than for the polycrystalline spectra, the data are qualitatively similar in that they suggest that the conductivity consists of two distinct parts: a Drude "peak" at low frequency, and a mid-infrared "mode" centered at about 1500 cm^{-1}.

The most recent experiments on $YBa_2Cu_3O_{7-x}$ involve the measurement of untwinned single crystals(16-20), where one can separately

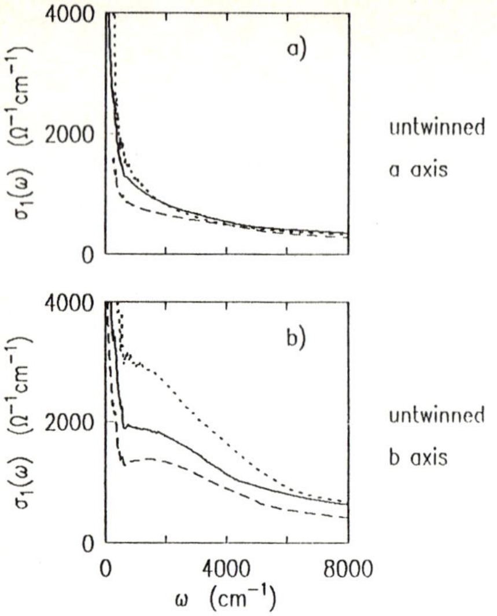

FIGURE 2

Normal state conductivity of untwinned $YBa_2Cu_3O_{7-x}$ crystals with $T_c \simeq 92$, 80 and 56 K (dotted, solid, dashed), from ref 17,18. The data in (a) show the conductivity for the infrared electric field polarized along the $\hat{a}$ direction, in which case one measures the conductivity of just the CuO_2 planes. The data in (b) show the conductivity for the infrared electric field polarized along the b direction, in which case one measures the conductivity of both the CuO_2 planes and the CuO chains. These data allow the mid-infrared bump in $YBa_2Cu_3O_{7-x}$ to be identified with the CuO chains.

measure the infrared conductivity along the $\hat{a}$ and b axies. For these untwinned crystals the data are observed to be significantly different in the $\hat{a}$ and b directions. The conductivity of an untwinned crystal with $T_c \simeq 80$ K taken with the electric field polarized along the $\hat{a}$ axis is shown in fig 1c. Normal state conductivity data from $Bi_2Sr_2CaCu_2O_{8-x}$ and $La_{1.85}Sr_{.15}CuO_4$, where there are no chains, are quite similar to the $\hat{a}$ axis data from the $YBa_2Cu_3O_{7-x}$ (see, e.g. ref 1, 21 and 22)

Conductivities from untwinned crystals for both the $\hat{a}$ and b directions are shown in fig 2. Regarding the origins of the a-b plane anisotropy, Rotter et al.(18) have stated that, "Two aspects of the structure of $YBa_2Cu_3O_{7-x}$ are of potential relevance to the a-b plane anisotropy of $\sigma(\omega)$:

1. $YBa_2Cu_3O_{7-x}$ contains CuO chains oriented parallel to the b axis, and
2. the lattice constant is about 2% larger in the b direction than along $\hat{a}$.

In all known models of transport, a larger lattice constant is expected to lead to a lower conductivity, hence the lattice constant difference has the wrong sign to account for the observed anisotropy (which is $\sigma_{1a}<\sigma_{1b}$ in all samples). The observation of both higher conductivity and more complexity in the b spectra instead indicates that these spectra are enhanced by the presence of chains parallel to this axis, as one might expect."

A very similar point of view is expressed by Cooper et al.(19), who also analyze the b axis conductivity as a sum of chain and plane contributions, and the $\hat{a}$ axis conductivity as the pure CuO_2 plane conductivity. From this viewpoint, the difference between the b and $\hat{a}$ axis conductivities is regarded as the chain contribution. Recent measurements of $PrBa_2Cu_3O_{7-x}$(20) seem to confirm the validity of this approach, in which the conductivity within the plane is treated as simply the sum of a two dimensional plane conductivity and a one dimensional chain conductivity. The data of Takenaka et al.(20) shows that replacing Y by Pr eliminates the plane conductivity in the infrared, but leaves the chain conductivity virtually unchanged (with respect to its magnitude in $YBa_2Cu_3O_{7-x}$), demonstrating that the chain conductivity is indeed a separate identifiable entity, at least in the infrared. (One should caution, however, that the d.c. conductivity may not be so readily separable into independent components. There the physics may be more complex because one is probing at effectively longer length scales.)

With this knowledge of the actual conductivities for each crystal axis one can understand the earlier data from twinned crystals. For the twinned crystals (fig 1b) $\hat{a}$ and b axis contributions are both present in the measured conductivity, and cannot be separated by any measurement. The ambiguity of this unresolved anisotropy is removed through the study of untwinned crystals. In particular, the data from untwinned $YBa_2Cu_3O_{7-x}$ crystals show that the feature in the twinned data which had been identified with a mid-infrared mode is associated with the chain response.

Figure 1 thus summarizes the development of our understanding of the normal state infrared conductivity of cuprate superconductors (for the a-b plane). The simplest way to understand this development is as the successive resolution of anisotropies within the cuprate crystal. In the first generation (fig 1a) the data was severely distorted by effects associated with the large in-plane/out-of-plane anisotropy(5,6). The second generation involved measurement of twinned crystals (fig 1b), in which the anisotropy within the a-b plane was unresolved(9-15). The third generation of experiments, measurement of untwinned crystals(16-19) (fig 2), resolves the in plane anisotropy, and allows the identification of the intrinsic conductivity of the CuO_2 planes in $YBa_2Cu_3O_{7-x}$.

With the untwinned crystals the measurement with the infrared electric field polarized along the $\hat{a}$ axis generates the conductivity of just the CuO_2 planes. As noted above, this conductivity is quite similar to the normal state conductivity of $Bi_2Sr_2CaCu_2O_{8-y}$ and $La_{1.85}Sr_{.15}CuO_4$, which have no chains(1,21,22). Although the a axis conductivity has no mid-infrared bump, it is important to emphasize that it does not follow a con-

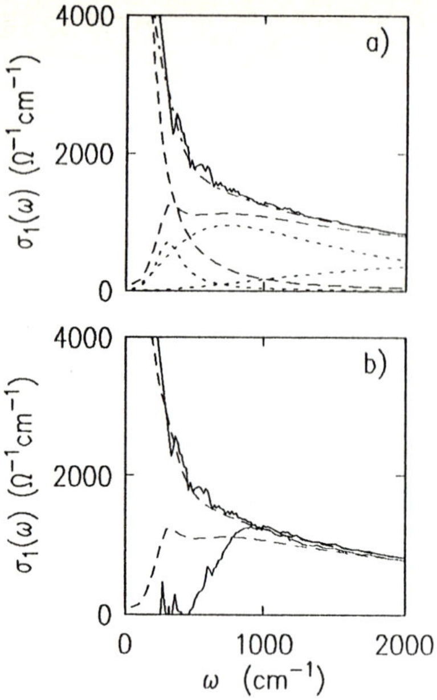

FIGURE 3
Two component model for the normal state conductivity is shown. The solid line (a) is the measured conductivity for the CuO_2 planes in $YBa_2Cu_3O_7$(17). The two dashed curves show the two components used for the fit. One is a Drude term that is peaked at $\omega=0$ and decreases like $1/\omega^2$above $\sim$200 cm^{-1}. The other is a "mid-infrared" term that is constructed from a sum of (three) Lorentz oscillator contributions, shown by the dotted curves, (after Kamaras et al.(23)). In part (b) the attempt to fit the superconducting state conductivity of untwinned $YBa_2Cu_3O_7$ (solid line), by collapsing the Drude term to zero width, leaving only the mid-infrared term at finite frequency is shown. This procedure does not provide a good fit to the superconducting state.

ventional Drude form. Instead it falls more slowly with frequency than the conventional $1/\omega^2$, roughly like $1/\omega^{1-\delta}$ with $\delta\sim0.2$ (for $\omega\lesssim5000$ cm^{-1}). As such, there is excess conductivity in the infrared compared with expectations based on the Drude model. How one attempts to understand the origin of this excess conductivity is a key issue for the normal state.

Two approaches have been considered. One is to postulate that the actual intraband part of $\sigma(\omega)$ follows the conventional Drude form, and that any excess comes from interband transitions. With this approach the interband transitions start at very low energy ($\sim200\pm200$ cm^{-1}), and the conductivity is usually fit by a conventional Drude (intraband) term and a additional (interband) term, which is made up of a sequence of Lorentz oscillators. Such a fit, based on ref 23, is shown in fig 3a. This is called the *"two component"* approach, since both interband and intraband components of $\sigma(\omega)$ are proposed to be significant even at low frequency.

Historically the primary support for this two component approach has come from the observation of a local maximum ("bump") in the mid-infrared conductivity, such as that shown in fig 1b or 1a. The absence of such a feature in the a-axis conductivity of untwinned crystals and in compounds such as $Bi_2Sr_2CaCu_2O_{8-y}$ seriously undermines the motivation for this approach. For example, according to Cooper et al.(19), "the absence of a distinguishable secondary absorption in the a-axis conductivity of moderately-doped $YBa_2Cu_3O_{7-x}$ places strong limitations on the possibility of a two-component absorption in the CuO_2 planes of $YBa_2Cu_3O_{7-x}$."

A secondary motivation for the two-component approach has been the belief that one might describe the change in the conductivity in the superconducting state, by collapsing the Drude term to a Dirac-δ function at $\omega=0$ and leaving the second (interband) part of the conductivity unchanged(23). This, however, does not work well for the a-axis conductivity of $YBa_2Cu_3O_7$, as shown in fig 3b and discussed in references 1 and 2.

The possibility of defining the interband component of $\sigma(\omega)$ as the measured conductivity of the superconducting state has also been considered. This is intriguing, however, one then finds that the intraband component, which must then be defined as $\sigma_{1n}(\omega)$-$\sigma_{1s}(\omega)$, would go to 0 rather abruptly at about 900 cm^{-1}. Such behavior is physically unreasonable, which indicates that this $\sigma_{1s}(\omega)$ cannot realistically be viewed as a distinct conductivity component. The data instead suggest that a threshold develops within the dominant conductivity component at about 500 cm^{-1}. Indeed, the observation that below T_c most of the conductivity below $\sim$500 cm^{-1} goes into the dissipationless response at $\omega=0$ (17,24,25), suggests that the low frequency conductivity is made up of only one component, as we discuss in the next paragraph.

The alternative approach, which we can call the single component picture, proposes that there is a frequency in the infrared (not too low) below which interband contributions to $\sigma(\omega)$ are not significant. In this case the measured conductivity provides a determination of the intrinsic form of the intraband $\sigma(\omega)$. One then concludes that the intraband dynamics are quite unusual, since $\sigma(\omega)$ falls like $1/\omega^{1-\delta}$ rather than $1/\omega^2$ ($\delta\sim0.2$) (see e.g., 1 and 2). Much theoretical effort has been put into explaining this unusual behavior, and to relating this unusual infrared phenomenology to other measured properties(17, 26-28). Due to the absence of a distinguishable secondary absorption in the normal state conductivity, this single component approach is at present rather widely favored in theoretical treatments of the infrared conductivity.

The question of where the interband contributions to the conductivity become significant is difficult to resolve because the conductivity falls, and then rises, smoothly and gradually. There are no obvious features, as seen in Cu e.g., that clearly signify the onset of interband absorption. One thing that provides a clue is the observation that the conductivity begins to rise above about 10,000 cm^{-1}(2), which indicates that the conductivity is mostly interband in this higher frequency range. The single component approach depends on the assumption that most (i.e. ~80% or more) of the conductivity below about 1000 cm^{-1} is of intraband origin (this is the crucial range for the superconducting and low energy normal state dynamics). Thus for the single component approach to be valid, a crossover from a primarily intraband to interband conductivity must occur somewhere between about 1,000 and 10,000 cm^{-1}. Although it would be useful to understand how and where the crossover occurs, it should be emphasized that such knowledge does not effect the phenomenology of the low energy dynamics, which is rather robust with respect to the crossover frequency as long as it is above about 1000 cm^{-1}.

The above discussion summarizes in a brief way the development of an understanding of the a-b plane normal state conductivity of high Meissner fraction cuprate superconductors. It can be summarized succinctly. Early data showed a maximum in the mid-infrared conductivity for many samples, leading to the belief in a second conductivity component in addition to the Drude term. More recent data from untwinned $YBa_2Cu_3O_{7-x}$ and $Bi_2Sr_2CaCu_2O_{8-y}$ crystals show a smoothly falling conductivity in the mid-infrared for the CuO_2 planes, in which a second component is not readily identifiable. The assumption of a single component conductivity for the low frequency range ($\omega \lesssim 1000\ cm^{-1}$) leads to an unusual phenomenology for the normal state, in which the frequency dependence of $\sigma(\omega)$ and the temperature dependence of the d.c. resistivity are intimately related(17,26,28). Details of modelling the normal state conductivity and the description in terms of frequency dependent scattering are discussed elsewhere(1,2,14,15,17-19).

We have discussed here the nature of the conductivity *in the normal state* of compounds such as $YBa_2Cu_3O_{7-x}$, $Bi_2Sr_2CaCu_2O_{8-y}$ and $La_{1.85}Sr_{.15}CuO_4$ that are good (high Meissner fraction) high T_c superconductors. An important issue not discussed here is the development of the infrared conductivity as a function of doping near the antiferromagnetic state. There the cuprates are close to an insulator metal transition, and the physics of (strong) localization may be relevant to understanding the infrared conductivity. Localization effects tend to suppress the d.c. conductivity and produce a conductivity as a function of frequency with a broad maximum at some characteristic frequency in the infrared, which depends primarily on the localization length. Conductivities following this general form are often observed in light and moderately doped materials such as $La_{2-x}Sr_xCuO_4$ and Y doped $Bi_2Sr_2CaCu_2O_{8-y}$. Another issue which has not been discussed is the temperature dependence of the conductivity in the superconducting state, which seems to reflect the development of an energy gap-like feature with highly unusual temperature dependence. Some references to these issues can be found in references (1), (2) and (25).

Acknowledgements: The authors acknowledge valuable discussions with P. W. Anderson, E. Abrahams, R. Bhatt, S. L. Cooper, M. V. Klein, P. A. Lee, P. B. Littlewood, D. J. Scalapino, I. Terasaki, S. Uchida, C. M. Varma,

References

1. Z. Schlesinger, L. D. Rotter, R. T. Collins, F. Holtzberg, C. Feild, U. Welp, G. W. Crabtree, J. Z. Liu, Y. Fang and K. G. Vandervoort, Physica C **185-189** 57, (1991)
2. Z. Schlesinger, L. D. Rotter, R. T. Collins, F. Holtzberg, C. Feild, U. Welp, G. W. Crabtree, J. Z. Liu, Y. Fang and K. G. Vandervoort, in *Physics of High Temperature Superconductors*, series in Solid State Sciences 106, Springer Verlag (1992)
3. Y. Tokura et al., Phys. Rev. B**41**, 11657 (1990)
4. F. Wooten, *Optical Properties of Solids*, (Academic Press, New York, 1972).
5. Z. Schlesinger, R. T. Collins, M. W. Shafer and E. M. Engler, Phys. Rev.B36,5275 (1987)
6. J. Orenstein and D. H. Rapkine, Phys. Rev. Lett. **60**, 968 (1988)
7. K. Kamaras, C. D. Porter, M. G. Doss, S. L. Herr, D. B. Tanner, D. A. Bonn, J. E. Greedan, A. H. O'Reilly, C. V. Stager and T. Timusk, Phys. Rev. Lett. **60**,969 (1988).
8. S. Tajima, S. Uchida, H. Ishii, H. Takagi, S. Tanaka, U. Kawabe, H. Hasegawa, T. Aita, and T. Ishiba, Mod. Phys. Lett. B **1**, 353 (1988).
9. Z. Schlesinger, R. T. Collins, D. L. Kaiser, and F. Holtzberg, Phys. Rev. Lett. **59**, 1958 (1987);
10. G. A. Thomas, J. Orenstein, D. H. Rapkine, M. Capizzi, A. J. Millis, R. N. Bhatt, L. F. Schneemeyer and J. V. Waszczak, Phys. Rev. Lett. **61**, 1313 (1988).
11. R. T. Collins, Z. Schlesinger, F. Holtzberg, P. Chaudari, and C. Field, Phys. Rev.B. 39, 6571 (1989).
12. J. Schutzmann, W. Ose, J. Keller, K. F. Renk, B. Roas, L. Schultz and G. Saemann-Ischenko, Europhysics Lett. 8, 679 (1989)
13. R. T. Collins, Z. Schlesinger, F. Holtzberg and C. Field, Phys. Rev. Lett. 63, 422 (1989).
14. Z. Schlesinger, R. T. Collins, F. Holtzberg, C. Feild, G. Koren and A. Gupta, Phys. Rev. B**41**, 11237 (1990)
15. J. Orenstein, G. A. Thomas, A. J. Millis, S. L. Cooper, D. H. Rapkine, T. Timusk, L. F. Schneemeyer and J. V. Waszczak, Phys. Rev. B**42**, 6342 (1990)

16. B. Koch, H. P. Geserich and TH. Wolf, Solid State Commun.71, 495 (1989)

17. Z. Schlesinger, R. T. Collins, F. Holtzberg, C. Feild, U. Welp, G. W. Crabtree, Y. Fang and J. Z. Liu, Phys. Rev. Lett.**65**, 801 (1990)

18. L. D. Rotter, Z. Schlesinger, R. T. Collins, F. Holtzberg, C. Feild, U. Welp, G. W. Crabtree, Y. Fang, K. G. Vandervoort, S. Fleshler and J. Z. Liu, Phys. Rev. Lett.**67**, 2741 (1991)

19. S. L. Cooper, A. L. Kotz, M. A. Karlow, M. V. Klein, W. C. Lee, J. Giapintzakis, and D. M. Ginsberg, Phys. Rev. B.**45**, 2549 (1992)

20. K. Takenaka, Y. Imanaka, K. Tamasaku, T. Ito and S. Uchida, preprint

21. S. Uchida, T. Ido, H. Takagi, T. Arima, Y Tokura and S. Tajima, Phys. Rev. B**43**, 7942 (1991), and S. Uchida Physica C**185-189** 28, (1991)

22. I. Terasaki, S. Takebayashi, I. Tsukada, A. Maeda and K. Uchinokura, Physica **C185-189** 1017, (1991)

23. K. Kamaras, S. L. Herr, C. D. Porter, N Tache, D. B. Tanner, S. Etemad, T. Venkatesan, E. Chase, A. Inam, X. D. Wu, M. S. Hegde, and B. Dutta, a) Phys. Rev. Lett. **64**, 84 (1990); b) Erratum, ibid, 1962 (1990)

24. T. Pham, M. W. Lee, D. H. Drew, U. Welp and Y. Fang, Phys. Rev. B.**44**, 5377 (1991)

25. R. T. Collins, Z. Schlesinger, F. Holtzberg, C. Feild, U. Welp, G. W. Crabtree, J. Z. Liu and Y. Fang, Phys. Rev. B**43**, 8701 (1991)

26. P. W. Anderson, in Strong Correlation and Superconductivity, edited by H. Fukuyama, S. Maekawa and A. Malozamoff (Springer-Verlag, Berlin, 1989), and Kanazawa proceedings (1991)

27. M. V. Klein, in Strong Correlation and Superconductivity, edited by H. Fukuyama, S. Maekawa and A. Malozamoff (Springer-Verlag, Berlin, 1989)

28. C. M. Varma, P. B. Littlewood, S. Schmitt-Rink, E. Abrahams and A. E. Ruckenstein, Phys. Rev. Lett. 63, 1996 (1989);

Resonant Raman Scattering in $Bi_2Sr_2Ca_{1-z}Y_zCu_2O_{8+\delta}$ Single Crystals

M. Boekholt[1], *G. Güntherodt*[1], *and V.V. Moshchalkov*[2]

[1]2. Physikalisches Institut, RWTH Aachen, Templergraben 55, W-5100 Aachen, Fed. Rep. of Germany

[2]Laboratorium voor Vaste Stof-Fysika, Katholieke Universiteit Leuven, Celesteinenlaan 200 D, B-3001 Leuven, Belgium

We report on resonance Raman scattering investigations of $Bi_2Sr_2Ca_{1-z}Y_zCu_2O_{8+\delta}$ single crystals ($0 \le z \le 0.85$), i.e. on compounds with Y-concentrations both in the metallic ($z \le 0.5$) and insulating ($z \ge 0.5$) regime. At the incident laser energy of 2.6 ± 0.1 eV, the 463-cm^{-1} "in-phase out-of-plane" and the 275-cm^{-1} "out-of-phase out-of-plane" vibrations of the oxygens situated in the CuO_2-planes as well as the Cu-vibration at 165 cm^{-1} show a resonance. The resonance energy ε_{res} is independent of the Y-concentration z and corresponds to the charge-transfer gap Δ_{CT}. An additional electronic scattering intensity only in metallic samples ($z \le 0.5$) gives evidence for the existence of narrow states near the Fermi energy, i.e. of the so-called Zhang-Rice singlets.

1. Introduction

Since the discovery of the $Bi_2Sr_2CaCu_2O_{8+\delta}$ (Bi-2212) high-T_c superconductor, a large number of Raman scattering studies have been published trying to clarify the characteristics of its phononic and electronic excitations. Only few reports [1-4] deal with the Raman investigation of the $Bi_2Sr_2Ca_{1-z}Y_zCu_2O_{8+\delta}$ solid solution series, which is of special interest because of the occurence of a transition from an antiferromagnetic charge-transfer insulator ($Bi_2Sr_2YCu_2O_{8+\delta}$) to a strongly correlated metallic state ($Bi_2Sr_2CaCu_2O_{8+\delta}$). The "metal-insulator transition" takes place for an Y-concentration of about $z \approx 0.5$. This z-value separates also the regime of superconductivity ($z \le 0.5$) from the regime of antiferromagnetic order ($z \ge 0.5$).

In Ref. 4 we reported in detail on the growth and the characterization of the $Bi_2Sr_2Ca_{1-z}Y_zCu_2O_{8+\delta}$ single crystals investigated here.

Springer Series in Solid-State Sciences, Vol. 113 Electronic Properties of High-T_c Superconductors
Editors: H. Kuzmany, M. Mehring, J. Fink

2 Results

Some A_g-symmetric Raman spectra of an insulating $Bi_2Sr_2Ca_{0.3}Y_{0.7}Cu_2O_{8+\delta}$ single crystal are shown in Fig. 1 as a function of different laser wavelengths λ_L. The scattering configuration is defined by symbols such as $Z(X,X)\bar{Z}$, which means that the incident light propagates along the Z-axis and is polarized along the X-axis, and the scattered light is polarized along the X-axis and propagates in the opposite direction along the -Z-axis. The axes X,Y,Z are chosen along the axes a,b,c of the crystallographic unit cell. The most remarkable feature of this series is a strong, sharp resonance of the 165-cm^{-1} Cu-mode at λ_L = 472.6 nm (ε_L = 2.62 eV). Likewise, a weaker resonance scattering of the 463-cm^{-1} "in-phase out-of-plane" vibrations of the oxygens situated in the CuO_2-planes can be seen by comparing just the areas

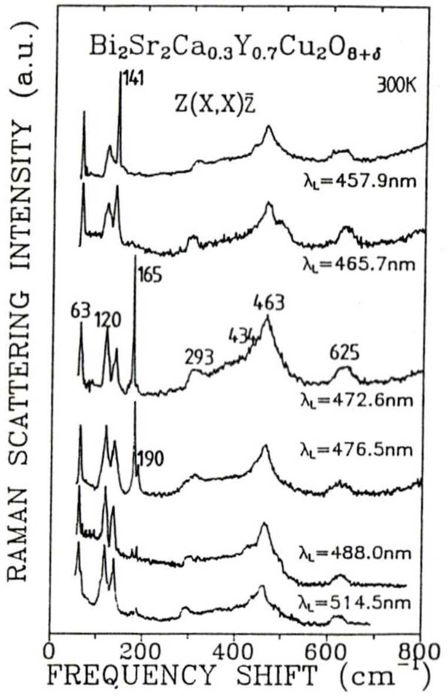

Fig. 1: Polarized room-temperature Raman spectra of A_g-symmetry (scattering geometry $Z(X,X)\bar{Z}$) taken on the ab-plane of a $Bi_2Sr_2Ca_{0.3}Y_{0.7}Cu_2O_{8+\delta}$ single crystal (z = 0.7) for different laser wavelengths λ_L.

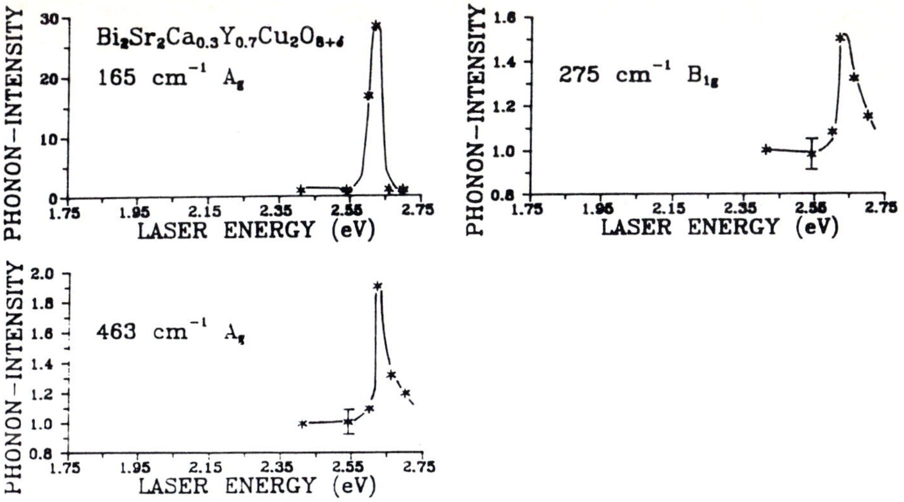

Fig. 2: Relative intensity of the 165-cm^{-1} Cu-mode and the "in-phase out-of-plane" 463-cm^{-1} and "out-of-phase out-of-plane" 275-cm^{-1} vibration of the oxygen atoms situated in the CuO_2-planes of a $Bi_2Sr_2Ca_{0.3}Y_{0.7}Cu_2O_{8+\delta}$ single crystal (z = 0.7) as a function of the incident laser energy ε_L. The solid lines are only a guide to the eye.

underneath this phonon peak for different λ_L. The corresponding B_{1g}-type "out-of-phase out-of-plane" 275-cm^{-1} phonon shows also a resonance in its intensity at the same λ_L.

For a quantitative analysis, the phonon intensities I_{Ph} of the different modes have to be plotted as a function of the incident laser energy ε_L. As outlined in Refs 4 and 5, only the phonons involving primarily motions of atoms situated in the CuO_2-planes (here the A_g-type 165-cm^{-1} Cu-mode as well as the 275-cm^{-1} B_{1g}-type and the 463-cm^{-1} A_g-type oxygen vibrations) show a resonance at $\varepsilon_{res} = 2.6 \pm 0.1$ eV. The error has been estimated as an upper limit by taking into account the phonon intensities at the next neighboring ε_L-values investigated. The other phonon modes detected in the spectra of Fig. 1 show a different $I_{Ph}(\varepsilon_L)$- behavior. Fig. 2 is thus restricted to the resonance curves of the phonons mentioned above, the Raman spectra of which are given in Fig. 1. The intensities plotted in Fig. 2 were normalized against the intensity of the 322-cm^{-1} phonon of CaF_2, whereby the phonon scattering intensities at ε_L = 2.41 eV were set equal to 1. The solid lines are only a guide to the eye. Both the 463-cm^{-1} "in-phase out-of-plane" and the 275-cm^{-1} "out-of-phase out-of-plane" oxygen vibration as well as the 165-cm^{-1} Cu-mode resonate at ε_L = 2.62 eV, i.e. at the same incident laser energy as the undoped $Bi_2Sr_2CaCu_2O_{8+\delta}$ [5]. Comparing the intensities at the resonance energy ε_{res} = 2.62 eV with those at the green laser line (ε_L = 2.41 eV), the strong enhancement of the Cu-mode compared to the oxygen vibrations is obvious.

In the charge-transfer insulators $Bi_2Sr_2Ca_{1-z}Y_zCu_2O_{8+\delta}$ ($z \geq 0.5$) the first conduction band above the Fermi energy ε_F is the upper Hubbard band (UHB) of Cu. The energy difference between the hybridized {Cu $3d_{x^2-y^2}$ - O $2p_{x,y}$} valence band and the UHB of Cu is the charge-transfer gap Δ_{CT}, which is the energy needed to transfer one hole from an oxygen atom situated in the CuO_2-planes to a Cu-atom. The Raman scattering intensity will be resonantly enhanced for phonons belonging to motions of the copper and the oxygen atoms situated in the CuO_2-planes if the incident laser energy coincides with Δ_{CT}. Thus the detected resonance energy ε_{res} = 2.6 eV ± 0.1 eV is attributed to Δ_{CT}. The excitation of an electron from the {Cu $3d_{x^2-y^2}$ - O $2p_{x,y}$} valence band to the UHB of Cu and its fast recombination are labeled in Fig. 3 by numbers 1 and 2.

The resonance Raman scattering experiments have been carried out for different Y-concentrations in $Bi_2Sr_2Ca_{1-z}Y_zCu_2O_{8+\delta}$ single crystals. The resonance energy in the $I_{Ph}(\varepsilon_L)$-curves of the phonons shown in Fig. 2 turned out to be the same for different z (ε_{res} = 2.6 ± 0.1 eV). This result is an indication for the z-independence of the charge-transfer gap.

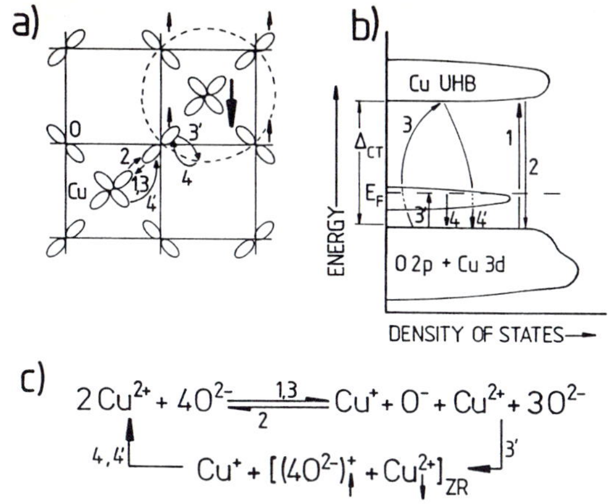

Fig. 3: Schematic representation of a part of a CuO_2-plane of the $Bi_2Sr_2Ca_{1-z}Y_zCu_2O_{8+\delta}$ crystals (a) and a part of the electronic density of states (b) (Ref. 4). The two possible recombination channels of an electron excited to the UHB (processes 1 and 3) correspond to the processes 2 and {3'-4-4'} in Fig. 3. The charge transfer inside the CuO_2-plane during the processes 1-2-3-3'-4-4' is outlined in Fig. 3c.

The polarized room-temperature Raman spectra as a function of λ_L taken in the B_{1g}-type scattering geometry $Z(X,Y)\bar{Z}$ on the ab-plane of a pure $Bi_2Sr_2CaCu_2O_{8+\delta}$ (z = 0) single crystal are shown in Fig. 4. As can be seen in Fig. 4, the B_{1g}-type electronic scattering intensity, which in "pure" Bi-2212 is flat for $\lambda_L \geq 514.5$ nm, is strongly enhanced when decreasing the incident laser wavelength towards the uv-region. For $\lambda_L \leq 488.0$ nm, the maximum electronic scattering intensity almost exceeds that of the B_{1g}-phonons. Its frequency position is for most of the wavelengths between $\Delta\tilde{\nu} \approx 450$ cm^{-1} (55 meV) and $\Delta\tilde{\nu} \approx 550$ cm^{-1} (68 meV). This increase of the electronic scattering intensity when decreasing λ_L is not detected in the B_{1g}-type spectra of insulating $Bi_2Sr_2Ca_{1-z}Y_zCu_2O_{8+\delta}$ crystals. The resonance energy ε_{res} determined from the phonon resonance curves

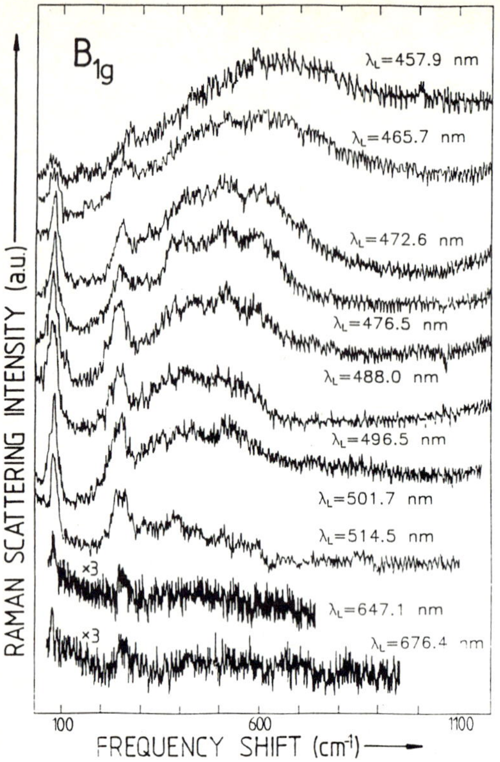

Fig. 4: Polarized room-temperature Raman spectra of B_{1g}-symmetry (scattering geometry $Z(X,Y)\bar{Z}$) taken on the ab-plane of a $Bi_2Sr_2CaCu_2O_{8+\delta}$ (z = 0) single crystal for different laser wavelengths λ_L.

coincides with the onset of the enhanced B_{1g}-type electronic scattering in metallic $Bi_2Sr_2Ca_{1-z}Y_zCu_2O_{8+\delta}$ ($z \leq 0.5$). This correspondence is in first place due to the condition $\varepsilon_L \geq \Delta_{CT}$ for an observation of both enhanced phonon and electronic scattering intensity (see Fig. 3b).

The interpretation of the enhanced electronic scattering in superconducting $Bi_2Sr_2Ca_{1-z}Y_zCu_2O_{8+\delta}$ ($z \leq 0.5$) may be based on the assumption of the existence of electron states inside the charge-transfer gap. Such states are often modeled in terms of the Zhang-Rice (ZR) singlets [6]. The latter correspond to the strong binding of a hole on a square of oxygen atoms with the hole on the central Cu^{2+} site. The spin of Cu^{2+} is compensated by the opposite spin of the oxygen hole shared among the four nearest-neighbor oxygen atoms forming a square. This concept is illustratesd in Fig. 3a. In metallic samples ($z \leq 0.5$), the Fermi energy lies within the ZR singlets (Fig. 3b). The second possible recombination channel (labeled 3-3'-4-4' in Fig. 3) of an electron excited to the UHB of Cu (3) involves the creation of an additional "optically pumped" ZR singlet (3'). In this case the hole in the O 2p orbital is transferred into a "collective" hole, residing simultaneously on all four oxygen atoms of a square, before this hole recombines with the excited electron in the UHB of Cu via the channel $Cu^{+}O^{-} \rightarrow Cu^{2+}O^{2-}$ (4-4'). This recombination process may occur by destroying a ZR singlet, freezing a hole on a fixed oxygen atom (4) and destroying this hole through its recombination with an excited electron in the Cu UHB (4'). The charge transfer within a CuO_2-plane during the processes 1-2-3-3'-4-4' is outlined in Fig. 3c. In insulating samples, the increase in B_{1g}-type electronic scattering intensity for $\varepsilon_L \geq \Delta_{CT}$ is not observed This is due to the fact that in insulating samples the second recombination process (labeled 3-3'-4-4' in Fig.3) is not possible because the Fermi energy is shifted out of these states. The width of empty correlated states probed by Raman scattering may roughly be estimated by the cut-off of the B_{1g}-type electronic scattering intensity in superconducting Bi-2212 (Fig. 4) to be about 60 - 80 meV.

When the spectral Raman shifts of $Bi_2Sr_2Ca_{1-z}Y_zCu_2O_{8+\delta}$ are extended to high frequencies, two-magnon scattering can be observed in insulating samples. Raman scattering failed to detect any magnons in superconducting, metallic $Bi_2Sr_2Ca_{1-z}Y_zCu_2O_{8+\delta}$. The unpolarized two-magnon Raman scattering intensity in insulating $Bi_2Sr_2Ca_{1-z}Y_zCu_2O_{8+\delta}$ is strongly enhanced for increasing z. From its maximum, which is at about $\Delta\tilde{\nu} = 2800 \pm 200\ cm^{-1}$ and which may correspond to 2.7*J in high-T_c superconductors {see, e.g., [1,2,7] and Refs therein}, a value of J = 130 ± 12.5 meV can be derived for the exchange coupling constant in antiferromagnetic $Bi_2Sr_2Ca_{1-z}Y_zCu_2O_{8+\delta}$.

The maximum of the two-magnon peak remains constant in frequency for the different laser wavelengths investigated (457.5 nm ≤ λ_L ≤ 514.5 nm). After taking into account the spectral sensitivity of the spectrometer, no significant change in the intensity of the two-magnon scattering as a function of λ_L could be observed. For example, in NiO the two-magnon scattering intensity as a function of ε_L [8] was found to be non-resonant and explained as a transition from a O 2p valence band to a Ni 3d conduction band. The possibility of a Raman process involving as initial state a Ni 3d valence band was excluded in [8]: In this case the two-magnon scattering intensity should be resonant as a function of ε_L because both bands involved in the Raman process belong to 3d-bands of a magnetic ion. However, in antiferromagnetic α-Fe_2O_3 the observed two-magnon Raman scattering intensity shows a resonance as a function of ε_L [8,9]. In this material the resonance was explained by a scattering mechanism involving only the 3d and 4p orbitals of the iron atom, the contributions of a transition involving the O 2p states were stated not to be important for the resonance. The conclusions made in [8,9] for NiO and α-Fe_2O_3 can be taken over to the case of Bi-2212 investigated here: In the framework of the electronic band structure of Bi-2212, the initial electronic state in the two-magnon Raman scattering process does hence not involve primarily Cu 3d bands, but more likely O 2p bands.

Acknowledgments: For financial support we thank the Deutsche Forschungsgemeinschaft through SFB 341. V.V.M. would like to acknowledge the support by the DAAD exchange program on superconductivity and by the SFB 341.

References

[1] S. Sugai, M. Sato, Jap. J. Appl. Phys. **28** (1989) L1361

[2] S. Sugai, M. Sato, Phys. Rev. **B40** (1989) 9292

[3] M. Boekholt, G. Güntherodt, L.I. Leonyuk, V.V. Moshchalkov, Physica C **185-189** (1991) 1035

[4] M. Boekholt, V.V. Moshchalkov, G. Güntherodt, Physica C **192** (1992) 191

[5] M. Boekholt, G. Güntherodt, Physica C **181** (1991) 179

[6] F.C. Zhang, T.M. Rice, Phys. Rev. **B37** (1988) 3759

[7] C. Thomsen in "Light scattering in Solids VI", ed. by M. Cardona and G. Güntherodt, Springer Topics in Applied Physics, Vol. 68 (Springer, Berlin 1991) p. 285

[8] R. Merlin, T.P. Martin, A. Polian, M. Cardona, B. Andlauer, D. Tannhauser, J. Magn. & Magn. Mater. **9** (1978) 83

[9] T.P. Martin, R. Merlin, D.R. Huffman, M. Cardona, Solid State Commun. **22** (1977) 565

Normal-State Infrared Response from Ellipsometric Measurements: $YBa_2Cu_3O_7$ and $PrBa_2CU_3O_7$

J. Humlíček

Masaryk University, Faculty of Science, Department of Solid State Physics, Kotlářská 2, 611 37 Brno, Czechoslovakia

Abstract. We perform quantitative estimates of the sensitivity of normal-incidence reflectance to measurement errors and to extrapolation beyond the range covered by measurements, which is needed to compute the Kramers-Kronig integral. A similar analysis is made for the ellipsometric technique, which provides both real and imaginary parts of the response functions at each photon energy. The feasibility of determination of the components of dielectric tensor for highly anisotropic materials is demonstrated. We discuss the mid- and near-infrared ellipsometric data obtained on oriented films of $YBa_2Cu_3O_7$ and $PrBa_2Cu_3O_7$.

1. Introduction

Almost all of the numerous investigations of the infrared (IR) optical response of high-T_c superconductors (HTSC) have used normal-incidence reflectance R [1]. However, the values of R are close to unity, changing little with changes of the dielectric function. Even more seriously, the complex response functions have to be determined from a single real R spectrum using the integral Kramers-Kronig relations; the procedure is sensitive to the accuracy of the extrapolations beyond the range of measurements.

Two independent quantities at each photon energy can be obtained by the ellipsometric technique, which measures changes of *polarization* after *oblique* reflection at the sample. The spectroscopic ellipsometry (SEL) has contributed substantially to consistent results for interband electronic structure of HTSC [2]. An extension of the SEL measurements to the near-infrared (NIR) with a dispersive spectrometer has revealed orientation-dependent plasma effects in $YBa_2Cu_3O_7$ [3]. Efficient SEL measurements in the mid-infrared region (MIR) became possible with an ellipsometer coupled to a Fourier-transform spectrometer [4]. The spectra are taken as series of interferograms at several fixed azimuths of the polarizers between the spectrometer, sample, and detector, with and without a phase-shifting retarder. The normal-state carrier dynamics of $YBa_2Cu_3O_7$ and $PrBa_2Cu_3O_7$ has already been studied using these measurements [5].

Since SEL is far from being well known, this contribution aims at several methodological points. We compare its sensitivity with the normal-incidence reflectance, discuss the problem of optical anisotropy, and explain selected features of the spectra of $YBa_2Cu_3O_7$ and $PrBa_2Cu_3O_7$.

Springer Series in Solid-State Sciences, Vol. 113 Electronic Properties of High-T_c Superconductors
Editors: H. Kuzmany, M. Mehring, J. Fink

2. Estimation of sensitivity

Let us assume an ideal interface between ambient and semi-infinite isotropic sample with the complex dielectric function $\varepsilon = \varepsilon_1 + \varepsilon_2$. The amplitude reflectivity $r = \sqrt{R}\exp(i\theta)$ at normal incidence is given by the Fresnel formula that can be easily inverted:

$$r = \frac{1-\sqrt{\varepsilon}}{1+\sqrt{\varepsilon}}, \quad \varepsilon = \left(\frac{1-r}{1+r}\right)^2 = 1 + \frac{4r}{(1-r)^2} \,. \tag{1}$$

The measured power reflectivity R has to be complemented by the phase θ in order to obtain ε. Assuming a small error δr of r, we can estimate the corresponding error $\delta\varepsilon$ of ε using the linear expansion $\delta\varepsilon \approx (\mathrm{d}\varepsilon/\mathrm{d}r)\delta r = -4\varepsilon/(1 - r^2)\delta r$. This error becomes very large for high magnitudes of ε, since $r^2 \to 1$ for $|\varepsilon| \to \infty$. To simulate the response of HTSC's, we use the classical Drude formula

$$\varepsilon(E) = \varepsilon_\infty - \frac{E_p^2}{E(E+i\Gamma)} = \varepsilon_\infty - \left[\frac{E}{E_p}\left(\frac{E}{E_p} + i\frac{\Gamma}{E_p}\right)\right]^{-1} \tag{2}$$

for ε at the photon energy E; here E_p is the (unscreened) plasma energy, Γ is the broadening energy, the real constant ε_∞ describes the background polarizability due to absorption at high energies. Figure 1 shows the spectral dependences of the magnitudes of the logarithmic derivatives, $\mathrm{d}\ln\varepsilon/\mathrm{d}r$, computed from Eqs. (1) and (2), which measure the ratio of the relative error $\delta\varepsilon/\varepsilon$ to δr. Although the real and imaginary parts of ε, $\delta\varepsilon$, and δr are mixed in the plotted quantity, it is useful for a quick orientation. We can see, e.g., that the relative accuracy of ~ 10 % in ε requires the errors of $\sqrt{R}\sin\theta$ and $\sqrt{R}\cos\theta$ to be less than ~ 0.01 for $E \approx 0.1E_p$, and this requirement becomes much more stringent with decreasing E.

Ellipsometric measurements performed at the angle of incidence φ provide the complex ratio $\rho = r_p/r_s$ of the amplitude reflectances for the p (parallel) and s (perpendicular) polarization with respect to the plane of incidence. The measured quantities are usually given as two ellipsometric angles, ψ and Δ, with $\rho = \tan\psi\exp(i\Delta)$ [4]. Similarly to Eq. (1), the dielectric function can be expressed explicitly from the Fresnel formulas for the isotropic sample, and differentiated with respect to ρ in order to estimate the errors within the linear expansion:

$$\varepsilon = \left(\frac{1+\rho}{1-\rho}\right)^2 \tan^2(\varphi)\sin^2(\varphi) + \sin^2(\varphi)\,, \; \frac{\mathrm{d}\varepsilon}{\mathrm{d}\rho} = (\varepsilon - \sin^2(\varphi))\frac{4}{1-\rho^2} \,. \tag{3}$$

Since $\rho \to 1$ for $|\varepsilon| \to \infty$, the relative error of ε diverges again for finite values of $\delta\rho$. However, a pronounced lowering of the magnitude of the logarithmic derivatives at a suitably chosen angle of incidence is seen in Fig. 1. With obvious extensions for the relative errors of ε_1 and ε_2, this analysis can be used to choose properly the angles of incidence. Moreover, several independent spectra at different angles of incidence overdetermine the problem, and allow us to test the internal consistency of the measured data.

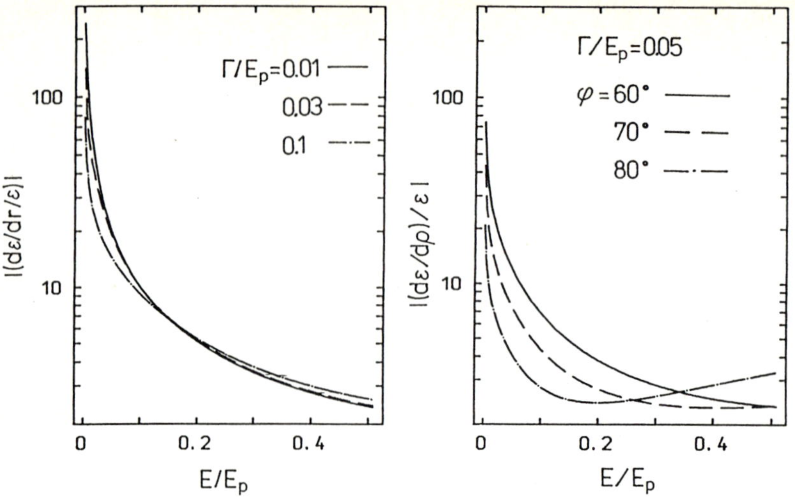

Fig. 1. Magnitude of the logarithmic derivative with respect to the amplitude reflectivity r at normal incidence (left), and with respect to the ratio ρ at oblique incidence (right); computed using the Drude formula with $\varepsilon_\infty = 1$.

3. Anisotropy in ellipsometric measurements

In the ellipsometric experiment on an anisotropic material, the light sees different tensor components of the response function that have to be recovered from the measured spectra. An approximative way to accomplish this has been found for weakly anisotropic samples [6]. We prefer to fit numerically the measured ψ and Δ spectra with the exact Fresnel formulas [3, 5]; this is eventually the best choice for the multiple-angle-of-incidence measurements mentioned above. Since the performance with highly anisotropic samples is of primary importance here, we have tested the ellipsometer with the lattice bands of crystalline quartz. Our results [7] demonstrate a complete separation of the lattice vibrations along the ordinary and extraordinary directions. In fact, comparing our spectra in MIR with the earlier work based on the reflectance [7], we observe definite improvements due to the ellipsometric technique.

4. Results on oriented films of $YBa_2Cu_3O_7$ and $PrBa_2Cu_3O_7$

Ellipsometric angles taken on the (110) and (001) $YBa_2Cu_3O_7$ films in MIR are shown in Fig. 2. The noise does not exceed a few degrees; it is even lower in some parts of the spectra, depending on the number of accumulations, spectral resolution, angle of incidence, and the dimensions of the samples. The simultaneous treatment of the data at several angles of incidence resolves the a-b–plane and c-axis components of the response functions, and confirmes the consistency within the noise level. The real part of in-plane conductivity computed from

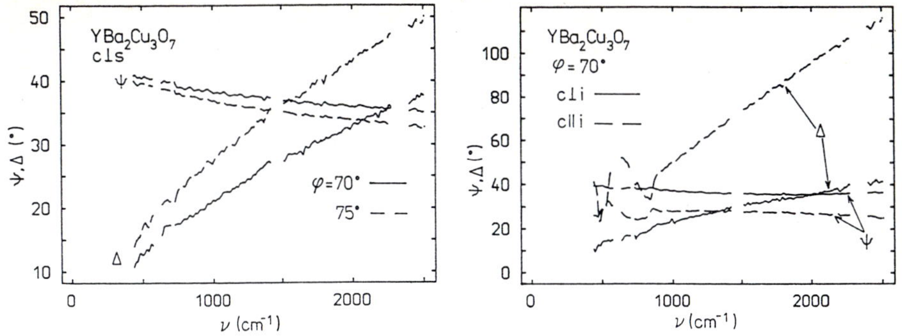

Fig. 2. Spectra of the (110) film with the c axis perpendicular and parallel to the plane of incidence (left); (001) film at two angles of incidence (right).

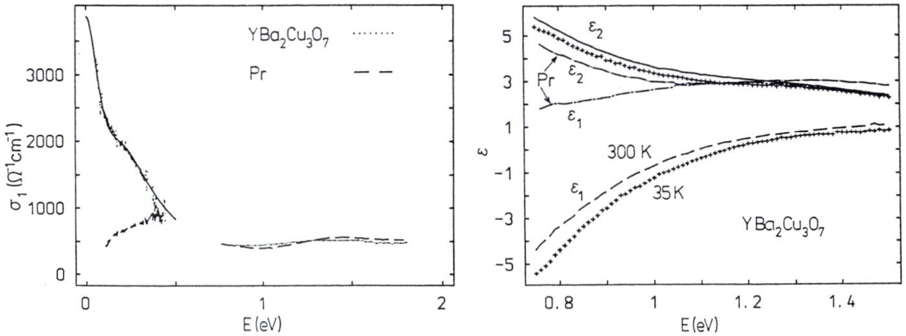

Fig. 3. Real part of the in-plane conductivity obtained ellipsometrically at room temperature (left); in-plane dielectric function of $PrBa_2Cu_3O_7$ at 300K, and $YBa_2Cu_3O_7$ at 300 and 35K (right).

this data is accurate to better than 10% except for the high-wavenumber end of the MIR range (above ~ 3000 cm$^{-1} \approx 0.37$ eV). The substitution of Y by Pr reduces dramatically the low-energy conductivity and the oscillator strength is taken over by the broad absorption band centered at ~ 0.3 eV. This change is also seen as a strong upward shift of ε_1 in NIR, as shown in Fig. 3.

The real part of ε for $YBa_2Cu_3O_7$ crosses zero at the photon energy of ~ 1.1 eV. Since ε_2 is fairly small, a well defined peak arises in the energy-loss function, $-Im(1/\varepsilon)$, near this energy. It describes longitudinal excitations in the plasma of carriers taking part in the infrared absorption. This plasma threshold is analogous to the $\varepsilon_1 = 0$ crossings for impurity carriers in IR, or all-valence electrons in UV, seen in the optical response of semiconductors [8]. The high-energy tail of ε is insensitive to spectral structures below the plasma energy, since, at sufficiently high frequencies, the carriers do not feel weak bonds. It depends merely on ε_∞ and the total oscillator strength, $F = 4\pi Ne^2/m^*$; here m^* and N are carrier effective mass and concentration, respectively. Both ε_∞ and F can be determined reliably from the ellipsometric spectra. The NIR data for $YBa_2Cu_3O_7$ were fitted with a single Drude term [3, 5], which is the high-energy limit of any sum of Lorentzian lineshapes. We have obtained $\varepsilon_\infty = (4.34 \pm 0.07)$ and $F = (7.07 \pm 0.14)$ eV^2. The concentration of carriers responsible for the IR response of $(5.1 \pm 0.1) \times 10^{21}$ cm^{-3} (or 0.89 ± 0.02 elemental charges per primitive cell) results from the spectral weight, assuming the free electron effective mass, $m^* = m_e$.

Acknowledgments. This work has been done in collaboration with M. Cardona, J. Kircher, and H.-U. Habermeier in Stuttgart, A. Röseler in Berlin, and benefited from the solid-state and optical background of our department in Brno. All these contributions are gratefully acknowledged.

References

[1] T. Timusk and D.B. Tanner, in *Physical Properties of High Temperature Superconductors*, Vol. I, ed. by D.M. Ginsberg (World Scientific, Singapore, 1989), p. 339.

[2] D.E. Aspnes and M.K. Kelly, IEEE J. Quantum Electron. **25**, 2378 (1989).

[3] J. Humlíček, J. Kircher, H.–U. Habermeier, M. Cardona, Y. Fang, U. Welp, K. Vanderwoort, and D. Crabtree, Solid State Commun. **79**, 637 (1991).

[4] A. Röseler, *Infrared Spectroscopic Ellipsometry* (Akademie-Verlag, Berlin, 1990).

[5] J. Humlíček, J. Kircher, H.–U. Habermeier, M. Cardona, and A. Röseler, Physica C **190**, 383 (1992).

[6] D.E. Aspnes, J. Opt. Soc. Am. **70**, 1275 (1980).

[7] J. Humlíček and A. Röseler, to be published. H. R. Philip, in *Handbook of Optical Constants of Solids*, ed. by E. D. Palik (Academic, Orlando, 1985), p. 719.

[8] H. Ehrenreich, in: *The Optical Properties of Solids*, ed. by J. Tauc (Academic, New York, 1966), p. 106.

Change of Electronic Structures with Varying Lattice Distortion and Metal Valence in Titanium and Vanadium Oxides

Y. Tokura and Y. Taguchi

Department of Physics, University of Tokyo, Tokyo 113, Japan

Abstract Filling-dependent electronic structures in titanium and vanadium oxides with perovskite-like structures have been investigated by measurements of optical conductivity spectra as well as by characterization of transport and magnetic properties. With use of orthorhombically distorted solid solutions , (R,A)TiO_3 and (R,A)VO_3 (R = rare earth and A = alkaline earth ions), a crossover behavior of the electronic states from the Mott insulator to Pauli metal has been unraveled as a function of the fillingness. The role of the electron correlation in the metal-insulator transitions manifests itself in filling-dependent enhancement of effective electron mass and in doping-induced ingap states.

1. Introduction

Unprecedently extensive studies on cuprate superconductors have revealed a number of important features in strongly correlated electron systems, in particular drastic changes in nature of electronic states with carrier-doping. With increasing or decreasing the formal valance of Cu, a transitional behavior has been observed in common to layered cuprate compounds from an anti-ferromagnetic insulator with localized d holes on Cu-sites to a normal metal through a high-T_c superconductor (or an unconventional metal above T_c). Here we present some results of recent experimental investigations[1-3] on changes of electronic structures in light transition metal (Ti and V) oxides with varying the formal valence of metal (or number of 3d electrons). The Ti^{3+} ($3d^1$) and V^{3+} ($3d^2$) oxides are mostly Mott insulating or otherwise barely metallic on the verge of the Mott-Hubbard transition. With change of the fillingness (or effective metal valence), the compounds undergo the phase change to good metals accompanying a critical change of electronic structures due to the filling-dependent effect of the electron correlation. According to Zaanen-Sawatzky-Allen scheme[4], the Ti- or V-based oxides with localized 3d electrons are the Mott insulators (in a narrow sense) in contrast to the fact that the undoped cuprate compounds are the charge-transfer insulators. In this sense, the investigations on the Ti- and V- based oxide compounds may bring about complementary information to that for high-T_c cuprate.

Control of the fillingness of the 3d bands can be done for solid solution systems, (R,A)MO_3, with perovskite-like structure[1,5,6,7]. Here R and A are trivalent rare earth and divalent alkaline earth ions, respectively, and M is Ti or V. The solid

Springer Series in Solid-State Sciences, Vol. 113 Electronic Properties of High-T_c Superconductors
Editors: H. Kuzmany, M. Mehring, J. Fink

solution can be formed for arbitrary ratio of R/A cations and the number of 3d electron per metal site can be scanned from 0 to 1 for (R,A)TiO_3 and from 1 to 2 for (R,A)VO_3. The crystalline lattice of these oxides often shows the orthorhombic distortion (of $GdFeO_3$ type) associated with alternating tilting of MO_6 octahedra. The tilting angle is sensitive to the ionic radii of the R/A ions or equivalently to the tolerance factor. Deviation of the M-O-M bond angle from 180° causes a reduction in one-electron band width (W) of the 3d state, since the hopping interaction of d electron is governed by supertransfer interaction via oxygen site. For example, $LaTiO_3$ with the bond angle of ca. 157° [8] is barely metallic around room temperature, whereas $YTiO_3$ (ca. 140° [8]) is obviously a Mott insulator associated with a fairly large charge gap ($>$ 0.5eV).

2. Metal-insulator phase boundary in titanium oxides with perovskite-like structures

To obtain a perspective on electron correlation effect and resultant electron localization in $Ti^{3+}(3d^1)$-based oxides, the electronic and magnetic phase diagram for $RTiO_3$ system (R=rare earth ion) is shown in Fig.1, which is based mostly on pioneering works by Greedan and his coworkers [8-11]. We have plotted the critical temperatures for the antiferromagnetic (AF) and ferromagnetic (F) phase transitions in various $RTiO_3$ compounds which are arranged according to their tolerance factors (or ionic radii of R's). (To be precise, the AF phase is weakly ferromagnetic due to canting of ordered spins.) The abscissa represents, as mentioned above, the magnitude of effective correlation strength or U/W. Mott

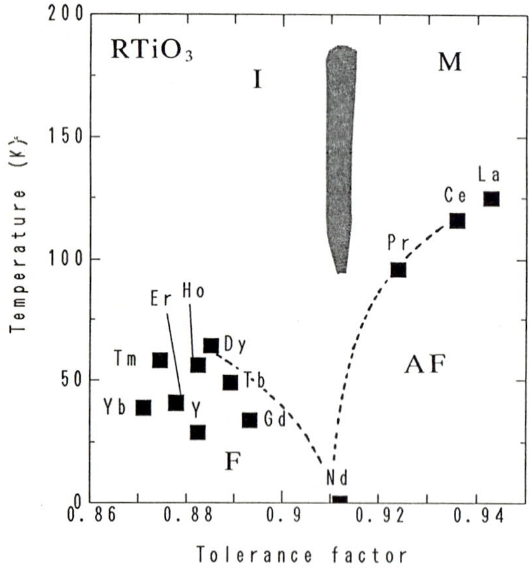

Fig.1 Electronic and magnetic phase diagram in slightly hole-doped (a few %) $RTiO_3$ with distorted perovskite-like ($GdFeO_3$ type) structures.

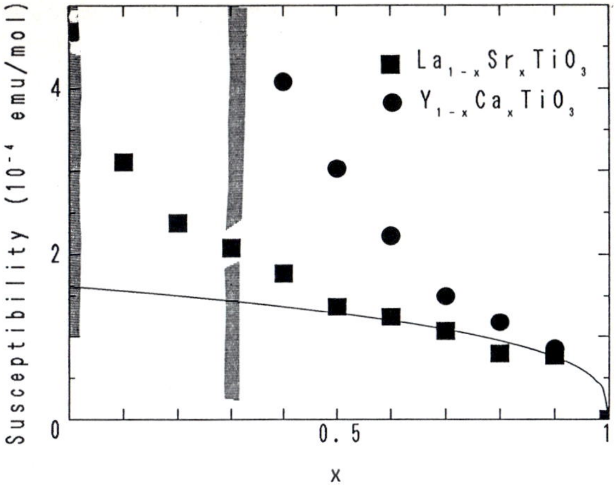

Fig.2 Fillingness dependence of magnetic susceptibilities in the metallic phase of $La_{1-x}Sr_xTiO_3$ and $Y_{1-x}Ca_xTiO_3$. Hatched vertical bars around x=0 and x=0.3 represent the insulator-metal phase boundaries for $La_{1-x}Sr_xTiO_3$ and $Y_{1-x}Ca_xTiO_3$, respectively. A solid line represents the x-dependence of density of states at Fermi level expected for the hypothetical parabolic (free electron-like) band.

insulator(I)-metal(M) phase boundary is likely to position around the critical tolerance factor for R=Nd compound, which appears to coincide approximately with the F-AF magnetic phase boundary at low temperature.

Concerning the high temperature metallic region on the right side of the phase diagram (Fig.1), however, some comments are needed: Transport properties in $LaTiO_3$ (and perhaps also in $CeTiO_3$ and $PrTiO_3$) are extremely sensitive to small nonstoichiometry of R ions and/or oxygens [12,13]. It has been reported [12] that better stoichiometric $LaTiO_3$ should show semiconducting behavior even up to room temperature, yet very slight deviation of the Ti^{3+} valence, e.g. +3.02-3.05, causes the metallic behavior at high temperatures above T_N. The exactly one electron-occupied case per Ti site for such a nearly simple cubic lattice may have a subtle problem concerning the correlation-induced charge gap and also be amenable to correlation-enhanced electronic instabilities. Therefore, the M-I phase diagram shown in Fig.1 should be interpreted as the one for slightly (a few %) hole-doped $RTiO_3$ systems. By contrast, the insulating compounds (on the left-hand side in Fig.1) associated with the ferromagnetic phase is definitely accompanied by the Mott-Hubbard gap and not too sensitive to the stoichiometry.

Doping-induced changes of electronic states have been investigated for two prototypical $RTiO_3$ compounds; $LaTiO_3$ with relatively weak correlation[1,2] and $YTiO_3$ with Mott-Hubbard gap [14] (see Fig.1). Carrier-doping or control of the fillingness was made by partial substitution of R sites with alkaline earth ions; i.e. $La_{1-x}Sr_xTiO_3$ and $Y_{1-x}Ca_xTiO_3$. We show in Fig.2 the insulator-metal phase boundary (hatched vertical bars) and variations of the nearly temperature-independent magnetic susceptibility in the metallic region [14]. The insulator-metal phase boundary closely sticks to the end (x=0) for $La_{1-x}Sr_xTiO_3$, but is observed around x=0.3 for $Y_{1-x}Ca_xTiO_3$. The Pauli paramagnetic susceptibility is observed to be critically enhanced on approaching the metal-insulator phase boundary from the metallic side. The increase of the magnetic susceptibility near the phase boundary may be ascribed to either the enhancement of density of states (or effective electron mass) at Fermi level or change of Stoner enhancement factor. Concerning the case of $La_{1-x}Sr_xTiO_3$, the fillingness dependence of specific heat density of states shows quite a parallel behavior with that of the magnetic susceptibility [2]. In accord with these observations, a similarly critical enhancement of carrier mass and its strong ω-dependence have been proved by (extended) Drude analysis of the optical conductivity spectra in $La_{1-x}Sr_xTiO_3$ [1].

3. Optical spectra in $La_{1-x}Sr_xTiO_3$ and $Y_{1-x}Ca_xTiO_3$

Electronic structures in the highly electron-correlated Ti^{3+}- and V^{3+}-based oxides have been spectroscopically investigated with varying electron fillingness (or carrier-doping). Optical conductivity spectra are shown in Fig.3 and Fig.4 for $La_{1-x}Sr_xTiO_3$ [1] and $Y_{1-x}Ca_xVO_3$ [3], respectively. As mentioned above (Fig.2), the former system shows a metallic behavior except for the composition region very close to x=0 or x=1, whereas the latter vanadium oxide system with a similar $GdFeO_3$-type structure undergoes a doping-induced Mott insulator-to-metal transition at the hole-doping level around x=0.5. The electronic structures as

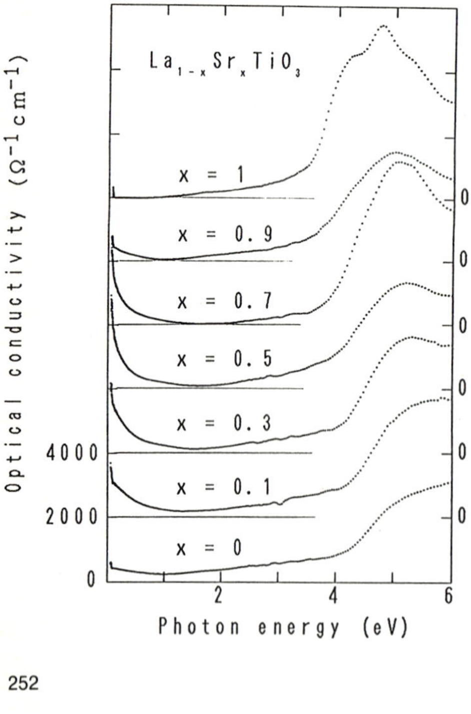

Fig.3 Spectra of optical conductivity in $La_{1-x}Sr_xTiO_3$ at room temperature.

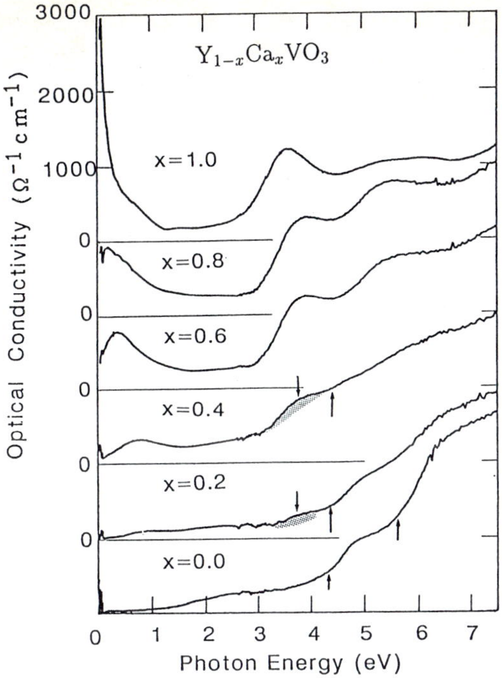

Fig.4 Spectra of optical conductivity in $Y_{1-x}Ca_xVO_3$ at room temperature.

probed by the optical conductivity spectra show a notable change not only upon the insulator-metal transition but also in the readily metallic region.

Spectra of the optical conductivity in $La_{1-x}Sr_xTiO_3$ (Fig.3) can be divided into two regions; infrared responses of charge-carriers below 1eV and charge-transfer type (O 2p to Ti 3d) interband transitions above 3eV. The absorption edge for the O 2p to Ti 3d transitions is clearly seen around 3.2 eV in the x=1 compound ($SrTiO_3$) with the empty 3d band and is observed to shift to ca.4.2 eV in the x=0 ($LaTiO_3$). Such an energy shift can be attributed to partial filling of the 3d band with decreasing x. On the other hand, the change of the infrared spectra is not monotonous with x. First, the infrared spectral weight in (barely) metallic $LaTiO_3$ (x=0) appears to be much suppressed and rather resemble that of the closed-shell insulator $SrTiO_3$(x=1). This indicates that $LaTiO_3$ is on the verge of the Mott insulator [1,13]. The spectral weight is increased with hole-doping procedure (or more correctly with decreasing the fillingness, 1-x, of the d-band). It reaches the maximum around x=0.5, and then decreases with further increasing x toward the end $SrTiO_3$.

Integrated spectral weight in the infrared region ($<$ 1eV) stands for the effective number of electrons (N_{eff}) which are relevant to low energy optical transitions. In terms of the Drude model, N_{eff} is equal to the ratio of the number density to effective mass of free carriers, i.e. $N/(m^*/m_0)$. The variation of spectral weight can be explained by x-dependent changes of N and m^*. On the basis of the one-electron band model, the carrier density N is equalized to the fillingness, 1-x. Therefore, the decrease of the spectral weight with decreasing x below x=0.5 can be interpreted as a correlation-induced enhancement of m^* which overwhelms an apparent increase of N[1]. The behavior is consistent with the critical enhancement of density of states at Fermi level in approaching the x=0 ($LaTiO_3$) compound, as probed by measurements of specific heat and magnetic susceptibility (see Fig.2).

Some qualitative differences are seen in filling-dependent change of optical conductivity spectra for $La_{1-x}Sr_xTiO_3$ (Fig.3) and $Y_{1-x}Ca_xVO_3$ (Fig.4). In a typical Mott insulator YVO_3 (x=0) with $3d^2$ configuration, the optical conductivity spectrum (shown in the bottom part of Fig.4) shows a threshold-like rise at 1.0-1.5 eV, apart from the optical phonon activity. The threshold photon energy is considered to correspond to the Mott-Hubbard gap. Further two absorption onset structures are observed below 7eV in YVO_3; around 4.3eV and around 5.6eV as indicated by upward arrows in Fig.4. These two absorption edges have been assigned to the charge-transfer type transitions from the O 2p valence states to the t_{2g}-and e_g-like V 3d states, respectively. The unoccupied t_{2g}-like state corresponds to the upper Hubbard band in this Mott insulator system.

The hole-doping procedure causes an appreciable change in the interband transition region. For the x=0.2 compound which still remains semiconducting or insulating, an additional transition is observed around 3.8 eV (indicated by a downward arrow in Fig.4) just below the interband (O 2p to upper Hubbard band) transition edge (indicated by a upward arrow). The new band grows with further hole-doping. Typically in the metallic $CaVO_3$ (x=1) sample, the optical conductivity shows the onsets at 3.0 eV and 4.5eV (or the peaks around 3.5eV and 5.0eV), which can be likewise assigned to the charge-transfer bands from the O 2p valence states to the t_{2g}- and e_g-like V 3d states, respectively. Obviously, these transitions are shifted to lower energy by about 1.5 eV, as compared with the corresponding transitions in YVO_3.

One of the important features observed in intermediately hole-doped samples (e.g. x=0.2 and 0.4) is that the two distinct lower-lying CT excitations are discernible, as indicated by downward and upward arrows in the spectra of X=0.2 and 0.4 samples (Fig.3). Since the initial state for the transitions is common, i.e. the topmost O 2p state, the observed optical conductivity spectra represent the double-stepped feature of the density of states for the unoccupied 3d (t_{2g}-like) states. In other words, the doping-induced new 3d states are formed near the Fermi level, which seems to coexist with the original upper Hubbard band. The upper Hubbard band as probed by the CT excitation spectra appears to collapse around x=0.5 where the insulator-metal transition takes place in $Y_{1-x}Ca_xVO_3$ system.

Such an ingap state is likely to be responsible also for the mid-infrared absorption band in the intermediately hole-doped compounds as typically seen for the x=0.2-0.6 samples. In the low-energy region where only the 3d bands are responsible for the transitions, a conspicuous change of the spectra is observed from the gap-like feature in YVO_3 to the Drude-like one in $CaVO_3$. With hole-doping the spectral weight below 1.5eV is critically increased. The onset of the optical conductivity is shifted to lower energy with x, showing a maximum in the mid-infrared region for the x=0.2-0.6 samples. With further increasing x, such a mid-infrared absorption tends to merge into the Drude-like absorption as typically seen for the x=1 ($CaVO_3$) spectrum.

The observed transitional behavior in the infrared region upon the insulator-metal transition for $Y_{1-x}Ca_xVO_3$ resembles those observed in cuprate superconductors, for example in $La_{2-x}Sr_xCuO_4$ [15] and $Pr_{2-x}Ce_xCuO_4$ [16]. Similarly to the present case, the layered cuprate compounds shows the mid-infrared absorption at the relatively low doping levels, the maximum of which shifts to lower energy and finally merges into the Drude-like absorption. Such a transitional behavior has been attributed to reshuffle of electronic structures and formation of the ingap states within the original charge-transfer gap upon carrier-doping. In layered cuprate compounds, the spectral weight for the ingap absorption is transferred from the charge-transfer excitation between the O 2p σ- and Cu 3d-like (upper Hubbard) bands. In the case of $Y_{1-x}Ca_xVO_3$, however, the infrared spectral weight in the hole doped samples appears not to come from the intensity of the optical transitions between the original Hubbard bands, but rather to borrow the intensity from the higher-lying transitions. This is perhaps because the energy positions of O 2p states relative to the V 3d band become closer with increasing x and hence the compounds show stronger hybridization between 2p and 3d orbitals in the higher-x samples.

We are grateful to Y.Fujishima, T.Arima, M.Kasuya, H.Eisaki, S.Uchida, A.Fujimori, Y.Iye and K.Kumagai for their collaboration throughout the present work.

References

[1] Y.Fujishima, Y.Tokura, T.Arima and S.Uchida, Physica C **185-189**, 1001 (1991); to be published in Phys. Rev. B.

[2] K.Kumagai, Y.Fujishima and Y.Tokura, unpublished; Y.Tokura et al. to be published.

[3] M.Kasuya, T.Arima, Y.Tokura, H.Aisaki and S.Uchida, to be published.

[4] J.Zaanen, G.A.Sawatzky and J.W.Allen, Phys.Rev.Lett. **55**, 418 (1985).

[5] Y.Maeno, S.Awaji, H.Matsumoto and T.Fujita, Pysica B, **165-166**, 1185 (1990).

[6] P.Dougier and P.Hagenmuller, J.Solid State Chem. **15**, 158 (1975).

[7] M.Sayer, R.Chen, R.Fletcher and A.Mansingh, J.Phys.C, **8**, 2059 (1975).

[8] D.A.MacLean, Hok-Nam Ng and J.E.Greedan, J.Solid State Chem., **30**, 35 (1979).

[9] J.E.Greedan, J.Less-Common Met. **111**, 335 (1985).

[10] D.A.MacLean and J.E.Greedan, Inorg.Chem. **20**, 1025 (1981).

[11] J.P.Goral, J.E.Greedan and D.A.MacLean, J.Solid State Chem. **43**, 244 (1982).

[12] F.Lichtenberg, D.Widmer, J.G.Bednorz, T.Williams and A.Reller, Z.Phys.B, **82**, 211 (1991).

[13] D.A.Crandles, T.Timusk and J.E.Greedan, Phys.Rev.B, **44** 13250 (1991).

[14] Y.Taguchi, Y.Tokura and T.Arima, to be published.

[15] S.Uchida, T.Ido, H.Takagi, T.Arima, Y.Tokura and S.Tajima, Phys.Rev. B **43**, 7942 (1991).

[16] S.L.Cooper et al. Phys.Rev.B **41**, 11605 (1990).

Tests for Nonreciprocal Optical Effects in High-Temperature Superconductors

A. Kapitulnik

Department of Applied Physics, Stanford University,
Stanford, CA 94305, USA

The existance of spontanous polar Kerr effect and Faraday effect in High-Tc films and crystals was tested using a Sagnac interferometer. Observation of these effects would be a strong evidence that the superconductivity in the cuprates is described by a theory that predicts broken time-reversal symmetry. No evidense of either polar Kerr rotation or Faraday effects were found when the data was analyzed for both a spatially fluctuating component (anticipating domains) and an absolute offset. The measurements were done with averaged sensitivity of less than 3μrad.

I. Introduction

It was proposed that superconductivity in the cuprates arises from a new type of ground state that spontanously [1,2]. This theory is based on the concept that in two spatial dimensions, one can obtain not only quantum ideal Bose and Fermi gases, but also quantum ideal gases of new types of particles that interpolate between those two extremes, hence obeying fractional statistics. Those particles are known generically as *anyons*. It was first pointed out by Laughlin and co-workers [3-5] that these gases form superfluids, and become superconductors if the anyons are electrically charged. Thus, similar to a magnetic material, an anyon superconductor will exhibit a spontaneous Hall effect and magneto-optical effects. Polarized light that go through such a sample will exhibit a non-reciprocal rotation of polarization equivalent to the Faraday effect (we denote the measured effect in this mode Θ_F). Similarly, in reflection, one expects to see an effect resembling the polar Kerr effect (we denote the measured effect in this mode Θ_K).

Several attempts have been made to observe these effects in the high-T_c cuprate superconductors. Experimental results to date have been contradictory. While we have reported some null results in transmission on YBCO [6] and BSCCO [7], K. B. Lyons et al. [8] at AT&T and H. J. Weber [9] at Dortmund have reported positive results in reflection and transmission on similar samples. Even the two positive results differ so much as to be irreconcilable. In the present paper we will avoid the analysis of other experiments and rather concentrate on the explanation of our own results. However, we emphasize that in most part the motivation for our recent experiments in reflection [10] was to resolve the discrepancies in the results of the various groups. The approach thus was to better duplicate the conditions in the experiments that yield positive results (e.g. wavelength, laser spot size etc.), while still retaining the fundamental advantages of our method of measurement over the other reported results.

The rotation of linearly polarized light that is called the Kerr effect, happens because the left- and right- circular components (RCP and LCP) acquire a difference in phase $\Delta\phi$ upon

Springer Series in Solid-State Sciences, Vol. 113 **Electronic Properties of High-T_c Superconductors**
Editors: H. Kuzmany, M. Mehring, J. Fink

reflection. In general, there will be a difference in the magnitude of the reflected components as well, resulting in an elliptically polarized beam. At the sample surface, RCP and LCP are equivalent except that the electric field vectors have opposite time dependence. Because the sample is not T preserving, it is possible for these two components to be treated differently, and hence produce an observable optical effect. However, detecting the Kerr effect by analyzing the polarization state is made difficult by birefringence and linear dichroism in the sample. Although these phenomena are T-preserving, they can, nevertheless, affect the polarization state of the light, because they couple from RCP to LCP and vice-versa. We have used a method in which $\Delta\phi$ is measured directly. Two beams are incident on the sample, one RCP and one LCP, and the difference in phase shift they acquire is measured by a Sagnac interferometer. Birefringence and dichroism couple some light into the other (circular) polarization state, but this component is later blocked by a polarizer.

II. Experiment

To search for broken T symmetry we have used a fiber optic Sagnac interferometer as described in Refs. [6,7,10]. It is however important to understand the basic ingredients of this method to appreciate the final result. In brief, light from a 670 nm laser diode (or in other cases from a 1060 nm source) is launched into polarization maintaining single mode optical fiber. After the light has passed through a polarizer it is purely single mode, both spatially and in polarization. The light is then split into two beams by a loop coupler. These two beams propagate in opposite directions around the loop, which contains a phase modulator, the sample, and 20 m (or ~1 km for the 1060 source) of polarization maintaining fiber. If the loop is a reciprocal path, meaning its optical length does not depend upon the direction of propagation, then the two beams will return to loop coupler precisely in phase and the maximum possible intensity will return through the polarizer and eventually to the detector. If the loop is nonreciprocal, then the intensity will reduce to $1+\cos(\Delta\phi)$ of the maximum. The system is actively biased with a phase modulator, to enable measurements of very small $\Delta\phi$. The drift of the system is approximately 5 μrad. Note that because of the two propagating beams, we have $\Delta\phi=2\Theta_F$ in the case of transmission , and $\Delta\phi=2\Theta_K$ in reflection. A bulk optics portion is then inserted into the loop to provide the selection of one of the eigenmodes of polarization, i.e. right or left circularly polarized light, that will pass through (or reflected from) the sample. The $1/e^2$ beam diameter was measured to be 15 - 18 μm. The immunity of this system to spurious signals as well as its high degree of rejection of reciprocal effects are discussed in our other publications [6,7,10].

The spatial filtering provided by the single-mode fiber requires that the sample, like the other components, be aligned precisely, both in angle and focus. Thermal expansion and other disturbances make this alignment difficult to maintain, especially if the sample holder is fixed to the cold finger. In the case of BSCCO crystals, which have rippled surfaces, this difficulty renders the experiment virtually impossible. To overcome this problem, the sample rotation and translation have been decoupled from each other and from the motion of the cold finger.

The sample holder is mounted mechanically via a thin wall stainless steel tube to a pair of goniometers outside the cryostat vacuum. These provide two rotation axes in the plane of the sample. The goniometers attach to the vacuum shroud with a flexible bellows. The sample holder is thermally grounded to the cold head with a flexible bundle of copper strands. This configuration allows the sample to be translated and tilted with five nearly decoupled degrees of freedom, while being isolated from the motion in the cryostat pump line and transfer tube. Samples were mounted with thermal grease to the sample holder. A Pt thin film thermometer mounted on the sample holder read within 15 Kelvin of the cold finger temperature. The Laser power used was 60μW.

Several BSCCO single crystals were studied, as well as YBCO films. The BSCCO crystals were grown from a near stoichiometric melt in a strong thermal gradient using a magnesia crucible. Details of the crystal growth method are reported elsewhere [11]. Magnetometry on similar samples from the same melt indicated a superconducting transition at T_c = 85 K. For transmission experiments, samples were cleaved to thicknesses between 600 Å and 2000 Å. The YBCO films were grown by single target off-axis sputtering [12]. The films thicknesses were between 50 Å and 800 Å, and had transition temperatures of ~85 K, measured by four-point resistivity and by ac susceptibility.

Samples were placed in the Sagnac loop as described and cooled to temperatures as low as 11 K in the transmission measurements and down to 40 K in the reflection experiments. At each temperature, the beam was moved to various points on the sample surface and the nonreciprocal signal $\Delta\phi$ was measured. A variance in the values of $\Delta\phi$ would indicate a random domain structure exists, whereas a constant offset would indicate a single handedness of the anyon state over the sample surface. Neither of these was seen to within the sensitivity of our apparatus. The upper limit on offset is set by the drift in the apparatus, 5 μrad. The variance measurements can be performed on a much shorter time scale than that of the drift. We have placed an upper limit on the variance at $\sigma_{\Delta\phi} \leq 1\mu$rad in transmission and at $\sigma_{\Delta\phi} \leq 3\mu$rad in reflection .

The apparatus was tested in several ways in both, transmission and reflection configurations. To check for rejection of reciprocal effects, linearly birefringent materials as well as optically active solution of sugar were used. No signal was observed down to the sensitivity of the apparatus. In fact, the rejection of reciprocal effects is several orders of magnitude better than our sensitivity. Non-reciprocal effects were observed when magnetic materials were studied. In transmission, we have used submonolayers of EuO (Curie temperature of ~70 K) to test the response of the system as well as its sensitivity. We have also used thin films of gd in both transmission and reflection. The ferromagnetic transition of Gd was clearly measured even in reflection with tilting fields as small as 70 Oe (this field which is only 3.5% of the saturation field produced a maximum signal of ~50μrad, or a Kerr angle of ~25μrad).

III. Results

Fig. 1 shows the row data from a typical measurement on 1000Å thin $Bi_2Sr_2CaCu_2O_8$ single crystal. As for all other cases, no signal was detected. Thus, it is important to carefully discuss this result in view of possible intrinsic difficulties that may reduce the signal.

Since the domains of broken T are presumably smaller than the spot size, the spatial resolving power of the apparatus is an important quantity to consider. Since the spot is an image of the optical mode propagating in the fiber, its profile is nearly gaussian. The $1/e^2$ radius, w, is

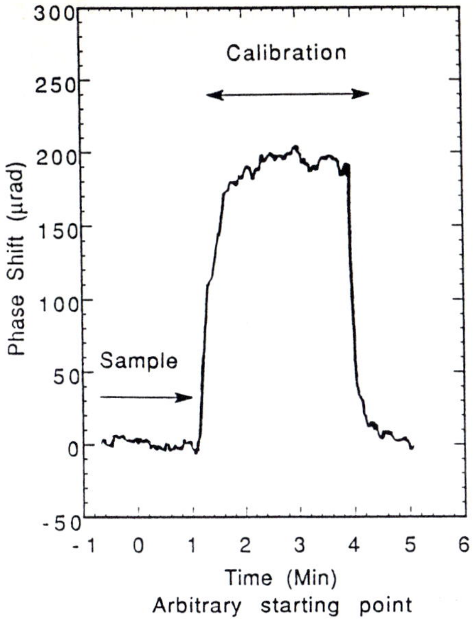

Fig. 1. Typical data for reflection from high quality $Bi_2Sr_2CaCu_2O_8$ single crystal at a temperature of 70 K. Between t=-1min and t=1min the figure shows time trace of the phase shift reading from the sample. At time t=1min, a calibration signal using Terbiumborosilicate was switched on as a reference.

9μm, measured with a knife edge. The spatial frequency response of the system falls to 1/e at a frequency of $f_c \approx 1/(2w)$, and decreases as $\exp[-(2wf_c)^2]$. Therefore, a domain pattern containing only frequencies above fc, for example, a structure periodic in the plane of the sample with a frequency $f > f_c$, would produce little or no fluctuation as the beam is scanned. However, it is unlikely that the anionic domains would order periodically. One would expect the geometry of the domains to be strongly constrained to grain boundaries and other types of disorder prevalent in these materials. Each domain will " choose" the sign of its chirality randomly. The resulting random patchwork would have no lower cutoff in spatial frequency and the signal will scale as (d/w) with d being the averaged domain size.

Assuming no periodic ordering of the domains, we have found the following:

1) No effect in transmission for a laser wavelength of 1060 nm to an accuracy of $\Theta_F \leq 1$ μrad in YBaCuO films of thicknesses 50, 200, 500, and 800 Å and BiSrCaCuO cleaved crystal of thickness 1000 Å . In these experiments the temperature was varied from room temperature down to 11 K and a magnetic field of 100 G was applied in some of the experiments in either field cooled or zero field cooled schedules.

2) No effect in transmission for a laser wavelength of 670 nm to an accuracy of $\Theta_F \leq 5$ μrad in BiSrCaCuO cleaved single crystals of thicknesses 600, 1000, and 1500 Å . The temperature was varied from room temperature down to 20 K and a magnetic field of 200 G was applied in some of the experiments in either field cooled or zero field cooled schedules.

3) No effect in transmission for a laser wavelength of 1060 nm to an accuracy of $\Theta_F \leq 1$ μrad in BiSrCaCuO cleaved crystal with a simultaneous exposure to a 633 nm radiation (photo-induced experiment), with and without magnetic field and with the temperature varied between room temperature and 20 K.
4) No effect in reflection for a laser wavelength of 670 nm to an accuracy of $\Theta_K \leq 2$ μrad in YBaCuO films of thicknesses 500, 800 and 2000Å and BiSrCaCuO crystals. The temperature was varied from room temperature down to 40 K and a magnetic field of 200 G was applied in some of the experiments in either field cooled or zero field cooled schedules. Some of the films used were identical to those used in the transmission experiments.

IV. Discussion

Our results put a very stringent bound on the existence of anyons in high-temperature superconductors.In fact, with the assumption of a single domain, we conclude that the rotation per Cu-O plane is no more than 2μrad. Of course, we realize that other complications and in particular the existence of very small domains may reduce the signal substantially. Our result is also in excellent agreement with the muon spin relaxation measurements [13] where a bound of 0.8 G was put to the internal magnetic field due to the disturbance of the muon, a number which is much smaller than any estimate that was done so far.

We realize however that there is still some discrepancies among the optical experiments. It is clear that all three experiments [6-10] do not agree with each other. First, the experiment of Weber et al. on BSCCO crystals is directly compared to the results presented here in both type of experiments (i.e. transmission and reflection) and wavelength. The observed position independent 5000μrad of rotation by Weber et al., which imply a single domain of chirality, will agree with our results only if the domain size in our sample is d ~ (5/5000)·15μm ~ 150Å. With the assumption that both experiments used high quality single crystals, it is hard to reconcile the 5 orders of magnitude difference in domain size between the samples used in this study and those used by Weber et al. Moreover, we would expect the results of Weber et al. in reflection from YBaCuO untwinned crystals to be directly compared to our results on YBaCuO films. In this case, Weber et al.'s result imply a domain size in the Stanford experiment of ~10Å. This length is much smaller than the typical crystallite size or twinning domains in the films.

The second point is the comparison between the reflection and transmission experiments. In a magneto-optic medium where the real and imaginary part of the indices of refraction are of the same order, all magneto-optic effects measured in terms of specific rotation (i.e. rotation per unit length) are of same order. This is easy to see if we write:

$$A=f_1(n,k)\sigma'_{xy}+f_2(n,k)\sigma''_{xy}$$

where A can either be the Faraday angle Θ_F, or the specific rotation associated with reflection Θ_K/δ, where the optical penetration depth δ or it can be the magnetic circular dichroism.

σ'_{xy} and σ''_{xy} are the real and imaginary parts of the off-diagonal term of the conductivity tensor which is the part that contains all the information about the magnetic state (or anyon state) [14].

The functions f_1 and f_2 depend on the optical properties of the material with the magnetic (anyon) contribution switched off. For all high Tc, n and k have been measured and therefore f_1 and f_2 are known for all three cases. It is thus found that all magneto-optic quantities mix n and k in a similar way. Thus, just based on this argument we expect transmission and reflection measurements to give a similar order of specific rotation . We therefore expect the reflectivity measurements of Lyons et al. to also agree with our measurements in both transmission and reflection modes. The results of Lyons et al. and Weber et al. dissagree even between each other in this respect because the beam size of Lyons et al. was very similar to ours. It is also important to note that those other two experiments show a completely different temperature dependence of the positive effect that they measure.

The possibility of observing a finite effect in reflection but no effect in transmission was considered by Dzyalushinskii [15]. He argues that if the layers order with alternating chirality (i.e. antiferromagnetic ordering) such that pairs of layers exist within each crystallographic unit cell (i.e. the AFM wavelength does not coincide with the lattice periodicity), no effect will be observed in a transmission experiment but in reflection a small effect, of size of one layer will appear. It is clear at this stage that since we present measurements in both transmission and reflection modes with no signal observed that this hypothesis is falsified. An important point should be added about the symmetry argument. Such an argument that predicts no effect in transmission is valid for an infinite system. For a system with a finite thickness, as are all our samples, and in particular if the samples have rough and irregular surfaces, a single layer effect may be observed despite the global symmetry argument.

In conclusion, we reported in this paper results that show no T breaking effects in either the rreal or the imaginary parts of the index of refraction. This finding in itself does not disprove the role of anyons in the materials investigated, however, it shows that if anyons do exist in high temperature superconductors, they exhibit much weaker optical effects in visible wavelengths than were previously deduced from measurements which did not benefit from the advantages of the Sagnac interferometer. We thus give a bound to the anyon theory of specific rotation of no more than 2μrad per Cu-O plane.

Acknowledgements

This work has been done in collaboration with S. Spielman, J.S. Dodge, M.M. Fejer, L. Lombardo, C.B. Eom and T.H. Geballe. I greatfully acknowledge useful discussions with R. Laughlin, B. Halperin and T. Lawrence. This work was supported by the National Science Foundation through the PYI program, by the AFOSR grant 91-0145 and by Stanford University Office of Technology Licensing. All samples for this research were made with support from Stanford Center for Materials Research through the MRL/NSF program.

References:

1. B.I. Halperin, J. March Russel and F. Wilszek, Phys. Rev. **B 40**, 8726 (1989).
2. X.G. Wen and A. Zee, Phys. Rev. Lett **62**, 2873 (1989).
3. R.B. Laughlin, Science **242**, 525 (1988).

4. V. Kalmayer and R. B. Laughlin, Phys. Rev. Lett. **59**, 2095 (1987).

5. C.B. Hanna, R.B. Laughlin and A.L. Fetter, Phys. Rev. **B 40**, 8745 (1989).

6. S. Spielman, K. Fesler, C.B. Eom, T.H. Geballe, M.M. Fejer and A. Kapitulnik, Phys. Rev. Lett. **65**, 123 (1990).

7. S. Spielman, J.S. Dodge, K. Fesler, L.W. Lombardo, M.M. Fejer, T.H. Geballe, and A. Kapitulnik, Phys. Rev. **B** (1992).

8. K.B. Lyons, J. Kwo, J.F. Dillon, Jr., G.P. Espinosa, M. McGlashan-Powell, A.P. Ramirez and L.F. Schneemeyer, Phys. Rev. Lett. **64**, 2949 (1990).

9. H.J. Weber, D. Weibrecht, D. Brach, H. Keiter, A.L. Shelankov, W. Weber, Th. Wolf, J. Geerk, G. LinkerG. Roth, P.C. Splittgerber-Hunnekes and G. Guntherodt, Solid State Comm. **76**, 511 (1990).

10. S. Spielman, J.S. Dodge, L.W. Lombardo, C.B. Eom, M.M. Fejer, T.H. Geballe, and A. Kapitulnik, (1991) submitted for publication.

11. L. Lombardo and A. Kapitulnik, to appear in J. of Crystal Growth, 1992.

12. C.B. Eom , J.Z. Sun, K.Y. Yamamoto, A.F. Marshall, K.E. Luther and T.H. Geballe, Appl. Phys. Lett. **55** , 595 (1989).

13. R.F. Kefl et al. Phys. Rev. Lett. **64**, 2082 (1990).

14. see e.g. R.W. White and T.H. Geballe, "Long Range Order in Solids", (Academic Press, New-York,1979) p. 317.

15. I. Dzyaloshinskii, in proceedings of the TCSUH Workshop on the Physics and Mathematics of Anyons, World Scientific Publishing, Singapore, 1991.

Search for Time Reversal Symmetry Violation in High-Temperature Superconductors

A.L. Shelankov

Institute of Physics, University Dortmund,
W-4600 Dortmund 50, Fed. Rep. of Germany and
A.F. Ioffe Institute, 194021 St. Petersburg, Russia

Abstract. In the anyon and flux phase models of high temperature superconductivity, the time reversal symmetry is spontaneously broken. We survey recent experiments, mainly optical, searching for the symmetry violation, and critically discuss attempts to reconcile the contradicting optical data.

Introduction

Attempts to understand the mechanism of high temperature superconductivity have lead to a lot of suggestions. The most exotic among them is the idea of anyon superconductivity put forward by Kalmeyer and Laughlin [1] (for a review see [2]). The idea exploits the fact that the charge carriers in the cuprates are confined to copper-oxygen planes and, in good approximation, may be considered as two dimensional(2D). As it has first been demonstrated by Laughlin in the theory of the quantum Hall effect, charge excitations in a strongly correlated 2D Fermi system do not need to be fermions: they may have fractional statistics - to be anyons. When two identical anyons are interchanged (in a counter-clockwise manner), their wave function acquires a phase factor $\exp(i\theta)$, and the "statistical angle" θ, $0 \leq |\theta| \leq \pi$, characterizes the actual statistics of the excitations which lies between bosonic ($\theta = 0$) and fermionic ($\theta = \pi$). The intermediate statistics is a result of specific spin correlations (in a chiral spin liquid [1]) and the anyon hypothesis represents itself an elegant way to describe the interaction between the charge and spin degrees of freedom. The anyon description of strong correlations is closely related, if not equivalent, to the theory of flux phases in the 2D Hubbard model [3]. There exist rather convincing theoretical arguments in favor of a superconducting ground state of a system of free anyons [1,2]. The superconductivity would be of electronic origin, and the critical temperature is believed to be high enough for present and future needs.

The anyon as well as the flux phase models, implicitly assume that the time reversal (T) and 2D reflection symmetry (P) are broken in the ground state: Under the T-transformation, when the wave function is changed to its complex conjugate, the statistical parameter defined via the phase factor $\exp(i\theta)$, changes its sign, $T\theta = -\theta$. An unambiguous definition of the above "counter-clockwise manner" can be made only if one specifies the direction of the normal to the 2D plane, $\mathbf{n}$, which "looks to the eye". Under P (mirror reflection in the plane $\perp$ to the 2D plane), the counter- and clockwise paths replace each other, so that $\mathbf{n}$ is reversed, $P\mathbf{n} = -\mathbf{n}$.

The special symmetry properties of a 2D system of identical particles with intermediate statistics can be characterized by a "statistical vector" $\mathbf{s} = \mathbf{n}\sin\theta$: the vector is odd relative to the T and P transformations and is even relative to the combined PT. Being P- odd, **s** is a 3D pseudovector. From the point of view of symmetry, the anyon (or flux phase) state is identical to a (Ising) ferromagnet - in the both cases the state is characterized by a T-odd pseudovector, **s** or the spin vector. Therefore, one may expect all the effects allowed by symmetry in magnets to exist in an anyon system. Depending on the distribution of the sign of **s** over adjacent copper-oxygen layers - alternating or uniform - the anyon system would be closer to an anti- or a ferromagnet. Macroscopic consequences of the broken symmetry have been analyzed by Halperin et al.[4].

The purpose of the paper is to discuss recent experiments motivated by the flux phase/anyon hypothesis and searching for manifestations of broken time reversal symmetry in high temperature superconductors. Most attention will be paid to the contradictory picture emerging from the optical data.

Experiment

All the experiments are based on the above argument that **s** is equivalent by symmetry to the spin in a magnet. As in a magnet, one may expect an internal magnetic field, $\mathbf{h} = 4\pi\gamma\mathbf{s}$, generated by the magnetization $\gamma\mathbf{s}$. The in-plane components of the dielectric tensor are expected to be asymmetric,

$$2\Delta \equiv \varepsilon_{xy} - \varepsilon_{yx} = A\,(\mathbf{h}_{eff})_z\ ,\ \mathbf{h}_{eff} = \mathbf{h} + B\mathbf{s}\ , \qquad (1)$$

so that spontaneous Faraday and dc Hall effects are allowed. The magneto- optical coefficients of the material would determine A, whereas the material constants γ and B must be provided by a microscopic anyon theory. At present, the theory [2, 4, 5] is unable to give definite quantitative predictions.

Direct measurements of magnetic fields by the muon spin rotation technique have been performed by Kiefl et al.[6]. The technique provides a local probe and would be sensitive in case of arbitrary distribution of **h** over layers. The samples were sintered powder of 123-compound (T_c= 90 K) and films of 2212 (T_c= 85 K). To check the possible role of screening of **h** by the Meissner currents, a 123-sample with very fine grains was also studied. Given experimental uncertainties, no anomalies were observed. The upper level for the magnetic field is evaluated as 0.8 G, much less then a theoretical estimate, 15 G [4].

Local magnetic fields have also been probed by Aronov and Masterov [7]. They use a disordered network of Josephson junctions formed by grown-in 2212 and 2223 phases. The system being placed in a very weak external magnetic field is known to show strong generation of even RF-harmonics. Were the local fields finite, they would influence individual Josephson junctions and lead to the even RF-harmonics generation in zero external field. The method is believed to be sensitive to the field varying on a (submicron) scale of the typical size of a junction. The zero field measurements above 77 K give a null result. Measured in units of the external magnetic field, the T-symmetry violation is found to be below 0.001 G.

Gijs et al.[8] have checked the Onsager symmetry in the resistivity tensor of 123-films. In case of uniform distribution of **s** , the macroscopic zero field Hall is expected, and it would violate the symmetry. Within the experimental resolution of few parts in 10000, no clear evidence for the violation is seen. Another test sensitive in case of uniform **s**, asymmetry of the magnetoresistance in the conditions of the Little-Parks effect, has also given a negative result [9].

Optical data

The first positive result has been reported by Lyons et al. [10] who made ellipsometric measurements of reflection of light (λ= 514 nm) by the 123 and 2212 crystals and films. Circular dichroism (CD) was observed, i.e. an effect predicted by theory [11] and signifying the asymmetry in ε Eq.(1). With the zero average, the CD-signal fluctuated when the 20μ beam spot scanned the surface. Depending on the sample, the mean square deviation exceeded the error level at temperatures below 200-300 K, and reached 100-300 μrad at $T \to 0$. The data were compatible with the picture of domains with random orientation of **s**.

Ellipsometric reflection and transmission measurements made by Weber et al.[12] have also been interpreted as evidence for T-symmetry violation. Rotation of polarization of light (630 nm) as a result of reflection from a one-domain 123-crystal was observed below 110 K. The rotation, of order of 0.01 rad, was almost uniform across the surface. The sign of it was random in different temperature runs. However, the cooling in external magnetic field (200-500 G) gave a (zero field) rotation with the sign controlled the direction of the "annealing" field. In transmission through thin (100 nm) single crystal samples of 2212, the rotation of polarization of order 0.001 rad, and the field cooling effect were also observed below 130 K.

Spielman et al.[13] have tested the asymmetry in ε by measuring circular birefrigence of 123-films. They used an interferometry fiber set-up which measures the difference between the phases of two circular light (1.06 μ) waves having traversed the sample in opposite directions. Only the part of the response which is due to T-symmetry violation (i.e.nonreciprocal), contributed to the output signal of their set-up. The measurements showed no trace of, either homogeneous or fluctuating, nonreciprocal signal within the sensitivity 2 μrad.

Discussion

As we see, the optical data reported by different groups are in conflict with each other. Being in qualitative contradiction with the null interferometry data [13], the positive results of [10] and [12] disagree with each other in the onset temperature, the magnitude of the effect, and its character - hardly any [12] versus strong fluctuations with zero average [10]. Although a full ellipsometric measurement allows to discriminate between non- and reciprocal responses [14], the apparatuses in [10, 12] do not, and the bulk of the ellipsometric data could be interpreted when the T-symmetry is valid. (The only exception is the magnetic annealing experiments [12] which, however, have not been independently reproduced so far.) Interpreted in favor of the T-symmetry violation, can the positive results of [10 and 12] be reconciled with the null of [13]?

The reconciliation proposed by Dzyaloshinskii , is reached in the following scenario [15]. In case of antiferromagnetic (AF) plane-to-plane ordering of **s**, the macroscopic T-symmetry is broken only if the chemical unit cell contains two Cu-O planes: it would be broken in the 123 and 2212, and preserved in one plane La-based compounds. The space symmetry of the 123 and 2212 includes the (3D) inversion I if $\mathbf{s} = 0$. When $\mathbf{s}$ is finite, only the combined TI is valid. In a crystal with this symmetry, the magnetoelectric effect is allowed, i.e.magnetic induction $\mathbf{B} = \mu\mathbf{H} + \alpha\mathbf{E}$, α being the magnetoelectric coefficient. The arguments based on the Onsager relation show that the effect does not lead to bulk rotation of polarization, and no circular birefrigence is allowed. In reflection , nonreciprocity $\sim\alpha$ is expected in case of the 123 and 2212, and zero is predicted for the one plain La-compounds. This scenario makes the contradiction in the optical data only seeming, and ascribes it to the distinction between the reflection and transmission modes.

In our opinion, the scenario is unable to resolve the contradiction. The point is that in the case when light propagates along the c-axis, as in [10 - 13], the effect is rather of the surface then bulk origin. In accordance with [15], $\alpha \sim ka\,\Delta$, where $k = \omega/c$ is the wave vector of light, a is the atomic distance, and Δ, Eq.(1), is the one layer asymmetry of ε. The effect is proportional to ka and, therefore, the nonreciprocity exhibited by a crystal and that for one layer are comparable. This points to importance of nonreciprocity in the boundary conditions for the macroscopic fields neglected in [15].

We believe that basic physics can be grasped in a semi-microscopic description where $\mathbf{D}$ and $\mathbf{E}$ are related locally, and subject to the standard boundary conditions, but Δ Eq.(1) is a periodic function of the coordinate z along the c-axis, $\Delta(z+a) = \Delta(z)$, a being the period of the $\mathbf{s}$-structure. The AF-ordering implies the space average $\langle\Delta(z)\rangle=0$. The TI-symmetry leads to $\Delta(z) = -\Delta(-z)$ if $z = 0$ belongs to a plane of the TI-centers; in case of one-plane materials, an additional relation, $\Delta(z + a/2) = - \Delta(z)$, holds. Here, we present only results for the case when the anisotropy and multiple reflections are ignored. The (normalized) circular dichroism in reflection, CD , reads

$$CD=4\,ka\,\mathrm{Im}\,\delta(\mathcal{Z})/(n^2-1), \quad a\delta(z) \equiv \int_0^z dz\,\Delta(z) - \int_0^a dz \int_0^z dz\,\Delta(z)/a, \tag{2}$$

where $\delta(z)$ is a periodic function with $\langle\delta\rangle=0$, $\mathcal{Z}$ is the position of the reflection plane, and n is the refraction index. If light traverses a film, $\mathcal{L} < z < \mathcal{R}$, placed on a substrate ($z < \mathcal{L}$), the "circular birefrigence" signal ϕ of [13] is given by

$$\phi = 2\,ka\,\mathrm{Re}\{\delta(\mathcal{L})/(n + n_s) - \delta(\mathcal{R})/(n_s + 1)\}\ , \tag{3}$$

n_s being the refraction index of the substrate.

Eqs.2 and 3 show: (i) The CD-effect in reflection is indeed of the order of $ka\,\Delta$, but its sign and the value depend on $\mathcal{Z}$, i.e. the effect is crucially sensitive to the manner the crystal is terminated. On the other hand, a higher symmetry of the one plain compounds does not forbid the effect. (ii) Indeed, $\phi = 0$ for a free standing ($n_s = 1$) ideal crystal, when the TI-symmetry leads to $\delta(\mathcal{L}) = \delta(\mathcal{R})$. (iii) The interference signal in transmission, ϕ , is expected to be of order of the CD in reflection in real situation when the substrate index $n_s \neq 1$, and, very probably, $\delta(\mathcal{L}) \neq \delta(\mathcal{R})$ due to the difference in the microscopic structures of the two interfaces of the film. The symmetry consideration of [15], and also of [16], appears to be irrelevant because of primary importance of the surface.

By these arguments,we do not think the TI-scenario [15, 16] is able to reconcile the data. The null result of the interferometric measurements in reflection [17] supports this point of view. Another possibility is discussed in [14]: In contrast to the interferometric technique measuring only coherent processes, the ellipsometric one is sensitive also to quasielastic scattering. If one believes that mainly the inelastic component shows nonreciprocity, the data may be reconciled. So far, however, the suggestion has been backed up by neither experiment nor a model.

The positive results meet also difficulties being confronted with recent findings of Krichevtsov et al.[18]. They have measured the magneto-optical constant (proportional to A in Eq.(1)) of the 123, which turned out to be not anomalously large. The circular effects of [10 and 12] would require homogeneous $\mathbf{h}_{eff}$ in Eq.(1) to be as high as 20-2000 kG [18] (and $\sim 10^3$ higher local fields in case of the AF-ordering). Although $\mathbf{h}_{eff}$ may be in any relation with real field $\mathbf{h}$, it would be not easy to build a theory where the anyon magnetic moment γ is compensated in a real solid with the very high precision needed to reconcile the optical data [10,12] with the null result of the magnetic field measurements [6-9].

In conclusion, the only known evidences in favor of a broken T-symmetry - the optical data in [10] and [12], (i) do not agree with each other; (ii) can not be reconciled with other optical measurements [13]; (iii) give the size of the effect, which hardly can be understood simultaneously with the magnetic data [6-9]; (iiii) allow interpretation where the T-symmetry is preserved. In this situation, the only conclusion possible is that no convincing experimental evidences in favor of broken T-symmetry in high-T_c's have been presented so far.

Acknowledgements

I would like to thank H. Keiter and W. Weber for numerous discussions and for reading the manuscript. This work has been supported by Deutsche Forschungsgemeinschaft.

References

1. V.Kalmeyer and R.V.Laughlin, Phys.Rev.Lett. **59**, 2095 (1987); R.V.Laughlin, Phys.Rev.Lett. **60**, 2677 (1988).
2. Proceedings of the TCSUH Workshop "Physics and Mathematics of Anyons ", eds.S.S.Chern, C.W.Chu and C.S.Ting, World Scientific (1991).
3. B.Baskaran, Z.Zou, and P.W.Anderson, Solid State Commun.**63**, 973 (1987); R.V.Laughlin in Ref.[2], p.22.
4. B.I.Halperin, J.March-Russell, and F.Wilczek, Phys.Rev.**B 40**, 8725 (1989); B.I.Halperin,in "Proceedings of the Second ISSP International Symposium on the Physics and Chemistry of Oxide Superconductors, Tokyo, Japan, January 16-18, 1991.
5. P.W.Wiegmann, Phys.Rev.Lett.**65**, 2070 (1990).
6. R.F.Kiefl et al, Phys.Rev.Lett.**64**,2082 (1990).
7. A.G.Aronov and V.F.Masterov, Pis'ma ZhETF **54**, 453 (1991).
8. A.M.Gijs et al., Phys.Rev.**B42**, 10789 (1990).
9. P.L.Gammel et al., Phys.Rev. **B41**, 2593 (1990).
10. K.B.Lyons et al., Phys. Rev. Lett., **64**, 2949 (1990); K.B.Lyons and J.F.Dillon, Jr, p.37 in [2].
11. X.G.Wen and A.Zee, Phys. Rev. **B41**, 240 (1990)
12. H.J.Weber et al., Solid State Commun. 76, 511 (1990); H.J.Weber in [2], p.52.
13. S.Spielman et al., Phys. Rev. Lett. 65, 123 (1990)

14. A.L.Shelankov and G.E.Pikus , to be published in Phys.Rev.B.
15. I.G.Dzyaloshinskii, Phys.Lett. A **155**, 62 (1991).
16. G.S.Canright and A.G.Rojo, Phys.Rev.Lett. 68, 1601 (1992).
17. A.Kapitulnik, this conference.
18. B.B.Krichevtsov, V.V.Pavlov, R.V.Pisarev, and A.B.Sherman, Pis'ma ZhETF **54**, 86 (1991); and Solid State Commun.(1992).

Far-Infrared Applications of High-Temperature Superconductors: Fabry-Pérot Resonators and Fast Detectors

K.F. Renk

Institut für Angewandte Physik, Universität Regensburg, W-8400 Regensburg, Fed. Rep. of Germany

Abstract. Far-infrared applications of high temperature superconductors, namely Fabry-Pérot resonators and fast detectors, are reported. At terahertz frequencies high finesse ($\sim$ 60 at 3 THz) is obtained for Fabry-Pérot resonators with $YBa_2Cu_3O_7$-on-MgO reflectors and fast, nonbolometric response with a response time < 100 ps is found for structured $YBa_2Cu_3O_7$ thin films at frequencies from 0.1 THz to nearly 10 THz.

Recently it has been shown that $YBa_2Cu_3O_7$ thin films are suitable for fabricating of Fabry-Pérot resonators [1] and that structured films are suitable for fast detection of radiation [2]. In this paper the present status of these developments is sketched.

A Fabry-Pérot resonator consists of two plane parallel reflectors. In conventional far-infrared Fabry-Pérot resonators the reflectors are metal mesh [3]; they are used for analysis of far-infrared laser lines and in infrared astronomy. For a superconducting Fabry-Pérot resonator reflectors consisted of two $YBa_2Cu_3O_7$ (YBCO) films on dielectric MgO [1] or Si [4] plates.

An electromagnetic field acting on a YBCO film (with c axis perpendicular to the film plane) accelerates the charge carriers according to Ohm's law, with a dynamical conductivity shown in Fig. 1 [5]. In the normal state the real part, σ_1, of the dynamical conductivity is larger than the imaginary part, σ_2, at far-infrared frequencies while in the superconducting state $\sigma_1 \ll \sigma_2$. Therefore, in the normal state ohmic losses are strong while in the superconducting state the current is mainly inductive and therefore only weak losses occur. Superconducting YBCO films, though they have still residual absorption, are well suitable for fabricating of Fabry-Pérot resonators, up to frequencies around the gap frequency (near 400 cm^{-1} or $2\Delta(0)/k_BT_c \approx 6$).

Fabry-Pérot resonators with YBCO-on-Si reflectors have shown high transmissivity but low finesse [4]. Higher finesse has been obtained for YBCO-on-MgO reflectors [6]. Each reflector consisted

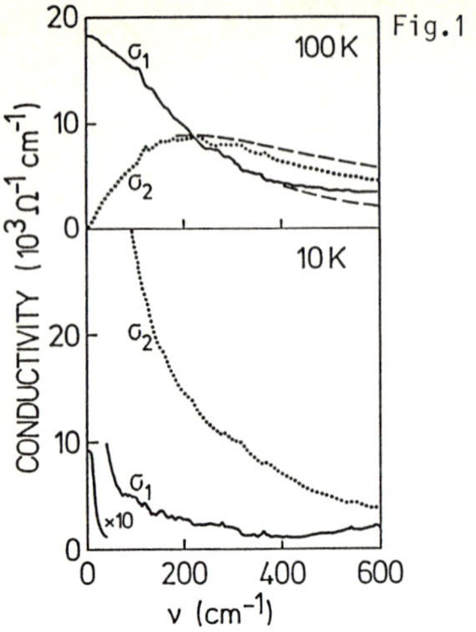

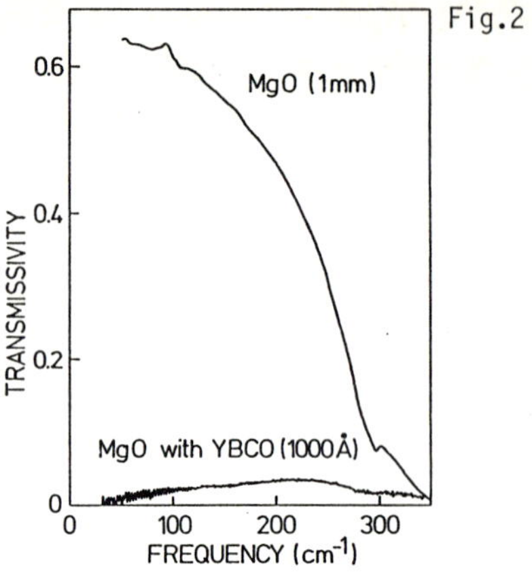

Fig. 1. Dynamical conductivity of YBCO in the (a,b) plane [5].

Fig. 2. Transmissivity of a MgO plate (1 mm thick) and of the plate covered with YBCO (1000Å thick).

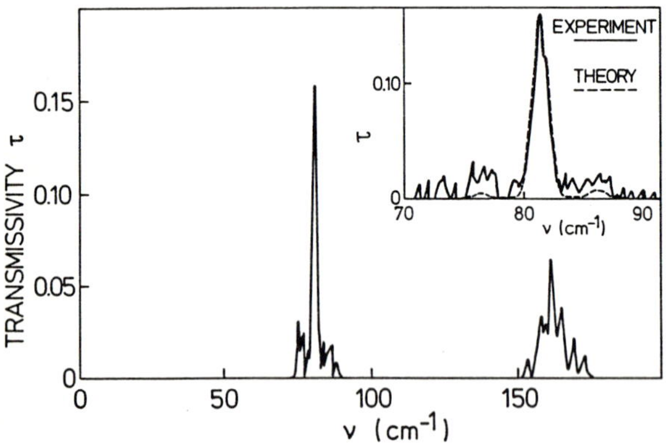

Fig. 3. Resonance curve of a Fabry-Pérot resonator.

of a YBCO film deposited on a MgO plate. The transmissivity of a MgO plate (Fig. 2) shows high transmissivity up to about 200 cm^{-1} and opacity above 300 cm^{-1} because of a reststrahlen band (at 400 cm^{-1}).

Two YBCO-on-MgO reflectors in parallel, with a distance of 63 μm between the YBCO films, had a transmission characteristic shown in Fig. 3, with the first and second order resonances. The peak-transmissivity (~ 0.15) was mainly restricted because of non-

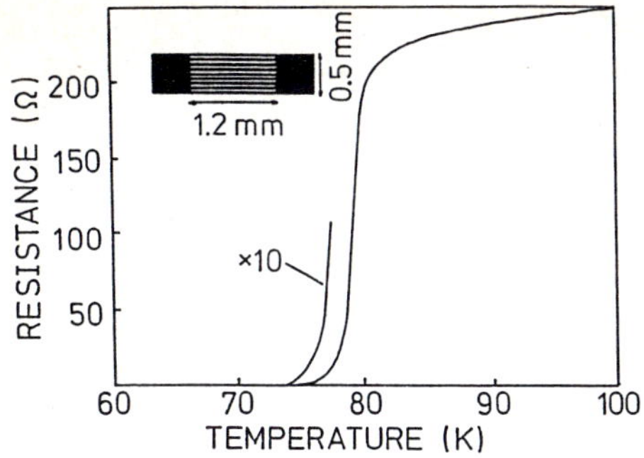

Fig. 4. Resistance of a structured YBCO film.

parallelism of the plates [6]. The finesse had a value of ~ 60 which is half the value reached with metal mesh Fabry-Pérot resonators [7]. There is a high contrast, between the resonances there was no intensity that could be measured with a Fourier infrared spectrometer. The resonances show sidebands (inset of Fig. 3) because of coupling of the main resonance (between the films) and the resonances within the MgO plates; the dashed line is calculated [6].

YBCO on MgO has also been used as outcoupling mirror of a p-germanium far-infrared laser [8].

For a basic description of YBCO film properties and superconducting Fabry-Pérot resonators see Ref.9, and for a description of fast detectors Refs. 9 and 10.

A variety of different studies have been performed with respect to both high sensitive bolometric detection, see for instance Ref.11, and fast detection (see Refs. 9 and 10). Fast far-infrared detection has been performed by use of polycrystalline films (12,9,10) and structured epitaxial YBCO films [2,13,14].

The structured YBCO film sample (Fig. 4, inset) consisted of 9 stripes (each 30 μm wide, film thickness $\sim$ 700Å). The sample was cooled to ~ 77 K and kept in a resistive state, at a resistance far below the normal state resistance (Fig. 4). A small current (0.1 mA) was applied to the sample. Irradiation of the sample with pulsed radiation resulted in a resistance change that was measured by detecting (by use of a fast oscilloscope) the voltage change over the sample.

The optical response to radiation pulses (duration 3 ps, wavelength 1.06 μm) of a Nd:YAG laser is shown in Fig. 5 [2]. At low power (lowest curve) there is a fast response with a time dependence given by the electronic equipment. This result shows that the detector has a fast response time, most likely below 100 ps. At

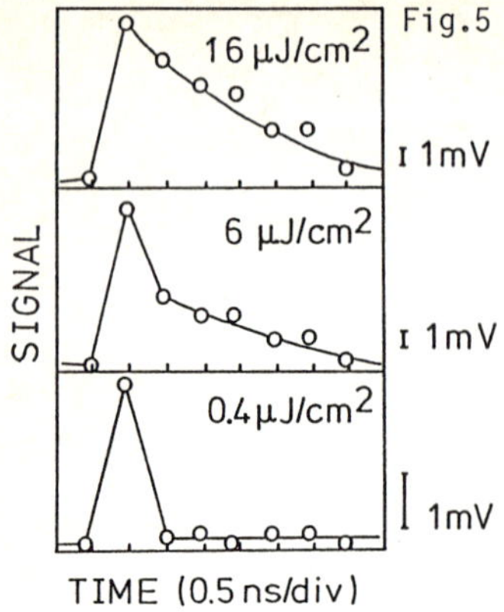

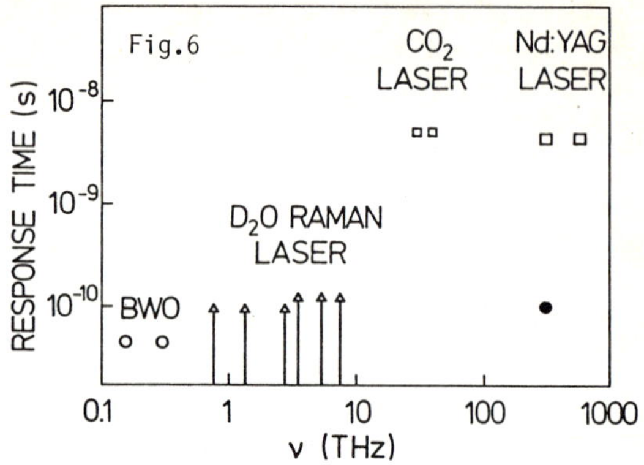

Fig. 5. Response of a YBCO film detector to 1.06 μm radiation.

Fig. 6. Response times at far-infrared wavelengths.

higher power density (Fig. 5) there occurs in addition to the fast signal a slow signal with a decay time of few ns.

The fast signal is attributed [2] to quasiparticle excitation and the slow signal to bolometric heating, with the electronic and phononic system in equilibrium. Accordingly, the fast response time corresponds to the electron-phonon relaxation time and the slow response time to escape of the heat from the film into the substrate.

It was found that the fast signal saturated [2], at a radiation pulse energy at which the condensate was fully broken up, while the bolometric signal did not saturate.

Nonbolometric response was also found in the far-infrared. Experimental response times (Fig. 6) are determined by the electronic equipment. Response times of few ps are suggested: This short response time follows from a mixing experiment performed with a backward wave oscillator (BWO, Fig. 6). The other far-infrared experiments habe been performed by use of a high pressure CO_2 laser or a D_2O Raman laser pumped with the CO_2 laser.

In summary, first experiments demonstrate the feasibility of high T_c thin films as partly transparent low-loss reflectors of Fabry-Pérot resonators for the far-infrared, and, structured thin films turn out to be suitable as detectors with response times of possibly few ps. The two devices make use of large energy gap values (namely the Fabry-Pérot resonator) and of the high T_c: A high operation temperature of the detector is the basis for fast (electron-phonon) relaxation processes and therefore for ultrafast response.

This work was supported by the Bundesministerium für Forschung und Technologie and the Bayerische Forschungsstiftung through the Bayerischer Hochschulverbund Hochtemperatur-Supraleiter (FORSUPRA).

[1] K.F. Renk, J. Betz, J. Schützmann, A. Prückl, B. Brunner, and H. Lengfellner, Appl. Phys. Lett. **57**, 2148 (1990).
[2] A.D. Semenov, G.N. Gol'tsman, I.G. Gogidze, A.V. Sergeev, E.M. Gershenzon, P.T. Lang, and K.F. Renk, Appl. Phys. Lett. **60**, 903 (1992).
[3] K.F. Renk and L. Genzel, Appl. Optics **1**, 643 (1962).
[4] A. Prückl et al., this volume.
[5] K.F. Renk, B. Gorshunov, J. Schützmann, A. Prückl, B. Brunner, J. Betz, S. Orbach, N. Klein, G. Müller, and H. Piel, Europhys. Lett. **15**, 661 (1991).
[6] P. Wiese, X. Riederer, J. Schützmann, B. Gorshunov, J. Betz, and K.F. Renk, Int'l. J.IR & MM Waves (1992).
[7] J.W.V. Storey, D.M. Watson, and C.H. Townes, Int'l. J. IR & MM Waves **1**, 15 (1980).
[8] A.V. Bespalov, P.T. Lang, J. Betz, and K.F. Renk, Appl. Phys. Lett. **58**, 2030 (1991).
[9] K.F. Renk, in: 'Studies of High Temperature Superconductors', ed. by A. Narlikar (Nova Science Publishers, Inc., New York, USA), 1992.
[10] K.F. Renk, in: *Tl-Based High Temperature Superconductors*, eds. A.M. Hermann and J.V. Yakhmi (Marcel Dekker, Inc.), 1992.
[11] Quing Hu and P.L. Richards, Appl. Phys. Lett. **55**, 2444 (1989).
[12] H. Lengfellner, Gi. Schneider, J. Betz, M. Hogan, W. Prettl, and K.F. Renk, Europhys. Letters **15**, 343 (1991).
[13] A.D. Semenov, P.T. Lang, K.F. Renk, and I.G. Gogidze, Solid State Commun. **80**, 507-510 (1991).
[14] G.N. Gol'tsman, A.D. Semenov, Y.P. Gousev, M.A. Zorin, I.G. Gogidze, E.M. Gershenzon, P.T. Lang, W.J. Knott, and K.F.Renk, Supercond. Science & Techn. **4**, 453 (1991).
[15] E.M. Gershenzon, G.N. Goltsman, A.D. Semenov, and A.V. Sergeev, Solid State Commun. **76**, 493 (1990).

Application of $YBa_2Cu_3O_{7-\delta}$ Thin Films on Silicon Substrates for Far-Infrared Fabry-Pérot Resonators

A. Prückl, J. Schützmann, S. Lipp, G. Lindner, B. Brunner, S. Vent, E. Pechen, and K.F. Renk

Institut für Angewandte Physik, Universität Regensburg,
W-8400 Regensburg, Fed. Rep. of Germany

We report on the use of $YBa_2Cu_3O_{7-\delta}$ thin films on silicon substrates as reflectors of a Fabry-Perot resonator in the far-infrared. The peak-transmissivity of the resonator increases with decreasing temperature. At $T \ll T_c$ we obtain a peak transmissivity of ~ 60 % and a quality factor of ~ 20 for frequencies, which are smaller than the superconducting energy gap. Because of the small absorption of silicon in the far-infrared, Fabry-Perot resonators with superconducting films on silicon can be used up to high frequencies.

Recently, Fabry-Perot resonators with $YBa_2Cu_3O_{7-\delta}$ (YBCO) thin films on MgO plates as reflectors have been reported [1]. In this paper we describe a Fabry-Perot resonator with YBCO films on plates of silicon that has high transparency at terahertz frequencies, up to a frequency (30 THz) where interband transitions set in.

YBCO films were prepared by laser deposition on (100) oriented silicon plates covered with yttria stabilized ZrO_2 (YSZ) buffer layers [2-4]. X-ray analysis showed that the YSZ buffer layers as well as the YBCO films were grown epitaxial with $\hat{c}$-axis perpendicular to the plane of the substrate.

The electrical resistivity ρ decreased linearly with decreasing temperature and had values in the range of 180 – 300 $\mu\Omega\cdot$cm at 300 K and a third of these values at 100 K. The resistivity and the a.c. susceptibility χ' showed sharp drops at the superconducting transition. The mid point of the resistive transition for different films was between 89 K and 91 K and zero resistance was reached between 87 K and 88.5 K. The mid point of the susceptibility drop was between 86 K and 88 K.

Our Fabry-Perot resonator, cooled by helium exchange gas in a cryostat with optical access, consisted of two reflectors, namely two parallel silicon plates each coated on one side with an epitaxial YBCO film. The films were arranged parallel face to face to each other and separated by a distance that determined the fundamental

Springer Series in Solid-State Sciences, Vol. 113 Electronic Properties of High-T_c Superconductors
Editors: H. Kuzmany, M. Mehring, J. Fink

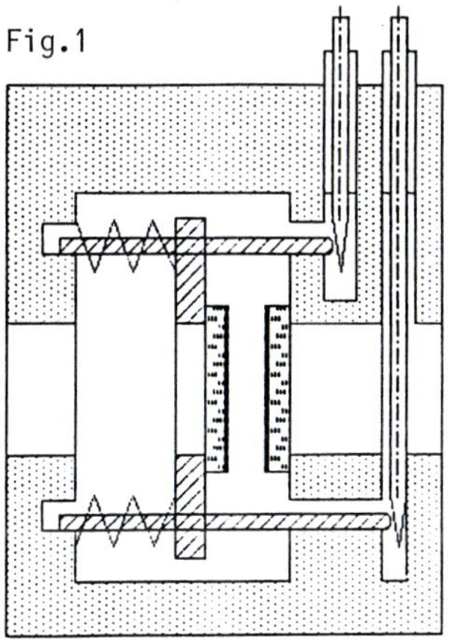

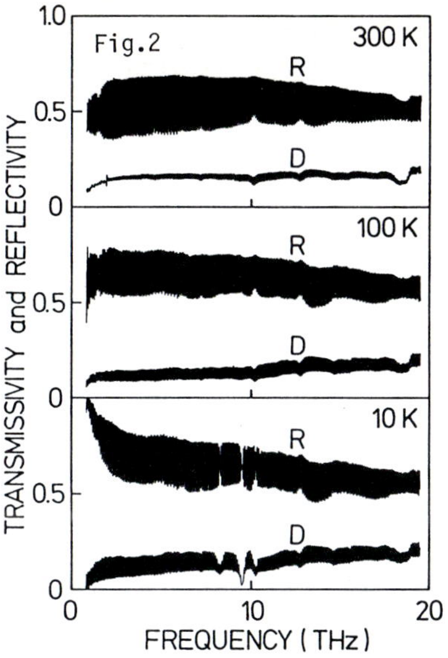

Fig. 1 Fabry-Perot resonator; width of the sample holder 2 cm, height 4 cm.

Fig. 2 Transmissivity D and reflectivity R (from film side) of a YBCO film (thickness $\sim$ 60 nm) on a silicon plate (thickness $\sim$ 0.52 mm).

resonance. For adjustment a special sample holder (Fig.1) was constructed. We fixed one of the reflectors with resinous glue on the base of the sample holder and the other on a frame that was adjustable with the help of screws. After a pre-adjustment with a microscope we inserted the sample holder in the cryostat and made a fine adjustment at each temperature seeking for maximum far-infrared peak-transmissivity. For the spectroscopic study we used a Fourier transform infrared spectrometer.

We first investigated the properties of the two reflectors separately and found that they had similar properties. Fig. 2 shows transmissivity D and reflectivity R of one of the reflectors for different temperatures. All curves show modulation because of interference within the silicon plate (refractive index $\sim$ 3.47, thickness $\sim$ 0.52 mm). Three absorption lines at 7.37, 8.40 and 9.57 THz (at 10 K) are due to shallow impurity centers (boron) and the band near 18 THz is due to multiphonon absorption in silicon. Most interesting is the result for small frequencies. With decreasing temperature the reflectivity increases indicating an increase of the dynamical conductivity.

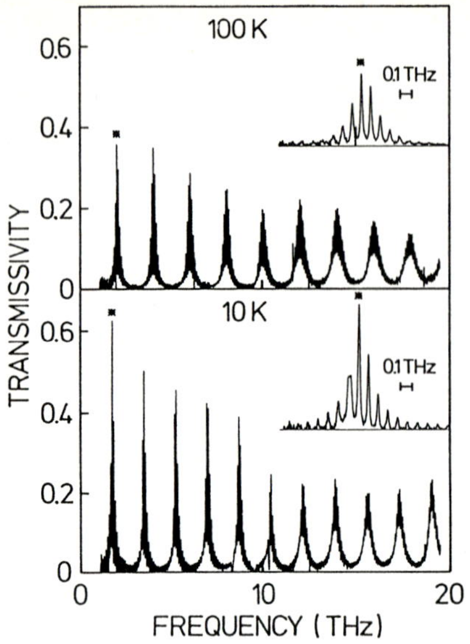

Fig. 3 Transmissivity of a Fabry-Perot resonator at 300 K and 10 K; insets, structure of the fundamental resonance.

While the average transmissivity is almost constant at small frequencies for temperatures above T_c it decreases strongly towards small frequencies for $T \ll T_c$; the behavior is characteristic for superconductors. Our results show that at low temperature modulation maxima of transmissivity and reflectivity almost coincide (as an extended representation of the curves shows) and that the sum of D and R at the maxima is near 1 and that the absorptivity is smaller than D. Residual absorption may be caused by free, unpaired carriers (for instance in the chains [5]) and imperfections in the film [6]. At temperatures above T_c the absorptivity is comparable with D, and increases with temperature.

The transmissivity curve of a resonator at 10 K is shown in the lower part of Fig. 3. There are main maxima at the frequencies $\nu_z \simeq z/2d$ where $z = 1, 2, \ldots$ is the order of resonance and $d \simeq 55$ μm the distance between the reflectors. The fine structure (inset) is due to coupling of the main resonances and the resonances in the silicon plates. The peak-transmissivity reaches 62% for the fundamental (z=1) resonance. The fundamental is the narrowest of the resonances and has a finesse $\nu / \Delta \nu \sim 20$ at 3 THz, where $\Delta \nu$ is the halfwidth of the resonance curve. The decrease of the peak-transmissivity and finesse in the range up to ~10 THz are mainly due to nonparallelism of the two reflectors. At higher frequencies the finesse decreases further because of lower reflectivity and the peak-transmissivity decreases because of absorption by shallow impurities in the silicon plates. There are several sources for non-parallelism, unplane original plates, stress induced by the YBCO films and unperfect adjustment. By improving the parallelism it should be possible to increase the finesse and even the already high peak-transmissivity.

The upper part of Fig. 3 shows the transmissivity curve of the resonator at 100 K. The peak-transmissivity of the main resonances at low frequencies is smaller than at 10 K, indicating larger absorptivity.

In conclusion, we have reported on far-infrared optical properties of YBCO films on silicon that belongs besides germanium and diamond to the materials of highest far-infrared transmissivity and demonstrated for the first time that high-T_c films on silicon plates are suitable for fabrication of Fabry-Perot resonators that can in principle be operated in a very large part of the far-infrared spectral range.

Financial support by the Bundesministerium für Forschung und Technologie, the Deutscher Akademischer Austauschdienst (DAAD), and the Bayerische Forschungsstiftung through the Bayerischer Forschungsverbund Hochtemperatur-Supraleiter (FORSUPRA) are acknowledged.

References

[1] K.F. Renk, J. Betz, J. Schützmann, A. Prückl, B. Brunner, and H. Lengfellner, Appl. Phys. Lett. **57**, 2148 (1990). **65**, 801 (1990).

[2] X.D. Wu, A. Inam, M.S. Hedge, B. Wilkins, C.C. Chang, D.M. Hwang, L. Nazar, T. Venkatesan, S. Miura, S. Matsubara, Y. Miyasaka, and N. Shohata, Appl. Phys. Lett. **54**, 754 (1989).

[3] D.K. Fork, D.B. Fenner, R.W. Barton, J.M. Phillips, G.A.N. Connell, J.B. Boyce, and T.H. Geballe, Appl. Phys. Lett. **57**, 1161 (1990).

[4] S.I. Krasnosvobodtsev and E.V. Pechen, Pis'ma Zh. Techn. Fiz. (St.Petersburg) **17**, 12 (1991).

[5] Z. Schlesinger, R.T. Collins, F. Holtzberg, C. Feild, S.H. Planton, U. Welp, G.W. Crabtree, Y. Fang, and J.Z. Liu, Phys. Rev. Lett. **65**, 801 (1990).

[6] K.F. Renk, B. Gorshunov, J. Schützmann, A. Prückl, B. Brunner, J. Betz, S. Orbach, N. Klein, G. Müller, and H. Piel, Europhys. Lett. **15**, 661 (1991).

Giant Voltages Upon Surface Heating in Normal $YBa_2Cu_3O_{7-\delta}$ Films Explained by an Atomic-Layer Thermopile

H. Lengfellner, G. Kremb, J. Betz, K.F. Renk, and W. Prettl

Institut für Angewandte Physik, Universität Regensburg,
W-8400 Regensburg, Fed. Rep. of Germany

Abstract. Large voltage signals have been observed beetween lateral contacts on epitaxial $YBa_2Cu_3O_{7-\delta}$ films, if the films were heated by pulsed laser irradiation or by heater wires. Our investigations show that the voltaic signals are thermoelectric in origin. A model is proposed which explains the voltages by an atomic layer thermopile formed by the layered structure of the material.

Recently, transient voltaic signals have been observed at room temperature in $YBa_2Cu_3O_{7-\delta}$ films in response to pulsed laser irradiation [1, 2]. A transverse Seebeck effect and pyro- and piezoelectric effects have been excluded by symmetry arguments [1, 3], a longidudinal Seebeck effect has been ruled out because of the magnitude of the voltaic singals [1]. We have performed experiments which show that the voltage signals are thermoelectric in origin and attribute the magnitude of the voltages to an atomic layer thermopile formed by the layered structure of the material [4].

$YBa_2Cu_3O_{7-\delta}$ films of about 500 nm thickness epitaxially grown on $SrTiO_3$ and MgO substrates were used for the measurements. Electric point contacts were made with silver epoxy paint on the film surface. A Nd:YAG laser ($\lambda = 1.06 \mu m$) with pulse duration $\sim$ 100 ns and pulse energy 10 mJ was used for film heating. Heating a film with the laser leads to a signal pulse of nearly 1 V (Fig. 1 a). From a heat propagation model [5] and bolometric measurements [6] we estimate a maximum temperature difference of $\Delta T = 50$ K between surface and bottom of the film for an energy density of 10 mJ/cm^2 of the laser pulse. The temporal behaviour of the signal is consistent with decay of the temperature gradient due to heat diffusion. Assuming film cooling by heat diffusion, $\Delta T(t)$ has also been calculated (dashed line Fig. 1) using a numerical method [4]. Irradiating the film through the transparent substrate leads to a reversed ΔT during laser heating and thus to a reversed signal polarity (Fig. 1 b). We note that a linear dependence of signal height on laser pulse energy was observed.

Springer Series in Solid-State Sciences, Vol. 113 Electronic Properties of High-T_c Superconductors
Editors: H. Kuzmany, M. Mehring, J. Fink

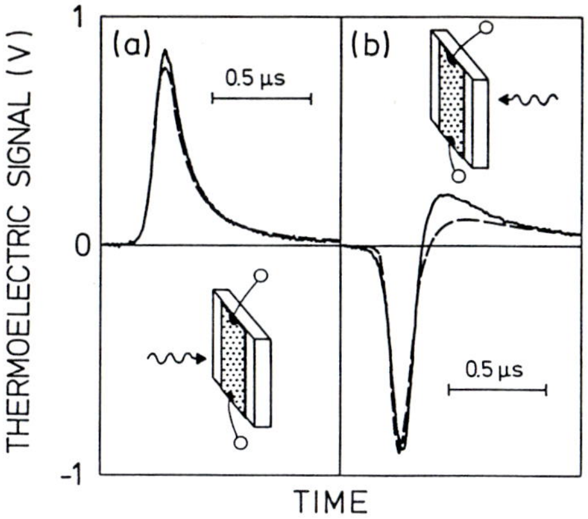

Fig. 1. Thermoelectric signal in response to pulsed laser heating, for different beam geometries (a) and (b). Dashed line: Calculated temperature gradient, normalized to signal maximum.

The spatial distribution of the electric potential in the plane of the film was determined by a series of point contacts on the film surface lying on the circumference of a circle of about 4 mm radius. The center of the circle was heated by the laser beam. The voltage signal of diametrically facing contacts was recorded and a sinus-like dependence of the signal height on the angle around the circle was obtained. Choosing, for instance, a contact pair with maximum signal, zero-signal was obtained for a contact pair at an angle of 90 °. These results indicate the creation of a dipolar electric source at the laser heated spot in the plane of the film with an oriented dipole axis and with a strength proportional to Δ T. This picture has been proven in more detail in an experiment where the signal obtained from a fixed contact pair has been recorded in dependence of heated spot position [4]. Instead of laser heating, films were also heated by a heater wire (Fig. 2), the heater power was several Watt. During heating a positive signal indicating a hot film surface and a colder substrate was obtained (Fig. 2 a). During a heating time $\sim$ 100s, the initially obtained temperature gradient became slightly reduced due to warming up of the substrate. When the film was heated through the substrate (Fig. 2 b) first the substrate had to be heated and a slowly increasing signal of reversed polarity was obtained. With an estimated Δ T $\sim 10^{-3}$ K the magnitude of the observed signal voltages is consistent with the laser heating experiment.

For an explanation of the large thermoelectric voltages we suggest a model based on a series connection of thermocouples,

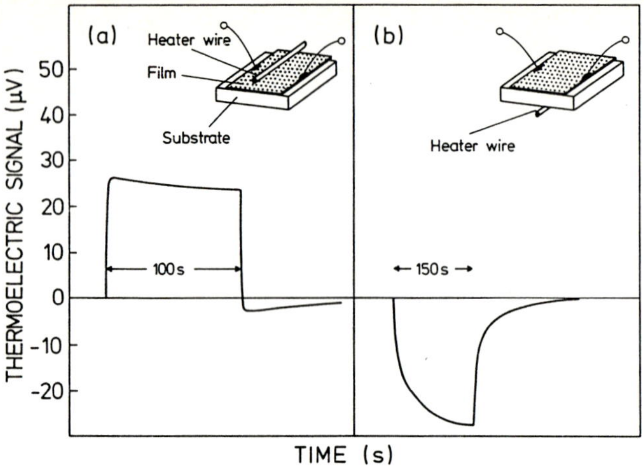

Fig. 2. Thermoelectric signal obtained in a wire heating experiment, for two heater configurations (a) and (b).

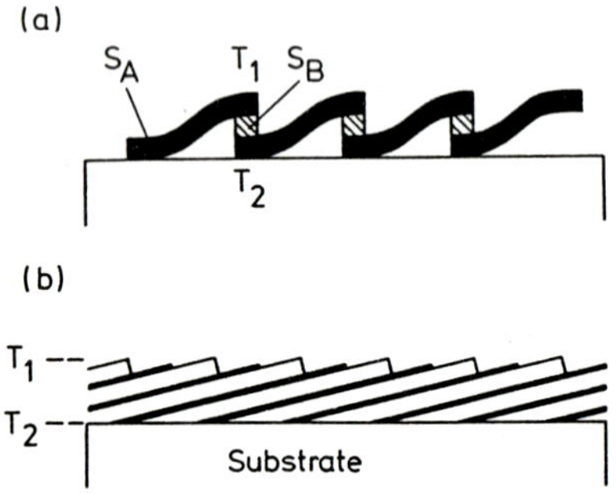

Fig. 3. (a) Plane thermopile made from materials with Seebeck coefficients S_A and S_B, temperature T_1 of upper contacts, T_2 of lower contacts.
(b) Plane thermopile formed by layers inclined with respect to the substrate, layer period $c \simeq 11$ Å for YBCO.

which may be formed by the high T_c materials in a natural way. In Fig. 3 (a), a plane thermopile is shown producing a voltage $U = N\ (S_A - S_B) \cdot \Delta$ T, where N is the number of elements, S_A - S_B is the difference of Seebeck coefficients of the two involved materials and $\Delta T = T_1 - T_2$ the applied temperature difference. A similar thermopile may be formed by a $YBa_2Cu_3O_{7-\delta}$ film with a c-axis inclined by a small angle α with respect to the surface normal. With film thickness D = 5000 Å, lattice constant c $\simeq$ 11 Å, Seebeck coefficients S_A for the CuO_2 planes and S_B for the material between the planes, a temperature difference $(T_1 - T_2) \cdot c/D$ between adjacent planes and a number $N = (d \cdot sin\alpha)/c$ of elements within a heated spot of diameter d we obtain

$$U = \frac{d \cdot sin\alpha}{D} \cdot \Delta T \cdot \Delta S$$

A value $\Delta S = 10\ \mu V/K$ may be estimated from measurements of the anisotropy of the Seebeck coefficient in $YBa_2Cu_3O_{7-\delta}$ single crystals [7]. Small angles α due to not precisely cut substrates have been reported by several groups [8, 9]. With a spot diameter d = 5 mm, $\alpha = 5°$, $\Delta T = 50$ K a value $U \simeq 0.5$ V is obtained comparable to the signal height in the laser heating experiment.

This work was supported by the Deutsche Forschungsgemeinschaft (H.L.), the European Community (W.P.) and the Bundesministerium für Forschung und Technologie (K.F.R.).

[1] C.L. Chang, A. Kleinhammes, W. G. Moulton, and L. R. Testardi, Phys. Rev. B.**41**, 11564 (1990).
[2] K. L. Tate, R. D. Johnson, C.L. Chang, E. F. Hilinski, and S. C. Foster, J. Appl. Phys. **67**, 4375 (1990).
[3] J. F. Scott, Appl. Phys. Lett. **56**, 1914 (1990).
[4] H. Lengfellner, G. Kremb, A. Schnellbögl, J. Betz, K.F. Renk, and W. Prettl, Appl. Phys. Lett. **60**, 501 (1992).
[5] S. Zeuner, H. Lengfellner, J. Betz, K.F. Renk, and W. Prettl, to be published
[6] H. Lengfellner, Gi. Schneider, J. Betz, M. Hogan, W. Prettl, and K.F. Renk, Europhys. Lett., **15**, 343 (1991).
[7] M.F. Crommie, A. Zettl, T.W. Barbee, and M.L. Cohen, Phys. Rev. **B 37**, 9734 (1988).
[8] H.S. Kwok, J.P. Zheng, and S.Y. Dong, Phys. Rev. **B 43**, 6270 (1991).
[9] J. Fujita, T. Yoshitake, T. Satoh, S. Miura, H. Tsuge, and H. Igarashi, Appl. Phys. Lett. **59**, 2445 (1991).

Study of Residual Absorption of High-T_c Thin Films by Means of Photothermal Interference Spectroscopy

D.N. Basov[2], M. Müller[1], A. Koller[1], J. Schützmann[1], E.V. Pechen[2], J. Betz[1], B. Brunner[1], and K.F. Renk[1]

[1]Institut für Angewandte Physik, Universität Regensburg, W-8400 Regensburg, Fed. Rep. of Germany
[2]Permanent address: P.N. Lebedev Physical Institute, Russian Academy of Sciences, Leninskii pr. 53, 117924 Moscow, Russia

Results of direct absorptivity measurements at ω=0.89 THz of thin films belonging to three different families of HTc compounds are reported. In all samples a significant decrease of absorption below T_c with nonzero values at $T<<T_c$ was observed. The real part of the complex conductivity as a function of temperature (for $T<T_c/2$) was evaluated from absorptivity together with normal state reflectivity data and was found to be of the order of $10^3\ \Omega^{-1}cm^{-1}$. This indicates the presence of a significant amount of either unpaired electrons or pairs with a binding energy lower than 0.89 THz in CuO planes. In addition, a considerable rise of the absorptivity for T<30 K was observed in $YBa_2Cu_3O_{7-x}$ samples.

Recently it was observed by means of both microwave and far-infrared (FIR) methods that $YBa_2Cu_3O_{7-x}$ compounds have residual intra-gap absorption that cannot be attributed only to sample imperfectness [1-4]. More profound understanding of the process responsible for low temperature loss mechanisms is expected on the basis of systematic absorptivity studies for a variety of HT_c materials. We demonstrate that a combination of normal state reflectivity and superconducting state absolute absorptivity measurements provides an opportunity to obtain $\sigma1$ values in the temperature region below $T_c/2$. This analysis was applied to the comparative study of thin films of three different families of metal-oxide superconductors.

Thin films of $YBa_2Cu_3O_{7-x}$ on $SrTiO_3$ (T_c=89 K), $Bi_2Sr_2CaCu_2O_{8-x}$ on MgO (T_c=79 K), $Bi_2Sr_2Ca_2Cu_3O_{10-x}$ on MgO (T_c=98 K) and $Tl_2Ba_2Ca_2Cu_3O_{10-x}$ on MgO (T_c=112 K) were prepared by means of laser ablation. The Y- and Bi-based films had almost perfect orientation of the c axis perpendicular to the substrate surface while the Tl-based film was found to be polycrystalline.In adition to the films a ceramic sample of $YBa_2Cu_3O_{7-x}$ (T_c=90 K) was studied.

The direct measurements of the absolute absorptivity (A) were carried out by means of novel calorimetric method - Fotothermal Interference Spectroscopy [5]. The experimental set up is shown in Figure 1. The sample is mounted in a flow-gas cryostat with its surface parallel to one of the beams of Jamin-type interferometer. Absorption of radiation of a FIR laser heats the sample and a gas volume close to the sample surface.The distance between interferometer beams is much larger than the thermaldiffusion length of the gas. The refractive index of the gas is temperature dependent that makes it possible to monitor radiation-induced optical length changes as an interference signal of a photodetector. Periodical heating of the sample with a chopping frequency f1 allows to measure radiation induced interference signals by

Springer Series in Solid-State Sciences, Vol. 113 Electronic Properties of High-T_c Superconductors
Editors: H. Kuzmany, M. Mehring, J. Fink

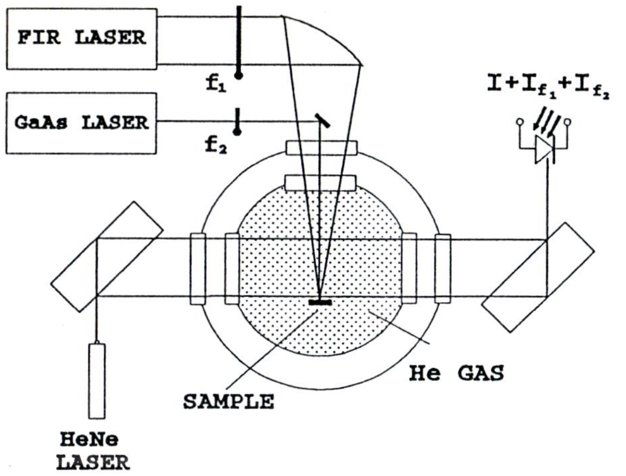

Fig.1. The Experimental set-up for Fotothermal Interference Spectroscopy

lock-in technique. The signal is proportional to the absorptivity of a sample but also dependent on the thermal properties of sample and gas. We have eliminated the influence of the thermal properties by a reference measurement,with a radiation of a GaAs laser, focused on the same point on the sample surface as the FIR radiation. The ratio of FIR-induced and reference signals corresponds to the relative absorptivity of the sample. Both FIR and reference laser beams are chopped at two slightly different frequencies f1 and f2 and corresponding signals are measured simultaneously by means of two separate Lock-In devices.The ratio of these signals that is the relative absorptivity of a sample is immediately obtained. The absolute value of absorptivity is then determined by a calibration using the sample with known absorptivities both in FIR and for radiation of GaAs laser.

The important advantage of the method compared with other calorimetric techniques [2,4] is the absence of effects concerned with overestimations of FIR absorptivity (for $\omega < 2$ THz) due to radiation leakage and absorption directly in thermosensitiv elements. That enables us to obtain reliable absorptivity data.

Figure 2 shows the absorptivity of different samples. Just below T_c a significant drop of absorptivity is observed in all the samples. At low temperature,however,all samples show residual absorption. The comparison of the absolute values of the residual absorptivities shows that polycrystalline samples (Tl-based film and $YBa_2Cu_3O_{7-x}$ pellet) exhibit higher absorptivity than oriented films. Partly the difference in A values can be attributed to the different screening due to superconducting condensate that less effective in polycrystaline materials rather than in crystals or films for the case of $E_{\perp}c$. A description of the influence of the screening effects on absorptivity for $T<T_c/2$ can be found from the relation:

$$A = \left(\frac{4\omega\varepsilon_0}{\sigma_2}\right)^{\frac{1}{2}} \frac{\sigma_1}{\sigma_2} \quad , \qquad (1)$$

where $\sigma 1$ and $\sigma 2$ are real and imaginary part of the complex conductivity.

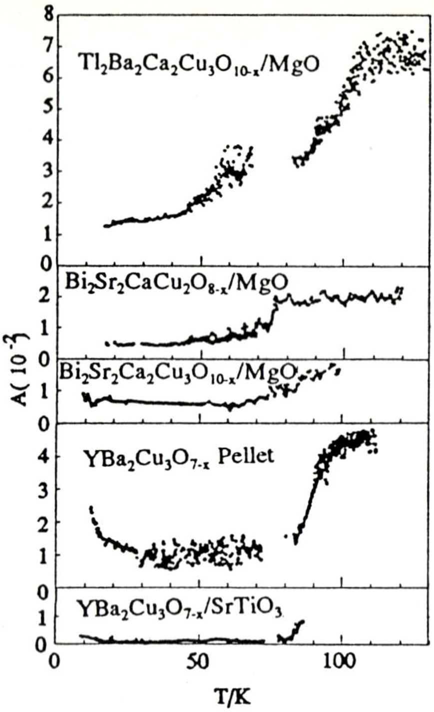

Figure 2. Absorptivity of different samples.

For $T < T_c/2$ $\sigma 2$ can be considered as independent of temperature. In case of London superconductors $\sigma 2$ is proportional to the square of the plasma frequency of condensed carriers. For high-T_c superconductors it is necessary to take into account the energy gap, 2Δ, and the normal state scattering rate, Γ. We used the programs of Brand and Bauer [7] for a description of the frequency dependence of $\sigma 1$ and $\sigma 2$. The input parameters:the Drude plasma frequency ωpD and Γ were determined by Drude model analysis of reflectivity data of our films in a wide frequency range;the analysis will be presented elsewhere [8].

Figure 3 presents $\sigma 1$ values obtained from (1) with gap values $2\Delta = 7kT_c$ for oriented films and 3 kT_c for polycrystalline samples. In all the samples $\sigma 1$ is of the order of $10^3\ \Omega^{-1}\ cm^{-1}$ not taking into account the low temperature rise observed in $YBa_2Cu_3O_{7-x}$ samples that will be discussed below. These large $\sigma 1$ values are typical for free carrier conductivity.Especially in case of chain-less compounds this indicates that free carriers contribute to the conductivity of the CuO planes. Experimentally we are not able to distinguish between absorption due to unpaired carriers and due to pairs with low binding energy (low compared to our probing frequency of 0.89 THz). So the question wether a large portion of carriers does not contribute to superconducivity or wether this is a wide distribution of binding energies still remains open.

An increase of absorptivity at temperatures below 30 K was observed in $YBa_2Cu_3O_{7-x}$ samples. This increase can be considered as occurring on the background of a temperature independent absorption (as in Bi-based samples) thus having a different origin than due to normal carriers or pairs with small binding energy in

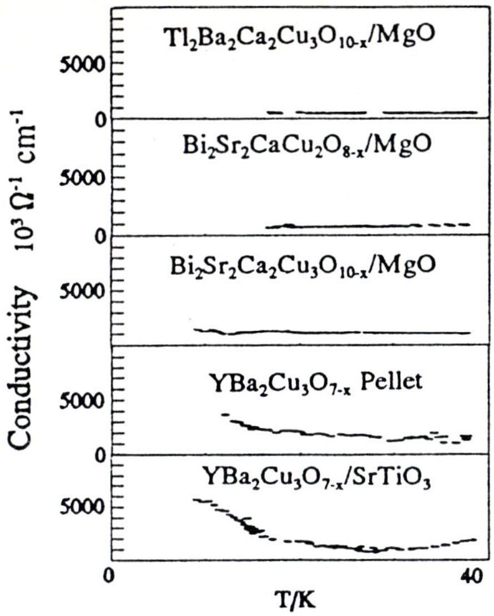

Figure 3. Conductivity of different samples

the CuO planes. We speculate that the rise of absorptivity may be caused by chain carriers or may be due to the absorption at twins booundaries.

In conclusion, we demonstrate that the combination of low temperature absorptivity data for a fixed FIR frequency, and reflectivity data in a wide frequency range allows to obtain $\sigma 1$ values at this frequency. For thin films of three different HT_c materials we found values of $\sigma 1$ of the order of $10^3\ \Omega^{-1}\ \mathrm{cm}^{-1}$ that give evidence of the presence of a significant amount of either unpaired carries or pairs with a wide distribution of binding energies in the CuO planes. In addition a rise of absorptivity below 30 K was observed in $YBa_2Cu_3O_{7-x}$ samples.

REFERENCES

1.Z.Schlesinger, R.T.Collins, F.Holtzberg, C.Feild, S.H.Blanton, U.Welp, G.W.Crab tree, Y.Fang, and J.Z.Liu.Phys.Rev.Lett4, 801 (1965).

2.T.Pham, M.W.Lee, H.D.Drew, U.Welp, and Y.Fang, Phys.Rev.B **44**, 5377 (1991).

3.K.F.Renk, B.Gorshunov, J.Schützmann, A.Prückl, B.Brunner, J.Betz, S.Obach, N.Klein, G.Müller, and H.Piel. Europhys.Lett., **15** (6) 661 (1991).

4.D.Miller, P.L.Richards, S.Etmad, A.Inam, T.Venkatesan, B.Dutta, X.D.Wu, C.B.Eom, T.H.Geballe, N.Newman, B.F.Cole. Appl.Phys.Lett.**59**, (18), 2326 (1991).

5.M.Müller, S.Basun, S.Glaser, and K.F.Renk.Appl.Phys.Lett.**59** (26), 3476 (1991).

6.K.F.Renk, J.Schützmann, A.Prückl, B.Roas, L.Schultz, and G.Saemann-Ischenko. Physica B **165 & 166**,1253 (1990).

7.E.H.Brand, M.Bauer.Proceedings of USSR-FRG Bilateral Seminar on Spectroscopy of HTc Superconductors.Tallin,USSR 1989.

8.D.N.Basov, M.Müller, A.Koller, J.Schützmann, E.V.Pechen, J.Betz, B. Brunner and K.F.Renk (not published).

Damping of Spin Excitations in the HTC-Cuprates: Undoped and Lightly Doped Material

P. Knoll[1], *S. Lo*[1], *P. Murugaraj*[2], *E. Schönherr*[3], *and M. Cardona*[3]

[1]Institut für Experimentalphysik der Universität Graz, Universitätsplatz 5, A-8010 Graz, Austria

[2]Centre for Materials for Electronics Technology, Panchayat Shopping Complex, Kolazhy, Trissur 680010, Kerala, India

[3]Max-Planck-Insitut für Festkörperforschung, Heisenbergstr. 1, W-7000 Stuttgart 80, Fed. Rep. of Germany

Abstract: The spin excitations of $YBa_2Cu_3O_x$ single crystals are examined using inelastic light scattering. This experimental method mainly investigates the spin excitations at the zone boundary. Starting from the insulating, antiferromagnetic material the spin scattering intensity decreases with increasing dopant concentration. Energy and lifetime of the zone edge spin excitations have been determined using a Heisenberg model extended by some extrinsic damping. With increasing doping concentration the spin excitation energy softens lightly and damping increases more significantly.

1. Introduction

The interplay between antiferromagnetism and superconductivity is one of the most fascinating phenomena in the HTc compounds. All known HTc-cuprates exist as a Mott insulating parent material with an antiferromagnetic ground state. Upon doping the antiferromagnetic order vanishes and superconductivity appears together with the metallic state. At higher doping concentrations superconductivity is suppressed but the metallic state is well established.

The low lying excitations of the electronic system are spin fluctuations in the pure antiferromagnetic state [1] and can be directly probed by either neutron scattering [2] or inelastic light scattering [3]. Both methods are in some way complementary: neutron scattering probes spin excitations around the zone centre but Raman scattering mainly sees zone boundary fluctuations in the B_{1g} scattering geometry. Both methods had given an exchange energy of the order of 100meV in rather good agreement with theoretical estimates within the three-band Hubbard model. There are, however, some difficulties in the interpretation of the Raman feature associated with the spin fluctuations. Compared with similar substances as K_2MnF_4 (S=5/2) and K_2NiF_4 (S=1) the Raman profile is much broader and has an asymmetric tail at the high energy side. R.R.P.Singh et al. [4] have shown that in the HTc cuprates (S=1/2) quantum fluctuations become important and cause asymmetric spectral weight at high Raman shifts. In the spin wave picture these quantum fluctuations correspond to higher order magnon processes and should be well separated from the 2-magnon scattering process. Using exact diagonalization techniques on a 4x4 lattice calculations of the Raman spectrum of the S=1/2 quantum Heisenberg model (as a limit t=0 of the t-J model) clearly show these separated peaks [5]. On the other hand, broad spectral features can be explained by introducing some additional damping mechanism. In the case of spin excitations of the HTc materials this has been first suggested by Weber and Ford [6]. Temperature dependent measurements have shown that rather good fit to the experimental data can be obtained using temperature and k-dependent magnon damping of the intrinsic magnon-magnon interaction and some additional damping mainly arising from magnon-phonon interaction [7]. We call this model the extended Heisenberg model.

2. The extended Heisenberg model

A widely accepted model of the CuO_2-plane is the three-band Hubbard model. In the undoped case the low-lying excitations can be described by a Heisenberg Hamiltonian [1]. Taking into account the spin-

Springer Series in Solid-State Sciences, Vol. 113 Electronic Properties of High-T_c Superconductors
Editors: H. Kuzmany, M. Mehring, J. Fink

lattice interaction the Heisenberg Hamiltonian is extended by the distance dependence of the exchange energy. Further interaction mechanisms should be described by some perturbing potential V which is also added to the starting Hamiltonian:

$$H = J\sum_{ij}\vec{S}_i\vec{S}_j + \vec{\nabla}J\cdot\sum_{ij}\vec{r}_{ij}\vec{S}_i\vec{S}_j + V \tag{1}$$

The actual calculation has been performed including a small anisotropy ($\sim 10^{-4}$) in the spin-spin interaction in order to stabilize the two-dimensional spin system at finite temperatures. The eigenvalues of that Hamiltonian can be approximately given by:

$$E_k = \epsilon_k + \sum\nolimits_k^{phon} + \sum\nolimits_k^{V} \tag{2}$$

where ε_k denotes the pure magnon energy in the spin wave approximation. Magnon-magnon interaction has been taken into account in second order yielding a complex energy ε_k [8]. So far, this kind of magnon calculation, together with the appropriate light scattering expression, has given best agreement with experimental two magnon Raman scattering on K_2MnF_4 and K_2NiF_4 up to temperatures well above the Nèel-temperature [9]. Additional magnon-phonon interaction influences the magnon energy by the complex self energy Σ_k^{phon} , which has been worked out by M.G.Cottam [10]. Using a simple lattice dynamical model of the CuO_2 plane with only one Cu-O stretch force constant the imaginary part of the magnon self energy at the zone edge can be estimated:

$$Im(\sum\nolimits_k^{phon}) \sim \frac{4aS^2\hbar}{vM\omega}\,(\vec{\nabla}J)^2\,[1 + n(T,\omega')] \tag{3}$$

The spin velocity v has to be taken from the magnon dispersion. S, a, M, ω are the magnitude of the spin, the lattice constant, the mass of copper and the longitudinal accustic frequency, respectively. The coupling constant ∇J has to be taken around $5000 cm^{-1} A^{-1}$ in order to explain the temperature dependent magnon scattering in the HTc materials [7]. The Bose-factor $n(T,\omega')$ contains the average of all possible magnon decay channels in the Brillouin zone. Further interaction mechanisms, as introduced by the phenomenological Hamiltonian V may change both real and imaginary parts of the spin excitations by the self energy Σ_k^V. Such kind of interaction may take place with free carriers as expected in the doped regime. This simple model will only hold for small carrier concentrations, where spinwaves still exist and perturbation theory holds. However, it should give a helpful base for the interpretation of the experimental data.

3. Doping dependence

Upon doping the two-magnon Raman peak qualitatively relaxes into a broad, featureless background [10] which exhibits temperature dependent changes associated with the superconducting gap. A similar background, which extends up to high Raman shifts [11], has stimulated some discussion about the unusual fermi liquid behavior and was related to the superconducting properties [12]. Spin excitations have also been suggested contributing to this background [10] and recent neutron scattering experiments clearly reveal spin excitations in the superconducting material [13]. We have performed two-magnon Raman measurements in the weakly doped regime on a multicrystal stack of $YBa_2Cu_3O_{6+x}$ prepared by the K_2CO_3 method [14]. The oxygen content had been changed and determined thermo-gravimetrically and was also checked by the Raman phonon spectra. The behavior of the B_{1g} magnon upon doping is shown in Fig.1. The strong $330 cm^{-1}$ B_{1g} phonon is present as well as a remainder of the $500 cm^{-1}$ phonon and a weak peak corresponding to the defect induced $580 cm^{-1}$ mode. An accurate estimate of the oxygen content within the laser spot is very difficult and, therefore, only rough estimates for the first and last spectrum are given. There is only a very small shift of the magnon peak at $\sim 2800 cm^{-1}$ to lower frequencies with increasing dopant concentration, while the magnon feature broadens and the

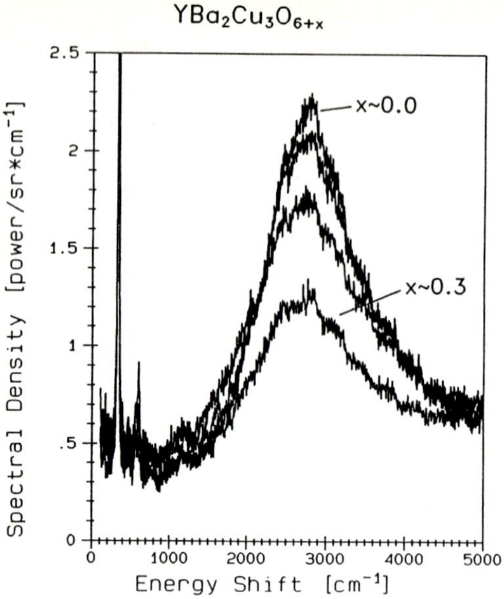

Fig.1: Raman spectra of the spin excitations for different doping concentrations (T=300K)

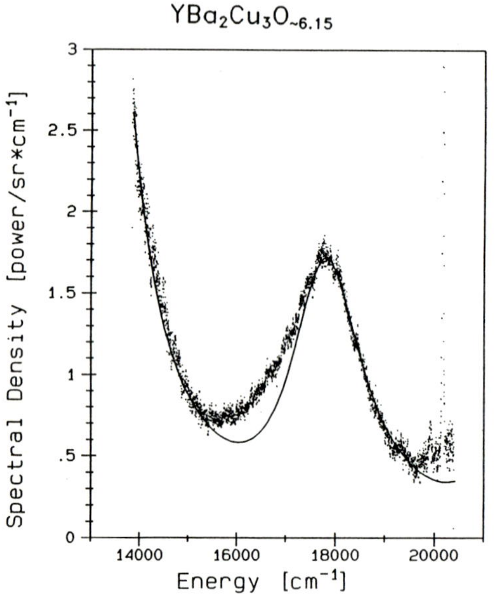

Fig.2: Experimental scattering intensity (dots) against absolut energy in comparison with calculated spectrum. The strong increase of intensity at low energies arises from sample dependent luminescence.

scattering intensity is significantly reduced. It seems that the magnon peak always sits on a doping independent background [15]. Such a background could arise from luminescence. Indeed, such luminescence is found on some samples as shown in Fig.2. The strong intensity increase below 15000 cm^{-1} scattered frequency depends on sample quality and does not shift with the exciting laser frequency. However, a good fit to all spectra can be obtained if the luminescence is approximated by a

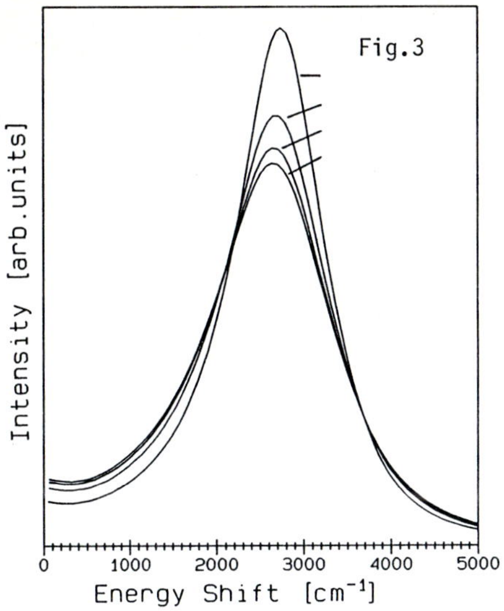

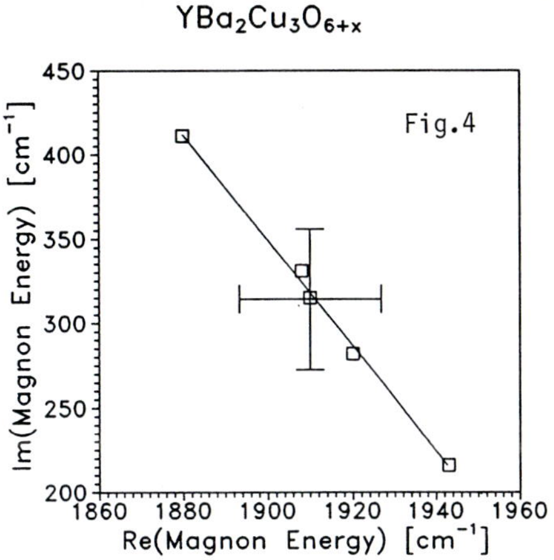

Fig.3: Pure two magnon behavior if only changes of damping and magnon energies are assumed. Values taken from a fit to the spectra of Fig.1.

Fig.4: Changes of real and imaginary part of the one magnon zone edge energy upon doping.

Lorentzian centered at 12600 cm^{-1}. The two magnon feature is calculated using the extended Heisenberg model and the same light scattering formalism as successfully applied to K_2MnF_4, K_2NiF_4 [8,9]. As Fig.2 shows, only discrepancies between calculated and measured spectra occur at the left edge of the magnon peak, most likely because of the neglect of high order magnon scattering in the latter. In Fig.3 the pure two-magnon Raman spectra are plotted as calculated with the complex one-magnon energy obtained from the fit to the experimental data of Fig.1. The displayed changes in scattered intensity correspond to the actually calculated relative values, without any scaling to the experimental data. Figure 3 clearly shows that there is a "background" at low energy shifts which tends to augment with increasing damping. On the other hand experiments indicate a significant decrease of scattering intensity with increasing doping concentration. Therefore, the "doping independent background" [15] definitely consists of spin excitations at low doping concentrations and, maybe some sample dependent luminescence. At higher doping concentrations maybe the charge excitation character becomes more dominant whereas the spin excitation intensity decreases. We expect a similar behavior of the "background" at high energy shifts which is not shown in Fig.3 because of the neglect of higher order processes.

A direct comparison of the change in magnon energy with changes in doping is difficult, as mentioned above. Therefore, in Fig.4. the measured change of the real part against imaginary part of the zone edge magnon energy due to doping (corresponding to the self energy contributions Σ_k^V of Equ.2) is plotted. The change of the real part is rather small but there is a significant increase in magnon damping. Such a behavior would be expected in the t-J model [16]. On the other hand, measurements indicate a strong decrease of magnon scattering intensity with increasing dopant concentration. This behavior may be explainable by assuming clusters around the dopant in which the antiferromagnetic spin ordering has been lost [17] and the two-magnon scattering mechanism is supressed.

Acknowledgments

This work was carried out in part as an Alexander von Humboldt fellow at the Max-Planck-Institut in Stuttgart. Financial support from the Austrian Science Foundation is greatly acknowledged.

References:

1. V.J.Emery and G.Reiter, Phys.Rev.B38,4547 (1988)
2. J.M.Tranquada, G.Shirane, B.Keimer, S.Shamoto, and M.Sato, Phys.Rev.B40,4503 (1989)
3. K.B.Lyons, P.A.Fleury, L.F.Schneemeyer, and J.V.Waszcak, Phys.Rev.Lett.60, 732 (1988)
4. R.R.P.Singh, P.A.Fleury, K.B.Lyons, and P.E.Sulewski, Phys.Rev.Lett.62, 2736 (1989)
5.E.Dagotto and D.Poiblanc, Preprint; S.Bacci et.al., Preprint
6.H.W.Weber and G.W.Ford, Phys.Rev.B40, 6890(1989)
7.P.Knoll, C.Thomsen, M.Cardona, and P.Murugaraj, Phys.Rev.42, 4842(1990)
8.see e.g. U.Balucani and V.Tognetti, Riv.Nuovo Cimento 6, 39(1976), G.Wenzel and M.Wagner, J.Phys.C11, 137(1978)
9. A.van der Pol, G.de Korte, G.Bosman, A.S. van der Wal, and H.W. de Wijn, Solid State Commun.19, 177(1976)
10. see e.g. K.B.Lyons and P.A.Fleury, J.Appl.Phys. 64, 6075 (1988)
11. see e.g. T.Staufer, R.Hackl, P.Müller, Solid State Commun. 79, 409 (1991)
12. C.M.Varma, P.B.Littlewood, S.Schmitt-Rink, E.Abrahams, and A.E.Ruckenstein, Phys.Rev.Lett. 63, 1996 (1989)
13. J.Rossat-Mignod, this volume, J.Rossat-Mignod, L.P.Regnault, C.Vettier, P.Burlet, J.Y.Henry, and G.Lapertot, Physica B 169, 58 (1991)
14. P.Murugaraj, J.Maier, and A.Rabenau, Solid State Commun.71, 167(1989)
15. D.Reznik, A.Kotz, S.L.Cooper, M.V.Klein, W.C.Lee, and D.M.Ginsberg, Physica C 185- 189, 1029 (1991)
16. G.Khaliullin and P.Horsch, preprint, J.Gan, N.Andrei, and P.Coleman, J.Phys.: Cond.Matter 3, 3537 (1991)
17. E.Sigmund and V.Hizhnyakov, in Springer Series in Solid-State Sciences 99, 366(1990)

Raman Study of the Order Parameter in Oxide Superconductors

R. Nemetschek, T. Staufer, O.V. Misochko, D. Einzel, R. Hackl, P. Müller, and K. Andres

Walther-Meissner-Institut für Tieftemperaturforschung,
Walther-Meissner-Str. 8, W-8046 Garching, Fed. Rep. of Germany

Abstract: We present Raman scattering results obtained from high quality single crystals of $Bi_2Sr_2CaCu_2O_{8+\delta}$ (Bi 2212) and $YBa_2Cu_3O_{7-\delta}$ (Y 123). The symmetry selection rules for the electronic scattering suggest the observed continuum to originate predominantly from the CuO_2 planes. The superconducting spectra exhibit gap-like structures which show that even at $T = 0$ a finite electronic density of states at energies well below the pair breaking threshold is an intrinsic feature of this material class. The temperature dependence of the superconducting order parameter is shown to be sensitive to the anisotropy.

1. Introduction

Inelastic scattering of light may provide informations about important properties of the electronic system of a material such as the carrier relaxation and the superconducting energy gap. Particularly the investigation of the gap has attracted considerable interest since the classical methods suffer from several disadvantages. Although the Raman method seems to be almost ideally suited for materials like the oxides with a short superconducting coherence length and a small carrier concentration, some fundamental questions remain open to date. For example, the origin of the electronic scattering in the normal and in the superconducting state is still subject to a controversial discussion. It is not clear, whether there exists a fully developed gap and which features are actually intrinsic. Contradictory results have been found for the low temperature limiting value and for the temperature dependence of the energy gap. In this contribution, we compare results of Raman scattering experiments recently obtained for Bi 2212 [1] single crystals with spectra measured earlier for Y 123 [2] in order to figure out common features.

2. Selection Rules

Comparing the main features of electronic scattering in Bi 2212 and Y 123 with significantly different unit cells and, consequently, different phonon excitations an almost quantitative agreement is found if the polarizations of the incident and the scattered light are given in the coordinate system of the Cu-O bonds. Therefore, we conclude that the electronic scattering comes predominantly from the CuO_2 planes. It turns out that a tetragonal unit cell is appropriate for the symmetry analysis. In this notation, the B_{1g} symmetry may be selected with the polarisations of the

Springer Series in Solid-State Sciences, Vol. 113 **Electronic Properties of High-T_c Superconductors**
Editors: H. Kuzmany, M. Mehring, J. Fink

incident and the scattered light perpendicular and at an angle of 45° with respect to the Cu-O bonds. In both compounds this specific polarization exhibits features being qualitatively different from those at the other three main symmetries. Among other things we find an almost temperature independent relaxation of the carriers in the normal state and the largest characteristic energy $2\Delta_o$ below T_c.

3. Origin of the Continuum

Inelastic scattering of light from elementary excitations implies the principle of detailed balance to hold [3]. In this case the ratio of the Stokes (ST) to the anti-Stokes (AS) intensities has to obey $I_{AS}/I_{ST} = (\omega_{AS}/\omega_{ST})^2 e^{-\omega/T}$ at all temperatures with $\omega_{AS(ST)}$, ω, and T being the absolute frequency of the scattered light for energy gain (loss), the frequency of the elementary excitation and the temperature, respectively. It has actually been shown for Tl 2212 [4] and for Tl 2201 [5], that the principle of detailed balance holds for the temperature range 30 K < T < 300 K. Therefore, scattering due to luminescence may be selected out for the small energy transfer part of the spectra, where the anti-Stokes intensity is sufficiently strong for a comparison with the Stokes side. The temperature dependence of the normal state electronic spectra at the B_{1g} symmetry can be described satisfactorily by applying the Bose factor (Fig. 1). If we exclude exotic explanations, this implies, that we indeed observe excitations of single particles subject to a temperature independent relaxation. Well below T_c, we find almost zero intensity at the B_{1g} configuration for frequencies less than 50 cm^{-1} i.e. a completely developed gap and excess intensity between 200 and 600 cm^{-1}. These features can be qualitatively accounted for in the framework of a conventional BCS theory [6,7] describing the peculiarities of a superconducting system in the vicinity of the Fermi energy. Therefore, it is tempting to conclude that in the energy range under consideration charge carriers give rise to the observed scattering.

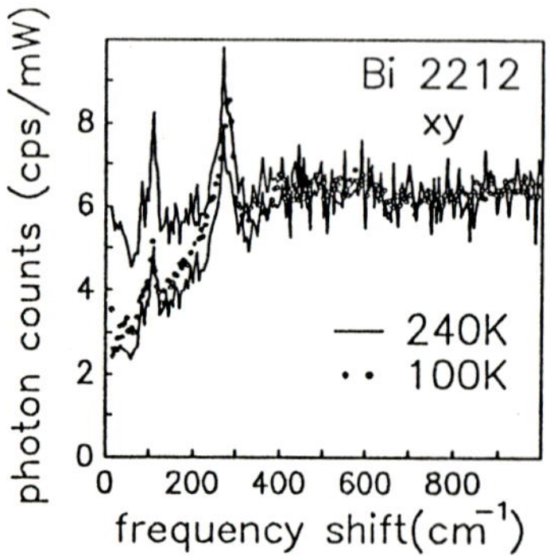

Fig. 1: B_{1g} symmetry spectra for Bi 2212 sample B2 (Ar annealed). The 100-K spectrum (dots) can be calculated by multiplying the 240-K spectrum (upper full line) with $\{1 + n(\omega,100\ K)\}/\{1 + n(\omega,240\ K)\}$ (lower full line).

4. Superconducting Gap

The BCS result for the Raman scattering cross section invokes the existence of a characteristic energy $2\Delta_0(T)$ which can be interpreted as the maximum binding energy of Cooper pairs. The Raman intensity is predicted to vanish well below and to display a maximum near $2\Delta_0$ [6,7]. An almost ideal spectrum of a superconductor is found at the B_{1g} symmetry of Bi 2212 (Fig. 2a). At all other symmetries a considerable scattering intensity is found at low frequencies and temperatures, which must be considered to be intrinsic in view of the vanishingly small cross section at the B_{1g} polarization. Therefore, the material appears to have a completely developed clean gap for a certain polarization, while for others only a reduced density of states is compatible with the data at low energies. In contrast to classical superconductors, the scattering cross section increases continuously from low frequencies up to a maximum located at symmetry dependent shifts between 300 and 500 cm^{-1} . At the B_{1g} symmetry the intensity for $\omega < 200\ cm^{-1}$ is approximately proportional to ω^3. The values for $2\Delta_0$ in Bi 2212 are approximately 8.0 kT_c for the B_{1g} symmetry and close to the BCS value of 3.5 kT_c for all other polarizations. The values found for Y 123 are some 20 % smaller.

We now address the temperature dependence of the electronic structures in different samples of Bi 2212. In crystals with an essentially non-metallic resistivity characteristic ρ_c (samples B1, B2), the maxima hardly change their positions upon heating from T = 20 K to T = T_c, while in sample B3 with a metallic temperature dependence of ρ_c and, consequently, a much less pronounced anisotropy than in samples B1 and B2 a softening by some 25% occurs (Fig. 3).

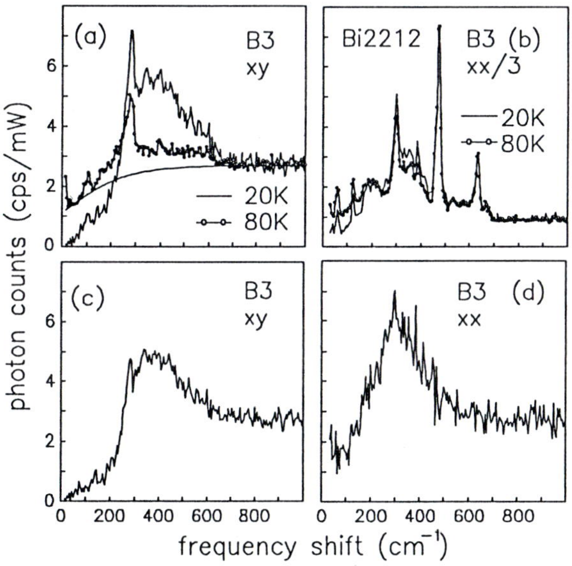

Fig. 2: Spectra for Bi 2212 sample B3 (O2 annealed). Below T_c a redistribution of intensity occurs which is characteristic for the superconducting state (a, b). In (c, d) the vibronic structures are subtracted.

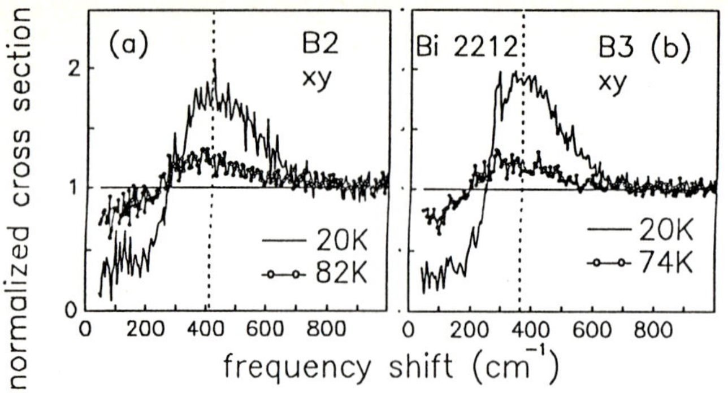

Fig. 3: Normalized electronic cross section $I_s(\omega,T)/I_n(\omega,T)$ below T_c for samples B2 (Ar) and B3 (O2). I_n is calculated assuming the same conventional temperature dependence below and above T_c.

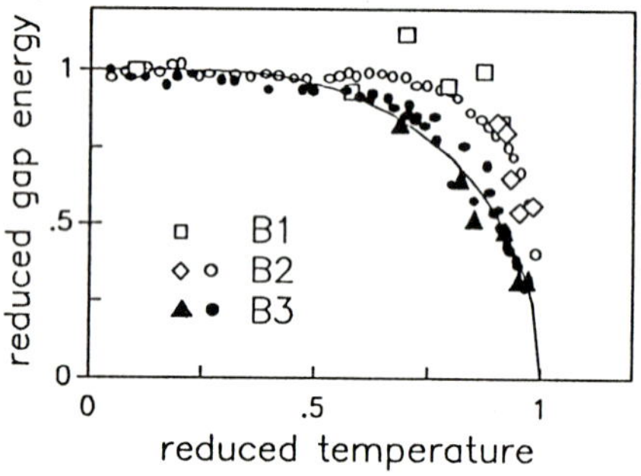

Fig. 4: Comparison of Raman and transport measurements. The squares, diamonds, and triangles represent the Raman data, the dots display the transport results [9].

The normalized cross section at T > 20 K is almost constant below 200 cm^{-1} (Fig. 3) and can easily be extrapolated to $\omega = 0$. According to the raw data $I_s(\omega = 0, T = 0) / I_n(0,0)$ is assumed to be zero in sample B3, but finite in B1 and B2. Since a real gap and a temperature independent carrier relaxation above T_c is found at the B_{1g} symmetry in B3, it seems reasonable to describe the temperature dependence of the normalized intensity at zero frequency within a conventional Fermi liquid model yielding $I_s(\omega = 0,T) / I_n(0,T) = 2/(e^{\Delta(T)/T}+1)$. At elevated temperatures, $0.5 < T / T_c < 1$, the gap $\Delta(T)$ can directly be determined (Fig. 4). It turns out that $\Delta(T)$ obeys the weak coupling BCS temperature dependence of the gap. It seems worthwhile to analyse the data of samples B1 and B2 in a similar way assuming, however, a temperature independent residual scattering intensity at $\omega = 0$. Up to 0.9 T_c the "gap" remains constant. For $0.9 < T / T_c < 1$, $\Delta(T)$ drops continuously to zero as required by a second order phase transition. Using the Ambegaokar-Baratoff formula for SIS tunneling junctions the energy gap can be determined from transport measurements [8]. A quantitative agreement between Raman and transport data is found (Fig. 4).

5. Conclusions

We have measured excitations of the carriers in both Y 123 and Bi 2212 above and below T_c. The orientation of the Cu-O bonds is found to determine the selection rules. The spectra at the tetragonal B_{1g} symmetry are indicative of a temperature independent relaxation of the carriers in the normal state and of an essentially clean gap in the superconducting state. At all other polarizations residual scattering intensity is found for low frequencies and temperatures being reminiscent of gapless superconductivity. The mobility of the carriers along the c-axis apparently determines the temperature dependence of the superconducting order parameter $\Delta(T)$. Therefore we believe that the observed deviations from the BCS prediction come from the 2-dimensional character of certain samples and are not indicative of the specific nature of the superconductivity in the oxides.

Acknowledgements: Many useful discussions with A. Zawadowski, A. Virosztek, and T.P. Devereaux are gratefully acknowledged. We are particularly indebted to H. Veith for precisely measuring the magnetic transition curves of our samples. Part of the work has been supported by the BMFT.

References

[1] T. Staufer, R. Nemetschek, R. Hackl, P. Müller, and H. Veith, Phys. Rev. Lett. **68**, 1069 (1992)

[2] R. Hackl et al. Phys. Rev. B **38**, 7133 (1988) and Physica C **162 - 164**, 1241 (1989)

[3] L.D. Landau and E.M. Lifshitz, Electrodynamics of Continuous Media (Oxford, Pergamon Press, 1960)

[4] A.A. Maximov, A.V. Puchnov, I.I. Tartakovskii, V.B. Timofeev, D. Reznik, and M.V. Klein to be published in Solid State Commun.

[5] unpublished results

[6] H. Monien and A. Zawadowski, Phys. Rev. B **41**, 8798 (1990) and references therein

[7] T.P. Devereaux, to be published in Phys. Rev. B

[8] R. Kleiner, F. Steinmeyer, G. Kunkel, and P. Müller, Phys. Rev. Lett. **68**, 2394 (1992)

[9] G. Kunkel, Diploma Thesis, Technische Universität München 1992 (unpublished) and R. Kleiner, private communication

Impurities and Raman Scattering in High-T_c Superconductors

O.V. Misochko[1] *and E.Ya. Sherman*[2]

[1]Walther-Meissner-Institut für Tieftemperaturforschung, Walther-Meissner-Str. 8, W-8046 Garching, Fed. Rep. of Germany
[2]Moscow Institute of Physics and Technology, 141700 Dolgoprudny, Russia

Abstract. Raman scattering (RS) by coupled electron-phonon excitations in a crystal with disturbed translational symmetry (e.g due to impurities) is investigated. Due to impurities the q=0 selection rule is broken and the phonon line shape can become asymmetric. In addition, for an anisotropic phonon dispersion, the line shape depends on the propagation direction of the phonon. It is shown that the impurity induced non-zero momentum of the phonons opens a new channel for scattering from electrons.

1. Introduction and experimental results

As it is known, in most of the high-temperature superconductors the chemical composition is not stoichiometric. Moreover, there is growing evidence that even in well-prepared samples microscopic disorder exists, whereby oxygen ions appear to be distributed over several neighboring potential minima. This fact permits to assume the availability of a random potential capable of strongly scattering electrons.

We have studied in detail the line shape of the high-energy Raman mode for thallium-based superconductor $TlBa_2Cu_3O_{7-x}$. The mode under study (520 cm^{-1}) refer to the displacement of the bridge oxygen. Fig.1 shows that the line shape of the 520 cm^{-1} phonon to be asymmetric. Its "half-width" from the high-frequency side, γ_+, is less than the "half-width" from the low-frequency side γ_-. The asymmetry factor $\chi = (\gamma_- - \gamma_+)/(\gamma_- + \gamma_+)$

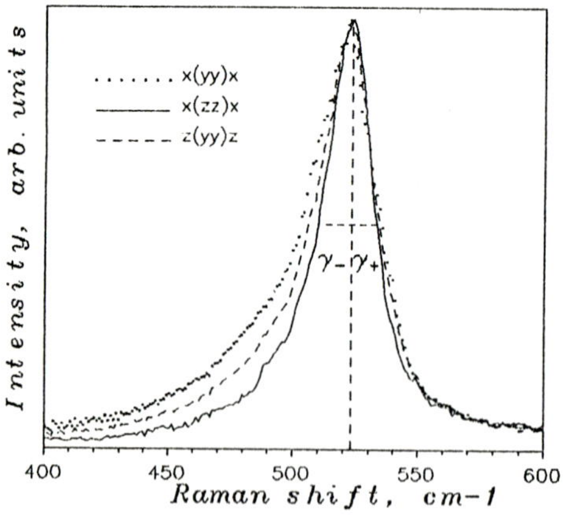

Fig.1. The Raman spectra of $TlBa_2CaCu_2O_{7-x}$ crystal showing the dependence of lineshape on polarization configuration. The spectra have been normalized to the intensity at the maximum.

Springer Series in Solid-State Sciences, Vol. 113 Electronic Properties of High-T_c Superconductors
Editors: H. Kuzmany, M. Mehring, J. Fink

for this line was about 0.1. The line-widths, frequencies and asymmetry were found to depend on the polarization geometry /1/. Therefore, a theory for Raman scattering must show how the polarization configurations affect the line shape.

2. THEORY AND DISCUSSION

To describe Raman scattering in dirty metal we should calculate renormalization of the vertex of the electron - phonon coupling by impurities. For the Γ-point phonons the calculations /2/ give

$$\Gamma = \gamma \frac{i}{\Omega_0 \tau} + \gamma \ , \tag{1}$$

where γ is the electron - phonon interaction constant, Ω_0 is the phonon frequency at the Γ-point of Brillouin zone, and τ - the elastic relaxation time. If $\Omega_0\tau \ll 1$ than $\Gamma \gg \gamma$. Hence, the impurities can drastically change the RS intensity.

Let us consider the phonon creation with momentum, which is considerably larger than the photon momentum and inverse light penetration depth. The diagrams we are interested in, are those in which a momentum can be transferred from one "bank" of diagram to another, thereby canceling a finite phonon momentum, Fig.2. For the density of probability of phonon creation with a finite component of momentum we obtain

$$w_i(q) = \frac{ln(1/\Omega_0\tau)}{k_F^2} \varphi_i \ (ql), \tag{2}$$

where l denotes the electron elastic free path, $\varphi_i(ql)$ is a dimensionless function, k_F denotes the Fermi momentum, and the index i marks the diagram type ("ladder" or "fan" ones). The dependence $\varphi_i \ (ql)$ is shown in Fig.3.

Taking into account the phonon dispersion, the dispersion law for a layered crystal being written down at small q in the following form

$$\Omega(q) = \Omega_0 + (\Omega_1 a^2)q^2 \ , \tag{3}$$

where Ω_1 denotes the characteristic width of the phonon zone, and a is the lattice constant. As a result of the fact that the phonon energy is differnt from Ω_0 at a momentum being different from zero, asymmetry of the phonon line must appear. The spectral density of the RS intensity $\rho(\omega)$ is a sum of the symmetric contribution $\rho_s(\omega)$ and asymmetric one $\rho_a(\omega)$, the latter is determined by the processes indicated in Fig.2. The $\rho_s(\omega)$ is a Lorenzian and for the $\rho_a(\omega)$ we have

$$\rho_a(\omega) = \int \frac{1}{q_z^2 + 1/\varkappa^2} \ (w_l(ql) + w_f(ql))\mathrm{Im}\ D^R(\omega,q) \frac{d^2q dq_z}{(2\pi)^3} \ . \tag{4}$$

For the asymmetry mechanism considered by us the asymmetry parameter is

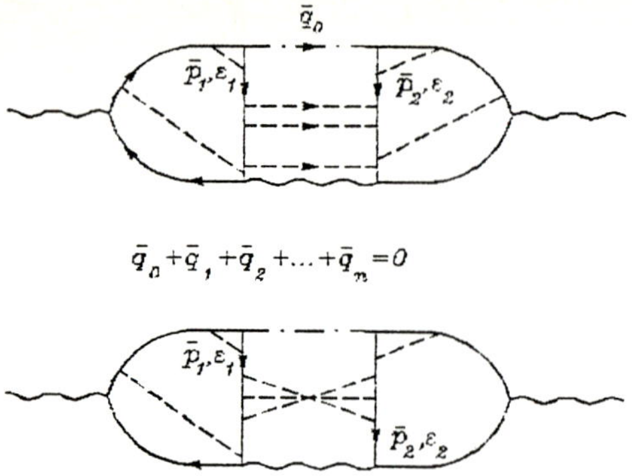

Fig.2. Diagrams describing emission of phonons with finite momentum. The same impurities are connected by dashed lines.

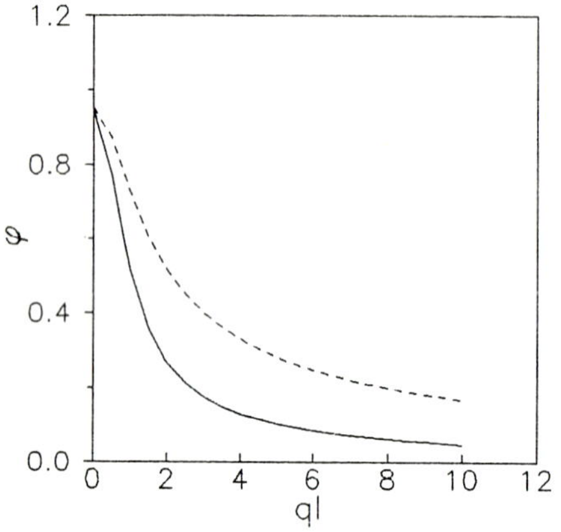

Fig.3. The function $\varphi(ql)$ in the expression for the density of probability of finite q phonon emission for the ladder (dashed line) and for the fan (solid line) diagrams.

$$\chi_i \sim \sqrt{\frac{\gamma}{\Omega_1}\frac{\ln(1/\Omega_0\tau)}{(k_F a)^2}}\ \frac{a}{l}\ ln\left((\gamma/\Omega_1)^{1/2}\frac{a}{l}\right) . \qquad (5)$$

For the realistic values of the parameters we have $\chi \approx 0.1$ from Eq.(5) what coincide with the value experimentally observed.

Moreover, as a result, an additional channel for electronic scattering is opening - due to emission of the phonon with the finite q it is possible to transfer energy to/from the electronic subsystem by "large" portions with not so large probability. The diagram for this type of scattering is shown in Fig.4., where the finite momentum of the electron - hole pair is canceled by the phonon momentum. Such a process is possible even in pure metals /3/, but due to singularity of electron spectrum near the Fermi level in dirty metals (a "diffuson" mode) it can be sufficiently changed by impurities and, for instance, give rise to a sufficient enhancement of RS intensity.

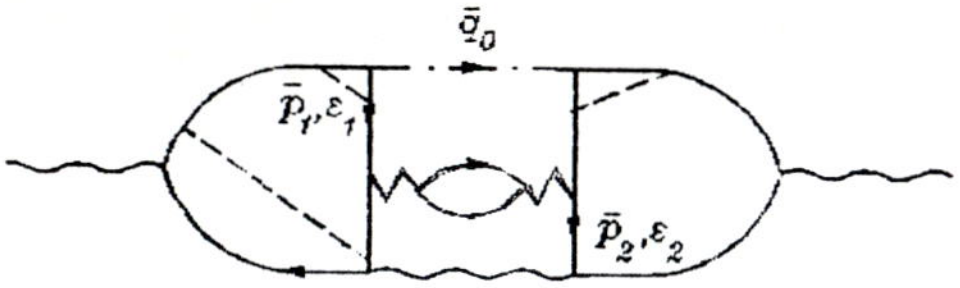

Fig.4. Diagrams describing excitation of electron-hole pair with finite momentum.

Acknowledgements. One of the authors (O.V.M) acknowledges support from Alexander von Humboldt Foundation.

References

1. O.V.Misochko and E.Ya.Sherman, accepted for Mod.Phys.Lett.B
2. O.V.Misochko and E.Ya.Sherman, submitted to Phys Rev.B
3. D.Reznik, A.Kotz, S.L.Cooper, M.V.Klein, W.C.Lee, and D.M.Ginsberg, Physica C 185-189 1029 (1991)

Polarization-Dependent Electronic Raman Scattering in Single Crystals of $REBa_2Cu_3O_{7-x}$

M. Mayer[1], *S. Lo*[1], *M. Pressl*[1], *P. Knoll*[1], *E. Holzinger-Schweiger*[2], *and G. Leising*[2]

[1] Institut für Experimentalphysik der Universität Graz, Universitätsplatz 5, A-8010 Graz, Austria
[2] Institut für Festkörperphysik der TU Graz, Petersgasse 16, A-8010 Graz, Austria

Abstract: The light scattering response of $REBa_2Cu_3O_{7-x}$ (RE = Sm, Nd, $Pr_{0.48}Y_{0.52}$) has been observed up to 7000cm^{-1} energy shifts for different scattering geometries. The experiments were performed in the Raman microprobe where selected areas of ca. 1μm are investigated. These areas were chosen by polarization microscopy. "Scanning multichannel technique" has been used in order to obtain well corrected spectra over a wide spectral range. The observed signal is very similar for all investigated samples regardless of their superconducting properties. In the Pr–Y system a small bump around 3000cm^{-1} was observed which may arise from spin excitations. The polarization dependent selection rules identify the long range scattering signal as an A_{1g} symmetry type. Contributions to the observed scattering signal from luminescence and insufficient suppression of the laser stray light are discussed.

1.Introduction

The Raman response of superconducting HTc samples has attracted considerable interest [1]. Electronic Raman scattering has probed the superconducting gap and its strange temperature dependence [2]. However, so far the origin of that electronic scattering is still mysterious. Even the normal conducting properties of that electronic signal show unusual scattering intensities which extend almost featureless up to high energy shifts [3].

The interaction of light with matter is described by the vector potential A which in the case of scattering experiments consist of the sum of the incident laser radiation A_i and the scattered radiation A_s. Because of the high frequency of the light the interaction takes place only with the electrons. The electron momentum p is replaces by p+(e/c)·A. Assuming only quasi free electrons with an effective mass m^* two types of interaction Hamiltonians are obtained:

$$H_A = \frac{e}{c}\left[\vec{p}\cdot\frac{1}{m^*}\vec{A} + \vec{A}\cdot\frac{1}{m^*}\vec{p}\right] , \qquad H_{AA} = \frac{e^2}{2c^2}\left[\vec{A}_i\cdot\frac{1}{m^*}\vec{A}_s\right] . \tag{1}$$

The H_{AA} term contributes to the scattering intensity in first order perturbation theory. This results in a Stokes scattering spectral density dependent on the energy transfer $\Omega=\omega_i-\omega_s$ and the momentum transfer q [4]:

$$\frac{dI_s(\Omega,q)}{d\Omega} = -\left(\frac{\omega_s}{\omega_i}\right)^2\left(\vec{e_i}\frac{1}{m^*}\vec{e_s}\right)\left(1+n(\Omega)\right)\frac{\hbar q^2 e^2}{4\pi c^4}\,\mathrm{Im}\left(\frac{1}{\epsilon(\Omega)}\right) . \tag{2}$$

This type of scattering is due to charge fluctuations (characterized by the dielectric function $\varepsilon(\Omega)$) and should peak at the plasma frequency. The selection rules of polarization of incident light e_i and scattered light e_s are given by the inverse effective mass tensor $1/m^*$ and should correspond to the totally symmetric representation in this simple treatment. In order to describe a broad, featureless electronic Raman response a strongly overdamped plasma frequency is required and some additional mechanism [5], as e.g. intervally scattering, contributing to the scattering intensities at low energy shifts. On the other hand the H_A term of the interaction Hamiltonian can contribute to the scattered intensity via second order perturbation and results in a scattering intensity proportional to matrix elements of the type

Springer Series in Solid-State Sciences, Vol. 113 Electronic Properties of High-T_c Superconductors
Editors: H. Kuzmany, M. Mehring, J. Fink

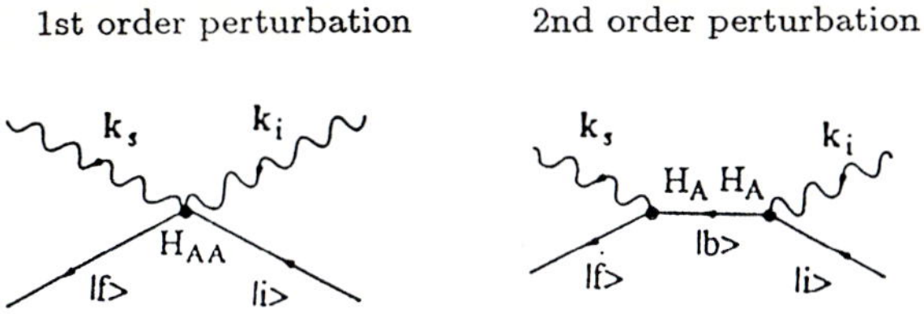

Fig.1: Feynman diagrams of the two lowest order Raman scattering processes corresponding to equ. 2 and 3.

$$I_s \sim \sum_b \left[\frac{\left\langle f \left| \vec{p} \cdot \vec{A} \right| b \right\rangle \left\langle b \left| \vec{p} \cdot \vec{A} \right| i \right\rangle}{\omega_i - \omega_f} \right]^2 \delta(\omega_i - \omega_f) . \tag{3}$$

The scattering process runs from an initial state <i| over a virtual state formed by the sum over all states <b| to the final state <f|. It can contribute to any symmetry species and is mostly dominated by interband scattering which should be significant at high energy shifts. In Fig.1 a diagrammatic representation of these two types of scattering are shown.

In this paper we report on long range Raman scattering experiments on different single crystals. The scattering intensities for different scattering geometries have been determined and quantitatively compared in order to find the symmetry properties.

2. Experimental setup

The experiments have been performed on single crystals of $SmBa_2Cu_3O_{6.7}$ with a T_c of 87K, of $NdBa_2Cu_3O_{6.5}$ and of $Pr_{0.48}Y_{0.52}Ba_2Cu_3O_7$ both showing no superconducting transition. The crystals were grown using the standard flux melt method [6]; The size of the crystals was around $800\mu m \times 800\mu m \times 90\mu m$. In order to obtain Raman spectra of all scattering geometries including that one of the xz plane the Raman microprobe has been used. The schematic experimental setup is shown in Fig. 2. The 457.9nm laser radiation was focused to a spot of $\sim 1\mu m^2$ (laser power less than 1mW). The

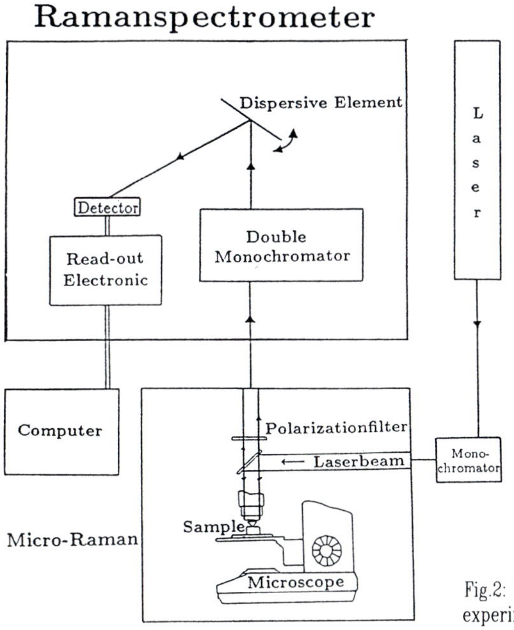

Fig.2: Experimental setup for the μ-Raman experiments

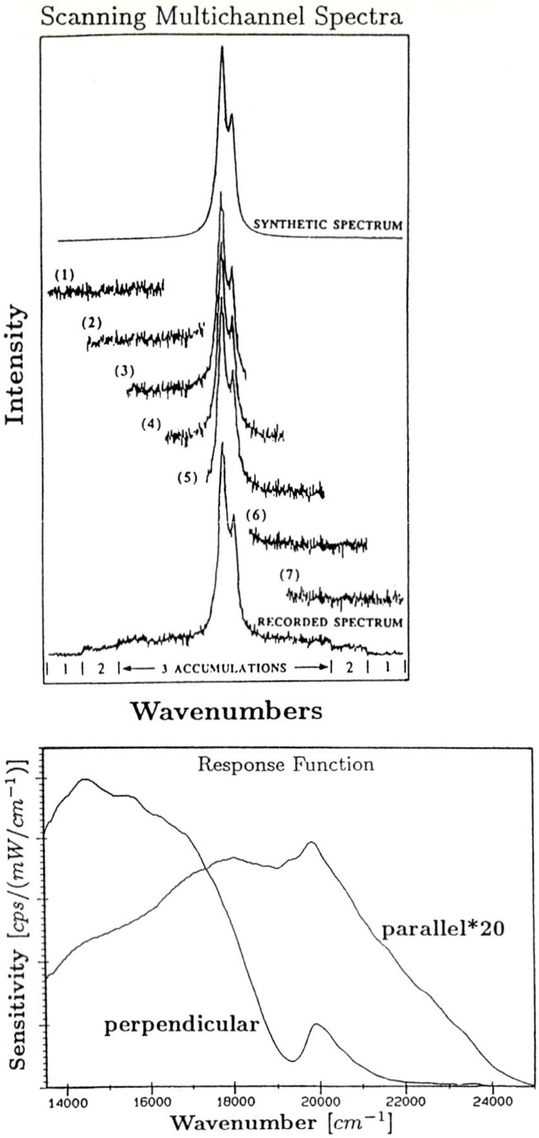

Fig.3: Upper picture: The scanning multichannel algorithm demonstrated with an artificial spectrum. Lower picture: The responsefunctions of the whole system for light polarized parallel and perpendicular to the entrance slit.

scattered light was analyzed by a Dilor triple spectrometer OMARS 89 and detected with an intensified diode array (512 diodes). In order to use the advantages of the multichanneldetektor together with a well calibrated long spectral scan "Scanning multichannel technique"[7] has been applied. In this spectroscopic technique the spectrum is obtained with a high overlap of each part of the spectrum seen by the mulitchannel detector as illustrated in Fig.3. The response function of the system is obtained measuring the irradiation of a OSRAM Wi17G black body calibration lamp under the same conditions and with the same alignment as the HTc single crystal measurements. However, the calibration is still tricky and special care has to be taken to avoid systematic errors as influence of the chromatic aberration and different illumination of the entrance slit. In our case a very small slit ($\sim 10\mu m$) irradiated by the calibration lamp has been placed perpendicular to the entrance slit instead of the sample. All obtained spectra were divided by the spectral sensitivity for the corresponding polarization direction. This procedure gives the corrected spectra the meaning of spectral densities proportional by some unknown factor to the units of mW/cm^{-1}.

3. Results

As a typical result the corrected spectra of $Pr_{0.48}Y_{0.52}Ba_2Cu_3O_7$ are shown in Fig.4. The scattering geometry is characterized using the Porto-notation: the symbols outside the brackets denote the direction of incident and scattered radiation; the symbols inside the brackets denote directions of polarizations of incident and scattered light. X' Y' denote rotation of the x, y axes by 45 degree, respectively. Because of twinning x and y direction can not be distinguished. The spectra of all the other investigated materials are very similar with the only difference that in the Pr-Y system a weak bump at around $3000cm^{-1}$ occurs in the yy and y'y' polarizations. Although spinfluctuations of the undisturbed antiferromagnetic crystals contribute mainly to x'y' polarizations this bump can arise from them because of strong perturbed and nearly suppressed antiferromagnetism. A comparison of the observed integrated intensities on the different crystals with respect to the different symmetry species are shown in Table 1.

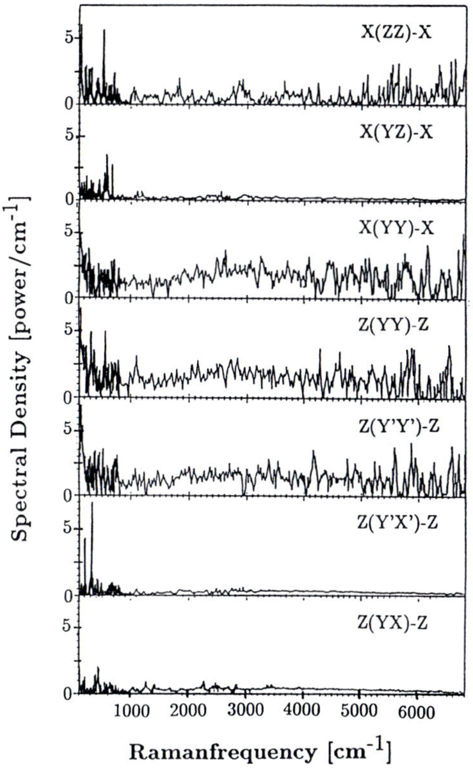

Fig.4: μ-Raman spectra for different scattering geometries on $Pr_{0.48}Y_{0.52}Ba_2Cu_3O_{\sim 6.8}$

Table 1: Integrated Raman intensities (1000–6800cm^{-1}) of the long range Raman response for different single crystals in different scattering geometries (point group D_{4h}).

Sample	Polarization Direction	Symmetry Species	Intensity
$SmBa_2Cu_3O_x$	x(zz)-x	A_{1g}	120
	x(yz)-x	E_g	28
	x(yy)-x	$A_{1g} + B_{1g}$	140
	z(yy)-z	$A_{1g} + B_{1g}$	175
	z(yx)-z	B_{2g}	29
	z(y'y')-z	$A_{1g} + B_{2g}$	152
	z(y'x')-z	B_{1g}	25
$NdBa_2Cu_3O_x$	x(zz)-x	A_{1g}	100
	x(yz)-x	E_g	15
	x(yy)-x	$A_{1g} + B_{1g}$	150
	z(yy)-z	$A_{1g} + B_{1g}$	190
	z(yx)-z	B_{2g}	16
	z(y'y')-z	$A_{1g} + B_{2g}$	170
	z(y'x')-z	B_{1g}	16
$Pr_{0.48}Y_{0.52}Ba_2Cu_3O_x$	x(zz)-x	A_{1g}	100
	x(yz)-x	E_g	25
	x(yy)-x	$A_{1g} + B_{1g}$	186
	z(yy)-z	$A_{1g} + B_{1g}$	155
	z(yx)-z	B_{2g}	30
	z(y'y')-z	$A_{1g} + B_{2g}$	144
	z(y'x')-z	B_{1g}	40

4. Discussion

The experimental results as summarized in Table 1 identify most of the scattered intensity as A_{1g} type. There is some smaller intensity in the zz polarizations as expected for a quasi two dimensional electronic system. But this zz intensity is rather strong and, in general, there are no significant changes between samples with different superconducting properties (and different electronic structure in the normal state). This makes electronic scattering in that high energy regime very unlikely in agreement with findings by D. Reznik et al.[8]. Spin excitations could contribute in principle. But this is also very unlikely as the scattering intensity is expected to strongly decrease with decreasing number of antiferromagnetically ordered spin pairs [9].

However, from an experimental point of view there is no good criterium to identify this signal as Raman scattering. At such high energy shifts Raman scattering of a featureless background can hardly be separated from luminescence. The antistokes spectrum vanishes very rapidly at higher energy shifts. At small energy shifts also luminescence may contribute to the antistokes side[10]. So far, there is no good experience with such small signals at high energy shifts in Raman spectrosopy. Therefore, influence of the spectrometer characteristics can not be excluded. We did an identical measurement on undoped silicon and find also some signal up to high energy shifts. The integrated intensity is about 80% of the signal found at the HTc cuprates of Table 1. This suggests that their may be some contributions from either luminescence (mainly from surface states) or some insufficient surpression of the laser light which does not pass the dispersive element and illuminates directly the detector. Further investigations are in progress to study such phenomena.

References:

1. for a review see e.g.: C.Thomsen, in Light Scattering in Solids VI, ed. by M.Cardona and G.Güntherodt (Springer Verlag, Heidelberg, 1991), p. 285
M.Cardona, Proc. of Int.Conf. on High Tc Superconductivity, ed. by S.K.Joshi, C.N.R.Rao, S.V.Subramanyam (World Scientific, Singapore, 1990), p.208
R.Feile, Physica C 159, 1 (1989)
2. R.Hackl et al. Phys.Rev. B 38, 7133 (1988)
T.Staufer, R.Nemetschek, R.Hackl, P.Müller, and H.Veith, preprint
3. C.M.Varma, P.B.Littlewood, S.Schmitt-Rink, E.Abrahams, A.E.Ruckenstein, Phys.Rev.Lett.63, 1996(1989)
T.Staufer, R.Hackl and P.Müller, Sol. State Commun. 75, 975(1990)
4. see e.g. G.Abstreiter, M.Cardona, and A.Pinczuk, in Light Scattering in Solids IV, ed. by M.Cardona and G.Güntherodt (Springer Verlag, Heidelberg, 1984) p. 5
M.V.Klein, in Light Scattering in Solids I, ed. by M.Cardona (Springer Verlag, Heidelberg, 1982)
5. A.Zawadowski and M.Cardona, Phys.Rev.B42, 10732(1990), a treatment taking into account a nesting fermi survace condition see A.Virostek and J.Ruvalds, Phys.Rev.Lett.67, 1657(1991)
6. D.L.Kaiser, F.Holtzberg, B.A.Scott, T.R.Mc Guier, Appl. Phys. Lett. 51, 1040(1987)
7. P.Knoll, R.Singer, and W. Kiefer, Appl. Spectr. 44, 776(1990)
8. D.Reznik et al. this volume
9. compare also P. Knoll et al. this volume
10. see e.g. K.Iwahana et al. in Springer Series in Solid State Sciences 63, 152(1985),
K.Iwahana, P.Knoll, and H.Kuzmany, phys.stst.sol.(b) 128, 735(1985)

Chain-Oxygen Vibrations and Phonon Anomalies Above T_c in $RBa_2Cu_3O_7$ and $YBa_2Cu_4O_8$

A.P. Litvinchuk, C. Thomsen, and M. Cardona

Max-Planck-Institut für Festkörperforschung,
Heisenbergstr. 1, W-7000 Stuttgart 80, Fed. Rep. of Germany

Abstract. The modes of B_{1u}-symmetry observed in the infrared spectra of $YBa_2Cu_3O_{7-\delta}$ and $YBa_2Cu_4O_8$ at $\nu \approx 277$ cm^{-1} and 500 cm^{-1}, respectively, are assigned to vibrations of the chain-oxygens. This assignment is reached by analysis of the corresponding eigenvectors, influence of Au, Pr, ^{18}O doping on these frequencies and comparison of infrared spectra of both materials. Anomalous softenings of oxygen-related phonon frequencies with decreasing temperature are found starting above T_c, the most pronounced ones occuring for $YBa_2Cu_4O_8$.

1. Introduction

Vibrations of atoms in the CuO_2 planes of oxide superconductors have been at the center of interest because of the natural conjecture that they should couple strongly to the superconducting carriers. It was indeed found in Raman spectroscopy that phonon frequencies, linewidths, and intensities experience considerable variations at the transition temperature T_c [1,2], a fact which led to the determination of a superconducting gap in $RBa_2Cu_3O_{7-\delta}$ (R = rare earth). In infrared (ir) spectroscopy, the odd B_{1u}-vibrations (z-direction) at $\vec{k} = 0$ were also found to show anomalies at T_c [3–5]; a detailed interpretation of the results, however, requires an understanding of the vibrational eigenmodes corresponding to each oscillator. Most authors believe that the ir modes at $\nu \approx 277$ cm^{-1} and 310 cm^{-1} in $RBa_2Cu_3O_7$ correspond to the out-of-phase and in-phase vibrations of the plane-oxygen [O(2) and O(3)]. We present here a number of experimental facts which evidence for the former as being due to chain-oxygen [O(1)] vibrations.

2. Results and discussion

It is current belief that the vibration at 277 cm^{-1} in $YBa_2Cu_3O_7$ is related to an anti-phase vibration in the z-direction of the O(2), O(3) oxygen atoms in the CuO_2 planes (see, e.g., [3,5]). Equivalent atoms in neighboring planes are in phase with each other, as is required by symmetry for ir-active (i.e. odd) vibrations. This means that in higher-symmetry tetragonal case (e.g. $YBa_2Cu_3O_6$) the oscillator strength (S) of this vibration should be exactly zero,

Springer Series in Solid-State Sciences, Vol. 113 Electronic Properties of High-T_c Superconductors
Editors: H. Kuzmany, M. Mehring, J. Fink

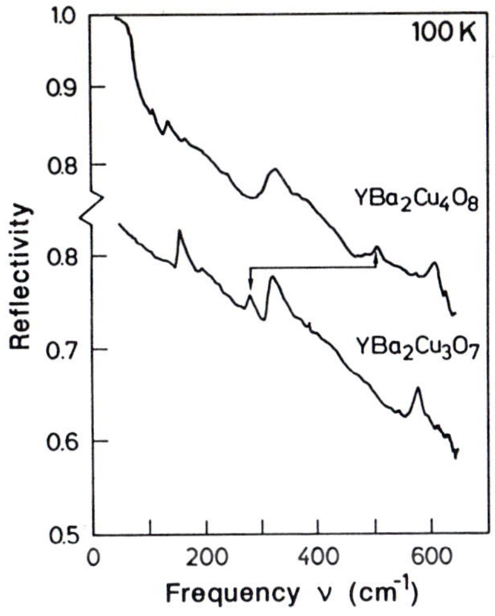

Fig. 1. Reflectivity spectra of $YBa_2Cu_4O_8$ and $YBa_2Cu_3O_7$ ceramics at $T = 100$K.

because charge displaced along z by oxygen in one inequivalent position (say O(2)) is exactly equal to that displaced by another (O(3)) in opposite direction. Taking into account existing orthorombicity one can expect (according to lattice dynamical calculations [6]) $S \leq 0.1$. Experimentally (see Fig. 1) the line at 277 cm^{-1} is as strong as other vibrational bands, especially at low temperatures. One finds much larger values of oscillator strength for both single crystals and ceramics [3,7] in contradiction with the nearly silent character of this mode.

In Fig. 1 we show the reflectivity spectra of both the 123 and 124 compounds. Apart from the effects of the double-chain, the compounds are isostructural and should hence possess similar phonon modes and frequencies. This seems to be true with one exception [8]. As may be seen from the figure, the strong mode at 277 cm^{-1} in 123 is not present in 124. In view of the assignment of the silent mode to this peak, this is a very surprising result. Furthermore, there is an additional peak in the 124 spectrum at 500 cm^{-1}. From a group-theoretical point-of-view, however, the number of ir-active modes is the same in both compounds. No new mode is expected. We may hence conclude that the 277 cm^{-1} (123) and 500 cm^{-1} (124) modes are actually the same (as indicated by arrows in Fig. 1), with a significantly different frequency in the two compounds.

Why should the frequency of this mode be so different in the two compounds? If we assume it to be the chain-oxygen vibration along z, the explanation follows naturally from the existence of double chains in 124. The z-vibration of the chain oxygen is a pure bending mode in 123 and should hence have a characteristically low frequency. In the double-chain compound the unit cell is face centered: there is a shift of $b/2$ in y-direction of two primitive cells adjacent in c-direction. Consequently the chain oxygen is placed under a copper atom and its z-direction vibration has predominately bond-stretching character. Its frequency should go up significantly as is observed in the spectra.

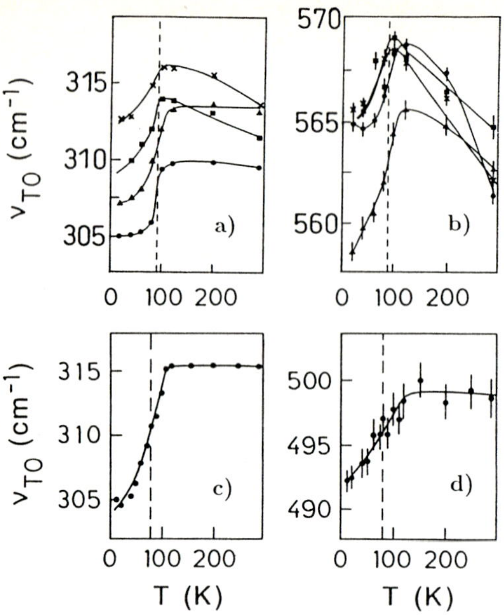

Fig. 2. Temperature dependence of TO-phonon frequencies for (a,b) $YBa_2Cu_3O_7$(**x** - undoped, ■ - 5%Au, ● - 10%Au, ▲ - 10%Pr) and (c,d) $YBa_2Cu_4O_8$. Vertical dashed lines mark T_c.

Thus, the comparison of the two spectra in Fig. 1 gives a strong indication that the 277 cm^{-1} mode in 123 is indeed a chain-related mode.

Results of substitution experiments further support this point. Gold is known to substitute for chain copper Cu(1) In the 123 structure. Pr, on the other hand, replaces Y in $(Y_{1-x}Pr_x)Ba_2Cu_3O_{7-\delta}$. For the 10%Au substitution we found the largest change of the TO-phonon frequency, $\Delta\nu/\nu$ = -4.0%, for the mode at 277 cm^{-1}, a surprising result if this mode were to be the silent one. As gold substitutes in the chain-copper site such an effect is rather expected for the chain-oxygen mode. For Pr in place of Y, on the other hand, the strongest change ($\Delta\nu/\nu$ = -1.6%) occurs for the 193 cm^{-1} mode, which is well known to be a vibration involving mostly the Y atom.

In order to further verify this new assignment we have also performed a site-selective oxygen-substitution experiment. By treating a sample of $ErBa_2Cu_3(^{16}O_{6.84-x}{}^{18}O_x)$ with $x = 0$ in ^{18}O atmosphere at low temperature (T = 300 C) we achieved an exchange of $x = 1.03$. Under this conditions the exchange with oxygen in the CuO_2 planes is suppressed and, to a first approximation, we may say that the O(1) oxygen position is substituted by ^{18}O while the other oxygen sites consist mostly of ^{16}O. If this were the case, we would expect a drop of the frequency for the chain-oxygen vibration. We found indeed this effect for the phonon in question (at $\nu \approx$277 cm^{-1}).

An unusual temperature dependence of the chain-oxygen vibration was found: the corresponding phonon frequency decreases with temperature for $T \leq$ 300 K. This anomaly does not have anything to do with superconducting transition since it occurs even in non-superconducting $PrBa_2Cu_3O_{7-\delta}$ [9]. In Fig. 2 the temperature dependence of phonon frequencies is shown for other oxygen-related modes. One can clearly see an onset of softening well above T_c for both 124 and also for *doped* 123, undopes 123 materials do not show this. The effect observed seems to be general for $RBa_2Cu_3O_7$ doped with transition metals and is not a particular property of metal dopants substituting for the chain Cu(1) site only, as was recently assumed [10].

3. Conclusion

We have presented evidence that the 277 cm^{-1} mode in the ir-spectra of $YBa_2Cu_3O_7$ is related to chain-oxygen vibrations and not to the CuO_2 planes as previously assumed. Anomalous softenings of oxygen-related vibrations were found to occure above T_c not only for $YBa_2Cu_4O_8$ but also for Au- and Pr-doped $YBa_2Cu_3O_7$.

Acklowledgments. Part of this work was performed by one of us (A.P.L.) under support from the Alexander von Humboldt Foundation (Bonn, Federal Republic of Germany). He thanks also the Max-Planck-Institut für Festkörperforschung for its hospitality.

References

[1] B. Friedl, C. Thomsen, and M. Cardona, Phys. Rev. Lett. **65**, 915 (1990).

[2] B. Friedl, C. Thomsen, H.-U. Habermeier, and M. Cardona, Solid State Commun. **78**, 291 (1991).

[3] L. Genzel, A. Wittlin, M. Bauer, M. Cardona, E. Schönherr, and A. Simon, Phys. Rev. B **40**, 2170 (1990).

[4] T. Zetterer, M. Franz, J. Schützmann, W. Ose, H.H. Otto, and K.F. Renk, Phys. Rev. B **41**, 9499 (1990).

[5] R. Gajić, J. Schützmann, J. Betz, T. Zetterer, H.H. Otto, P.E. Obermayer, and K.F. Renk, Solid State Commun. **78**, 65 (1991).

[6] R. Liu, C. Thomsen, W. Kress, M. Cardona, B. Gegenheimer, F.W. de Wette, J. Prade, A.D. Kulkarni, and U. Schröder, Phys. Rev. B **37**, 7971 (1988).

[7] R.T. Collins, Z. Schlesinger, F. Holtzberg, and C. Feild, Phys. Rev. Lett. **63**, 422 (1989).

[8] A.P. Litvinchuk, C. Thomsen, P. Murugaraj, and M. Cardona, Z. Phys. B **86**, 329 (1992).

[9] A.P. Litvinchuk, C. Thomsen, and M. Cardona, Solid State Commun. **80**, 257 (1991).

[10] H.S. Obhi and E.K.H. Salje, J. Phys.: Condens. Matter **4**, 195 (1992).

Phonon Softening and Electron–Phonon Interaction in $YBa_2Cu_3O_{7-\delta}$

R. Feile[1,2], *R. Li*[2], *U. Weimer*[2], *C. Tomè-Rosa*[3], *and H. Adrian*[3]

[1]Institut für Technische Physik, Universität des Saarlandes, W-6600 Saarbrücken, Fed. Rep. of Germany

[2]Institut für Physik, Johannes-Gutenberg-Universität, W-6500 Mainz, Fed. Rep. of Germany

[3]Institut für Physik, TH Darmstadt, W-6100 Darmstadt, Fed. Rep. of Germany

Abstract. We report on the Raman scattering investigation of the 335 cm^{-1} phonon of A_g (pseudo-B_{1g}) symmetry in thin $YBa_2Cu_3O_{7-\delta}$ films on various substrates. The experiments yield values for the phonon softening below T_c, which differ from sample to sample. We find a linear relation between the softening and the inverse asymmetry parameter of the phonon Fano-like lineshape, when these parameters, obtained from different samples, are compared with each other. In contrast to this, the onset temperatures for the softening are the same for these samples.

Optical phonons in the high temperature superconductors have received much attention because they exhibit self-energy effects below the superconducting transition temperature as observed by Raman [1-3] and IR spectroscopy [4,5]. Especially $YBa_2Cu_3O_{7-\delta}$ (123), its isostructural rare earth substitutes [6], and recently $YBa_2Cu_4O_8$ (124) [7] have been subject to many detailled spectroscopical investigations. The self-energy effects are most pronounced for the A_g (pseudo B_{1g}) phonon with an energy of 335 cm^{-1} in the 123-compound indicated by the softening of its frequency below T_c. The amount of softening reflects the electro-phonon interaction, and is predicted to be sensitive to the position of the phonon relative to the superconducting gap [8]. This had been verified by Raman experiments on a series of rare earth (R) compounds $RBa_2Cu_3O_{7-\delta}$ [6].

In this contribution we present some Raman data from $YBa_2Cu_3O_{7-\delta}$ films on different substrates. The results exhibit a unique relation between the phonon energy shift below T_c and the asymmetry of the lineshape.

The samples consisted of a series of films prepared on MgO, $SrTiO_3$ and on $LaAlO_3$ substrates by sputtering techniques as described elsewhere [9,10]. Their thicknesses ranged between 200 nm and 2 μm. The films had been characterized by resistance and susceptibility measurements. X-ray and Raman scattering [10,11] confirmed the epitaxy of the films. Raman measurements had been performed from room temperature through the superconducting transition. Details of the experimental setup have alredy been published elsewhere [12, 13].

The Raman experiments focused mainly on the spectral region around the 335 cm^{-1} phonon. All the spectra measured exhibited the typical asymmetric line for this phonon. Examples are shown in Fig. 1. To treat the spectral function we refer to Refs. [3,14] where the authors attributed the asymmetry to the coupling of the phonon to an electronic continuum, leading to the widely called Fano interference. The lineshape is given by

$$I(E) = \pi\varrho(E)T_e^2\,\frac{(q+\varepsilon)^2}{1+\varepsilon^2}\,,\quad \text{with } \varepsilon = \frac{E-E_p}{\Gamma}\,,\quad \text{and } q = \frac{T_p}{\pi T_e}\cdot\frac{1}{V\cdot\varrho(E)} + \frac{R(E)}{\pi\varrho(E)}\,. \tag{1}$$

Springer Series in Solid-State Sciences, Vol. 113 **Electronic Properties of High-T_c Superconductors**
Editors: H. Kuzmany, M. Mehring, J. Fink

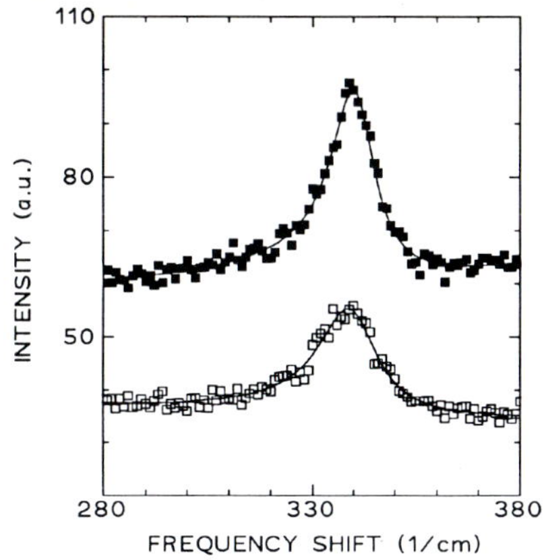

Fig.1: Examples for the lineshape of the pseudo B_{1g} phonon. The full lines give the results of fits using the Fano lineshape.

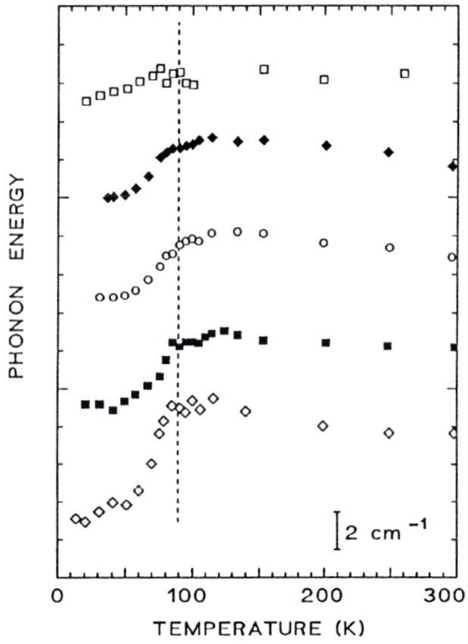

Fig.2: Temperature dependence of the renormalized phonon energy for the pseudo B_{1g} phonon in some of the various films on different substrates. The data are displayed on a relative scale for clarity. They give the results from films on $SrTiO_3$ (1,5), $LaAlO_3$ (2,3), and MgO (4), numbered from above. There is obviously no correlation of the temperature dependence with the substrate. The vertical line indicates a mean superconducting transition temperature.

$E_p = E_0 + V^2 \cdot R(E)$ is the renormalized phonon energy, E_0 gives the intrinsic phonon energy without electron-phonon interaction, $\varrho(E)$ is the electronic density of states, $R(E)$ its Hilbert transform, T_p, T_e are the electronic and phononic scattering amplitudes, respectively, and V defines the electron-phonon coupling strength. A large q value gives a symmetric Lorentzian lineshape, thus the inverse of this parameter, 1/q, may serve as an appropriate measure for the asymmetry of the lineshape. The spectral function (1) has been fitted to the phonon spectra with E_p, q, the linewidth Γ, and the intensity $I_0 = \pi \varrho(E) T_e^2$ as the adjustable parameters. The results of the fits have been plotted in Figure 1 in addition to the experimental spectra.

Figure 2 shows the temperature dependence of the renormalized phonon energy for the series of films on a relative scale. The data exhibit the typical decrease of the phonon energy at low temperatures. The onset temperatures for the softening

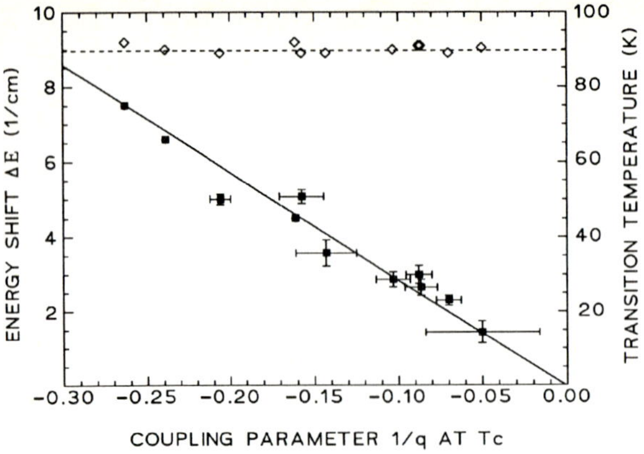

Fig.3: Energy shifts for the pseudo B_{1g} phonon at 335 cm^{-1} in various samples of $YBa_2Cu_3O_7$ (one exception is the datapoint for the highest energy shift taken from the Er-compond [15]) plotted versus the inverse asymmetry parameter at a temperature close above T_c (full symbols). The open symbols give the transition temperatures of the samples for comparison. The error bars are the σ-confidence regions for the parameters give by the fitting routine (no errors are given for data from the literature [15,16])

in different films coincide with the resistively determined transition temperatures. One clearly observes that some films exhibit a larger softening than others.

From our first work on films of these materials [13] we got the impression that the total frequency shift of the 335 cm^{-1} phonon between T_c and T=0, ΔE, is correlated with the asymmetry of the phonon line. As the asymmetry exhibited some temperature dependence, we took its value close to T_c, $1/q(T_c)$, as reference. In Figure 3 we have plotted ΔE versus $1/q(T_c)$ for the various samples. The linear relation between these two parameters becomes obvious. A complete discussion of the results will be given elsewhere [17].

At a first glance this linear relation directly reflects that the softening is proportional to the electron-phonon interaction constant $V \cdot \varrho(E)$ which also enters the asymmetry parameter $q \sim 1/V \cdot \varrho(E)$ as shown in (1). In this case, however, the transition temperature, as e.g. given by the BCS-theorie: $T_c \sim \exp(-1/V \cdot \varrho(E))$, would also vary for the different samples. In Figure 3 we have also plotted the transition temperatures for the films indicated by the onset of the softening which coincide with the resistively determined T_c's. Obviously the samples exhibit the same transition temperature with a minor scattering of their individual values. Thus, the phonon renormalization below T_c and the superconducting transition temperatures are not directly related to each other. Either, the value for T_c does not rely on the electron-phonon interaction, or, the phonon renormalization is subject to processes additional to the electron-phonon coupling. Zeyher and Zwicknagl [8] showed that additional electron scattering from impurities or inhomogeneities can reduce the renormalization effects of the phonons below T_c. Whether this can also change the asymmetry of the phonon lineshape is an open question, which has to be answered to understand our finding.

This work is supported by the 'Bundesministerium für Forschung und Technologie', grant 13N5705, and the 'Sonderforschungsbereich Darmstadt-Frankfurt-Mainz',

SFB 252. One of us (C.T.R) is financially supported by Conselho Nacional de Defenvolvimento Cientifico e Tecnològico do Brasil-CNP q.

References

1. C . Thomsen, M. Cardona, in *The Physical Properties of High-Temperature Superconductors*, ed. by D.M. Ginsberg, World Scientific, Singapore, 1989
2. R. Feile, Physica C159 (1989) 1, and references therein
3. S.L. Cooper, M.V. Klein, Comments Cond. Mat. Phys.15 (1990) 99,
4. T. Timusk, D.B. Tanner , in *The Physical Properties of High-Temperature Superconductors*, ed. by D.M. Ginsberg, World Scientific, Singapore, 1989
5. L. Genzel, A. Wittlin, M. Bauer, M. Cardona, E. Schönherr and A. Simon, Phys. Rev. B40 (1989) 2170
6. C. Thomsen, M. Cardona, B. Friedl, C.O. Rodriguez and O.K. Anderson, Solid State Commun. 75 (1990) 219
7. E.T. Heyen, M. Cardona, J. Karpinski, E. Kaldis, and S. Rusiecker, to appear in Phys. Rev. B
8. R. Zeyher and G. Zwicknagl, Z. Phys. B78, (1990) 175
9. C. Tomè-Rosa, G. Jacob, M. Maul, A. Walkenhorst, M. Schmitt, P. Wagner, P. Przyslupski, H. Adrian, Physica C 171 (1990) 213
10. U. Weimer, R. Feile, P. Leiderer, U. Poppe, J. Schubert, J. Fröhlingsdorf, B. Stritzker and W. Zander, Physica C168 (1990) 359
11. R. Li, U. Weimer, R. Feile, C. Tomè-Rosa, and H. Adrian, Physica C 175 (1991) 89
12. R. Feile, P. Leiderer, J. Kowalewski, W. Assmus, J. Schubert and U. Poppe, Z. Phys. B73 (1988) 155
13. R. Feile, U. Schmitt, P. Leiderer, J. Schubert and U. Poppe, Z. Phys. B72, (1988) 161, ibid. B73 (1988) 141
14. M.V. Klein in *Light Scattering in Solids I*, ed. M. Cardona, Topics in Applied Physics Vol.8, Springer-Verlag, Berlin, 1975
15. B. Friedl, C. Thomsen, and M. Cardona, Phys. Rev. Lett. 65 (1990) 915
16. S.L. Cooper, M.V. Klein, B.G. Pazol, J.P. Rice, and D.M. Ginsberg, Phys. Rev. B 37 (1988) 5920
17. R. Li et al., to be published

Phonon Behavior in the Bi–Sr–Ca–Cu–O-System

O. Flor[1], *B. Stadlober*[2], *M. Pressl*[1], *P. Knoll*[1], *P. Planinic*[3], *N. Brnicevic*[3], *M. Unterweger*[1], *and O. Buresch*[4]

[1]Institut für Experimentalphysik der Universität Graz, Universitätsplatz 5, A-8010 Graz, Austria

[2]Walther-Meissner-Institut für Tieftemperaturforschung, Walther-Meissner-Str. 8, W-8046 Garching, Fed. Rep. of Germany

[3]Rudjer Boskovic Institute, Bijenicka 54, 41011 Zagreb, Croatia

[4]Max-Planck-Institut für Festkörperforschung, Heisenbergstr. 1, W-7000 Stuttgart 80, Fed. Rep. of Germany

Absract: The phonon-Raman spectrum of $Bi_{2-x}Pb_xSr_2Ca_{n-1}Cu_nO_{2n+4+d}$ had been studied in detail. The $630cm^{-1}$ phonon which is assigned as a z-vibration of the oxygen between the CuO_2 and the BiO layers and of the oxygens of the BiO layers shows a sample dependent shoulder at $650cm^{-1}$. This shoulder is interpreted as a mode arising from different oxygen ordering in the BiO layers and from excess oxygen. Substituting Bi with Pb increases the amount of 2223 phase and the intensity of that shoulder decreases.

1. Introduction

So far, several mode assignments of the phonon-Raman spectra in the Bi-Sr-Ca-Cu-O System have been done [1-5]. Difficulties arise from the fact that no simple crystal structure exists [6-8]. Different oxygen arrangements in the BiO layers combined with oxygen vacancies and excess oxygen disturb the idealized structur. This idealized structure is shown in Fig.1 and belongs to the space group I4/mmm. The oxygens of the CuO_2, BiO and SrO layers are denoted as O1, O3 and O2, respectively. Usually this idealized crystal structur is used if symmetry considerations are done. The most accurate mode assignment can be obtained by comparing with calculated phonon frequencies [9] as it has been done by Cardona at al.[1]. However, such calculations also start with an idealized structure and become very unaccurate for the phonons of the BiO layers. On the other hand, vibrations of the CuO layer should be rather independent of the O disorder of the BiO planes.

In this paper we present new results of the behavior of some special modes and discuss their mode assignment.

2. The $630-650cm^{-1}$ mode

The strongest Raman feature of the Bi-Sr-Ca Cu O system is the $630-650cm^{-1}$ mode. Single crystal measurements [5,2] had shown a very strong scattering intensity if incident and scattered radiation are polarized along the z-direction. In analogy to the $YBa_2Cu_3O_x$ system (the $500cm^{-1}$ mode has the same polarization properties) one would assign that mode to a z-vibration of the O2 atom. In contrast to $YBa_2Cu_3O_x$ the frequency is around $130cm^{-1}$ higher which requires additional repulsive force in the movement. This additional repulsion can be caused by an out-of-phase movement of the oxygens O3 of the BiO layers. The strong z-Raman-polarization may be caused by electronic transitions between the BiO band and a CuO_2 band which are parallel in some parts of the Brillouin zone. Vibrations of the oxygen atom placed between the BiO and CuO_2 layers can couple rather strong to matrix elements of this electronic transition.

The $500cm^{-1}$ mode of the $YBa_2Cu_3O_x$ system is known to be very sensitive to the oxygen content of the CuO chains. This is because the vibration of the oxygen between the CuO_2 plane and the CuO chain

Springer Series in Solid-State Sciences, Vol. 113 Electronic Properties of High-T_c Superconductors
Editors: H. Kuzmany, M. Mehring, J. Fink

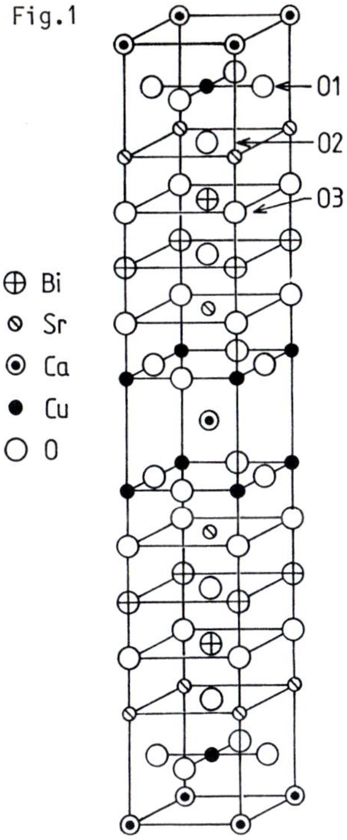

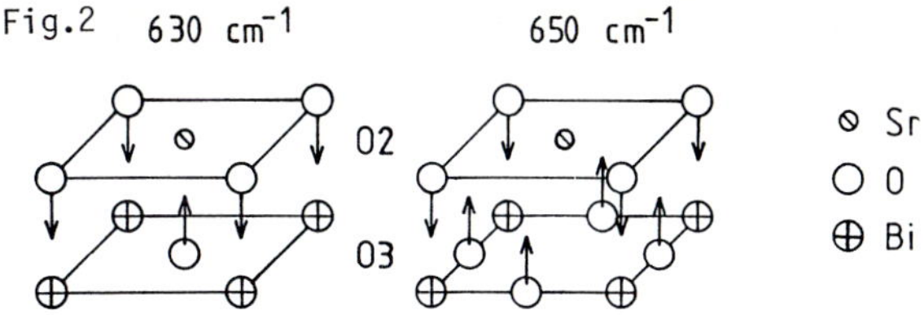

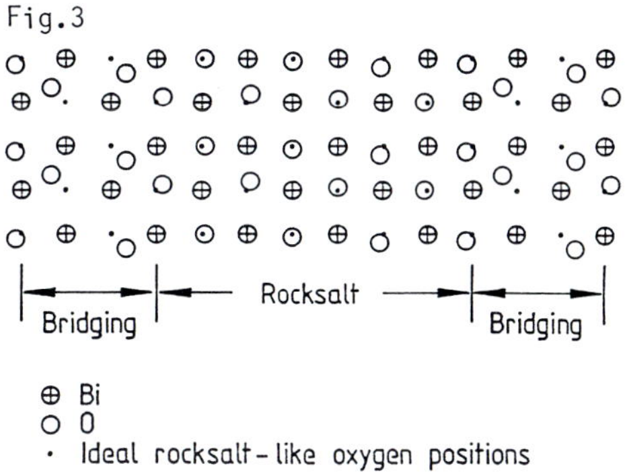

Fig.1: Idealized Structure of $Bi_2Sr_2CaCu_2O_8$. The notation of the atomes is indicated as used in that work

Fig.2: Two extrem cases (rocksalt and bridging position) of oxygen arrangement in the BiO layers. Arrows indicate the atomic displacement of the corresponding vibration

Fig.3: suggested superstructur of the BiO layers showing the continous transition of rocksalt to bridging position of O3.

(denoted as O4 in $YBa_2Cu_3O_x$) feels the repulsive potential of the near oxygen of the CuO chain. This repulsive potential increases the frequency and also pushes the O4 away which increases the Cu-O distance. If the oxygen content is reduced this repulsive potential decreases which lowers the frequncy and the O4-Cu distance at the same time [10]. A similar behavior is expected in the Bi system. The $630cm^{-1}$ mode should be sensitive to the oxygen ordering and content of the BiO layers. And indeed, in most samples a shoulder at $650cm^{-1}$ is found dependent on sample quality and preparation. How that frequency can be assigned to atomic movements is illustrated in Fig.2. The SrO and BiO layers are shown for two different oxygen arrangements in the Bi layers. If O3 is in the so called "rocksalt position" O2 and O3 are rather far away and the frequency is at $630cm^{-1}$. There is also the possibility to place the O3 between the Bi atoms which is denoted as the bridging position. This type of structure has been suggested by von Schnering et al. [8] and offers the possibility of a high amount of excess oxygen. In this position together with some excess oxygen the O-O distance is much smaller which increases the vibrational frequency to $650cm^{-1}$. Considering the second BiO layer one finds again that in the rocksalt position the two O3 atoms of the two BiO layers are rather far separeted and the Bi-O bond dominates the frequency. In the bridging position the two O3 atoms come closer together which increases the frequency.

Actually not one of the two oxygen arrangements of fig.2 have been found [11] but a superstructure arising from a transition of the rocksalt position to the bridging position as shown in Fig.3. We do not believe that the superstructure for itself has a disturbing potential to the ordinary $630cm^{-1}$ phonon which is large enough to produce a second peak. But the excess oxygen which can

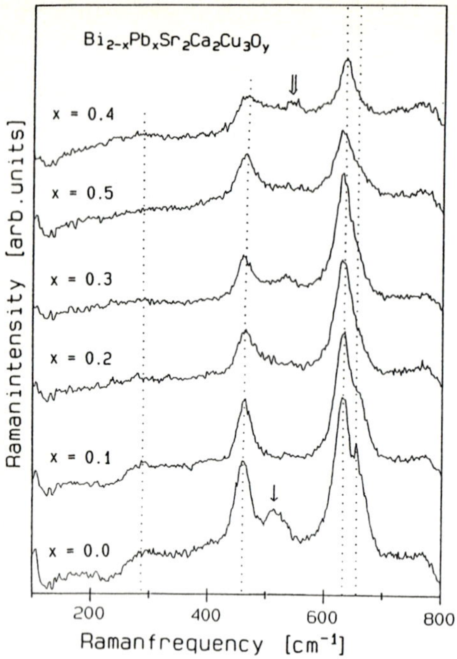

Fig.4: Behavior of the Phonon Ramanspectrum upon Pb substitution. The dotted lines indicate the positions of intrinsic phonon modes.The arrows indicate impurity phases.

enter the structure in the bridging position may cause the shoulder at 650cm^{-1}. In this way the shoulder at 650cm^{-1} probes the superstructure and the excess oxygen as well.

Substituting Bi with Pb is known to stabilize the 2223 110K phase. The structural changes between the 2212 and the 2223 phase are only one block of $CaCuO_2$ which should not influence the vibrations of the BiO layers and their surrounding. Fig.4 shows the Raman spectra for samples with different Pb content. For Pb amounts larger than x=0.3 nearly pure 2223 phase is present. Clearly one can see that the shoulder at 650cm^{-1} decreases with increasing lead content. This behavior is interpreted as a change of superstructur and excess oxygen in agreement with other investigations [12]. A similar behavior is found in the $Bi_2Sr_{2-x}La_xCaCu_2O_{8+d}$ system [2].

3. The 460cm^{-1} mode

The second prominent peak of the Bi-system is the 460cm^{-1} mode. In contrast to the 630cm^{-1} feature, the argumentation for a mode assignment is not straightforward and there are some discrepancies. This mode is either assigned as a CuO_2 plane vibration [3] or as a BiO plane vibration [1,2]. If this mode corresponds to the BiO planes -e.g. as an oxygen in-phase counterpart to the 630cm^{-1} mode - one expects a shoulder similar to the 630cm^{-1} vibration.
On the other hand, the in-phase counterpart of the out-of-phase B_{1g} mode of the CuO_2 planes is expected at lower frequencies and should have a much smaller intensity. We think that this mode is a more complicated mixture of several atomic movements, may be with main components of the 01 and 02 atoms. However, regardless of its exact assignment this mode shows a different temperature dependence. Fig.5 shows two spectra of ceramic samples taken at 300K and 77K. In contrast to the 630-650cm^{-1} feature which is not influenced by temperature, the 460cm^{-1} is shifted to higher frequencies upon cooling. Within the resolution of the spectra the halfwidth is nearly unchanged.

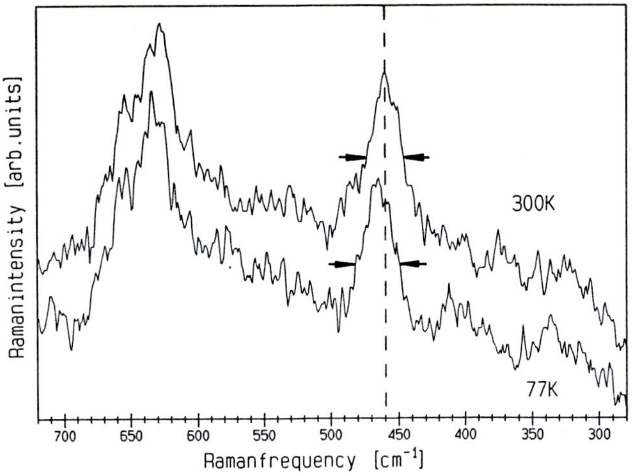

Fig.5: The 460cm^{-1} mode at two different temperatures. The dashed line indicates the frequency shift, the arrows indicate the halfwidth.

Acknowledgements
This work has been supported by the Austrian Science Foundation

References

1. M.Cardona, C.Thomsen, R.Liu, H.G. von Schnering, M.Hartweg, Solid State Commun.66, 1225 (1988)
2. R.Liu, Dissertation MPI f.Festkörperphysik and Univ. Stuttgart, (1990)
3. M.Boekholt, A.Erle, P.C.Splittgerber-Hünnekes, and G.Güntherodt; Solid State Commun. 74, 1107 (1990)
4. G.Burns, C.V.Chandrasehakdar, F.H.Dacol, M.W.Shafer, and P.Strobel, Solid State Commun., 67, 603 (1988)
5. P.Knoll, B.Stadlober, M.Pressl, and N.Brnicevic, Physica C 162-164, 1097 (1989)
6. S.A.Sunshine, T.Siegrist, L.F.Schneemeyer, D.W.Murphy, R.J.Cava, B.Batlogg, R.B. van Dover, R.M.Fleming, S.H.Glarum, S.Nakahara, R.Farrow, J.J.Krajewski, S.M.Zahuarak, J.V.Waszczak, J.H.Marshall, P.Marsh, L.W.Rupp,Jr., and W.F.Peck, Phys.Rev.B38, 893(1988)
7. P.Bordet, J.J.Capponi, C.Capponi, C.Chaillout, J.Chenavas, A.W.Hewat, J.L.Hodeau, M.Marezio, J.L.Tholence and D.Tranqui, Physica C 156, 189(1988)
8. H.G.von Schnering, L.Walz, M.Schwarz, W.Becker, M.Hartweg, T.Popp, B.Hettich, P.M[ller, and G.Kämpf, Angew. Chemie 100, 604 (1988)
9. J.Prade, A.D.Kulkarni, F.W.de Wette, U.Schröder, and W.Kress, Phys.Rev.B.39, 2771 (1989)
10. P.Knoll in "Oxygen disorder effects in High-Tc Superconductors", Ed. J.L.Moran-Lopez, Plenum Publishing Corp., 211 (1990)
11. Y.LePage, W.R.McKinnon, J.M.Tarascon, and P.Barboux, Phys.Rev.B40, 6810(1989)
12. Y.Ikeda, M.Takano, Z.Hiroi, K.Oda, H.Kitaguchi, J.Takada, Y.Miura, Y.Takeda, O.Yamamoto, and H.Mazaki, Jap. J.of Appl. Physics 27, L2067(1988)
Y.Matsui, S.Takekawa, H.Nozaki, and A.Umezono, Jap.J.of Appl.Physics 28,L602(1989)
G.Miehe, T.Vogt, H.Fuess, and M.Wilhelm, Physica C 171, 339 (1990)

Optical and Electrical Properties of Rare-Earth Substituted Ceramic Samples of the Y–Ba–Cu–O-System

E. Holzinger-Schweiger, K.D. Aichholzer, G. Leising, and H. Kahlert

Institut für Festkörperphysik der TU Graz,
Petersgasse 16, A-8010 Graz, Austria

We report the preparation of fully (Nd, Sm, Er, Yb, Pr) and partially (Pr) rare earth (RE) substituted ceramic Y–Ba–Cu–O samples. The cell parameters and the phase purity are characterized by x-ray powder diffraction. The temperature dependence of the electrical resistivity of the samples was determined and the room temperature values are compared with the results of the optical conductivity derived by Kramers-Kronig analysis from IR-reflectivity measurements.

Since the discovery of the 1–2–3–compound $Y_1Ba_2Cu_3O_{7-\delta}$ (YBC) various substitutions in this system were investigated. It was soon found that all lanthanides except Ce and Tb can fully replace Y in the structure [1] [2] [3]. (Pm was not used because of its radioactivity). Almost all of these substituted YBC's have a superconducting transition, only $Pr_1Ba_2Cu_3O_{7-\delta}$ shows a semiconducting temperature behaviour of the resistivity. Systematic studies of replacing Y by Pr show a decreasing transition temperature and a vanishing superconductivity around 50% substitution [4]. An investigation of the T_c-depressing behaviour of Pr in the 1–2–3–system might be one way towards the understanding of the mechanism of superconductivity in the perovskites.

The different ceramic samples were prepared by solid-state reactions, starting with oxides and carbonates. RE_2O_3 (RE=Y, Nd, Sm, Er, Yb) and/or Pr_6O_{11} $BaCO_3$ and CuO were ground in molar ratios, calcinated at about 900°C, reground and pressed to pellets. The pellets were annealed at about 915°C and reground again. The powder was sieved with a 100 micron sieve and then pressed with 6 t/cm^2 to pellets for the third heat treatment under oxygen flow at about 930°C. This procedure results in pellets with a slightly structured surface. The composition of the samples ($RE_1Ba_2Cu_3O_{7-\delta}$ with RE=Y, Nd, Sm, Er, Yb, Pr and $Y_{1-x}Pr_xBa_2Cu_3\,O_{7-\delta}$ with $x = 0$ to 1 in steps of 0.1) was controlled by EDX (energy dispersive x-ray analysis) in an electron microscope. For resistivity measurements the samples were contacted in Van der Pauw geometry with gold wires and silver paste. The measurements were done in a closed cycle helium cryostate down to 30 K and the temperature measured with a calibrated silicon diode. x-ray powder diffraction measurements were done on all samples with a Siemens D500 diffractometer. About 12 to 20 well defined peaks for 2ϑ between 5 and 85 degrees were used to do a least square unit cell refinement.

For IR-reflectivity measurements the plellets were polished. For a reflectivity reference, the surface was covered with a gold film of about 200nm and then measured again to correct the influence of the surface roughness. For the IR-reflection measurements two spectrometers were used: from 200 to 4000 cm^{-1} a Perkin-Elmer 684 IR spectrometer and from 40 to 250 cm^{-1} and from 50 to 500 cm^{-1} a Bomem DA8 with different mylar beamsplitters.

$RE_1Ba_2Cu_3O_{7-\delta}$ (RE= Y, Nd, Sm, Er, Yb) : Tab. 1 shows the calculated lattice parameters and the resistive transition temperatures of the samples. Only the Y- and Er-sample show a sharp transition and a T_{co} above 90 K. This is in good agreement with the high phase purity estimated from x-ray measurements. The samples with Nd, Sm and Yb contain phase impurities between 5 and 20%,which in the Y- and the Er-samples are below 5%. Fig. 1 shows the optical conductivity σ in the region from 0 to 1000 cm^{-1} .

Springer Series in Solid-State Sciences, Vol. 113 Electronic Properties of High-T_c Superconductors
Editors: H. Kuzmany, M. Mehring, J. Fink

Table 1: Lattice parameters for RE substituted ceramics (estimated standard deviation in parentheses refer to the last digit), the midpoint of the resistive transition ($T_{c1/2}$) and the temperature at which ρ vanishes (T_{co})

RE	a [Å]	b [Å]	c [Å]	$T_{c1/2}$	T_{co}
Y	3.8222 (3)	3.8918(7)	11.694 (5)	94.6	94.1
Nd	3.8683 (5)	3.9277 (12)	11.772 (4)	82.5	78.4
Sm	3.8499 (2)	3.9096 (5)	11.737 (4)	90.5	87.2
Er	3.8196 (3)	3.8904 (7)	11.693 (6)	95.0	94.2
Yb	3.8100 (4)	3.8800 (9)	11.660 (7)	92.1	89.9

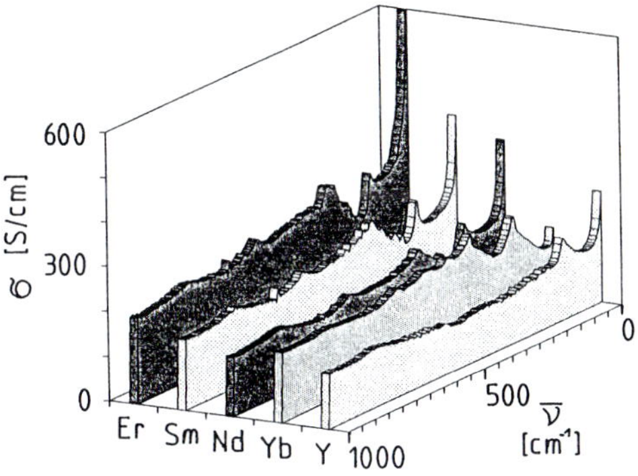

Figure 1: Optical conductivity of the RE substituted ceramic samples between 0 and 1000 cm^{-1}

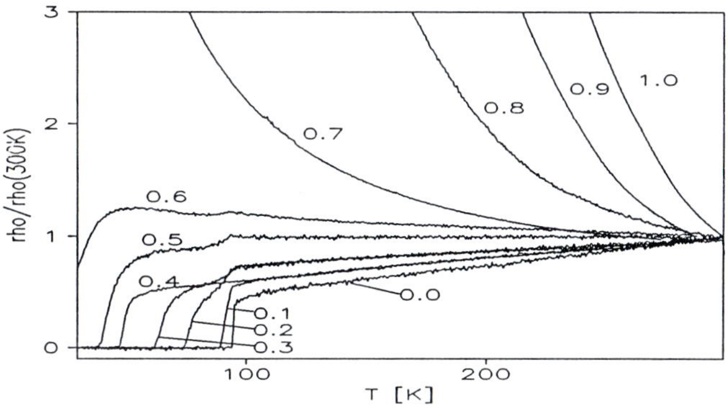

Figure 2: normalized resistivity versus temperature for the samples $Y_{1-x}Pr_xBa_2Cu_3O_{7-\delta}$ for different x–values

The phonon-peak around 150 cm^{-1} which corresponds to the RE vibrations [5] [6] [7] shifts to higher wavenumbers when Y is replaced by heavier RE. The Cu-O stretching modes around 340 and 580 cm^{-1} vary with the substitutional element.

$Y_{1-x}Pr_xBa_2Cu_3O_{7-\delta}$: Fig. 2 shows the normalized resistivity curves of the different Pr substituted samples. The superconducting transition shifts towards lower temperatures with increasing Pr content and vanishes at about $Pr_{0.6}$. Pr-doped YBC covers the whole range of metallic / superconducting to semiconducting resistive behaviour.

The lattice parameters calculated from the x-ray powder diffraction measurements (Fig. 3) increase monotonically as a function of the Pr concentration, in good agreement with other

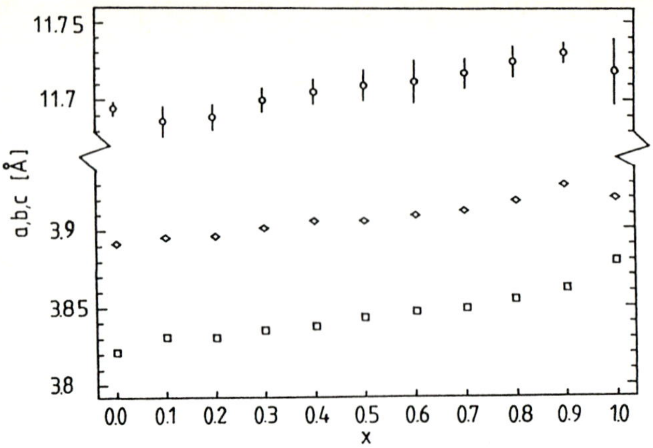

Figure 3: Lattice constants in dependence of the Pr content x of $Y_{1-x}Pr_xBa_2Cu_3O_{7-\delta}$ (error bars for a and b are within the size of the symbols)

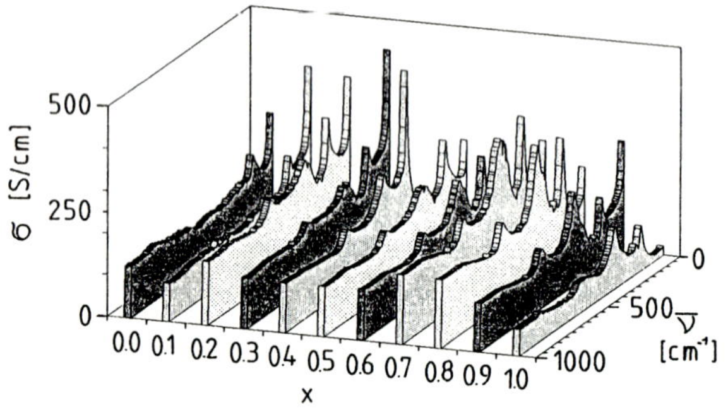

Figure 4: Optical conductivity versus wavenumber of $Y_{1-x}Pr_xBa_2Cu_3O_{7-\delta}$

x-ray measurements [8] or neutron diffraction studies [9]. The optical conductivity (Fig. 4) shows a shift of the phonon peaks to higher wavenumbers with increasing Pr concentration. The extrapolated values of the optical conductivity for $\nu = 0$ cm^{-1} differ between a factor 1.2 ($Pr_{0.8}$) and 5 ($Pr_{0.4}$) from the measured dc resistive values. This can be explained by the different densities of the sintered samples and by intragrain and intergrain (e.g. phase impurities) effects.

Conclusion : Investigations of superconducting and non superconducting ceramic samples of the 1–2–3–system with Y fully substituted by Nd, Sm, Er and Yb or partially substituted by Pr up to 50% were performed. The samples showed more phase impurities than the pure $Y_1Ba_2Cu_3O_{7-\delta}$ when prepared with the same solid state reaction. The RE substitutions in the 1-2-3 system show a orthorhombic structure with varying cell volume. The optical conductivity calculated from reflectivity measurements showed characteristic phonons. The substitution of Nd, Sm, Er, Yb leads to a peakshift for the 150 cm^{-1}–phonon towards higher wavenumbers for higher RE-ion masses. In case of partial Pr–substitution the phonons around 150, 340, and 580 cm^{-1} are shifted to higher wavenumbers with increasing Pr–content.

This work on ceramic samles is preliminary for more detailed studies on RE substituted single crystals, which are necessary to get information about the intrinsic properties and the anisotropy of the system.

Acknowledgement : The authors want to acknowledge Dr.P.Pölt from the Zentrum für Elektronenmikroskopie der TU-Graz who did the EDX-measurements.

This work was supported by the Austrian Fonds zur Förderung der wissenschaftlichen Forschung project number P8178.

References

[1] P.H.Hor, R.L.Meng, Y.Q.Wang, L.Gao, Z.J. Huang, J.Bechtold, K.Forster, C.W.Chu, Phys.Rev.Lett. 58 (1987) 1891

[2] J.M.Tarascon, W.R.McKinnon, L.H.Green, G.W.Hull, E.M.Vogel, Phys.Rev.B 36 (1987) 226

[3] H.C.Yang, M.H.Hsieh, H.H.Sung, C.H.Chen, H.E.Horng, Y.S.Kan, H.C.Chen, J.C.Jao, Phys.Rev.B 39 (1989) 9203

[4] J.K.Liang, X.T.Xu, S.S.Xie, G.H.Rao, X.Y.Shao, Z.G.Duan, Z.Phys.B - Cond. Matter 69 (1987) 137-140

[5] M.Cardona, L.Genzel, R.Liu, A.Wittlin, Hj.Mattausch, F.Garcia-Alvarado, E.Garcia-Gonzalez, Solid State Comm. 64/5 (1987) 727-732

[6] C.Thomsen, R.Liu, A.Wittlin, L.Genzel, M.Cardona, W.König, M.V.Cabanas, E.Garcia, Solid State Comm. 65/3 (1987) 219-222

[7] R.Feile, Physica C 159 (1989) 1-32

[8] J.Horn, H.C.Semmelhack, H.Börner, B.Lippold, U.Boehnke, M.Wurlitzer, M.Krötsch, Physica C 170 (1990) 343-349

[9] J.J.Neumeier, T.Bjornholm, M.B.Maple, J.J.Rhyne, J.A.Gotaas, Physica C 166 (1990) 191-196

Far-Infrared Properties of $Y_{1-x}Pr_xBa_2Cu_3O_y$ Ceramics

D. Macko, M. Kašpárková, I. Sargánková, and P. Diko

Institute of Experimental Physics, Slovak Academy of Sciences, Solovjevova 47, 043 53 Košice, Czechoslovakia

Abstract. FIR reflectance measurements have been performed on orthorhombic and tetragonal ceramic samples of $Y_{1-x}Pr_xBa_2Cu_3O_y$ (x=0.2, 0.4 and 0.6). The temperature and Pr-concentration dependencies of electronic and phonon features have been studied.

1. Introduction

Among all $LBa_2Cu_3O_7$ (L123) compounds (L - a lanthanide) that are isostructural to Y123, only Pr123 is nonmetallic and nonsuperconducting.

The single-phase $Y_{1-x}Pr_xBa_2Cu_3O_7$ system is of special interest since its superconductivity is gradually suppressed with increasing Pr concentration.

2. Experimental Results and Discussion

Reflectivity measurements of polycrystalline orthorhombic (x=0.2, 0.4 and 0.6) and tetragonal (x=0.0, 0.2, 0.4 and 0.6) samples $Y_{1-x}Pr_xBa_2Cu_3O_y$ were performed with a Bruker IFS 113v spectrometer for the range 20-4500 wavenumbers [cm^{-1}] (wn) at temperatures 5-300 K with resolution of 0.5 wn. The orthorhombic samples with x=0.2 and 0.4 were superconducting below the transition temperature $T_c \simeq 63$ K and 36 K, resp.. The orthorhombic x=0.6 sample was nonsuperconducting. For more details of the experiment and the sample preparation see [1].

Fig.1 shows IR spectra for the orthorhombic sample with Pr concentration x=0.2. These spectra contain all the features typical for the spectra of Y123 ceramic superconductors including gap-like manifestations at different frequencies.

The gap-like sudden drops in the reflectivity above ~65 wn on the orthorhombic x=0.2 sample and above ~29 wn on the orthorhombic x=0.4 sample are observed at temperatures $T<T_c$. Using the methods of a gap determination for ordinary metals in superconducting state [2] we determined the gap-frequencies: 60-65 wn (i.e. $2\Delta_1/k_BT_c \simeq 1.37$-$1.48$) for x=0.2 sample ($T_c \simeq 63$ K) and ~ 29 wn ($2\Delta_1/k_BT_c \simeq 1.44$) for x=0.4 sample ($T_c \simeq 36$ K).

According to [3] a wide band around 450 wn (Fig.1) in the reflectivity of the orthorhombic x=0.2 sample at temperatures $T<T_c$ correlates with the electronic B_{1g} and A_{1g} peaks observed in continuum Raman measurements. Elsewhere, the band is interpreted to be a manifestation of the superconducting energy gap with $2\Delta \sim 8k_BT_c$ [4]. It is interesting that the maximum of the broad peak for our 60-K sample is almost identical with that for 90-K superconductors (460-480 wn) [4]. This band is

Springer Series in Solid-State Sciences, Vol. 113 **Electronic Properties of High-T_c Superconductors**
Editors: H. Kuzmany, M. Mehring, J. Fink

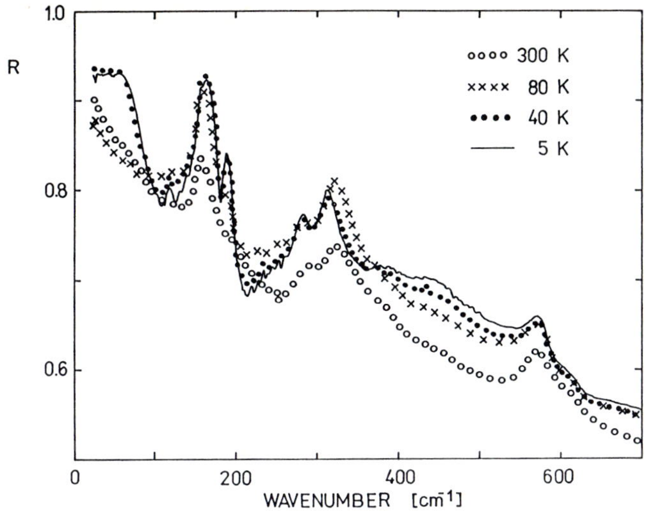

Fig.1 The reflectivity spectra of the orthorhombic x=0.2 sample at T=300 K, 80 K, 40 K and 5 K.

not seen in the reflectivity of orthorhombic samples with Pr content x=0.4 and 0.6.

The orthorhombic **E || c** phonon mode at 155 wn, referred to as the Ba mode [5], is according to our measurements almost independent of both concentration and temperature.

IR-active orthorhombic **E || c** phonon modes at 280 wn and 320 wn correspond to vibrations of CuO_2 planes [6,7]. An apparent softening and a sharpening of the 320 wn mode at the temperature change from 80 K to 40 K was observed on the x=0.2 sample (Fig.1). From such phonon behaviour it can be estimated, in the framework of the theory of Zeyher and Zwicknagl [8], that the energy gap $2\Delta_2$ lies above the mentioned phonon frequency. Frequency of the phonon mode of the x=0.2 sample ($T_c \simeq 63$ K) lies in the same range as the equivalent mode of the undoped Y123 sample ($T_c \simeq 90$ K), i.e. the application of this theory leads to the conclusion that the energy gap is not proportional to the critical temperature.

With increasing Pr content (orthorhombic x=0.4 and 0.6 samples) the phonon structure in this range becomes more complex (Fig.2). The 280 wn phonon mode becomes less apparent. The local reflectivity maximum at 320 wn for the x=0.2 sample, interpreted as one phonon mode, is shifted and changed with increased Pr content to a complex broad phonon feature with the maximum at 360-370 wn. The observed IR shift of the reflectivity maximum is larger than could be expected from [5] where the influence of lanthanides (except of Pr) on the phonon structure of L123 samples was studied. In our opinion this complex broad feature for orthorhombic sample x=0.6 is probably a combination of two (or more) phonons at which it consists probably also of **E || ab** modes (due to a decrease of a conductance in ab-planes).

Position of the **E || c** phonon mode at 570 wn of the orthorhombic x=0.2 sample, which may be probably connected with vibrations of apical oxygen O(4) in the c-direction [7], is temperature independent. The corresponding orthorhombic modes

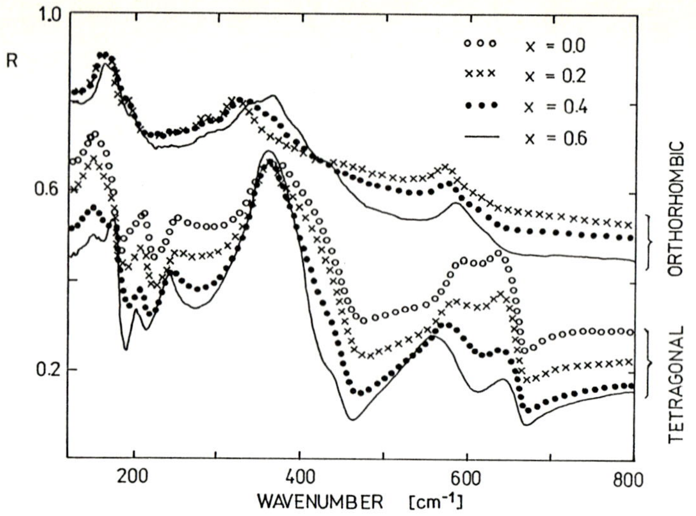

Fig.2 The reflectivity spectra of orthorhombic samples in normal state at T=80 K and of the tetragonal samples at T=300 K.

in x=0.4 and x=0.6 samples show hardening by ~1.5 wn and ~4 wn, resp., with decreasing temperature. With increasing Pr content this mode is shifted towards higher energies, with maximum shift of 11-12 wn at T=5 K.

Fig.2 shows IR spectra of the orthorhombic samples in normal state at T=80 K and of the tetragonal samples at T=300 K, for various Pr concentrations.

For the tetragonal x=0.0 sample the phonon modes at 150 wn, 212 wn, 250 wn, 360 wn, 590 wn and 637 wn are observed. A comparison of these spectra with the results of the polarized measurements on the tetragonal Y123 single crystals [9,10] has shown that the modes at 150 wn, 212 wn and 637 wn are polarized in c-direction and the modes at 250 wn and 590 wn are polarized in ab-plane. The broad reflectivity peak at 360 wn consists of two modes (the higher frequency mode is polarized in c-direction and the lower frequency one is done in ab-plane).

An analysis of the reflectance spectra (Fig.2) for orthorhombic and tetragonal samples shows that the influence of the Pr doping is similar in the both phases only for two phonon modes: 1. The increase of Pr content almost does not change the positions of the Ba phonon modes at 150 wn for orthorhombic samples and at 155 wn for tetragonal samples. 2. The frequencies of the orthorhombic phonon mode at 570 wn and of the tetragonal phonon mode at 637 wn (both modes correspond to vibrations of apical O(4) in c-direction [7,9]) increase with Pr doping.

In tetragonal phase we have not found an analogy of the concentration behaviour of the orthorhombic 280 wn and 320 wn modes (i.e. frequency increase of the phonon position with an increase of the ionic radius of lanthanide in L123 system [5]). The narrowing of the tetragonal 360 wn peak from the higher frequency side with increasing Pr content indicates that the higher frequency mode of this peak (assigned as Cu(2)-O(2)-O(3) vibration in c-direction [9]) does not shift towards the higher energy with increasing Pr content (the assignment of atom positions is by [6]).

The 590 wn mode, the lower frequency part (LFP) of the 360 wn peak and the 250 wn mode of tetragonal Y123 samples correspond to **E || ab** vibrations. The 590 wn phonon is assigned as Cu(2)-O(3) stretch mode [9,10]. The assignment of the other two **E || ab** modes, in which a role of oxygen is significant [7], is not unambiguous [9,10,11]. The concentration independence of the maximum position of the 360 wn peak with Pr doping (i.e. concentration independence of the LFP of the 360 wn feature), an softening of the 250 wn and 590 wn modes with Pr doping, together with taking into account mutual positions of CuO_2 planes, apical oxygen O(4) and Y atoms in primitive cell, lead us to the assignment of the 250 wn mode as Cu(2)-O(2)-O(3) mode by [9] and to the assignment of the LFP of the 360 wn feature as apical oxygen O(4) mode as is admitted by Feile [11].

In conclusion, we observed different gap-like manifestations in the reflectance spectra of the Pr-doped Y123 samples. Their interpretation is questionable. Also explanations of Pr-induced shifts of some orthorhombic and tetragonal phonons are not clear and will be discussed elsewhere.

References

[1] D. Macko M. Kašpárková, I. Sargánková, P. Diko, V. Bodák, to be published in Physica C

[2] Z. Schlesinger, R. T. Collins, J. A. Calise, D. G. Hinks, A. W. Mitchell, Y. Zheng, B. Dabrowski, N. E. Bickers and D. J. Scalapino, Phys. Rev. B **40**, 6862 (1989).

[3] E. Seider, M. Bauer, L. Genzel and H.-U. Habermeier, Z. Phys. B - Condensed Matter **83**, 1 (1991).

[4] Z. Schlesinger, R. T. Collins, F. Holtzberg, C. Feild, S. H. Blanton, U. Welp, G. W. Crabtree, Y. Fang and J. Z. Liu, Phys. Rev. Lett. **65**, 801 (1990).

[5] M. Cardona, R. Liu, C. Thomsen, M. Bauer, L. Genzel, W. König and A. Wittlin, Solid State Commun. **65**, 71 (1988).

[6] L. Genzel, A. Wittlin, M. Bauer, M. Cardona, E. Schönherr and A. Simon, Phys. Rev. B **40**, 2170 (1989).

[7] M. K. Crawford, W. E. Farneth, E. M. McCarron III and R. K. Bordia, Phys. Rev. B **38**, 11 382 (1988), and ref. wherein.

[8] R. Zeyher and G. Zwicknagl, Z. Phys. B - Condensed Matter **78**, 175 (1990).

[9] I. B. Ferreira, M. Bauer, L. Genzel, P. Murugaraj and J. Maier, in the Proc. of the 3rd Int. Conf. on Phonon Phys. and 6th Int. Conf. on Phonon Scattering in Condensed Matt., Vol. 1, edited by S. Hunklinger, W. Ludwig, G. Weiss (World Sci. Publ. Co. Pte. Ltd., 1989) p.331.

[10] A. V. Bazhenov and V. B. Timofeev, Physica C **162-164**, 1247 (1989).

[11] R. Feile, Physica C **159**, 1 (1989).

Influence of the Oxygen Content on the Optical Conductivity Function of $YBa_2Cu_3O_x$ ($6 \leq x \leq 7$)

M. Dürrler[1], *A. Zibold*[1], *K. Widder*[1], *H.P. Geserich*[1], *Th. Wolf*[2], *G. Roth*[3], *G. Bräuchle*[4], *A. Erb*[5], *G. Müller-Vogt*[5], *and J. Kircher*[6]

[1]Institut für Angewandte Physik, Universität Karlsruhe, Kaiserstr. 12, W-7500 Karlsruhe, Fed. Rep. of Germany
[2]Kernforschungszentrum Karlsruhe, Institut für Technische Physik, Postfach 3640, W-7500 Karlsruhe, Fed. Rep. of Germany
[3]Kernforschungszentrum Karlsruhe, Institut für Nukleare Festkörperphysik, Postfach 3640, W-7500 Karlsruhe, Fed. Rep. of Germany
[4]Physikalisches Institut, Universität Karlsruhe, Kaiserstr. 12, W-7500 Karlsruhe, Fed. Rep. of Germany
[5]Kristall- und Materiallabor, Universität Karlsruhe, Kaiserstr. 12, W-7500 Karlsruhe, Fed. Rep. of Germany
[6]Max-Planck-Institut für Festkörperforschung, Heisenbergstr. 1, W-7000 Stuttgart 80, Fed. Rep. of Germany

Abstract. We have performed polarized reflection measurements on twinned single crystals of the system $YBa_2Cu_3O_x$ in the energy range between 50 meV and 6 eV and in the stoichiometry range between x=6 and x=7 at room temperature. By fitting a Lorentz-Drude model and by Kramers-Kronig analysis the spectral distributions of the components of the conductivity function parallel and perpendicular to the ab-plane were determined, showing contributions of infrared active phonons, free carrier absorption and interband transitions.

1. Introduction

The optical properties of $YBa_2Cu_3O_x$ are very anisotropic. Moreover they show a strong dependence on the oxygen content of the crystals. While $YBa_2Cu_3O_6$ is a semiconductor, $YBa_2Cu_3O_7$ is the well known high–T_c superconductor. Therefore the transition regime $6 \leq x \leq 7$ is of particular interest. Within the regime a metal–semiconductor transition takes place and simultaneously the superconducting properties are developing [1].

2. Experimental

Twinned crystals of $YBa_2Cu_3O_{7-\delta}$ were grown by three different techniques described elsewhere [2,3,4]. The sizes of the free-standing crystals were about (2-4)mm x (1-4)mm x (0.2-1.5)mm. In order to achieve different oxygen contents and a homogeneous oxygen distribution the crystals with an oxygen content of x=6.0, 6.2, 6.33, 6.42, 6.46, 6.52, 6.61, 6.78, 6.92 and 7.00 were obtained by annealing for several days between 450 °C and 650 °C in an atmosphere of flowing

Springer Series in Solid-State Sciences, Vol. 113 **Electronic Properties of High-T_c Superconductors**
Editors: H. Kuzmany, M. Mehring, J. Fink

oxygen and argon with subsequent quenching [5]. The oxygen stoichiometries were determined indirectly by roentgenographic analysis of the cell parameters and then cross-checked by SQUID-measurements of the transition temperature T_c. The crystals with an oxygen content of x=6.1, 6.36, 6.85 were obtained by annealing in vacuum [6]. The average error of the stoichiometry values is $\Delta x \approx 0.04$.

Reflection measurements at near–normal incidence were carried out in the spectral range between 50 meV and 6 eV with a single beam set up, especially designed for small samples. The spectra were obtained on microtwinned (001) surfaces ($R_{\|ab}$) or on an average of (100) and (010) surfaces. In the latter case polarized light was used with the electric field perpendicular ($R_{\|ab}$) and parallel to the c–axis ($R_{\|c}$).

3. Results and Discussion

Selected reflectance spectra $R_{\|ab}$ und $R_{\|c}$ of $YBa_2Cu_3O_x$ are shown in Fig. 1. The spectra $R_{\|ab}$ represent an average of the excitation processes polarized parallel to the a- and to the b-axis respectively [4]. A pronounced anisotropy of the transport properties between ab-plane and c-direction is visible not only in $YBa_2Cu_3O_7$ but also in the oxygen reduced samples. As Fig.1 shows $YBa_2Cu_3O_6$ is a typical semiconductor with constant values of the reflectivity between 0.2 eV and and 1 eV, where no optical excitations take place. Between 50 meV and 100 meV the spectra are modulated by infrared active phonons , between 1 eV and 6 eV by interband transitions. The sequence of the spectra $R_{\|ab}$ in Fig. 1 (left side) between x=6 and x=7, i.e. with increasing oxygen stoichiometry parameter x, first shows a plasma edge of the free charge carriers at x=6.2, subsequently shifted to higher energies. In $R_{\|c}$ (Fig. 1, right side) a plasma edge is visible not before $x > 6.8$.

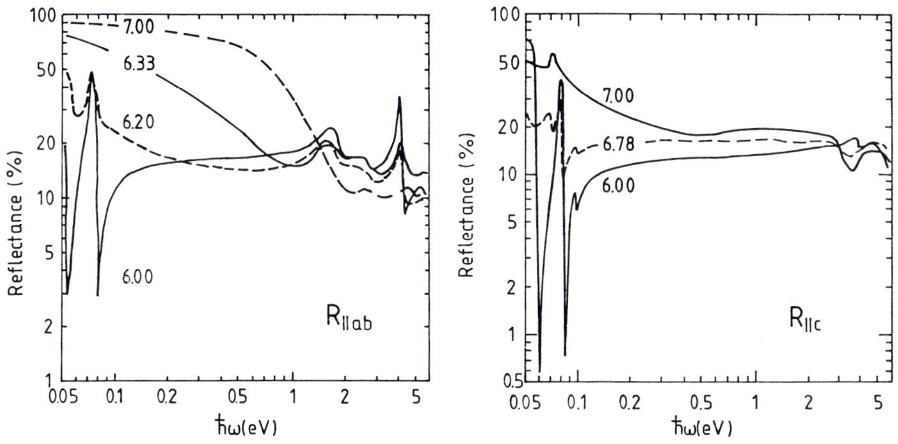

Fig.1 Polarized reflectance spectra of $YBa_2Cu_3O_x$ with the electric field parallel (left side) and perpendicular (right side) to the ab-plane at 300 K. The numbers denote the oxygen content x of the samples.

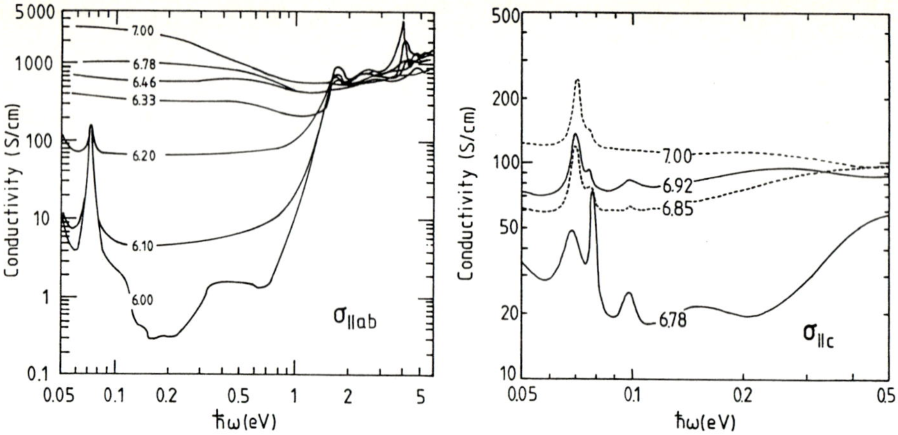

Fig.2 Real part of the conductivity parallel (left side) and perpendicular (right side) to the ab-plane.

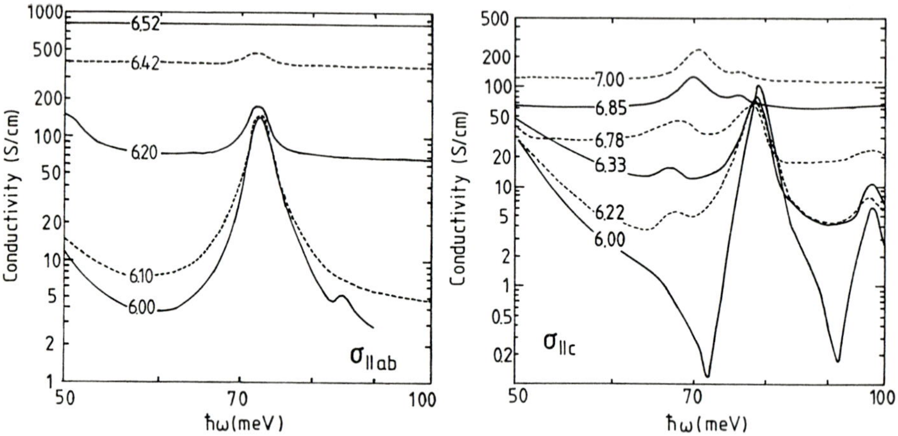

Fig.3 Real part of the conductivity parallel (left side) and perpendicular (right side) to the ab-plane (phonon regime).

For the discussion of the transport properties selected spectra of the conductivity functions $\sigma_{\|ab}$ and $\sigma_{\|c}$ are shown in Fig. 2. In Fig. 2 (left side) a strong increase of $\sigma_{\|ab}$ in the infrared between x=6.1 and x=6.3 by nearly two orders of magnitude is observed. This is the result of an increased free carrier absorption and corresponds to the appearance of a plasma edge in $R_{\|ab}$ at x=6.2. Both features point to the occurance of a semiconductor-metal transition well below the superconducting and tetragonal to orthorhombic phase transition at x=6.4 [1]. In Fig. 2 (right side) $\sigma_{\|c}$ is drawn in a reduced scale, in order to show the distinct increase of the conductivity function (free carrier absorption) between x=6.78 and x=6.85.

The conductivity is displayed by selected spectra in Fig. 3 for the phonon regime of the spectra. The structure at 72.6 meV (585 cm^{-1}) in the spectrum

$\sigma_{\|ab}$ of $YBa_2Cu_3O_6$ is assigned to a stretching vibration mode of the oxygen-atoms in the Cu(2)-plane. It can be observed up to an oxygen stoichiometry of x=6.46. Above x=6.5 its amplitude in the reflectivity spectrum is less than the error of ±1%, due to the increasing contribution of free charge carriers. Both eigenfrequency and dipole strength of this vibration mode decrease between x=6.1 and x=6.2. As the average bond distances in the Cu(2)-planes are not changed the decrease in the dipole strength must be due to a reduced ionic and an increased covalent character of the plane bonds [1]. This also causes an electronic shielding of the lattice vibration and therefore a softening of about 0.6 meV (5 cm^{-1}). The softening correlates with the simultaneous appearing of a plasma edge in the spectrum $R_{\|ab}$.

The structure at 78.5 meV (635 cm^{-1}) in $\sigma_{\|c}$ corresponds to the stretching mode of the bridging oxygen O(1). With increasing oxygen content the phonon mode softens by about 3 meV (25 cm^{-1}). This can be explained by the insertion of the chain oxygen which enlarges the Cu(1)-O(1) bond distance [1]. Similar to the behaviour of the O(2),O(3)-stretching mode in $\sigma_{\|ab}$ the softening of the stretching mode correlates with the increase of the free carrier absorption between x=6.78 and x=6.85.

The bending mode of the chain oxygen (O(4)) in $YBa_2Cu_3O_7$ with an eigenfrequency of 70.2 meV (566 cm^{-1}) does not exist in $\sigma_{\|c}$ of $YBa_2Cu_3O_6$. The dipole strength of this mode increases with the oxygen content of the samples. In contrast to the other phonon modes the modulation of the conductivity function $\sigma_{\|c}$ of $YBa_2Cu_3O_7$ by this mode is very pronounced. Simultaneously the eigenfrequency is increased very much, which can be explained by the reduction of the Ba-O(4)-bond length [1].

References

1.R.J.Cava, A.W.Hewat, E.A.Hewat, B.Batlogg, M.Marezio, K.M.Rabe, J.J.Kralewski, W.F.Peck Jr., and L.W.Rupp: Physica C **165**, 419 (1990)

2.T.Wolf, W.Goldacker, B.Obst, G.Roth, and R.Flückiger: J. Cryst. Growth **98**, 1010 (1989)

3.P.Murugaraj, J.Maier, and A.Rabenau: Solid State Comm. **71**, 167 (1989)

4.A.Zibold, M.Dürrler, H.P.Geserich, A.Erb, and G.Müller-Vogt: Physica C **171**, 151 (1990)

5.K. Kishio, J.Shimoyama, T.Hasegawa, K.Kitazawa, and K.Fuecki: Jap. Journ. of Appl. Physics **26**, L1228 (1987)

6.J.Kircher, M.K.Kelly, S.Rashkeev, M.Alouani, D.Fuchs, and M.Cardona: Phys. Rev. B **44**, 217 (1991)

Effect of Cu–O Planes and Oxygen Content on Optical Properties of BISCO Crystals

K. Kamarás[1,2], *S.L. Herr*[1,3], *F. Gao*[1], *B. Andraka*[1], *G.R. Stewart*[1], *D.B. Tanner*[1], *K. Remschnig*[4], *J.-M. Tarascon*[4], *and S. Etemad*[4]

[1]Department of Physics, University of Florida, Gainesville, FL 32611, USA
[2]Max-Planck-Institut für Festkörperforschung, Heisenbergstr. 1, W-7000 Stuttgart 80, Fed. Rep. of Germany
[3]Physics Department, Virginia Commonwealth University, Box 2000, Richmond, VA 23284-2000, USA
[4]Bell Communications Research, Red Bank, NJ 07781, USA

Abstract. We have studied the infrared and optical reflectivity of high quality BISCO crystals at room temperature: three 2201 samples (n=1) varying from semiconducting to perfect linear ρ(T) behaviour as a function of oxygen content, and a 2212 superconductor (n=2, T_c=91 K). We analyze the data in a two-component model (Drude conductivity + midinfrared absorption). We find that the Drude part in the 2201 metallic samples changes in width but its intensity remains constant as oxygen is added; the transition to 2212, on the other hand, increases the plasma frequency considerably. The oscillator strength of the MIR band depends only on the number of Cu-O layers, being twice as large for n=2 than for n=1. We conclude that oxygen content in the 2201 samples changes the mean free path but not the carrier concentration, while the new Cu-O plane in 2212 acts as a source of carriers for both the Drude and MIR absorption.

1. Introduction

Although a considerable amount of information has been accumulated by now [1], an unambigous explanation of the optical properties of high T_c materials is still missing. Recently, emphasis has been shifted to systematic investigations to clarify the role of individual "building blocks" of these systems, by polarization [2] or doping [3, 4] studies.

In this paper we compare optical properties of 2201 BISCO crystals with varying oxygen concentration in the Bi-O planes and a 2212 superconducting crystal. This allows us to probe the contribution of the Bi-O planes and that of a second Cu-O plane to the frequency dependent conductivity.

2. Experimental

Our samples were large area ($> 5x5mm^2$) single crystals of the 2201 compound whose conducting properties were changed by annealing in different at-

Springer Series in Solid-State Sciences, Vol. 113 Electronic Properties of High-T_c Superconductors
Editors: H. Kuzmany, M. Mehring, J. Fink

mospheres from semiconducting to metallic to a metal with very low resistivity (called "supermetal" in the following). Details about preparation, annealing and transport properties are given in Ref. [5]. The 2212 sample was grown from BiO flux [6]. The transition temperature, determined by magnetic susceptibility, was 91 K for this sample.

Reflectivity measurements were performed by a Bruker 113v FTIR spectrometer and a home-made grating spectrometer based on a Perkin-Elmer monochromator. Near-normal incidence spectra were taken at room temperature with unpolarized light. The surface of the crystals is oriented normal to the c-axis, thus we obtain the average ab-plane response this way.

3. Results and discussion

Reflectance spectra of the four crystals are shown in Fig. 1. To illustrate the changes in the spectra caused by chemical modification, we show in Fig. 2. the difference in optical functions upon going from the semiconductor to the metal (Step 1), the metal to the "supermetal" (Step 2), and from the "supermetal" to the superconductor (Step 3). Steps 1 and 2 involve oxygen addition to the Bi-O planes, while Step 3 means introduction of a new CuO_2 plane. The difference curves of optical conductivity and effective number of carriers have been calculated by performing a Kramers-Kronig transformation on the reflectivity data of Fig. 1. and subtracting the respective functions from each other.

Oxygen addition to the Bi-O planes has different consequences in Steps 1 and 2: in the former, the conductivity below 1000 cm^{-1} increases strongly, but the latter only shifts the spectral weight towards lower frequencies (ΔN_{eff} is near zero above 2000 cm^{-1}). A striking increase is caused by Step 3 in both the far and mid-infrared, the shape of $\Delta\sigma$ and the two distinct steps in ΔN_{eff} suggesting a two-component process.

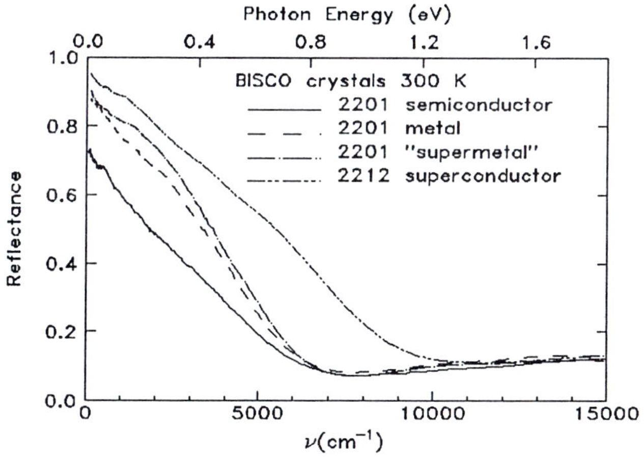

Figure 1: Reflectance spectra of the four crystals

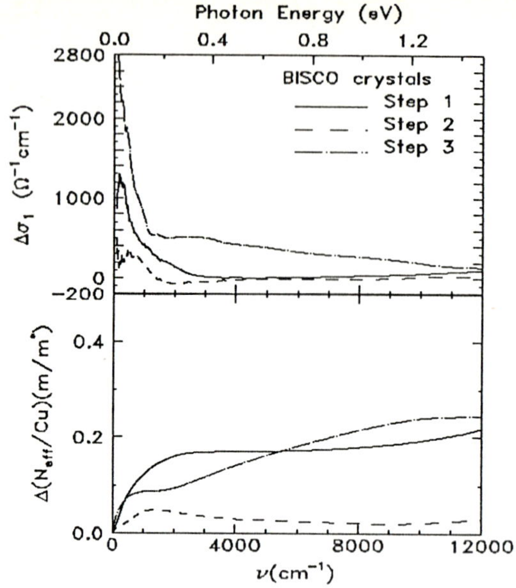

Figure 2: Changes in conductivity (upper panel) and effective number of carriers (lower panel) on chemical modification (see text)

On the basis of the observed changes, we regard Step 1 as addition of free carriers to the CuO_2 planes through increased charge transfer, Step 2 as an ordering process increasing the mean free path but not the concentration of the carriers, and Step 3 as addition of both free and bound carriers. Fits of the reflectivity curves to Drude-Lorentz dielectric functions confirm the above assignments [?].

The strong mid-infrared contribution to $\Delta\sigma$ which appears during Step 3 is of special importance. In $YBa_2Cu_3O_{7-\delta}$, the midinfrared absorption above 2000 cm^{-1} has been attributed entirely to the CuO chains; in our materials, by analogy, it should correspond to the BiO planes. However, the fact that the intensity in the midinfrared doubles by adding a new CuO plane suggests the absorption up to 1 eV to be an intrinsic property of the conducting planes. It remains to be seen whether the enhancement is simply a consequence of increased transfer of holes from the charge reservoirs or if coupling between adjacent planes is important.

This research was supported by DARPA Grant No. MDA-972-88-J-1006 (University of Florida), the Joseph H. DeFrees Grant of Research Corporation No. C-2943 and the Jeffress Memorial Trust Grant No. J-241 (Virginia Commonwealth University). One of us (K.K.) thanks the Alexander-von-Humboldt-Foundation for support.

References

[1] D. B. Tanner and T. Timusk, in *Physical Properties of High Temperature Superconductors*, vol. 3, Donald M. Ginsberg, Ed., World Scientific, Singapore, to be published.

[2] Z. Schlesinger, R. T. Collins, F. Holtzberg, C. Feild, S. H. Blanton, U. Welp, G. W. Crabtree, Y. Fang and J. Z. Liu, *Phys. Rev. Lett.* **65**, 801 (1990).

[3] S. Uchida, T. Ido, H. Takagi, T. Arima, Y. Tokura and S. Tajima, *Phys. Rev. B* **43**, 7942 (1991).

[4] J. Humlíček, J. Kircher, H.-U. Habermeier, M. Cardona and A. Röseler, *Physica C* **190**, 383 (1992).

[5] K. Remschnig, J. M. Tarascon, R. Ramesh and G. W. Hull, *Physica C* **175**, 261 (1991).

[6] B. Andraka, private communication

[7] S. L. Herr, K. Kamarás, F. Gao, B. Andraka, G. R. Stewart, S. Etemad and J. M. Tarascon, *Bull. Am. Phys. Soc.* **36**, 418 (1991).

Optical Anisotropy and Electron–Phonon Coupling in $Bi_2Sr_2CaCu_2O_8$ Single Crystals

A. Zibold[1], *K. Widder*[1], *M. Dürrler*[1], *A. Gaymann*[1], *H.P. Geserich*[1], *N. Nücker*[2], *V.M. Burlakov*[3], *and P. Müller*[4]

[1]Institut für Angewandte Physik, Universität Karlsruhe, Kaiserstr. 12, W-7500 Karlsruhe, Fed. Rep. of Germany
[2]Kernforschungszentrum Karlsruhe, Institut für Nukleare Festkörperphysik, Postfach 3640, W-7500 Karlsruhe, Fed. Rep. of Germany
[3]Institute of Spectroscopy, Russian Academy of Sciences, Troitzk, 142092 Moscow Region, Russia
[4]Walther-Meissner-Institut für Tieftemperaturforschung, Walther-Meissner-Str. 8, W-8046 Garching, Fed. Rep. of Germany

Abstract. We have determined the polarized reflectance spectra $R_{||a}$, $R_{||b}$ and $R_{||c}$ of the high temperature superconductor $Bi_2Sr_2CaCu_2O_8$ in the normal state. By fitting a Lorentz–Drude model or by performing a Kramers–Kronig analysis, respectively, the spectral distribution of the tensor components of the real and the imaginary part of the dielectric function were obtained. The optical results reveal a low electrical anisotropy within the (001) plane and a very high anisotropy between the in–plane conductivity and the conductivity perpendicular to this plane. The spectrum $R_{||c}$ gives evidence for the interaction between infrared–active phonons and the low–energy part of interband transitions.

1. Introduction

There are several publications, reporting the reflectance spectra of $Bi_2Sr_2CaCu_2O_8$ in the normal state [1–5]. The results, published up to now, however, do not show the complete information about the tensor components of the dielectric function of this orthorhombic compound. In particular, there are very limited informations about the optical excitations for the electrical field parallel to the c–axis, including the electrical coupling between the Cu–O planes and about the electrical anisotropy, resulting from the orthorhomic distortion within the (001) plane.

2. Experimental

The reflection measurements for the direction of polarization parallel to the a– and to the b–axis, respectively, were performed on a freshley cleaved (001) surface. The reflectance spectrum $R_{||c}$, however, was obtained on a (100/010) surface. A shiny surface was prepared by cutting a single crystal of $Bi_2Sr_2CaCu_2O_8$, embedded in epoxy, perpendicular to the (001) plane by a wire saw. The obtained surface was subsequently smoothed by repeated cutting with a diamond knive using an ultramicrotome.

Springer Series in Solid-State Sciences, Vol. 113 **Electronic Properties of High-T_c Superconductors**
Editors: H. Kuzmany, M. Mehring, J. Fink

3. Results and Discussion

Fig.1 shows the polarized reflectance spectra of $Bi_2Sr_2CaCu_2O_8$. The electric field of the incident light was polarized parallel to the crystallographic axes. Therefore Fig.1 represents the complete information about the optical anisotropy of $Bi_2Sr_2CaCu_2O_8$ in the energy range between 30 meV and 6 eV.

Fig.1 shows that the reflectance spectra $R_{\|a}$ and $R_{\|b}$ differ significantly in the energy range above 1 eV whereas the reflectance values at the plasma edge and in the low-energy regime coincide within photometric accuracy. For a quantitative discussion the tensor components of the energy loss function Im $(-1/\epsilon)$ and of the conductivity function $\sigma = \epsilon_2\epsilon_0\omega$ are plotted in Figs. 2 and 3. It is obvious from Fig.3 that the orthorhomic distortion of the metal-oxygen layers has an effect both on the interband transitions and on the free carrier absorption. This distortion, resulting in an elongation of about 1 percent for all metal-oxygen distances parallel to the b-axis, compared to the corresponding distances parallel to the a-axis, leads to a reduced overlap of the atomic orbitals and hence to a reduced band width for electrons propagating along the b-axis. Therefore the corresponding band gap is increased and the absorption edge is shifted to higher energy, thus reducing $\epsilon_{1L\|b}$, the interband contribution to the real part of the dielectric function, and consequently the reflectivity $R_{\|b}$ above 1 eV. In the low energy regime, however, the influence of the orthorhombic distortion onto the free carrier absorption, has to be taken into account

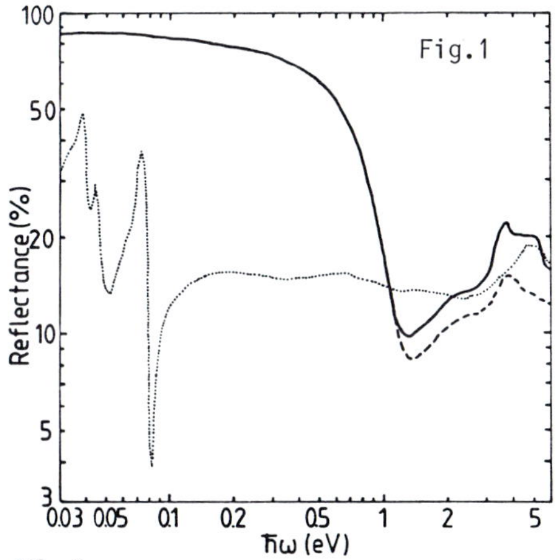

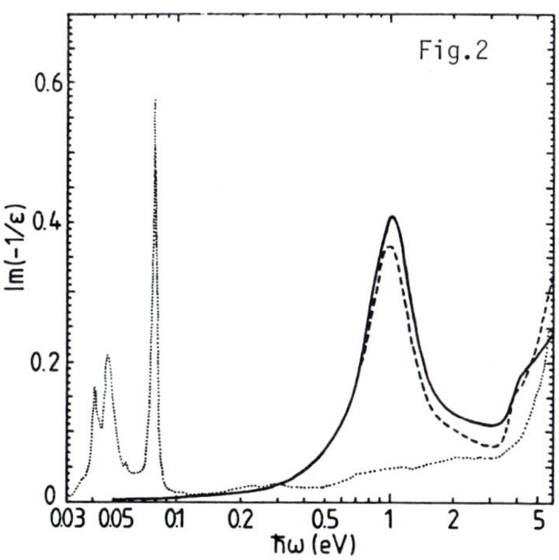

Fig.1
Polarized reflectance spectra of a $Bi_2Sr_2CaCuO_8$ single crystals, T = 300K. Full line: $R_{\|a}$, dashed line: $R_{\|b}$, dotted line: $R_{\|c}$.

Fig.2
Energy loss function of $Bi_2Sr_2CaCu_2O_8$. Full line: Im $(-1/\epsilon_{\|a})$, dashed line: $Im(-1/\epsilon_{\|b})$ dotted line: Im $(-1/\epsilon_{\|c})$.

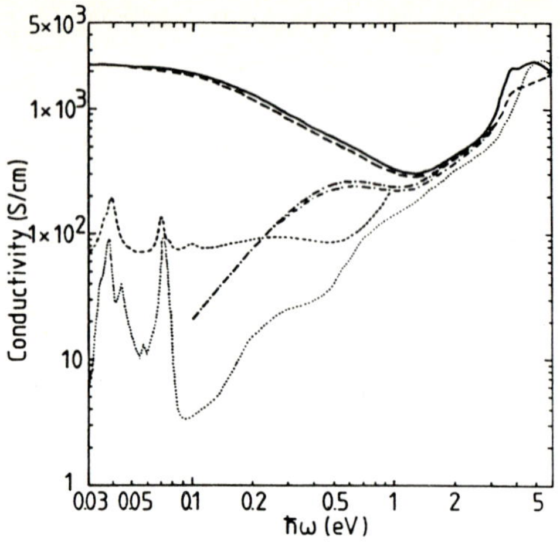

Fig.3
Conductivity function of $Bi_2Sr_2CaCu_2O_8$. Full line: $\sigma_{\parallel a}$, dashed line: $\sigma_{\parallel b}$, dotted line: $\sigma_{\parallel c}$, dashed dotted lines: interband contributions, shortly dashed line: $\sigma_{\parallel c}$ of $YBa_2Cu_3O_7$

which is generally represented by the oscillator strength $\omega_{p,u} = Ne^2/m^*\epsilon_0$, where $\omega_{p,u}$, N and m* are the unscreened plasma frequency, the concentration and the effective mass of the free carriers. As the decrease of the band width is correlated with an increase of the effective mass it is expected that the oscillator strength for the polarization parallel to the b–axis, $\omega_{p,u\,\parallel b}$, is reduced, compared to $\omega_{p,u\,\parallel a}$. This is confirmed experimentally by the value of the oscillator strength $\omega_{p,u\parallel b} = 7.78 \times 10^{30}/s^2$ which is about 7 percent lower than $\omega_{p,u\parallel a} = 8.38 \times 10^{30}/s^2$. Band structure calculations [6] as well as the results of angle–resolved photoemission spectroscopy [7] have shown nearly quadratic Fermi surfaces, arising from the Cu–O layers, as a main feature of the electronic structure of $Bi_2Sr_2CaCu_2O_8$. The present results indicate that optical spectroscopy is a very sensitive tool to determine precisely small deviations from this nearly quadratic symmetry.
In contrast to the optical behaviour of heavily doped semiconductors the oxide superconductors do not show a pronounced absorption gap between the free carrier absorption and the charge transfer excitations. Rather, in the energy range below the charge transfer gap, i.e. below 1.4 eV, an additional oscillator–like mid infrared absorption is observed. This general behaviour is confirmed by the conductivity spectra $\sigma_{\parallel a}$ and $\sigma_{\parallel b}$ of $Bi_2Sr_2CaCu_2O_8$ (Fig.3).
As expected from the crystallographic anisotropy of $Bi_2Sr_2CaCu_2O_8$, Fig.1 shows that the difference between the reflectance spectrum $R_{\parallel c}$, polarized perpendicular to metal–oxygen layers, and the in–plane polarized spectra $R_{\parallel a}$ and $R_{\parallel b}$ is much larger than the optical anisotropy within these layers. This is evident from the lack of any indication for metallic conduction along

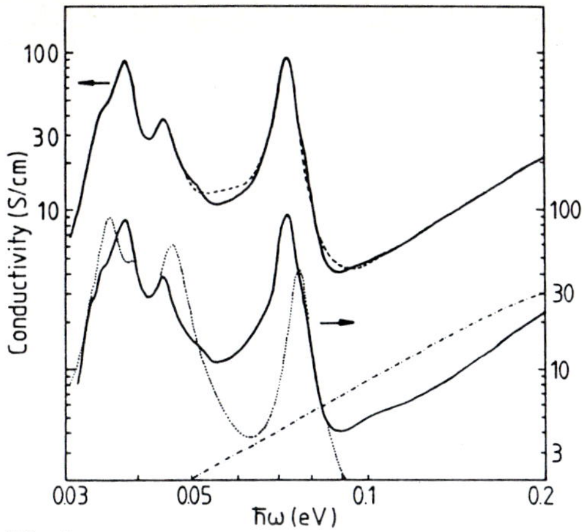

Fig.4

Conductivity function $\sigma_{||c}$ of $Bi_2Sr_2CaCu_2O_8$ in the phonon region. Full lines: experimental spectrum, dashed line: a fit, including electron−phonon interaction, dotted line: bare phonon spectrum, dashed−dotted line: bare electronic excitation spectrum.

the c−axis because $R_{||c}$ does not show a plasma edge and because, as a more sensitive feature, the well−pronounced minimum of the phonon structure near 80 meV confirms the absence of a contribution of free carriers to $\epsilon_{1||c}$. On the other hand $\sigma_{||c}$ shows optical excitations in the mid infrared regime with a minimum value of 3 S/cm at 90 meV. This mid infrared absorption is higher by a factor of 30 as compared to the dc−conductivity $\sigma_{dc||c} = 0.1$ S/cm, found in $Bi_2Sr_2\,CaCu_2O_8$ [8].
For a description of the experimental spectrum $\sigma_{||c}$ we used a Fano resonance model [9], which takes into account an interaction between lattice vibrations, represented by a set of Lorentzian oscillators and electronic excitations, represented by a single oscillator, which describes the absorption spectrum of these excitations below 230 meV. From the frequency shift of the phononic excitations of about 4 percent we conclude that the phonons under consideration are strongly coupled to electronic excitations (Fig.4).

References

[1] M.K.Kelly, P.Barboux, J.−M.Tarascon and D.E. Aspnes, Phys.Rev.B 40(1989)6797.

[2] M.P.Petrov, A.I.Grachev, M.V.Krasinkova, A.A.Nechitailov, V.V.Poborchii, S.I.Shagin and S.V.Miridonov, JETP Letters 50(1989)29.

[3] I.Terasaki, S.Tajima, H.Eisaki, H.Takagi, K.Uchinokura and S.Uchida, Phys.Rev.B41(1990)865.

[4] J.Humlicek, E.Schmidt, L.Bocanek, M.Garriga and M.Cardona, Solid State Comm. 73(1990)127.
[5] J.H.Kim, I.Bozovic, D.B.Mitzi, A.Kapitulnik and J.S.Harris, Phys.Rev.B 41(1990)7251.
[6] H.Krakauer and W.E.Pickett, Phys.Rev.Lett.60(1988)1665.
[7] G.Mante, R.Claessen, T.Buslaps, S.Harm, R.Manzke, M.Skibowski and J.Fink, Z.Phys.B80(1990)181.
[8] S.Martin, A.T.Fiory, R.M.Fleming, L.F.Schneemeyer and J.V.Waszczak, Phys.Rev.Lett.60(1988)2194.
[9] V.M.Burlakov, S.V.Shulga, J.Keller and K.F.Renk, to be published

Midgap Electronic States in Semiconducting $YBa_2Cu_3O_{6+x}$: A NIR Excited Raman Investigation

G. Ruani[1], *V.N. Denisov*[2], *A.G. Mal'shukov*[2], *V.M. Burlakov*[2], *R. Zamboni*[1], *and C. Taliani*[1]

[1]Istituto di Spettrroscopia Molecolare, C.N.R., Via de'Castagnoli, I-40126 Bologna, Italy
[2]Permanent address: Institute of Spectroscopy, Russian Academy of Sciences, Troitsk, 142092 Moscow Region, Russia

Abstract. Raman scattering exciting at 1.16 eV and luminescence measurements in the same spectral range have been performed in the semiconducting parent compounds of the HT_c superconducting system $YBa_2Cu_3O_{6+x}$. In the Raman spectrum of the $YBa_2Cu_3O_6$ the dominant features are the E_u(LO) phonon modes due to the Frölich mechanism. A new strong resonant band at 507 cm^{-1} with several overtones appears with oxygen doping in the Raman spectrum. Site selective isotope oxygen substitution confirms the assignement of this band to A_g vibrations of O(4) atoms adjacent to the short oxygen O(1) chain. Luminescence emission, with a peak at about 1.3 eV, was observed in samples with very low oxygen concentration. Both Raman and luminescence data were described in the framework of a model where the existence of a narrow midgap band, associated with the O(4)-Cu(1)-O(4) complex, is assumed.

1. Introduction

In the tetragonal semiconducting phase [1] of $YBa_2Cu_3O_{6+x}$ electronic correlations are strong. So far there is no reliable quantitative approach to the metal-insulator transition in the high-T_c oxides, and also the origin of the insulating gap and the nature of the electronic states filling the gap upon doping is not clear. In this context measurements of Raman spectra of the semiconducting phase with excitation at photon energy lower than the energy gap can provide useful information.

In this paper we present the results of the near infrared (NIR) excited Raman scattering and luminescence measurements of $YBa_2Cu_3{}^{18}O_{6+x}$ and $YBa_2Cu_3{}^{16}O_{6+x}$ ceramics; preliminary results were presented in Ref [2].

2. Experimental

The ceramic samples preparation of $YBa_2Cu_3O_{6+x}$ with different oxygen content and oxygen isotope substitution is reported elsewhere [3].

The NIR excited Raman spectra were performed in a back-scattering configuration with 4 cm^{-1} resolution with an FT spectrometer exciting at 1.16 eV (25 mW within a spot of about 300 μm). The luminescence spectra in the range of 0.7 - 1.4 eV were obtained using the same experimental apparatus. Measurements were

Springer Series in Solid-State Sciences, Vol. 113 Electronic Properties of High-T_c Superconductors
Editors: H. Kuzmany, M. Mehring, J. Fink

performed at different temperature and excitation energies (2.41 and 2.54 eV) with a laser spot of about 2 mm of diameter and laser power less than 5 mW.

We conventionally label the oxygen content with x = 0, 0.05 to indicate two different levels of doping of our samples with very low oxygen content.

3. Results and Discussion

3.1. Raman Scattering

The oxygen doping dependence of the visible excited Raman scattering of $YBa_2Cu_3O_{6+x}$ is well known [4], showing only a minor shift of the bands and a small redistribution of their intensities. The IR excited Raman spectrum of $YBa_2Cu_3{}^{18}O_6$ shows three strong bands at 387, 552 and 459 cm^{-1} (Fig. 1a), where the two formers are absent in the visible excited spectra. At the same time for ω_i = 1.16eV, the 320 cm^{-1} band (340 cm^{-1} in $YBa_2Cu_3{}^{16}O_6$), which usually is the strongest in visible excited Raman spectra [5], is not detected. Despite of the factor $\propto\omega_i^4$, the strong bands clearly observed for ω_i = 1.16 eV indicate their resonance enhancement suggesting the presence of a dipole electronic transition deep inside the semiconducting gap. Upon doping a new resonance feature at 477 cm^{-1}, together with overtones, appears in the Raman spectrum (Fig. 1b). In order to confirm the attribution of this peak to vibration of the O(4) atoms in microscopic domains of the orthorombic phase [6] we have performed site selective ^{16}O isotope substitution in $YBa_2Cu_3{}^{18}O_6$. In Fig. 2b the spectrum after 30' annealing of the sample at 200°C in air is shown. At this temperature annealing, the oxygen ^{16}O of the atmosphere can diffuse only in the basal plane but not in others oxygen sites.A new peak at 477 cm^{-1}, together with a weak overtone, appears at the same frequency of the main band of the $YBa_2Cu_3{}^{18}O_{6,2}$ spectrum excluding the assignment of this mode to oxygen O(1) vibrations. After further annealing at 300°C, where a partial substitution of the

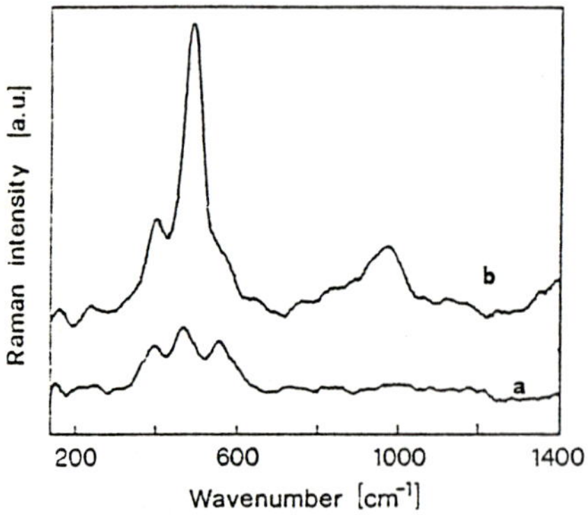

Fig. 1 FT-Raman spectra of $YBa_2Cu_3{}^{18}O_{6+x}$: a) x=0 b) x=0.2.

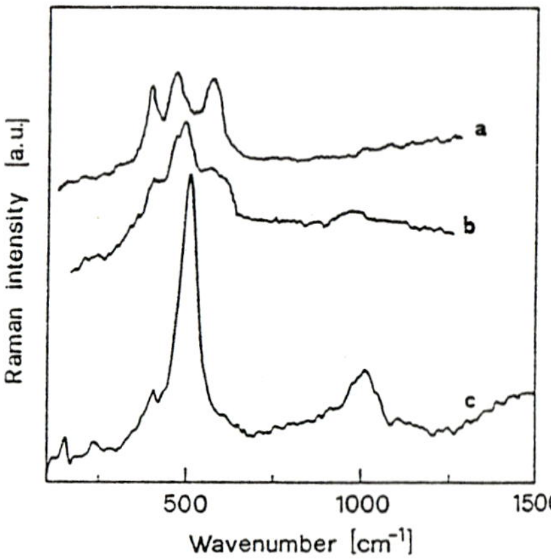

Fig. 2 FT-Raman spectra of $YBa_2Cu_3{}^{18}O_{6.0}$: a) as grown, b) after 30' at 200°C in air, c) after 60' at 300°C in air.

oxygens in the O(4) site takes place, the Raman spectrum drastically changes (Fig. 2c) becoming similar to the one of Fig. 1b approximately shifted by 20 cm^{-1} to the higher energy except for the shoulder clearly seen at 552 cm^{-1} in Fig. 1b. The absence of this feature indicates its related to vibrations of oxygen atoms in CuO_2 layers which were not isotopically substituted. Thus we conclude that all oxygen vibrational bands that appears in the IR excited Raman spectra of $YBa_2Cu_3O_{6+x}$, except the one at highest energy, are associated with vibrations of the apex oxygen atoms.

3.2. Luminescence

The luminescence spectra obtained exciting at 2.41 and 2.54 eV have showed no difference. As shown in Fig 3, the intensity of low temperature luminescence spectra for three samples with $x = 0$, 0.05 and 0.15 decreases with the increasing of oxygen doping. For samples with $x \geq 0.2$ no signal has been observed. In Fig. 4 the luminescence spectra at different temperatures for the sample with $x = 0.15$ are reported. The luminescence peak is shifted towards higher energies and increasing in intensity with decreasing temperature; at liquid helium temperature it is near the high frequency limit of our detector sensitivity.

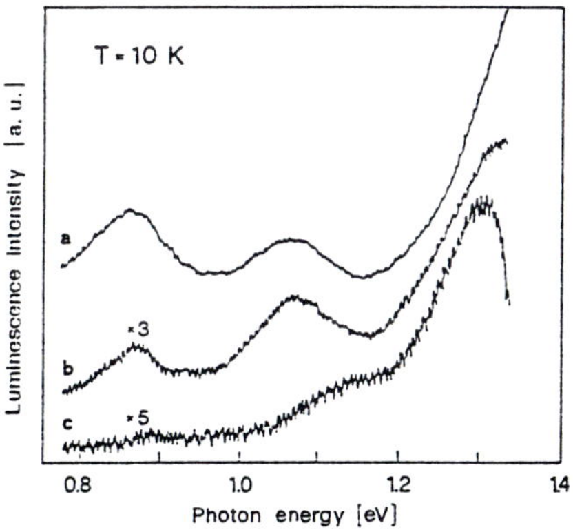

Fig. 3 Luminescence spectra at 10 K of $YBa_2Cu_3O_{6+x}$: a) x=0 b) x=0.05 c) x=0.15.

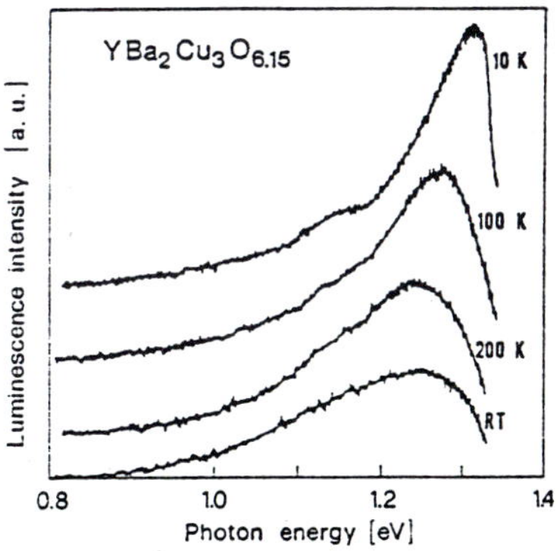

Fig. 4 Luminescence spectra of $YBa_2Cu_3O_{6.15}$ exciting at 2.41 eV at different temperatures.

3.3 The Model

One should expect that an insulating gap would provide opportunities for the appearance of narrow midgap electronic transitions, which can serve as resonance for the Raman scattering. From our luminescence measurements we can conclude that a narrow electronic band is present inside the semiconducting gap already at $x = 0$. At a higher oxygen content the luminescence only decreases. This decrease is due to the increasing number of localized electronic states that acts as channels for nonradiative decay. Therefore we cannot unambiguously exclude that the luminescence is due to radiative recombination of electrons and holes at localized levels appearing with very low doping. However, a relative narrowness of the band observed in luminescence compared to the very broad midgap absorption associated to oxygen O(1) [7] strongly suggests that this band is not a defect band.

Cu(1) atoms at x = 0 do not have localized magnetic moment [8] (d^{10} state), unlike Cu(2) atoms which are in the d^9 state. Hence, the d^{10} band of Cu(1) is at least below the upper Hubbard empty d^{10} conduction band. The former band is narrow since it is weakly hybridized with electronic states of the planes from which the O(4)-Cu(1)-O(4) complexes are well separated when x = 0. Upon doping, holes initially appear on Cu(1) sites [9], *i.e.* Cu(1) d^{10} should be above the valence band.

The assumption about a narrow midgap band gives a clue for the understanding of the resonance Raman scattering at 1.16 eV and luminescence in the near infrared. The latter is due to radiative transitions of excited electrons from the conduction band into the empty Cu(1) midgap state (O(4)p_z-Cu(1)$3d_{(z^2-r^2)}$-O(4)p_z antibonding band). Excited electrons on Cu(2)-O(2,3) planes are in an attractive Coulomb field of heavy holes on O(4)-Cu(1)-O(4) creating excitonic states near the bottom of the conduction band. Such states provide a most effective channel for luminescence. Transitions from the midgap electronic band to excitonic states below the bottom of the conduction band can account for the observed resonance effects in Raman spectra of $YBa_2Cu_3O_{6+x}$. The 412 cm^{-1} (the frequencies are related from now on to the ^{16}O compounds) peak is the E_u(LO) phonon seen in reflectance measurements near 420 cm^{-1} [10] that becomes Raman active near resonance due to the Frölich mechanism [11]. Other E_u(LO) modes, rather weak but reproducible in all samples, are also seen in the IR excited Raman spectra at 181 cm^{-1}, 250 cm^{-1} and 638 cm^{-1}, which were observed in IR reflectance measurements [10] at 199 cm^{-1}, 266 cm^{-1}, 637 cm^{-1} respectively. We have assigned the 507 cm^{-1} vibrational band to A_g vibrations of O(4) atoms in unit cells containing dopant oxygen atoms on O(1) chain sites where the Cu(1) atoms are in the d^9 configuration [9], as in $YBa_2Cu_3O_7$. Resonance transitions will be from the valence band to empty levels related to O(1) impurities with a strong admixture of charge-transfer transitions from O(1) to Cu(1). These transitions strongly interact with the A_g O(4) vibrations leading to shifted positions of the O(4) atoms in the excited state and hence to strong overtones.

4. Conclusions

The strong coupling of O(4) vibrations to charge fluctuations on Cu(1)-O(4) leading to shifted positions of O(4) atoms for different charged states of Cu(1)-O(4) may give rise to appearance in the ground state of double-well adiabatic potentials for O(4) atoms associated with different charged states of Cu(1)-O(4) complex (seen by EXAFS measurements [12] in $YBa_2Cu_3O_7$). According to Ref. [13] this can have a strong impact on superconducting properties of $YBa_2Cu_3O_{6+x}$ suggesting a crucial role played by apex oxygen vibrations in high-T_c oxides [14-15].

Acknowledgements

We wish to thank Dr. E. Schönherr for kindly suplly us ceramic sample of $YBa_2Cu_3{}^{18}O_{6+x}$. Financial support by National Research Council of Italy, C.N.R., under the Progetto Finalizzato "Superconductive and Cryogenic Technologies" is acknowledged.

References

1. H. Eskes, M.B.J. Meinders and G.A.Sawatzky, Phys. Rev. Lett. **67**, 1035 (1991).
2. G. Ruani, R. Zamboni, C. Taliani, V.N. Denisov, V.M. Burlakov and A.G. Mal'shukov, Physica C, 185-189, 963 (1991).
4. C. Thomsen, R. Liu, M. Bauer, A. Wittlin, L.Genzel, M. Cardona, E. Schöherr, W. Bauhofer and W. König, Solid State Commun., **65**, 55 (1988).
5. E.T. Heyen, R. Liu, C. Thomsen and M. Cardona in "Electronic Properties of High-T_c Superconductors and Relative Compounds", edited by H.Kuzmany, M. Mehring and J. Fink, (Springer-Verlag, Berlin Heidelberg 1990), p.324.
6. R. Zamboni, G. Ruani, A.J.Pal and C. Taliani, Solid State Commun, **70**, 813 (1989).
7. G.A. Thomas, D.H. Rapkine, S.L. Cooper, S.W. Cheong, A.S. Cooper, L.F. Schneemayer and J.V. Waszczak, Phys. Rev. B, **45**, 2474 (1992).
8. B. Batlogg Proc. of High Temperature Superconductivity, Los Alamos Symposium, 1989, Los Alamos (Addison-Wesley,1990).
9. H. Tolentino, A.Fontaine, A.M.Flank, P.Lagarde, J.Y.Henry, J. Rossat-Mignod, T. Gourieux, G. Krill and F. Studer in "Electronic Properties of High-T_c Superconductors and Relative Compounds", edited by H.Kuzmany, M. Mehring and J. Fink, (Springer-Verlag, Berlin Heidelberg 1990), p. 176
10. M. Bauer, L.B. Ferreira, L. Genzel, M. Cardona, P. Muragaraj and J. Maier, Solid State commun, **72**, 551 (1989).
11. M. Cardona in "Light Scattering in Solids II", ed. M. Cardona and G. Güntherodt (Springer, 1982)
12. J. Mustre de Leon, S.D. Conradson, A.R. Bishop and I. Batistic, Phys Rev. Lett., **65**, 4675 (1990).
13. A.G. Mal'shukov, JETP Lett. **48**, 429 (1988); Solid State Commun. **77**, 57 (1991).
14. K.A. Müller, Z. Phys. B **80**, 193 (1990).
15. D. Mihailovic, C.M. Foster, K.F. Voss and N. Herron, Phys. Rev. B **44**, 237 (1991).

Optical Absorption due to Pr^{3+} 4f–4f Transitions in $PrBa_2Cu_3O_x$ ($x \approx 6$)

R. Boyn[1], *H. Zimmermann*[1], *U. Müller*[1], *G. Jakob*[2], and *H. Adrian*[2]

[1]Humboldt-Universität Berlin, Fachbereich Physik, Invalidenstr. 110, O-1040 Berlin, Fed. Rep. of Germany

[2]Technische Universität Darmstadt, Institut für Festkörperphysik, Fachbereich 5, Hochschulstr. 8, W-6100 Darmstadt, Fed. Rep. of Germany

Abstract: Transmission spectra of $PrBa_2Cu_3O_x$ films ($x \approx 6$, thickness about 5 µm) on $LaAlO_3$ substrates have been measured in the range 1000 to 8000 cm^{-1}, at temperatures between 4.2 and 100 K. Several absorption bands are found, which are clearly due to Pr^{3+} 4f–4f transitions. The fine structure and width of these bands are obviously related to crystal-field splitting.

1. Introduction

It seems that, so far, optical absorption spectra due to transitions between 4f-like states in $LnBa_2Cu_3O_x$ materials have not been observed. Such data are of considerable interest since they should give information i) on the charge state of the Ln ions and ii) on the electronic interactions with the CuO_2 planes. It is expected that the simple crystal-field model provides a good starting-point for analysing such spectra, just as in the case of neutron scattering data /1,2/. The first aspect (i) is particularly important in the Ln=Pr case because of the 3+/4+ charge state problem, which arises in the discussion of the origin of the nonmetallic behaviour of $PrBa_2Cu_3O_7$ (e.g. /3/).

The difficulty concerning the experimental observation of optical 4f–4f transitions in the high-T_c materials lies in their small oscillator strengths and, in many cases, their overlap with more intense transitions of other types. Our idea has been to start such studies (for Ln=Pr) at reduced oxygen content, using sample thicknesses adapted to the 4f–4f oscillator strengths.

2. Results and Discussion

$PrBa_2Cu_3O_7$ films of thickness about 5 µm were grown by high-pressure reactive sputtering on $LaAlO_3$ substrates (for details see /4/). An X-ray diffraction diagram showing preferential c-axis orientation is presented in Fig. 1. In the as-grown state (x=7) the samples are opaque throughout the investigated range (1000 to 8000 cm^{-1}), which is expected from ellipsometric data /5/ for our film thickness. After annealing in streaming Ar(400° C, one week), which should lead to an oxygen content x about 6, we obtained the transmission spectra shown in Fig. 2 a and b. These exhibit several bands, which can be naturally assigned to 4f–4f transitions from the $^3H_4$ ground levels to various excited levels of Pr^{3+} as indicated in Fig. 2a and Fig. 3. Note that the centroids of the bands correspond to the positions of the Pr^{3+} free-ion levels /6/, while Pr^{4+} should give rise to only a single band ($^2F_{5/2} \longrightarrow {}^2F_{7/2}$) somewhat above 2000 cm^{-1}. This

Springer Series in Solid-State Sciences, Vol. 113 Electronic Properties of High-T_c Superconductors
Editors: H. Kuzmany, M. Mehring, J. Fink

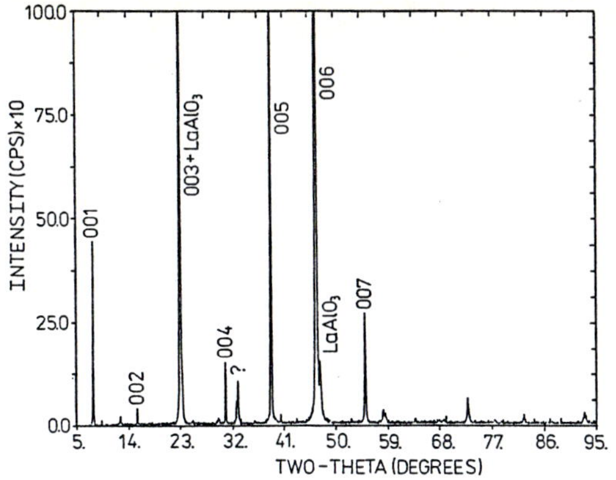

Fig. 1. X-ray diffraction diagram (x=7 state)

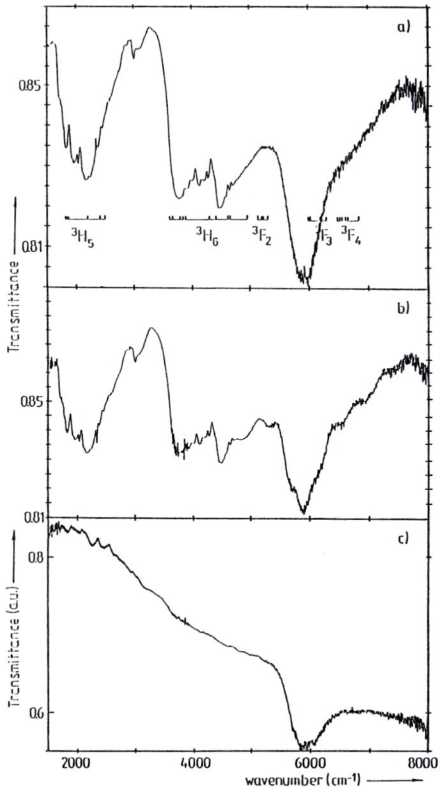

Fig. 2. Transmission spectrum of a sample a) at 4.2 K and b) at 100 K. c) Transmission spectrum of a substrate from the same origin. The measurements have been performed by means of a Bruker IFS 88 Fourier transform spectrometer. In Fig. 2a the relevant final-state manifolds of Pr^{3+} as well as crystal-field splittings estimated by us are indicated.

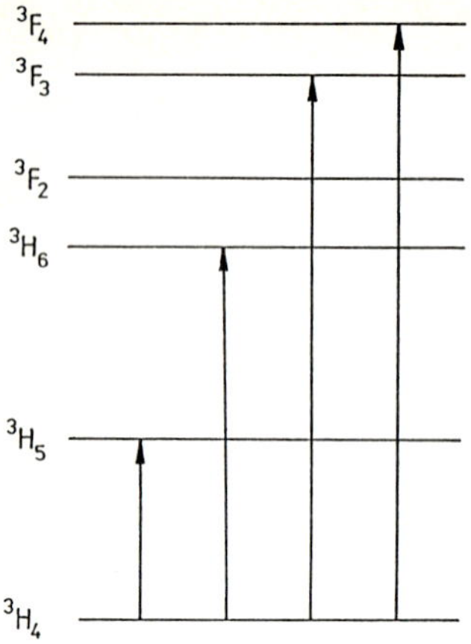

Fig. 3. Free-ion levels of Pr^{3+} and transitions manifesting themselves in the spectra of Fig. 2a and 2b.

result is consistent with the growing evidence (e.g. /3,5/) that the Pr charge state is near 3+ even for x=7. We mention that the band related to $^3H_4 \longrightarrow {}^3F_3$, $^3F_4$ transitions is appreciably affected by atmospheric water absorption not completely compensated in the spectrometer.

Since for x≈6 the atomic configuration around the Pr site should have nearly inversion symmetry, one would expect magnetic dipole transitions ($/\Delta J/ = 0,1$) rather than electric dipole transitions to be dominant. The high intensity of the $^3H_4 \longrightarrow {}^3H_6$ transitions, which are magnetic dipole forbidden, suggests the presence of low-symmetry crystal-field components, as have also been inferred from neutron scattering data /2/.

The fine structure and the width of the $^3H_5$ and $^3H_6$ band should be mainly due to crystal-field splitting. We demonstrate this in Fig. 2a by an estimate of such splittings which is based on crystal-field parameters taken from /1/ and the Stevens operator equivalents method /6/. (We have put $B_2^2 = B_2^4 = B_2^6 = B_6^6 = 0$, assuming D_{4h} symmetry as a first approximation.) Obviously the calculated overall-splittings are consistent with the widths of the observed bands. On the other hand, there is poor agreement with respect to the individual splitting components. This is not surprising because we have neglected J-mixing, which should be very important in view of the near overlap of some of the splittings. A more careful analysis is in progress.

Within the present experimental accuracy, there is no appreciable temperature dependence of line positions and intensities. In particular, there is no significant line shift in the range (about 8K) where an antiferromagnetic phase transition in the Pr subsystem has been found /7/(Fig. 4). It should be noted that all the transitions observed are expected to start from the $^3H_4$ quasi-triplet ground state component, which is separated from the higher $^3H_4$ components by about 400 cm^{-1} /2/; this explains the absence of "hot lines".

The absorption coefficient due to the 4f-4f transitions is estimated to be about 100 cm^{-1}. For the oscillator strengths corresponding to the fine structure lines we get values of the order 10^{-6}, which is typical for this class of transitions.

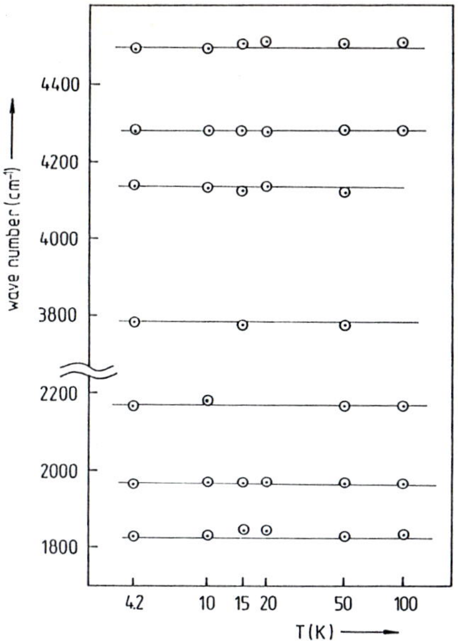

Fig. 4. Plot of selected line positions vs temperature.

References

/1/ G.L. Goodman, C. K. Loong, and L. Soderholm, J. Phys. Condens. Matter 3, 49 (1991)

/2/ V. Nekvasil, E. Holland-Moritz, H.D. Jostarndt, U. Walter, and G. Hilscher, J. Magnetism Magn. Mat., in the press

/3/ J. Fink, N. Nücker, H. Romberg, M. Alexander, M. B. Maple, J. J. Neumeier, and J. W. Allen, Phys. Rev. B 42, 4823 (1990)

/4/ C. Tome-Rosa, G. Jakob, M. Maul, A. Walkenhorst, M. Schmitt, P. Wagner, P. Trzyslopski, and H. Adrian, Physica C 171, 231 (1990)

/5/ J.Kircher, J. Humlicek, D. Fuchs, H.-U. Habermeier, M. Cardona, and A. Roeseler, Physica C 185-189

/6/ Handbook on the Physics and Chemistry of Rare Earths, Ed. K. A. Gschneidner and L. Eyring, Vol. 5, North Holland 1982

/7/ G. Wortmann and I. Felner, Solid State Commun. 75, 981 (1990)

Part VII

Theory

One- and Two-Particle Excitations in Doped Mott-Hubbard Insulators

P. Horsch[1] *and W. Stephan*[2]

[1]Max-Planck-Institut für Festkörperforschung,
Heisenbergstr. 1, W-7000 Stuttgart 80, Fed. Rep. of Germany
[2]King's College London, Strand, London WC2R 2LS, UK

Abstract. Recent analytical and numerical results for the single-particle spectral function and the optical conductivity of two-dimensional Hubbard and t-J models are reviewed. These models are considered relevant for the copper-oxide superconductors which are usually classified as doped charge-transfer insulators. We shall (1) briefly discuss based on a study of the 3-band Hubbard model why the charge-transfer gap and the low-lying excitations of the doped systems may be described by the more simple 1-band Hubbard model, which reduces in the strong coupling limit to the t-J model. The subsequent discussion covers the following topics: (2) the Green's function for a single hole in the $t-J$ model, (3) the suppression of staggered magnetization at small doping concentration as a result of the motion of the holes, (4) the spectral function and Fermi surface at moderate doping, i.e in the spin liquid phase, and (5) the doping dependence of the optical conductivity.

1 Introduction

Shortly after the discovery of superconductivity in the copper oxides by Bednorz and Müller [1] it was suggested by Anderson [2] that the phenomenon of high temperature superconductivity must be explained in the framework of doped Mott-Hubbard insulators. This prompted a renaissance in the study of the Hubbard model and its strong coupling limit, the $t-J$ model, which are now widely accepted to be relevant models that describe the low energy physics in these compounds. In spite of the huge efforts made, there is still no consensus on the mechanism of high temperature superconductivity (HTSC'y)[3, 4]. These models have a long history, dominated until recently by applications to the study of magnetism and correlation effects in transition metals and their compounds [5, 6].

Given these models a natural strategy is to ask the question:' To which extent are these models able to describe the peculiar normal state properties of these compounds?' This is the strategy we will follow, yet we will limit ourselves to the discussion of the single-particle Green's function which may be measured e.g. in angular resolved photoemission (Sections 3 and 5) and to the discussion of the optical conductivity in Section 6.

The theoretical difficulty is due to the strong coupling of the carriers to the spin-degrees of freedom, i.e. the d^9-configurations of the undoped material. This strong coupling between bare charge and spin degrees of freedom is evident from the rapid disappearance of antiferromagnetic long-range order upon doping, e.g. in $La_{2-x}Sr_xCuO_4$ at about $x \sim 0.02$[7] . Hence there is no straightforward perturbative approach to calculate these quantities.

The results presented are predominantly from exact diagonalization calculations of finite clusters. This technique has the advantage that a minimal amount of information is required as input for the calculation. The calculations may then be performed successfully even in cases where physically based intuition is lacking at the outset. This is not often the case with approximate calculations, where a built in bias is necessary in order to begin at all. Of course, the possibility and necessity for introducing subjective bias occurs also with diagonalization, at the stage where one attempts to interpret and analyze the results. For the problems of interest here it is generally not possible to reliably extrapolate to the thermodynamic limit. Nevertheless, the results from small systems can be very useful in extracting some essential aspects of the physics of the model, and provide strong constraints for approximate treatments.

In Section 3 we discuss the calculation of the Green's function in the dilute doping limit in a framework where the holes are described as spinless (slave-) fermions coupled to antiferromagnetic spin waves. The solutions obtained from standard Green's function techniques in selfconsistent Born approximation are in close agreement with the corresponding Green's function from exact diagonalization. The same technique is used in Section 4 to determine the doping dependence and suppression of magnetic order.

We begin in Section 2 with a brief review of the origin of the single-band Hubbard and t-J model physics in these systems. This is not entirely trivial since the copper-oxides fall into the class of the charge-transfer (CT) insulators or semiconductors [8]. That is, an optical excitation involves the creation of a hole in oxygen p-states and an electron essentially in a copper d_{10}-configuration. We shall describe here, why nevertheless this charge-transfer type gap does not show the physics as in a usual semiconductor but rather the features of a Mott-Hubbard gap.

2 Photoemission spectra of the 3-band Hubbard model

There is considerable evidence both from bandstructure calculations[9] and from various spectroscopic investigations[10] that the generic properties of the copper oxygen planes can be discussed in the framework of a 3-band Hubbard model formed by the Cu $d_{x^2-y^2}$ and the O p_x and p_y orbitals pointing towards the neighbouring Cu atom [11, 12]:

$$
\begin{aligned}
H_{3B} &= \epsilon_d \sum_{i\sigma} d_{i\sigma}^{+} d_{i\sigma} + \epsilon_p \sum_{j\sigma} p_{j\sigma}^{+} p_{j\sigma} + t_{pd} \sum_{ij\sigma} (d_{i\sigma}^{+} p_{j\sigma} + h.c.) + t_{pp} \sum_{jj'\sigma} p_{j\sigma}^{+} p_{j'\sigma} \\
&+ U_d \sum_{i} n_{i\uparrow}^{d} n_{i\downarrow}^{d} + U_p \sum_{j} n_{j\uparrow}^{p} n_{j\downarrow}^{p} + U_{pd} \sum_{ij} n_i^d n_j^p . \qquad (1)
\end{aligned}
$$

Here (i, j) and (j, j') represents $Cu - O$ and $O - O$ neighbors, so that this Hamiltonian contains two hopping terms, as well as site energies ϵ_i and Coulomb interactions U_i for the two types of sites, i on Cu and j on O. In the following we will not consider t_{pp} and U_{pd}. We note, however, that if U_{pd} were sufficiently large a very different scenario from what we discuss below would emerge [13, 14]. It is appropriate to use the hole notation, since there is one hole per unit cell in the undoped case. Hence the vacuum state $|0>$ corresponds to the electronic configuration $|d^{10}p^6>$. As $\epsilon_d < \epsilon_p$ this hole occupies a d-level forming a d^9 state. The hybridization $t_{pd} \sim 1.5eV$ is substantial and leads to a large covalent splitting into bonding and antibonding bands, which form the bottom and top of the p-d band complex. The Fermi level is in the middle of the antibonding band as shown in Fig. 1a, consistent with the LDA-bandstructure which predicts a metal. The local Coulomb interaction U_d is crucial for the semiconducting properties. According to Zaanen, Sawatzky and Allen[8] we may distiguish two cases: (1) The Mott-Hubbard case ($t_{pd} < U_d < \epsilon$) shown in Fig 1b where the conduction band develops a correlation gap of order U_d and (2) the charge-transfer regime ($t_{pd} < \epsilon < U_d$) where the lower Hubbard band (LHB) is pushed below the oxygen level (Fig.1c). The HTSC's fall into this latter category (typical parameters are $\epsilon \sim 3eV, t_{pd} \sim 1.5eV$ and $U_d \sim 9eV$)

If Fig.1c would constitute the final answer, this model would be unable to describe the strong coupling of the holes to the spins, since the holes would occupy the nonbonding band (NB) (which is dispersionless as long as the hopping between oxygen $t_{pp} = 0$).

The exact spectral function, e.g. for the process of hole creation

$$
A_{n\sigma}(\omega) = \frac{1}{\pi} Im \langle \psi_0(N) | c_{n\sigma} \frac{1}{E + H - i\delta} c_{n\sigma}^{\dagger} | \psi_0(N) \rangle, \qquad (2)
$$

calculated by means of the Lanczos algorithm (Fig.2) shows instead a quite different electronic structure in the vicinity of the gap [15, 17]. Due to an intrinsic strong Kondo exchange coupling between the O-hole and the Cu-spin the valence band is split into (local) singlet (S) and triplet (T) states.

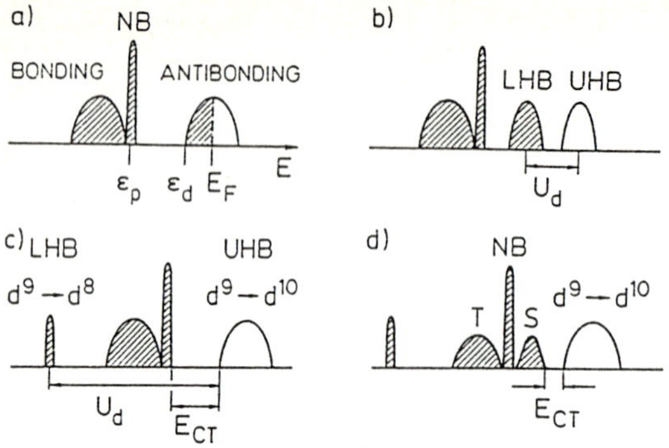

Fig.1: Sketch of the density of states for the 3-Band model: a) bandstucture result in the half-filled case, b) Mott-Hubbard , c) charge transfer insulator without and d) with singlet-triplet splitting.

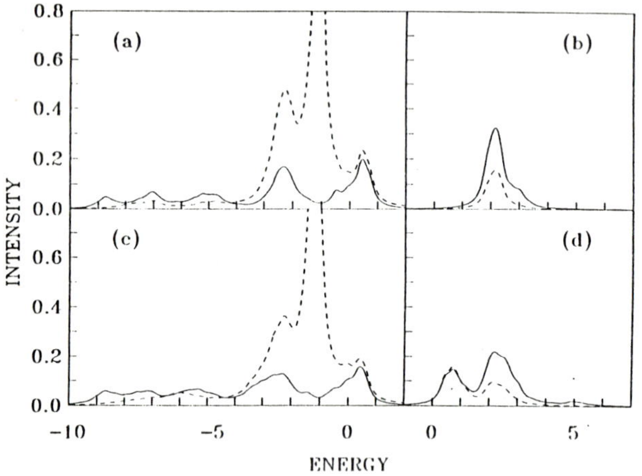

Fig.2: Photoemission spectra (PES) for $\epsilon = \epsilon_p - \epsilon_d = 2$, $U_d = 6$, $U_p = 3$, $U_{pd} = 0$, with $t_{pd} = 1$ taken as unit of energy, ($\delta = 0.1$). Figs. 2(a,b) show PES and inverse PES on Cu (solid) and on O (dashed lines), respectively, for the undoped initial state Figs. 2(c,d) represent calculations starting from an initial state with one extra hole, which implies a doping concentration of 25% in the $4 \times CuO_2$-cluster studied. From reference [15].

The singlet band is pushed above the nonbonding states and forms the lower edge of the gap. This corroborates the picture developed by Zhang and Rice[16] based on perturbative arguments in the physical range of parameters. Closer inspection shows that the basic physics of the singlet or $d^9 L_h$-state is quite similar to that of the d^8-configuration, i.e. the *Cu*-spin is compensated by the additional hole, except that its energy is much

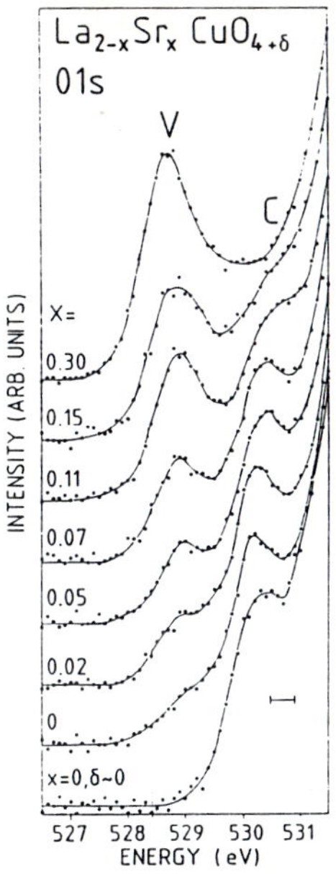

Fig.3: XAS spectrum of $La_{2-x}Sr_xCuO_4$ for various doping concentrations from Ref. [21]. The peak at 530 eV is interpreted as UHB.

lower. Hence the singlet band acts now as LHB, that is, the CT-gap shows essentially the physics of a one-band Hubbard model with $U_{eff} \sim E_{CT}$ and t_{eff} given by the hopping matrix element of the d^9L_h-states. For a more detailed discussion of the doping dependence and the electron doped case we refer to Ref.[17]. Similar studies of the 3-band Hubbard model have been performed by several groups and techniques[18, 19, 20].

Experimentally the most appealing evidence that this picture is relevant for the copper oxides comes from XAS[21, 22], which shows nicely the expected characteristic decrease of states in the UHB upon hole doping (Fig.3)[23, 24]. Also the energy scale in Fig. 3 appears to be consistent with the standard parameter sets[26, 25] used in the calculation of the spectra in Fig.2.

3 Single hole in the $t - J$ model: AF-spin polaron

The Green's function for a hole in a *fixed* spin background has been discussed in great detail in the context of transition metal oxides in the 60th. In this case the Green's function is local and fully incoherent[5, 6]. The first clear evidence of quasiparticle formation in the 2D $t - J$ model

$$H_{t-J} = -t \sum_{\langle i,j\rangle\sigma} \left((1 - n_{i,\bar{\sigma}})c^{\dagger}_{i,\sigma}\tilde{c}_{j,\sigma}(1 - n_{j,\bar{\sigma}}) + h.c.\right) + J \sum_{\langle i,j\rangle} \left[\vec{S}_i\vec{S}_j - \frac{n_i n_j}{4}\right] \quad (3)$$

came from a series of exact diagonalization studies[15, 27]. The problem is complicated by the fact that quantum fluctuations play a crucial role.

We will describe here a slave fermion technique[28, 29], which to our knowledge is the only other approach which was until now successful in reproducing the diagonalization results for the full Green's function [30, 31, 32, 33]. In a first step of the reformulation of the problem holes are described as spinless (slave) fermion operators, i.e. on the A sublattice a spinless fermion creation operator is defined as $h_i^+ = c_{i\uparrow}$ while the corresponding operator $c_{i\downarrow} = h_i^+ S_i^+$ is expressed as a composite operator, and similarly for the B-sublattice. The kinetic energy then reads $H_t = -t\sum_{i,j(i)}(h_i h_j^+ a_j + \text{h.c.})$, that is, each hop of the fermion is connected with a spin-flip. The spin dynamics is described within linear spin wave theory (LSW) which provides a satisfactory approximation for the 2D spin-1/2 HAF[34]. After performing the usual steps, i.e. Holstein-Primakoff, i.e. $S_i^+ \sim a_i$, and Bogoliubov transformation, the $t - J$ Hamiltonian takes the form:

$$H_{t-J} = \frac{zt}{\sqrt{N}} \sum_{k,q} \left[h_k^+ h_{k-q} \alpha_q \left(u_q \gamma_{k-q} + v_q \gamma_k\right) + \text{h.c.}\right] + \sum_q \omega_q \alpha_q^+ \alpha_q . \quad (4)$$

Here $\alpha_q = u_q a_q - v_q a_{-q}^+$ and $\omega_q = szJ\sqrt{1-\gamma_q^2}$ are the spin wave annihilation operator and energy, $\gamma_q = \frac{1}{2}(\cos q_x + \cos q_y)$ and $u_q(v_q)$ are the usual Bogoliubov coherence factors[32]. The kinetic energy in (3) appears now as the coupling term to the spin waves. Otherwise (4) is similar to the small polaron Hamiltonian although a kinetic energy term for the fermions is absent. As for the copper oxides $t > J$ this poses a strong coupling problem and a selfconsistent technique is required.

The selfconsistentent Born approximation for the fermion (holon) Green's function $G^h(k,\omega) = (\omega - \Sigma(k,\omega))^{-1}$ amounts to the summation of all non-crossing diagrams. Here in contrast to the 'phonon' polaron problem vertex corrections turn out to be of minor importance[32, 33]. The self-energy

$$\Sigma(k,\omega) = \frac{z^2 t^2}{N} \sum_q \frac{M^2(k,q)}{\omega - \omega_q - \Sigma(k-q, \omega - \omega_q)}, \quad (5)$$

with $M(k,q) = (u_q \gamma_{k-q} + v_q \gamma_k)$ has to be solved selfconsistently. Typical numerical results for the spectral function $A(k,\omega) = -(1/\pi)\text{Im}G^h(k,\omega+i\delta)$ are shown in Fig.4 for a 4×4-cluster which allows a direct comparison with the corresponding results from exact diagonalization[27]. The spectra show a bound state (quasiparticle) at low energy and a broad incoherent continuum of multi-magnon excitations distributed over an energy range of almost the free band width ($8t$).

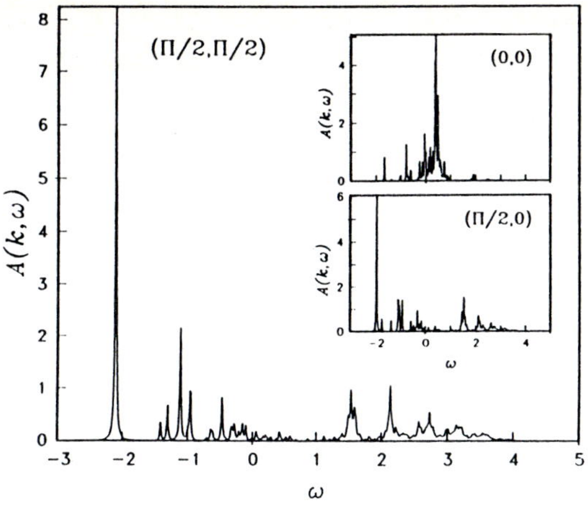

Fig.4: Spectral function $A(k,\omega)$ at wavevector $\vec{k} = (\pi/2, \pi/2)$ for a cluster of 4×4 sites and $J = 0.2$ as calculated in Born approximation. Insets: Spectra for $\vec{k} = (0,0)$ and $\vec{k} = (\pi/2, 0)$. From Ref.[32].

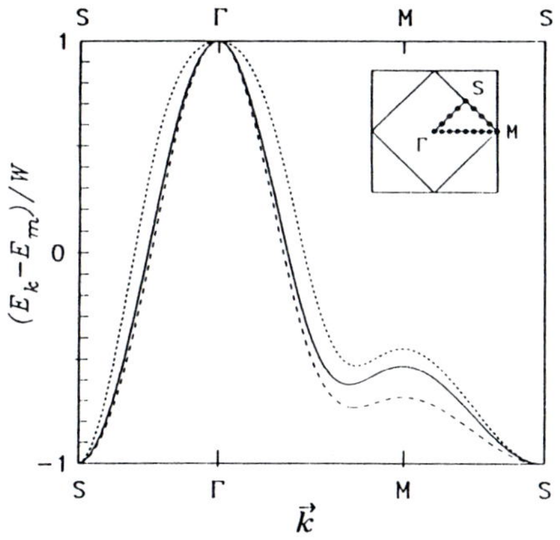

Fig.5: Dispersion relation E_k of the QP band normalized by the bandwidth $W = E_\Gamma - E_m$ where $E_\Gamma = E(0,0)$ and $E_m = E(\pi/2, \pi/2)$ along symmetry lines in the AF-BZ: large-J limit (solid line), $J = 0.01$ (short-dashed line), and $J = 0.8$ (long-dashed line). Inset: allowed k-points along the symmetry lines for a 16×16 lattice.

Perhaps surprisingly, the quasiparticle has dispersion (shown in Fig.5) with a bandwidth of $W \sim J$ for $J < t$ and $\sim t^2/J$ for $J >> t$. This motion results from the coherent emission and reabsorption of spin waves and is quite different from the standard picture associated with polarons. At sufficiently small doping concentration the holes are expected to form hole pockets around $(\pm\pi/2, \pm\pi/2)$.

It has been argued recently by Anderson [35] that the quasiparticle spectral weight $a_k = | < k|c_{k\sigma}|0 > |^2$, where $|k >$ denotes the single hole ground state with momentum k, should vanish in the thermodynamic limit. In such case a Fermi liquid type picture would certainly not apply. On the other hand the present framework combined with finite size scaling gives a finite spectral weight in the thermodynamic limit [32]; — a similar conclusion for the problem of a localized hole ($t/J \rightarrow 0$) was obtained by Sorella [36] and Malshukov and Mahan [37]. However, Sorella finds in his Monte Carlo calculations for the Hubbard model indications that in that case a_k may vanish. Reiter [38] obtained directly $< k|c_{k\sigma}|0 > \neq 0$ from the wave function, he further points out that the vanishing spectral weight within the semiclassical approach of Shraiman and Siggia [39], which was used in Ref.[35], is due to the neglect of quantum fluctuations.

4 Doping dependence of staggered magnetization

The slave-fermion formalism has been used recently to study the spin wave renormalization of 2D doped antiferromagnets by Gan, Andrei and Coleman[40] and by Igarashi and Fulde[41]. Gan et al. showed that doping leads to a softening of the long wavelength spin waves and to a damping of short wavelength spin waves due to the decay into particle-hole excitations in a coherent band. Igarashi and Fulde [41] pointed out the very important contribution of the incoherent background.

Also for the rapid disappearance of antiferromagnetic long-range order the fast incoherent motion of the carriers within the spin-polaron bag is crucial[42]. The appropriate quantity to study is the staggered moment $m(\delta) = 1 - 2 < b^+b >$ which after Bogoliubov transformation reduces to

$$m(\delta) = m_o(1 - \varphi(\delta)), \tag{6}$$

where $m_o = 2 - \sum_p (1 - \gamma_p^2)^{-1/2}$ is the staggered moment of the two-dimensional antiferromagnet without holes and the reduction factor due to the holes is

$$\varphi(\delta) = \frac{2}{m_o} \sum_p < a_p^+ a_p - \gamma_p a_p a_{-p} > /(1 - \gamma_p^2)^{1/2}. \tag{7}$$

If there are no holes the expectation values in (7) vanish and the function $\varphi = 0$. However, there are a finite number of spin-wave excitations in the doped system even at $T = 0$ resulting from the mutual interaction between spin-waves and carriers. As for the copper oxides $t > J$ the coupling term in (4) is strong. Thus the function $\varphi(\delta)$ increases quickly with doping and the Néel-order parameter $m(\delta)$ goes to zero.

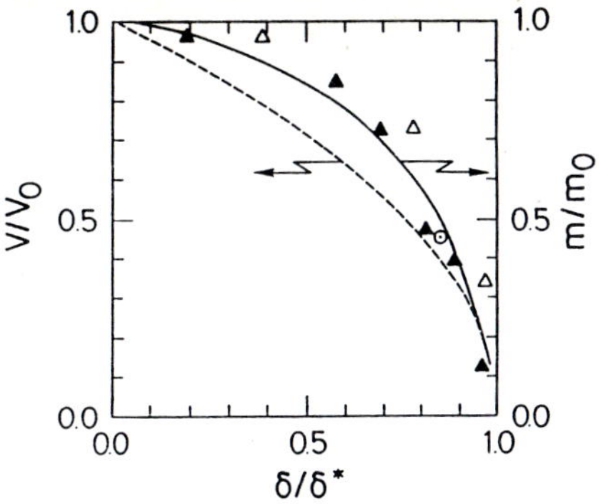

Fig.6: Data of the normalized spin wave velocity v/v_0 and staggered moment m/m_0 as a function of the hole concentration: theory for $J/t = 0.25$ (dashed and solid curves). From Ref.[42].

To calculate $\varphi(\delta)$ and the staggered moment (6) we need the boson Green's functions $D_\tau(p) = < -T_\tau a_p a_p^+(\tau) >$ and $F_\tau(p) = < -T_\tau a_{-p} a_p(\tau) >$ which describe the spin waves [43].

These may be evaluated using a dominant pole representation of the Green's function for the holes but keeping the incoherent contributions . The momentum dependence of the hole polarizability is approximated by the interpolation formula $\Pi(p)/\Pi(0) = 1/\left[1 + (p/2k_0)^2\right]$, which decreases as p^{-2} at large momentum as for a free fermion gas. We summarize here only some results of Ref.[42].

The reduction factor is found to be

$$\varphi(\delta) = \frac{k}{m_0}(8\delta^*/\pi)^{1/2}(K_k - E_k)\ ,\ k^2 = \delta/\delta^*, \tag{8}$$

where K_k and E_k are complete elliptic integrals, and

$$\delta^* \simeq (J/zt)/(1 + \frac{1}{z}\ln(zt/2J)), \tag{9}$$

defines the concentration where the spin wave velocity $v = v_0(1 - \delta/\delta^*)^{1/2}$ vanishes[42]. At $J/t = 0.25$ this concentration is $\delta^* \simeq 0.04$. The staggered moment $m(\delta)$ (6) vanishes at a slightly different critical concentration $\delta_c \simeq \delta^* - \delta^* \cdot exp(-m_o\sqrt{\pi/2\delta^*})$. This exponentially small difference is presumably a result of the approximations. The staggered moment is in qualitative agreement with the numerical results obtained by Lee and Feng[44] for a staggered RVB-type wave function. A comparison with experimental results is shown in Fig.6. The experimental data is from internal field measurements [45] of $(La_{1-x}Ba_x)_2CuO_4$ (open triangles); ordered moment [46] (solid triangles) and spin-wave velocity [47, 48](circle) for $YBa_2Cu_3O_{6+x}$.

5 Electron Green's function in the spin-liquid phase

We focus here on the most interesting region of moderate doping, $\sim 10\%-15\%$, where the spin system is strongly affected by the presence of holes. The antiferromagnetic correlation length ξ is already short. We have performed calculations on various 2D clusters from $N = 16$ to 20 sites using the Lanczos algorithm[49] . The smallest doping level which truly represents a system with a finite density of holes is 2 holes per cluster, since otherwise the important ingredient of hole-hole interactions is not yet present.

Finite cluster results for the electronic momentum distribution $n(\vec{k}) = \langle \tilde{c}^{\dagger}_{\vec{k},\sigma} \tilde{c}_{\vec{k},\sigma} \rangle$ of two hole systems suggest that already at 10% doping this strongly correlated 2D model exhibits a large electronic Fermi surface consistent with Luttinger's theorem[49] . This is in agreement with the results of Monte Carlo simulations for the Hubbard model at $U = 4$ [50]. We find no indication of the formation of hole pockets, which one would expect if a rigid band picture based on the single hole result were valid[51]. This is a consequence of the short correlation length and hole-hole interactions, – both features are not present in the single hole problem.

The spectral function $A(\vec{k}, \omega)$ for an 18-site cluster with 2 holes is shown in Fig.7, where the 'electron' notation is used, i.e. photoemission of elec-

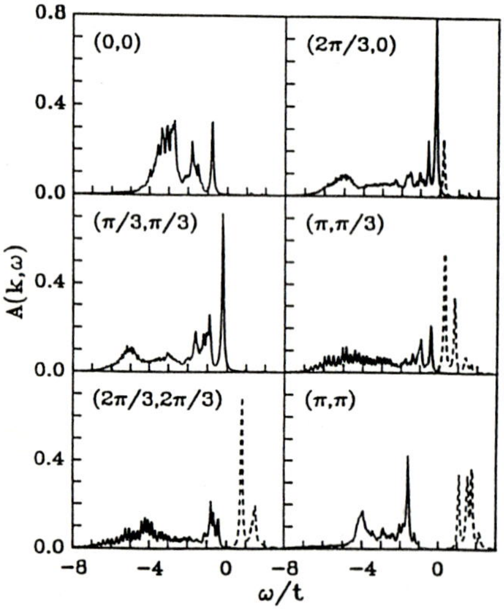

Fig.7: Spectral function for the single-particle Green's function for an $N = 18$ site cluster with $J = 0.4$, measured in the 2 hole ground state. The solid (dashed) lines correspond to annihilation (creation) of an electron. A Lorentzian broadening of $\delta = 0.05t$ has been used to plot the δ-functions appearing in eq. (2). From reference [49].

trons appears as usual along the negative energy axis. The chemical potential is at $\omega = 0$.

The simplest interpretation of the large quasiparticle (QP) like peak in the hole part of the spectrum at $(\pi/3, \pi/3)$ and the similar peak in the electronic part at $(2\pi/3, 2\pi/3)$ is in terms of a "band" crossing the Fermi level between these two points. This is consistent with our interpretation of the momentum distribution as

$$n(\vec{k}) = \int_{-\infty}^{\mu} A(\vec{k}, \omega) d\omega . \quad (10)$$

Due to the limitation to small system sizes, however, it is not possible to decide whether or not $n(\vec{k})$ is discontinuous at the Fermi energy, and whether the QP-pole strength remains finite there in the thermodynamic limit or not[52, 53] .

The quasiparticle band follows a simple tight binding dispersion $\epsilon_{\vec{k}} = -2t_{eff}(\cos k_x + \cos k_y) + \epsilon_0$, where $t_{eff} = 0.24$ (0.15) for $J = 0.4$ (0.2) respectively, and $\epsilon_0 = 0.16$ (0.08) is a small shift of the center of the band. This dispersion reflects the dominance of nearest neighbor hopping with bandwidth of approximately $4J$ in contrast to the single hole case where the QP dispersion is determined by processes within a given antiferromagnetic sublattice. Remnants of such a dispersion may still be seen in the dispersion of the boundary of the continuum. The large continuum is a second characteristic feature of these spectra, note that the energy scale is given by t which is of order 0.3 eV. A more complete discussion may be found in [49] and a comparison with experiment in [54].

6 Doping dependence of optical conductivity

The infrared [55] and optical properties [56] differ considerably from those of usual doped semiconductors, particularly noteworthy is a strong midinfrared absorption pointing to the importance of electron-vibrational coupling or some other electronic mechanism. A very complete overview of the spectral changes upon doping has been given by Uchida and coworkers both for hole-doped $La_{2-x}Sr_xCuO_4$[57] and electron-doped $Nd_{2-x}Ce_xCuO_4$ [56] which behave quite similarly. Figure 8 shows their results for $La_{2-x}Sr_xCuO_4$. We note the following features: (1) a rapid reduction of interband absorption and (2) the appearance of absorption in the gap upon doping, (3) the appearance of a Drude absorption peak which merges for x=0.15 and 0.20 with the midinfrared absorption and may be described by a frequency dependent relaxation rate $\frac{1}{\tau} \sim \omega$ [58] (4) in the overdoped case, x=0.34,

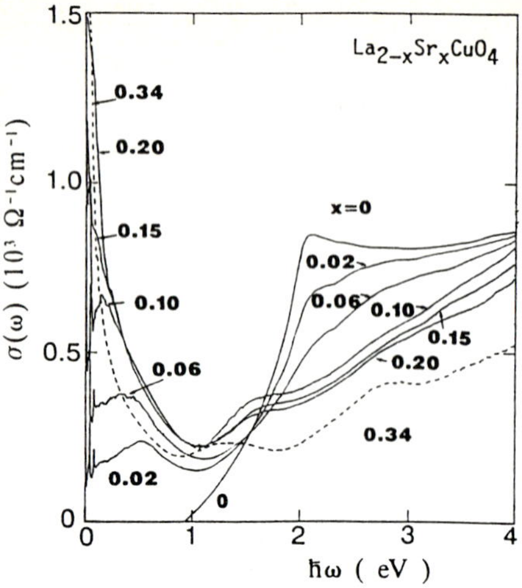

Fig.8: Doping dependence of optical conductivity for $La_{2-x}Sr_xCuO_4$. From Ref. [57].

the spectrum changes into a conventional Drude form with a Fermi liquid like $\frac{1}{\tau} \sim \omega^2$.

To calculate the real, i.e. absorptive, part of the optical conductivity we start from the Kubo formula

$$Re\sigma_{\alpha\beta}(\omega) = -\frac{1}{\pi\omega} Im\langle\psi_0|j_\alpha \frac{1}{\omega + E_0 - H + i\delta} j_\beta|\psi_0\rangle, \tag{11}$$

where $j_\alpha = ieat \sum_{l,\sigma} \left(\hat{c}^\dagger_{l+\alpha,\sigma}\hat{c}_{l,\sigma} - h.c.\right) e^{i\vec{q}\cdot\vec{x}_{\vec{l}}}$ is the current operator.

We discuss the optical conductivity for the two-dimensional (one-band) Hubbard model, with Hamiltonian given by

$$H = -t \sum_{\langle i,j\rangle\sigma} \left(c^\dagger_{i,\sigma}c_{j,\sigma} + h.c.\right) + U \sum_i n_{i,\uparrow}n_{i,\downarrow} \tag{12}$$

in standard notation. The Hubbard model has three energy scales on which interesting optical effects may be expected; U, t, and $J = 4t^2/U$ in decreasing order for the parameter range of interest here. Let us first consider the two larger energy scales, U and t. In the half-filled case ($n_h = 0$) a Mott-Hubbard gap for charge excitations Δ_{MH} is expected, perhaps for U above some critical value for spatial dimensionality larger than one. The application of the current operator in (11) necessarily creates a state with one doubly occupied site and one empty site, that is a state belonging to the upper Hubbard band (UHB). This then immediately leads to an absorption band centered near U. It is expected that the spectral intensity of this interband transition will decrease upon hole doping, reflecting the decreased probability of generating a doubly occupied site upon applica-

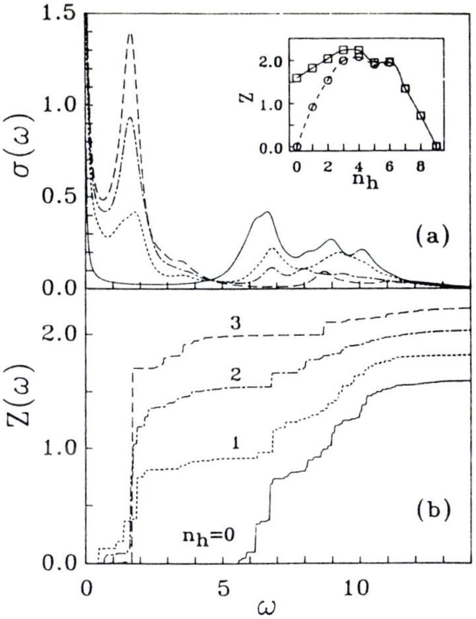

Fig. 9: Frequency dependent optical conductivity (a) and integrated conductivity (b) for 3×3 Hubbard model with open boundary conditions and $U = 8$ ($t = 1$). A large broadening $\delta = 0.4$ has been used in (a) in order to display $\sigma(\omega)$ for several fillings, resulting in a finite conductivity for $\omega < \Delta_{MH}$ at zero doping for example. The actual thresholds may be seen in (b), where $Z(\omega)$ has been calculated with $\delta \to 0$. Curves are labeled by the number of holes away from half-filling, as specified in (b). Inset: Doping dependence of integrated conductivity $Z(\infty)$ (squares) indicating the total sum rule, and the absorption in the lower Hubbard band $Z(\Delta_{MH} \approx 5.5)$ (circles). The lines are merely guides to the eye. From reference [59].

tion of the current operator. Additional absorption will also appear at low energy due to the possibility of intraband transition within the lower Hubbard band (LHB).

The results of numerical calculations on 3×3 Hubbard model clusters with OBC in Fig. 9(a) support the simple picture outlined above. In the absence of holes (solid line) there is a gap $\Delta_{MH} \approx U - 3t$. With hole doping, spectral weight is transferred to the low energy region $\omega \approx t$, and the lower edge of the UHB shifts to higher energy. This upward shift is a direct consequence of the narrowing of the UHB upon doping. These trends are in good agreement with experiment[57, 56] , and imply effective parameters $t \approx 0.2 - 0.3$ eV and $U \approx 2.0$ eV for Nd_2CuO_4, for example. The integrated conductivity

$$Z(\omega) = \int_0^{\omega} d\omega' \sigma(\omega') \tag{13}$$

is shown in Fig.9b to illustrate a further interesting point: not only does intensity shift from the energy region of the UHB to the LHB with hole doping, also the total sum rule $Z(\infty) = \frac{1}{2}(ea)^2 < -H_t >_x$ increases, at least up to doping levels $\approx$ 30% [59]. This point is important because the observation of such dependence would be a clear indication of the dominance of correlation effects even in the range of doping where metallic behavior exists[58] . The spectral weight $Z(\Delta_{MH})$ measures the weight of transitions within the lower Hubbard band ($Z(\Delta_{MH}) \sim n_h$). This information is summarized in the inset of Fig. 6a. Beyond $n_h \sim 30\%$ there is almost negligible weight in the UHB, i.e. both sum rules merge and scale proportional to the electron concentration n_e.

To study the physics on scale J and t the t-J model is more appropriate, because it is possible to diagonalize larger clusters, and we refer to discussion in Refs.[59, 60, 61]. We would like to stress that even in the large U-limit Hubbard and $t - J$ models are not identical, e.g. the Drude weights have a quite different J-dependence as result of the neglect of 3-site hopping terms in the $t - J$ model [62]. Finally we note that the Drude absorption (which is strictly an absorption at $\omega = 0$ in these models, as there are no impurities included in the calculation) and the mid-infrared absorption are in this framework a direct consequence of the structure of the single-particle Green's function, i.e. the Drude absorption follows from the QP-peak and the infrared absorption from the incoherent part.

7 Summary

We have tried to give an overview of the single- and two particle excitations and their dependence on doping for three models which are widely discussed and considered relevant for the description of the copper oxide superconductors. The selection, of course, is to a large extent subjective and oriented on our own work. Clearly these studies can only give partial answer to the questions:' Do these models contain the relevant low energy physics, what is this physics, and may it explain high-temperature superconductivity'? Nevertheless we think that the comparison with many beautiful experimental data from various forms of photoemission and optical conductivity with rather unusual features shows the finger prints of the Hubbard ($t - J$) model.

References

[1] J.G. Bednorz and K.A. Müller, Z. Phys B **64**, 189 (1986).

[2] P.W. Anderson, Science **235**, 1196 (1987).

[3] H. Fukuyama, in:'Materials and Mechanisms of Superconductivity III', eds. M. Tachiki, Y, Muto, and Y. Syono (North Holland, Amsterdam, 1991).

[4] Yu Lu, in:'Recent Progress in Many-Body Theories', eds. C.E. Cambell and E. Krotscheck (Plenum, New York, 1992).

[5] L.N. Bulaevskii, E.L. Nagaev, and D.L. Khomskii, Zh. Eksp. Teor. Fiz. **54**, 1562 (1968) [Sov. Phys.-JETP. **27**, 836 (1968)];

[6] W. Brinkman and T.M. Rice, Phys. Rev. B **2**,1324 (1970).

[7] R.J. Birgeneau and G. Shirane, in 'Physical properties of HTSC's', ed. D.M. Ginsberg (World Scientific, Singapore, 1989).

[8] J. Zaanen, G.A. Sawatzky, and J.W. Allen, Phys. Rev. Lett. **55**, 418 (1985).

[9] L.F. Mattheiss, Phys. Rev. Lett. **58**, 1028 (1987); W.E. Pickett, Rev. Mod. Phys. **61**, 433 (1989).

[10] J. Fink et al., in 'Earlier and Recent Aspects of Superconductivity', eds. K.A. Müller and G. Bednorz (Springer, Berlin, 1991).

[11] C.M. Varma, S. Schmitt-Rink, and E. Abrahams, Solid State Commun. 62 (1987) 681.

[12] V.J. Emery, Phys. Rev. Lett. **58**, 2794 (1987); V.J. Emery and G. Reiter, Phys. Rev. B 38 11938 (1988).

[13] A.E. Ruckenstein and C.M. Varma, in Ref.[3], p. 134.

[14] W. Stephan, W. v.d. Linden, and P. Horsch, Phys. Rev. B **39**, 2924 (1989).

[15] P. Horsch et al, Physica C 162-164 (1989) 783, and Helv. Physica Acta 63 (1990) 345.

[16] F.C. Zhang and T.M. Rice, Phys. Rev. B **37**, 3759 (1988).

[17] W. Stephan and P. Horsch, in: Dynamics of Magnetic Fluctuations in High-T_c Materials, eds. G. Reiter, P. Horsch, and G. Psaltakis (Plenum, New York, 1991).

[18] Y. Ohta, T. Tohyama, and S. Maekawa, Phys. Rev. Lett. **66**, 1515 (1991), and Phys. Rev. B **43**, 2968 (1991).

[19] P. Fulde, in 'Physics of High-Temperature Superconductors', ed. S. Maekawa and M. Sato (Springer, Berlin, 1992); P. Unger and P. Fulde, to be published.

[20] G. Dopf, J. Wagner, P. Dieterich, A. Muramatsu, and W. Hanke, preprint.

[21] H. Romberg et al. Phys. Rev. B 42 (1990) 8768.

[22] C. T. Chen et al., Phys. Rev. Lett. 66 (1991) 104.

[23] H. Eskes, M.B.J. Meinders, and G.A. Sawatzky, Phys. Rev. Lett. **67**, 1035 (1991).

[24] M.S. Hybertsen et al., preprint.

[25] H. Eskes, G.A. Sawatzky, and L.F. Feiner, Physica C **160**, 424 (1989)

[26] M.S. Hybertsen, M. Schlüter, and N. Christensen, Phys. Rev. B **39**, 9028 (1989).

[27] K.J. von Szczepanski, P. Horsch, W. Stephan and M. Ziegler, Phys. Rev. B **41** 2017 (1990); E. Dagotto, R. Joynt, A. Moreo, S. Bacci, and E. Gagliano, ibid. **41**, 9049 (1990).

[28] S. Schmitt-Rink, C.M. Varma and A.E. Ruckenstein, Phys. Rev. Lett. **60**, 2793 (1988)

[29] C.L. Kane, P.A. Lee and N. Read, Phys. Rev. B **39**, 6880 (1989).

[30] G. Martinez and P. Horsch, Int. J. Mod. Phys. B **5**, 207 (1991).

[31] F. Marsiglio, A. Ruckenstein, S. Schmitt-Rink, and C. M. Varma, Phys. Rev. B **43**, 10882 (1991).

[32] G. Martinez and P. Horsch, Phys. Rev. B **44**, 317 (1991).

[33] Z. Liu and E. Manoussakis, Phys. Rev. B **45**, 2425 (1992).

[34] E. Manoussakis, Rev. Mod. Phys. **63**, 1 (1991).

[35] P.W. Anderson, Cargese lectures (1990).

[36] S. Sorella, preprint.

[37] A.G. Mal'shukov and G.D. Mahan, Phys. Rev. Lett. **68**, 2200 (1992).

[38] G.F. Reiter, preprint.

[39] B.I. Shraiman and E. Siggia, Phys. Rev. Lett. **60**, 740 (1988); Phys. Rev. B **42**, 2485 (1990).

[40] J. Gan, N. Andrei and P. Coleman, J. Phys.: Cond. Matter **3**, 3537 (1991).

[41] J. Igarashi and P. Fulde, Phys. Rev. B (to be published).

[42] G. Khaliullin and P. Horsch, preprint.

[43] A.A. Abrikosov, L.P. Gorkov, and I.E. Dzyaloshinski, 'Methods of Quantum Field Theory in Statistical Physics', (Prentice Hall, Englewood Cliffs, 1963).

[44] T.K. Lee and Shiping Feng, Phys. Rev. B **38**, 11809 (1988).

[45] Y. Kitaoka et al., Physica C **153-155**, 733 (1988)

[46] M.J. Jurgens et al., Physica B **156-157**, 846 (1989).

[47] J. Rossat-Mignod et al., Physica B **169**, 58 (1991).

[48] J. Rossat-Mignod et al., in: Dynamics of Magnetic Fluctuations in High T_c Materials, eds. G. Reiter, P. Horsch and G. Psaltakis (Plenum, New York, 1991).

[49] W. Stephan and P. Horsch, Phys. Rev. Lett. **66**, 2258 (1991).

[50] A. Moreo et al, Phys. Rev. B **41**, 2313 (1990).

[51] S.A. Trugman, Phys. Rev. Lett. **65**, 500 (1990).

[52] C.M. Varma et al., Phys. Rev. Lett. **63**, 1996 (1989).

[53] P.W. Anderson, Phys. Rev. Lett. **64**, 1839 (1990).

[54] P. Horsch and W. Stephan, in 'Electronic Properties and Mechanisms in HTSC's', ed. K. Kadowaki and T. Oguchi (Springer, Berlin, 1992).

[55] T. Timusk and D.B. Tanner, in 'Physical Properties of HTSC's', ed. D.M. Ginsberg (World Scientific, Singapore, 1989).

[56] S. Uchida, Mod. Phys. Lett. B **4**,513 (1990).

[57] Y. Tokura et al., in Proceedings of the second International Symposium on Superconductivity, Tsukuba, Japan (Springer, Berlin, 1990).

[58] S. Uchida, in Ref.[54].

[59] W. Stephan and P. Horsch, Phys. Rev. B **42**, 8736 (1990).

[60] I. Sega and P. Prelovsek, Phys. Rev. B **42**, 892 (1990).

[61] A. Moreo and E. Dagotto, Phys. Rev. B **42**, 4786 (1990).

[62] W. Stephan and P. Horsch, Int. J. Mod. Phys. B **6**, 589 (1992).

Consistent Description of High-T_c Superconductors with the Three-Band Hubbard Model: Quantum Monte Carlo Studies

G. Dopf[1,2], *J. Wagner*[1], *P. Dieterich*[1], *A. Muramatsu*[1,2], *and W. Hanke*[1]

[1]Physikalisches Institut, Universität Würzburg, W-8700 Würzburg, Fed. Rep. of Germany

[2]HLRZ, KFA Jülich, W-5170 Jülich, Fed. Rep. of Germany

A direct comparison of quantum Monte Carlo results with experimental data on electronic excitations and magnetic properties leads to a set of parameters for the three-band Hubbard model that consistently describes salient features of high-T_c superconductors in the normal state. Furthermore, for the same universal parameter set, the interaction vertex for the pairing correlation function in the extended s-channel is found to be attractive with a doping dependence closely resembling the behaviour of T_c on doping.

1 Introduction

A considerable effort was invested in recent years towards a determination of the relevant parameter region for different models for high temperature superconductors (HTS). Among the most popular ones, the three-band Hubbard model (3BH) is closest to the real systems. Several groups proposed sets of parameters that were derived using different approximation schemes like constrained local density calculations[1] together with a mean-field treatment[2], the Anderson impurity model[3] complemented with experimental spectroscopic data[4], cluster calculations[5, 6], and Lanczos exact diagonalization for small clusters[7].

We present in this review a summary of recent results[8, 9, 10, 11] obtained from quantum Monte Carlo (QMC) simulations for the 3BH model which allow us to test such parameter sets a) beyond the mean-field approximation, and b) with the capability of extrapolating information relevant to the thermodynamic limit of several quantities. On the basis of our QMC simulations, it is shown for the first time, that a parameter set exists which consistently reproduces a large variety of characteristic features of the HTS. Most remarkable is the fact that one and the same parameter set yields an attractive pairing vertex with the correct (i. e. experimentally observed) s*–symmetry and doping dependence.

We consider the following version of the 3BH model:

$$H = \sum_{\substack{i,j \\ \sigma}} \varepsilon_{ij} c^{\dagger}_{i\sigma} c_{j\sigma} + \frac{1}{2} \sum_{\substack{i,j \\ \sigma\sigma'}} U_{ij} n_{i\sigma} n_{j\sigma'}, \tag{1}$$

where $c^{\dagger}_{i\sigma}$ creates a hole in the Cu-$3d_{x^2-y^2}$- and in the O-$2p_x$- or $2p_y$-orbital depending on the site i. ε_{ij} includes the on-site energies ε_d (Cu) and ε_p (O) with $\Delta = \varepsilon_p - \varepsilon_d$ and a Cu-O hopping t_{Cu-O} (O-O hopping t_{O-O}), while U_{ij} describes the on-site Coulomb energies U_d and U_p and the inter-site Cu-O interaction U_{pd}. In the following, we express all parameters in units of t_{Cu-O}.

Springer Series in Solid-State Sciences, Vol. 113 Electronic Properties of High-T_c Superconductors
Editors: H. Kuzmany, M. Mehring, J. Fink

The QMC algorithms used allows (i) for finite temperature simulations of a grand canonical ensemble with an exact updating in the Monte Carlo procedure, and for $T = 0$ calculations with the projector QMC formalism[11, 12, 13, 14].

2 Normal State Properties

We start by directly comparing the charge transfer gap (CTG) from QMC simulations and experiments for the 3BH model. The required values of the different parameters of the model for a quantitative agreement with the experimental value of the CTG are then used for the calculation of the normal state properties as well as for the superconducting properties of the model.

As discussed in previous publications[8] rather large values of $U_d = 6$ and $\Delta = 4$ are required to fit the experimental CTG. The parameters U_{pd} and t_{O-O} have opposite effects on the CTG, which tend to cancel for generally accepted values. Therefore in that what follows our parameter set is zero fixed to $U_d = 6$ and $\Delta = 4$ with all other parameters set equal to zero.

The most salient characteristics of the high-T$_c$ superconductors besides the superconductivity itself are the magnetic properties. The parameters chosen above lead to a value of the local magnetic moment of $< s_z^2 >\sim 0.84$ that implies that approximately 90% of the moment corresponding to a spin-$\frac{1}{2}$ is localized on the Cu-site. This value is almost not changed as a function of doping reaching $< s_z^2 >\sim 0.78$ at 50% doping[15]. This result agrees with neutron scattering experiments[16], where no dependence on doping was found in the integrated intensity. In the absence of doping, the HTS are insulators with antiferromagnetic long-range order[17] as a result of electronic correlation.

To decide whether the 3BH model also exhibits antiferromagnetic long-range order, we performed finite size studies with system sizes up to 10×10 unit cells with three sites each and inverse temperatures (projection parameters) up to $\beta = 30$ ($\Theta = 80$)[10, 11].

To study magnetic order in the system, we have computed the magnetic structure form factor $S(\vec{q})$[10] in particular $S(\pi,\pi)$ vs. the linear system size (in units of the lattice constant) for $U_d = 6$ and the charge-transfer energies $\Delta = 4$ and $\Delta = 1$. These calculations were done with the projector method.

The finite value of $S(\pi,\pi)/N$ versus $1/N_x$ signals long-range AF order. The case $\Delta = 4$ that gives a charge transfer gap of $\Delta_{ct} \simeq 1.2t_{pd}$ ($\simeq 1.7$ eV) in quantitative agreement with experiments, leads to a staggered magnetization of $m = \sqrt{3m_z^2} = 0.42\pm0.11$, whereas we find for $\Delta = 1$ a value of $m = 0.22\pm0.04$. Since the parameter set with $\Delta = 4$ leads to an agreement with experiments for several quantities, as remarked above, it is interesting to compare the values obtained for the order parameter with the corresponding ones in the S-$\frac{1}{2}$ antiferromagnetic Heisenberg model and in the one-band Hubbard model. For the first one, $m = 0.60 \pm 0.04$[18], showing that fluctuations are stronger in the 3BH model. On the other hand, a similar value of the staggered magnetization can be obtained in the one-band Hubbard model only with relatively large coupling constants ($U \gtrsim 6-8$)[19]. Therefore, if an identification of both models is to be made, this is possible only in the strong coupling regime of

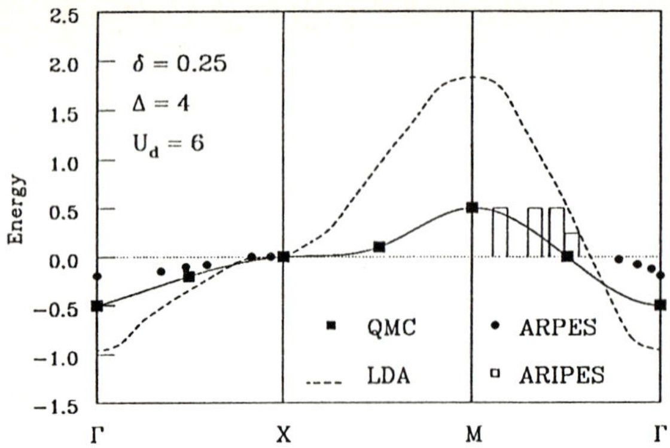

Figure 1: Dispersion of the Zhang-Rice states in the irreducible part of the Brillouin zone. The dashed line gives the LDA-bandstructure. The experiments are also depicted in the figure.

the one-band Hubbard model. Our QMC results also show that both the weak and strong-coupling case scale as $1/\sqrt{N}$, implying that fluctuations are well described by spin-wave theory[20].

We turn now to the dynamical properties for one-particle excitations. A central and controversial issue in the high-T_c cuprates concerns the nature of carriers near the Fermi surface. The most crucial experimental results until now stem from angle-resolved photoemission (ARPES) and inverse photoemission (ARIPES)[21, 22] measurements that clearly show the existence of a dispersive band crossing the Fermi surface. The topology of the Fermi surface is in general agreement with LDA-bandstructure calculations[23], however the Fermi velocity is quite different. This indicates that electronic correlations renormalize considerably the results obtained in the frame of a one-particle treatment.

In the grand canonical QMC method we can calculate the Matsubara thermodynamic Green's function. In order to evaluate the spectral density we have to perform an analytic continuation. We used a modified least-squares fit[24] to obtain the spectral density $A(\vec{k},\omega)$[9]. The results of the least-squares fitting procedure are most reliable for small excitation energies. For each $\vec{k}$-vector we extracted the energy of the state closest to the Fermi energy. These states have both copper and oxygen weight and are mainly of Zhang-Rice character[7]. In Figure 1 we show results for a lattice of 4×4 unit cells and for the above defined parameter set. The doping is $\delta = 0.25$ and the inverse temperature is $\beta = 10$. We see that concerning the Fermi surface and the Fermi velocity the dispersion of the Zhang-Rice states is in good agreement with ARPES and ARIPES experimental data which were measured in $Bi_2Sr_2CaCu_2O_8$[21] at a doping concentration of about 20%[25]. This result demonstrates that the 3BH model describes accurately also the one-particle excitations of the superconducting oxides. The LDA bandstructure (dashed line) totally overestimates the Fermi velocity although the locus of the Fermi energy is given correctly.

Using an exact diagonalization study for a 2×2 system we have also addressed the question whether the present system can be well described by a

Fermi liquid picture[9]. For a doping concentration of 50 % the imaginary part of the self-energy vanishes in a broad region around the Fermi energy. This clearly indicates the existence of long-living quasiparticles and the Fermi liquid picture is appropriate. However, for a doping of $\delta = 0.25$ the corresponding Zhang-Rice state has a finite lifetime in the immediate vicinity of E_F and the Fermi liquid picture with well defined quasiparticles at the Fermi energy breaks down. We suggest that at doping levels $\delta \lesssim 0.25$, which are relevant for the high-T_c cuprates, the system is better described as a Luttinger liquid[9].

3 Superconducting Properties

Next we address the question of whether or not the 3BH model has an attractive pairing interaction. To this end we consider the interaction vertex of pairing correlation functions for the extended s-wave symmetry of the order parameter. The interaction vertex[26, 27] is defined as the difference between the equal time pairing correlation function (P_α)

$$P_\alpha = \langle \Delta_\alpha \Delta_\alpha^\dagger \rangle \,, \tag{2}$$

where $\Delta_\alpha^\dagger$ denotes a pair-field operator, and the corresponding quantity for two fully dressed one-particle excitations that propagate without interaction ($\bar{P}_\alpha$). A positive interaction vertex means that the interaction enhances pairing. We have considered different symmetry channels. For an explicit definition of the underlying operators Δ_α see Ref. [24].

Figure 2 displays the dependence of the vertex for extended s-wave symmetry of the order parameter as a function of doping. We take into account only those contribution for two holes separated by one lattice constant both on the *Cu*- and on the *O*-sublattices. The (inverse) temperature of the simulation is $\beta = 10$, the lowest temperature attainable without running into minus sign problems. It can be seen that a distinct maximum appears for a doping of $\delta \sim 20\%$ and the overall shape of the curve is very reminiscent of the corresponding experimental curve for T_c in $La_{2-x}Sr_xCuO_4$[28]. On the contrary, in the case of d-wave symmetry, the maximum is always found at zero doping.

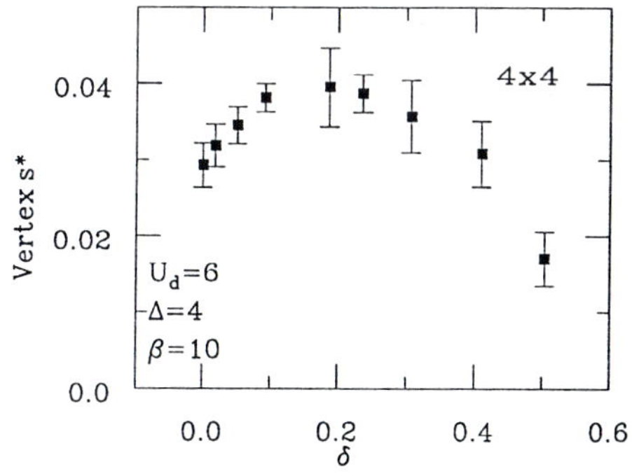

Figure 2: Extended s-wave vertex as a function of doping.

In contrast to the presently studied three-band model, the results by Moreo and Scalapino[26] for the one-band Hubbard model do not show such a marked variation of the vertex as a function of doping. For other parameter regions ($\Delta \sim 1$), where charge fluctuations dominate over spin fluctuations, again the maximum is obtained for zero doping but now for both s- and d-wave symmetry. We have also examined the case of nodeless s-wave, i.e. pairs formed either on-site on both Cu or O or such pairs that are separated by half a lattice constant (in x-, y- or both directions). With and without $U_{pd} = 0.5$ the vertex remained negative or zero within error bars for all doping concentrations. Therefore, for the values of U_{pd} consistent with parameter determinations in the literature[1]–[7], it is seen that the corresponding operator does not play any role for superconductivity.

Since the simulations were performed at finite temperatures, long-range order is not going to set in as a consequence of the Mermin-Wagner theorem[29]. But one could expect that the system undergoes a Kosterlitz-Thouless phase transition at a certain finite temperature as in the negative-U Hubbard model[30]. We have simulated systems with 4×4, 6×6 and 8×8 elementary cells with 3 atoms each. No measurable change was detected for the different sizes. However, contrary to the one-band case, where the pairing function levels off at around $\beta \sim 6$, the results for the three-band model seem to have not yet reached convergence in temperature[8]. Again the results differ in the parameter region $\Delta \sim 1$, where already at $\beta \sim 8$ a convergent behavior is observed. Thus although off-diagonal (quasi) long-range order is not obtained in our simulations, we have shown that the relevant temperature scale for superconductivity was still not reached for the extended s-channel with the parameter set used in the present model. This fact implies that the 3BH model remains a serious candidate for superconductivity induced by electronic correlation in contrast to the one-band Hubbard model, where numerical results failed up to now to show any evidence for superconductivity in the experimentally relevant symmetry channel of the order parameter.

4 Summary

In summary, we have determined a parameter set for the 3BH model that leads to a quantitative agreement with experimental results for the CTG and for the most prominent magnetic properties.

In the undoped case antiferromagnetic long-range order is found both in the weak ($U_d = 6, \Delta = 1$) and strong ($U_d = 6, \Delta = 4$) coupling situations. The structure form factor scales in both regions as $1/\sqrt{N}$, where N is the number of Cu-sites in the system. Fluctuations are therefore well described by spin-wave theory. Moreover, our numerical results show that the 3BH model gives a very accurate description of the low-lying one-particle excitations in the high-T_c superconductors. We can reproduce the experimentally observed Fermi surface and Fermi velocity quantitatively. Finally and most importantly, the same parameter set gives an attractive interaction vertex in the extended s-channel of the pairing functions, where the doping dependence suggestively resembles the one of T_c as found in experiments. The features above are not obtained in other parameter regions.

References

[1] A. K. McMahan, J. F. Annett, and R. M. Martin, Phys. Rev. B **42**, 6268 (1988), *and references therein.*

[2] J. B. Grant and A. K. McMahan, Phys. Rev. Lett. **66**, 488 (1991).

[3] A. K. McMahan, R. M. Martin, and S. Satpathy, Phys. Rev. B **39**, 6650 (1988).

[4] H. Eskes and G. A. Sawatzky, Phys. Rev. Lett. **61**,1415 (1988).

[5] F. Mila, Phys. Rev. B **38**, 11358 (1988).

[6] H. Eskes, L. H. Tjeng, and G. A. Sawatzky Phys. Rev. B **41**, 288 (1990).

[7] J. Wagner, W. Hanke, and D.J. Scalapino, Phys. Rev. B **43**, 10517 (1991).

[8] G. Dopf, A. Muramatsu, W. Hanke, Phys. Rev. Lett. **68**, 353 (1992).

[9] G. Dopf, J. Wagner, P.Dieterich, A. Muramatsu, W. Hanke, Phys. Rev. Lett. **68**, 2082 (1992).

[10] G. Dopf, A. Muramatsu, W. Hanke, Europhys. Lett. **17**, 559 (1992).

[11] G. Dopf, A. Muramatsu, W. Hanke, Int. J. Mod. Phys. C **3**, 79 (1992).

[12] R. Blankenbecler, D. J. Scalapino, and R. L. Sugar, Phys. Rev. D **24**, 2278 (1981).

[13] J. E. Hirsch, Phys. Rev. B **31**, 4403 (1985).

[14] S. R. White, R. L. Sugar, and R. T. Scalettar, Phys. Rev. B **38**, 11695 (1988).

[15] G. Dopf, A. Muramatsu, and W. Hanke, Phys. Rev. B **41**, 9264 (1990).

[16] R. J. Birgeneau, et al. Phys. Rev. B **38**, 6614 (1988).

[17] Y. Endoh, et al. Phys. Rev. B **37**, 7443 (1988); J. M. Tranquada, et al. Phys. Rev. Lett. **60**, 156 (1988).

[18] J. D. Reger and A. P. Young, Phys. Rev. B **37**, 5978 (1988).

[19] J. E. Hirsch and S. Tang, Phys. Rev. Lett. **62**, 591 (1989).

[20] D. A. Huse, Phys. Rev. B **37**, 2380 (1988).

[21] G. Mante, et al. Z. Phys. B **80**, 181 (1990).

[22] C. G. Olson, et al. Phys. Rev. B **42**, 381 (1990); T. Takahashi, et al. Phys. Rev. B **39**, 6636 (1989).

[23] H. Krakauer and W. E. Pickett, Phys. Rev. Lett. **60**, 1165 (1988).

[24] S. R. White, et al. Phys. Rev. Lett. **63**, 1523 (1989).

[25] W. A. Groen, et al. Physica C **165**, 55 (1990).

[26] A. Moreo and D. J. Scalapino, Phys. Rev. B **43**, 8211 (1991).

[27] S. R. White, et al. Phys. Rev. B **39**, 839 (1989).

[28] J. B. Torrance, et al. Phys. Rev. B **40**, 8872 (1989).

[29] N. D. Mermin and H. Wagner, Phys. Rev. Lett. **17**, 1133 (1966).

[30] A. Moreo and D. J. Scalapino, Phys. Rev. Lett. **66**, 946 (1991).

Relation Between Transition Temperature, London Penetration Depth and Kosterlitz-Thouless Behavior in Superconductors

T. Schneider

IBM Research Division, Zurich Research Laboratory,
CH-8803 Rüschlikon, Switzerland

Abstract. We sketch the theory of London superconductors with a complex order parameter undergoing a phase transition dominated by thermal fluctuations. Thus, the theory is essentially that of superfluid helium, appropriately modified. We derive relations between the transition temperature T_c, the London penetration depth, the phase correlation length, the fall of T_c with reduced thickness in thin slabs and the corresponding appearance of Kosterlitz-Thouless behavior. Our analysis of recent electronic-specific heat, μSR measurements and experiments on ultrathin slabs reveal that this scenario applies to a large class of superconductors that includes the cuprates, bismuthates and fullerenes.

The discovery of superconductivity in the cuprate [1], bismuthate [2] and doped C_{60} [3] materials has introduced a new class of superconductors having the common property of short correlation length and penetration depth amplitudes [4-7]. In ordinary superconductors, the amplitude of the correlation length is very large and the transition is extremely well described by a mean field treatment of the Ginzburg-Landau theory [8], which was shown by Gor'kov [9] to be equivalent to the BCS theory close to the transition temperature T_c. However, the mean field approximation does not account for most second-order phase transitions (e.g. superfluid helium). This failure is due to the neglect of thermal fluctuations which become crucial in systems with short correlation length amplitude. Standard estimates of the critical region show that in BCS superconductors the range of temperatures around T_c, within which thermal fluctuations are important, is small, $(T - T_c)/T_c < 10^{-14}$, while in the cuprates it appears to be much larger [10,11] and comparable to that in superfluid He [12], namely $< 10^{-2}$. To substantiate this finding we analyzed the electronic specific heat of $Bi_2Sr_2Ca_2Cu_3O_x$ [13], $YBa_2Cu_3O_{7-x}$ [14,15] and $Tl_2Ba_2Ca_2Cu_3O_{10}$ [16] in

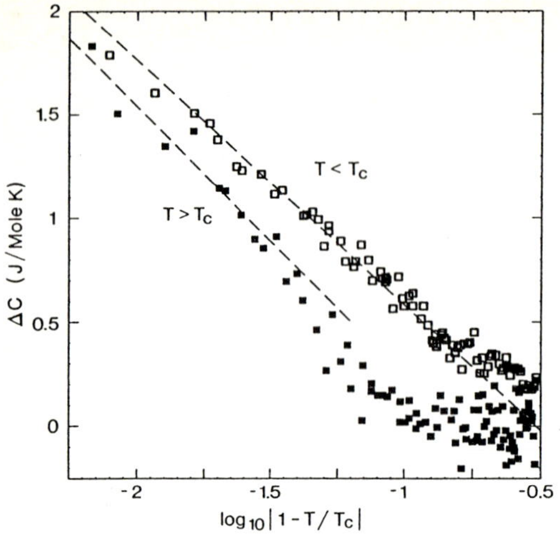

Fig. 1. Electronic specific heat of $Bi_2Sr_2Ca_2Cu_3O_x$ plotted versus $\log|T/T_c - 1|$. The data was taken from Fig. 11a of Ref. 13. For comparison we included straight lines with the slope ratio $A^+/A^- = 1.1$.

close analogy to work on superfluid He [12]. For the power law $C^{\pm} = (A^{\pm}/\alpha)\ |t|^{-\alpha}$, where $t = 1 - T/T_c$ is sufficiently small, the data should fall into two branches for $A^+ \neq A^-$. The indices + and − denote $T > T_c$ and $T < T_c$, respectively. Indeed, $C^{\pm} = (A^{\pm}/\alpha)\exp(-\alpha \ln\ t) = (A^{\pm}/\alpha)(1 - \alpha \ln\ t)$. For superfluid He the values of the parameters are $A^+/A^- \approx 1.1$ and $\alpha \approx -0.03$ [12]. In Fig. 1 we plotted the electronic-specific heat of $Bi_2Sr_2Ca_2Cu_3O_x$ [13] versus $\ln\ t$ and found remarkable consistency with the essential characteristics of the λ-like singularity in He. The experimental data for $YBa_2Cu_3O_{7-x}$ [14,15] and $Tl_2Ba_2Ca_2Cu_3O_{10}$ [16] plotted in this form exhibit the same essential features. From Fig. 1 it can also be seen that the critical region is indeed $< 10^{-1}$. However, it should be kept in mind that it is difficult to extract the electronic contribution, because the phonon part dominates around the rather high transition temperatures. Close to T_c, however, the phonon contribution can be subtracted in a controlled fashion [13-16]. More severe is the rounding of the specific heat, presumed to arise from such effects as sample inhomogeneities, impurities or internal stress. Owing to the unsurpassed sample quality, these rounding effects are absent in the superfluid transition of He, and the asymptotic behavior of the specific heat can be followed very close to T_c. Nevertheless, the remarkable consistency between the specific heat of superfluid He and the cuprate superconductors cited above strongly suggests (i) that the superconducting transition shares its universality class with the superfluid transition in He, and (ii) that thermal fluctuations invalidate a mean field or BCS treatment in superconductors with short correlation length. In view of this, the critical properties should be well described by the partition function associated with the appropriate Ginzburg-Landau-Wilson functional (GLW), which reads

$$\mathscr{H}[\psi] = \int dx\, dy\, dz \left(\frac{\hbar^2}{2M_\parallel} |\nabla_\parallel \psi|^2 + \frac{\hbar^2}{2M_\perp} \left| \frac{\partial}{\partial z} \psi \right|^2 + \alpha |\psi|^2 + \frac{\beta}{2} |\psi|^4 \right) . \tag{1}$$

$\psi(r) = |\psi(r)| \exp(i\varphi(r))$ is the complex order parameter which has the two components $\psi(r) = \psi'(r) + i\psi''(r)$. To account for uniaxial anisotropy in the superconductors we introduced the effective masses $M_\parallel$ and $M_\perp$ parallel and perpendicular to the layers, respectively. The partition function reads

$$z = \int d[\psi]\, e^{-\beta \mathscr{H}[\psi]} \, , \quad \beta = 1/k_B T \, . \tag{2}$$

Rescaling the z-coordinate and the temperature appearing in the partition function by

$$\bar{z} = \left(\frac{M_\parallel}{M_\perp} \right)^{1/2} z, \quad \bar{T} = \left(\frac{M_\perp}{M_\parallel} \right)^{1/2} T \tag{3}$$

we obtain an isotropic system with effective mass $M_\parallel$ at temperature $\bar{T}$ and which has the universal properties in common with superfluid helium and the three-dimensional (D) xy-model. Keeping this in mind, we continue with T and z and rescale at the end to obtain the results of interest. In this context it is important to recognize that pronounced effective mass anisotropy enhances the thermal fluctuations in the corresponding isotropic system. Indeed, taking current estimates for $(M_\perp/M_\parallel)^{1/2}$, namely 10 for YBCO and 60 for BISCO, one obtains very high temperatures $\bar{T} = (M_\perp/M_\parallel)^{1/2}\, T$ in the vicinity of T_c and in turn strong thermal fluctuations. This enhancement combined with the short correlation length appears to explain the occurrence of the λ-like singularity in the specific heat.

Here we concentrate on relations between the transition temperature T_c, the London penetration depth, the fall of T_c with reduced thickness in thin slabs and the corresponding appearance of Kosterlitz-Thouless (KT) behavior. Indeed, muon-spin relaxation (μSR) and bulk measurements of the magnetic field penetration depth suggest that many superconductors, including the cuprate, bismuthate, Chevrel-phase and fullerene materials, have the unique property in common that their transition temperature scales with the square of the inverse zero temperature penetration depth [4-7,17]. Although this seems to be unrelated at first glance, T_c was found to drop with reduced thickness in ultrathin slabs of YBCO, M unit cells thick ($M = 1,2,3,4,...$), accompanied with signs of KT behavior in the temperature dependence of the resistance and in the current-voltage characteristic [18-22]. In the following, we corroborate these experimental findings in terms of the properties of the model defined by the GLW functional (1) and the assumption that the amplitude of the correlation length is small compared to the magnetic penetration depth. In this case London's description of the electrodynamic properties is valid.

An important feature of the $n = 2$ universality class is the fact that in the ordered state defined by $<\psi'(r)> \neq 0$ and $<\psi''(r)> = 0$, the decay of the correlation function

$$C_{\parallel}^{\varphi} = <\psi''(r)\,\psi''(0)> \tag{4}$$

is not exponentially fast for $r \to \infty$. For $D = 3$ it decays to zero very slowly, explicitly, as follows [23-27]:

$$C_{\parallel}^{\varphi}(r) = A <\psi'(r)>^2 \frac{1}{\rho r}\ , \quad \frac{A}{r} = \int d^3k\, e^{i\mathbf{k}\cdot\mathbf{r}} \frac{1}{k^2}\ , \tag{5}$$

where ρ is a temperature-dependent stiffness constant. This behavior allows us to define the phase correlation length [23-27]

$$\xi_{\parallel}^{\varphi} = \frac{1}{<\psi'(r)>^2} \lim_{R\to\infty} \int_{r<R} \frac{r^2 dr}{R^2}\, C_{\parallel}^{\varphi}(r) = \frac{4M_{\parallel} k_B T}{\hbar^2 n_B}\ , \tag{6}$$

where n_B denotes the bulk density of electrons in the condensate. Approaching T_c from below, the leading temperature dependences of $\xi_{\parallel}^{\varphi}$ and n_B are given by

$$\xi_{\|}^{\varphi}(t) = \xi_{\|0}^{\varphi}\ t^{-\nu}\ ,\quad n_{\mathrm{B}}(t) = n_{\mathrm{B}0}\ t^{\nu}\ ,\quad t = 1 - \frac{T}{T_{\mathrm{c}}} \tag{7}$$

with $\nu \approx 2/3$. The terms $\xi_{\|0}^{\varphi}$ and $n_{\mathrm{B}0}$ are the amplitudes of the phase correlation length and single electron density in the condensate. Away from T_{c} there are correction terms to the leading behavior (7), but in the limit $T \to T_{\mathrm{c}}$, $n_{\mathrm{B}}(t)\ \xi_{\|}^{\varphi}(t)$ tends to $n_{\mathrm{B}0}\ \xi_{\|0}^{\varphi}$. Thus, combining Eqs. (7) and (8) we obtain in the limit $T \to T_{\mathrm{c}}$ the relation $T_{\mathrm{c}} = (\hbar^2/4M_{\|}k_{\mathrm{B}})\ n_{\mathrm{B}0}\ \xi_{\|0}^{\varphi}$, which is valid for isotropic systems at temperature $\overline{T}$. With the aid of Eq. (3), rescaling to the anisotropic case yields

$$T_{\mathrm{c}} = \frac{\hbar^2}{4M_{\|}k_{\mathrm{B}}}\ n_{\mathrm{B}0}\xi_{\|0}^{\varphi} = \frac{\hbar^2}{4M_{\perp}k_{\mathrm{B}}}\ n_{\mathrm{B}0}\ \xi_{\perp 0}^{\varphi} = \frac{\hbar^2 c^2}{16\pi e^2 k_{\mathrm{B}}}\ \frac{\xi_{\|0}^{\varphi}}{\lambda_{\|0}^2}\ . \tag{8}$$

In the last step we used expression $1/\lambda_{\|}^2 = 4\pi n_{\mathrm{B}} e^2/M_{\|}c^2$ for the penetration depth, valid for London superconductors, where $\xi_0 \ll \lambda$. The term c denotes here the velocity of light. Thus, the characteristic length scales for spatial variations of the phase and the spatial variations of the electromagnetic effects are not independent but related to T_{c} by Eq. (8). From the derivation it is clear that this relation is a characteristic of superconductors with a complex order parameter, a short phase correlation length amplitude and a large penetration depth.

Recently, an empirical relation between T_{c} and $1/\lambda_{\|}^2(0)$ was established in a variety of superconductors by μSR experiments [4-7,17]. For each family of superconductors, T_{c} initially increases with increasing $1/\lambda_{\|}^2(0)$, then shows saturation followed by suppression. This behavior has been verified for various cuprates, bismuthates, Chevrel-phase and fullerene systems [4-7]. The generic feature is that in each family the initial increase in T_{c} versus $1/\lambda_{\|}^2(0)$ is nearly linear with a slope close to that found in other groups. Unfortunately, however, an interpretation of these findings with the aid of Eq. (8) is not straightforward. Indeed, Eq. (8) involves the amplitudes of the penetration depth and the phase correlation length, but not their zero temperature values. Moreover, at this point, the temperature dependence of the penetration depth has not been measured with an accuracy sufficient to expose deviations from the mean field behavior and to determine the amplitude $\lambda_{\|0}$. Nevertheless, because the temperature dependence of the two-fluid model, $n_{\mathrm{B}}(t) = n_{\mathrm{B}}(0)(1 - t^4)$, provides a reasonable overall description of the available experimental data, it is reasonable to replace the amplitudes in Eq. (8) with the zero temperature values of the penetration depth and phase correlation length to obtain an approximate version of this equation. In view of this, the occurrence of saturation followed by suppression of T_c in the plot T_c versus $1/\lambda_{\parallel}^2(0)$ is then readily understood, because $T_c\lambda_{\parallel}^2(0)$ itself depends on the phase correlation length (Eq. (8)).

For systems becoming finite in one direction, this scenario also implies a dimensional crossover from D=3 critical behavior to KT behavior. Indeed, the phase transition in any $n=2$, D=3 system, finite in one direction and infinite in the two remaining ones, will be a KT-type transition with no long-range order even below T_c [26]. The KT transition is due to vortex unbinding which occurs with increasing temperature in strictly 2D systems. Nevertheless, the essential KT predictions are also expected to hold for slabs, provided one is sufficiently close to T_c [26]. Clearly the lateral dimension must always be large compared to the thickness. Finite size scaling then describes the crossover from 3D to 2D behavior in terms of a crossover scaling function, connecting the areal condensate density n with the bulk counterpart n_B [26]. The fall of T_c with reduced thickness is then given by [27]

$$\frac{T_c(d)}{T_c} = \frac{n_B(T_c)}{n_{B0}} \quad \frac{d}{\xi_{\perp 0}^{\varphi}} x_c \ , \tag{9}$$

where $T_c = T_c(d=\infty)$ is the bulk transition temperature. Thus, the fall of $T_c(d)$ is fully determined by the temperature dependence of the superfluid bulk density or, equivalently, by the inverse parallel penetration depth squared. The term x_c is of order unity and depends on details of the boundary conditions. It is important to emphasize that this scenario only applies if the physics remains unchanged as the slabs become thinner. The ideal sample is an ultrathin and isolated single crystal for which quantum size effects can be neglected. From this point of view layered superconductors appear to be promising materials.

Recently, it became possible to fabricate thin YBCO slabs, M unit cells thick $M = 1,2,3,4,\ldots$ as a sandwich or superlattice with thick PrBCO slabs in between. PrBCO is presumed to be insulating. These experiments provide clear evidence for the fall of $T_c(d)$ [18-22].

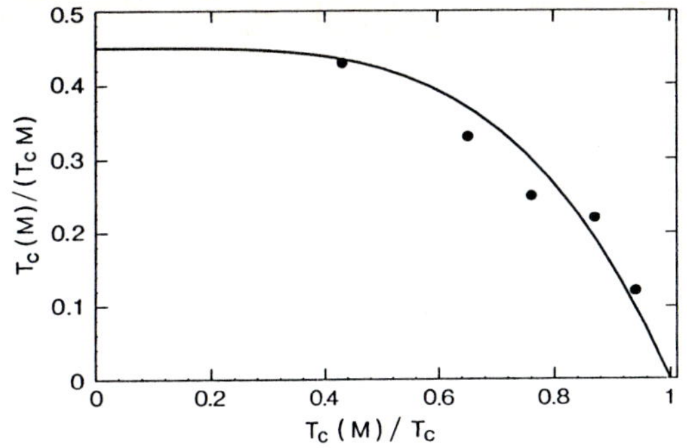

Fig. 2. $T_c(M)/(T_cM)$ versus $T_c(M)/T_c$ for YBCO slabs $M = 1,2,3,4,8$ unit cells thick. For comparison we included the temperature dependence resulting from the temperature dependence of the two-fluid model for the bulk condensate density with $x_c d/\xi^{\varphi}_{\perp 0} \simeq 0.45$.

In Fig. 2 we plotted the estimates available for the zero resistance transition temperatures for various YBCO slabs [18-22], M unit cells thick, in terms of $T_c(M)/(T_cM)$ versus $T_c(M)/T_c$, where $d = Mc$. The term c is the lattice spacing perpendicular to the layers and M the number of YBCO unit cells. The resulting experimental points simply probe the temperature dependence of the superfluid bulk density. In YBCO this quantity is well approximated by the two-fluid expression $n_B(T)/n_{B0} \approx (1 - (T/T_c)^4)$. The resulting behavior has been included in Fig. 2 with $x_c C/\xi^{\varphi}_{\perp 0} \approx 0.45$. For $C = 12$ Å and $\xi^{\varphi}_{\perp 0} \approx 3$ Å, we arrive at $x_c \approx 0.1$. In this context we emphasize that x_c depends on the boundary conditions and the quality of the slabs, including their boundaries. Indeed, x_c measures the relative distance over which the order parameter decays. In view of this it is interesting to compare the x_c values from different systems. A Monte Carlo study of the layered and isotropic xy-model with free boundaries yields $x_c \approx 1$, while the experimental data for He^4 films gives $x_c \approx 0.3$ [28]. In the Monte Carlo experiments the layers are clearly flat on an atomic scale by construction and free boundaries are imposed, while the substrates of He^4 films are certainly rough on this scale. Nevertheless, the experimental estimates for the fall of T_c in the YBCO slabs are remarkably consistent with a dimensional crossover from D = 3 to D = 2. Additional confirmation comes from the observation of KT behavior in the width of the resistive transition and the current voltage characteristic of slabs a few unit cells thick [20,21].

To summarize, we explored the properties of London superconductors with uniaxial mass anisotropy, short correlation length and a complex order parameter. On this basis we related the bulk T_c to the London penetration depth and the correlation length of the phase fluctuations. The fall of T_c with reduced slab thickness and the corresponding appearance of KT behavior follow then naturally from the dimensional crossover controlled by the slab thickness, the temperature dependence of the condensate bulk density and the relative healing length. In these superconductors the fluctuations of the magnetic field can be neglected, but thermal fluctuations drive the transition at H_{c2} first order [29]. Our analysis of the μSR and electronic-specific heat data provide strong evidence for a class of superconductors for which thermal fluctuations are essential. These extreme type II superconductors have short phase correlation and large penetration depth amplitudes. They obey relations (8) and (9) and should exhibit the characteristic critical properties of the $n=2$, $D=3$ universality class [24]. For YBCO we have the most complete experimental evidence for this scenario. In close analogy to Fig. 1, the electronic-specific heat exhibits a λ-like singularity, the phase correlation length is short and the penetration depth is large, T_c falls with reduced thickness and is accompanied by the appearance of KT behavior (Fig. 2). However, the conditions necessary in order that this scenario be valid are simply a short phase correlation length and a large penetration depth. In these superconductors, the 3D thermal fluctuations are essential and uniaxial anisotropy even enhances these fluctuations (Eq. (3)). Accordingly a mean field or BCS treatment is not applicable. As outlined here, the theory of superfluid He, appropriately modified, appears to be adequate.

It is a pleasure to thank D. Ariosa, H. Beck, G. Bednorz, D. Bormann, J.-P. Locquet, H. Keller, Ch. Rossel and A. Schmidt for stimulating discussions and K.A. Müller for valuable comments and suggestions.

References

[1] J.G. Bednorz and K.A. Müller, Z. Phys. B 64, 189 (1986)

[2] L.F. Mattheiss, E.M. Giorgy and D.W. Johnson, Phys. Rev. B 37, 3745 (1988)

[3] A.F. Hebard et al., Nature 350, 600 (1991)

[4] Y.J. Uemura, G.M. Luke, B.J. Sternlieb, J.H. Brewer, J.F. Carolan, W.N. Hardy, R. Kadono, J.R. Kempton, R.F. Kiefl, S.R. Kreitzman, P. Mulhern, T.M. Riseman, D.LI. Williams, B.X. Yang, S. Uchida, H. Takagi, J. Gopalakrishnan, A.W. Sleight, M.A. Subramanian, C.L. Chien, M.Z. Cieplak, Gang Xiao, V.Y. Lee, B.W. Statt, C.E. Stronach, W.J. Kossler and X.H. Yu, Phys. Rev. Lett. 62, 2317 (1989)

[5] Y.J. Uemura, L.P. Le, G.M. Luke, B.J. Sternlieb, W.D. Wu, J.H. Brewer, T.M. Riseman, C.L. Seaman, M.B. Maple, M. Ishikawa, D.G. Hinks, J.D. Jorgensen, G. Saito and H. Yamochi, Phys. Rev. Lett. 66, 2665 (1991)

[6] Y.J. Uemura, Nature 352, 605 (1991)

[7] H. Keller, W. Kündig, I.M. Savic, H. Simmler, B. Stäuble-Pümpin, M. Warden, D. Zech, P. Zimmermann, E. Kaldis, J. Karpinski, S. Rusiecki, J.H. Brewer, T.M. Riseman, J.W. Schneider, Y. Maeno and C. Rossel, Physica C 185-189, 1089 (1991)

[8] V.L. Ginzburg and L.D. Landau, Zh. Eksp. Teor. Fiz. 20, 1064 (1950)

[9] L.P. Gor'kov, Sov. Phys. JETP 7, 505 (1958); 37, 1407 (1960)

[10] A. Kapitulnik, M.R. Beasley, C. Castellani and C.D. Di Castro, Phys. Rev. B. 37, 537 (1988)

[11] L.N. Bulaevskii, V.L. Ginzburg and A.A. Sobyanin, Sov. Phys. JETP 68, 1499 (1988)

[12] G. Ahlers, Rev. Mod. Phys. 52, 489 (1980)

[13] W. Schnelle, E. Braun, H. Broicher, H. Weiss, H. Geus, S. Ruppel, M. Galffy, W. Braunisch, A. Waldorf, F. Seidler and D. Wohlleben, Physica C 161, 123 (1989)

[14] W. Schnelle, E. Braun, H. Broicher, R. Dömel, S. Ruppel, W. Braunisch, J. Harnischmacher and D. Wohlleben, Physica C 168, 465 (1990)

[15] M.B. Salamon et al., Physica A 168, 283 (1990)

[16] E. Braun, W. Schnelle, H. Broicher, J. Harnischmacher, D. Wohlleben, C. Allgeier, W. Reith, J.S. Schilling, J. Bock, E. Preisler and G.J. Vogt, Z. Phys. B 84, 33 (1991)

[17] B. Pümpin, H. Keller, W. Kündig, I.M. Savic, J.W. Schneider, H. Simmler, P. Zimmermann, E. Kaldis, S. Rusiecki, C. Rossel and E.M. Forgan, J. Less Common Metals 164&165, 994 (1990)

[18] J.M. Triscone, Ø. Fischer, O. Brunner, L. Antognazza, A.D. Kent and M.G. Karkut, Phys. Rev. Lett. 64, 804 (1990)

[19] Q. Li, X.X. Xi, X.D. Wu, A. Inam, S. Vadlamannati, W.L. McLean, T. Venkatesan, R. Ramesh, C.W. Hwang, J.A. Martinez and L. Nazar, Phys. Rev. Lett. 64, 3086 (1990)

[20] D.H. Lowndes et al., Phys. Rev. Lett. 65, 1160 (1990)

[21] T. Terashima, K. Shimura and Y. Bando, Phys. Rev. Lett. 67, 1362 (1991)

[22] S. Vadlamannati, Q. Li, T. Venkatesan, W.L. McLean and P. Lindenfeld, Phys. Rev. B 44, 7094 (1991)

[23] M.E. Fischer, M.N. Barber and D. Jasnow, Phys. Rev. A 8, 1111 (1973)

[24] P.C. Hohenberg, A. Aharony, B.I. Halperin and E.D. Siggia, Phys. Rev. B 13, 2986 (1976)

[25] P.C. Hohenberg and B.I. Halperin, Rev. Mod. Phys. 49, 435 (1977)

[26] V. Ambegaokar, B.I. Halperin, D.R. Nelson and E.D.D. Siggia, Phys. Rev. B 21, 1806 (1980)

[27] T. Schneider, submitted to Z. Phys. B.

[28] T. Schneider and A. Schmidt, submitted to J. Phys. Soc. Jpn.

[29] E. Brezin, D.R. Nelson and A. Thiaville, Phys. Rev. B 31, 7124 (1985)

"Small" Masses and Strong Coupling in High-T_c Superconductors and in Heavy-Fermion Compounds

G.M. Eliashberg

L.D. Landau Institute for Theoretical Physics,
Chernogolovka, 142 432 Moscow Region, Russia

Abstract. Competition between short-ranged correlations and the Luttinger sum rule lead to a peculiar duality of the electron spectrum: two different effective masses have to be attributed to the same Fermi excitation. One of them corresponds to the band width measured by photoemission spectroscopy, the other may be much smaller in the highly correlated system. The residual Coulomb repulsion between excitations is reduced, and this, probably, has a direct relation to the high-T_c problem. A phenomenological description of these phenomena in the framework of Fermi-liquid theory is discussed in connection with high-T_c superconductivity and heavy-fermion physics.

1. Introduction

The original Bednorz und Müller finding [1] gave rise to the discovery of a wonderful family of copper-oxide compounds whose properties change drastically with relatively small variations of their composition. We have here (sometimes within the same matrix) an insulating phase (antiferromagnetic), high-T_c superconductors and a metallic phase with no superconductivity at all. There is now a wide agreement that these materials are in the region of metal-insulator transition promoted by short-ranged Coulomb correlations. The high-T_c phase is closer by composition to the metal-insulator transition and we can expect here correlation effects to be more pronounced as compared with a nonsuperconducting metallic phase. This is obviously in favour of Anderson's statement that the mechanism of superconductivity "uses, rather than finesses the strong natural repulsive interactions of electrons in narrow bands" [2].

The narrow band physics is described usually in the framework of a tight-binding approach, which implies that electrons remain in atomic-like states. In a one-band picture close to half-filling the importance of the on-site repulsion V becomes evident, and using a Hubbard model we can treat it separately. The immediate conclusion is that if V is of the order or larger than the bandwidth

Springer Series in Solid-State Sciences, Vol. 113 **Electronic Properties of High-T_c Superconductors**
Editors: H. Kuzmany, M. Mehring, J. Fink

the essential (may be, the most) part of the one-particle denstiy of states is pushed out from the original band to the lower and upper Hubbard subbands and a gap develops around the Fermi level, the gap width being of the order of V. This gives us some representation of what is the "Mott insulating state", but our understanding will be essentially incomplete would be forget the Luttinger sum rule [3]. The latter imposes a strong limitation on the possible evolution of the electron spectrum so that a certain part $a < 1$ of the one-electron density of states has to survive at the Fermi level as long as the symmetry is unchanged. Therefore, a competition between the short-ranged correlations and the Luttinger sum rule results in a peculiar interplay between the itinerant and localized parts of the electron spectrum, and the parameter a here is an important quantitative characteristic. Introducing this parameter explicitly we provide a consistent phenomenological description of the correlated Fermi system. In the following sections we will show that it is, in fact, a slightly reformulated Fermi-liquid theory.

2. The kinematic one-electron spectrum and the Luttinger-sum rule

For the following discussion it is convenient to use the one-electron Green functions $G^R(x, x', \epsilon), G^A(x, x'\epsilon)((x, x')$ include space and spin coordinates), which are analytical functions of the energy variable in the upper and lower half-planes correspondingly [4]. We define also the self-energy operator $\hat{\Sigma}(\epsilon)$:

$$[\hat{G}^{R(A)}(\epsilon)]^{-1} = H_0 - \mu N - \epsilon - \hat{\Sigma}^{R(A)}(\epsilon) ,$$

and all the consideration will be related to systems, where the following relation is fulfilled:

$$(\hat{\Sigma}^R - \hat{\Sigma}^A)_{\epsilon=0} = 0 \; ; \; T = 0 \, . \tag{1}$$

In this case $[\hat{G}^R(0)]^{-1} = [\hat{G}^A(0)]^{-1}$ has the properties of the one-electron Hamiltonian and its eigenvalues ξ_d constitute the rigorously defined one-electron spectrum for the itinerant electron system. Let's call it kinematic spectrum by the reasons which will be clarified in sec. 3. In terms of ξ_d there exists at zero temperature a remarkable expression:

$$N = \frac{1}{2\pi i} \sum_{\alpha} [\ln(\xi_d + i\delta) - \ln(\xi_d - i\delta)] \; ; \; \delta \to +0 \, , \tag{2}$$

which simply means that (like in the free particle case) the total number of electrons N is equal to the number of properly defined one-electron states below the Fermi level. Luttinger and Ward [5] derived this sum rule for the uniform Fermi-liquid, and it is the most elegant and fruitful proof of the famous Landau statement [6] that Fermi momentum does not depend on interaction. For the crystal case d corresponds to the band index n, to the wave number $\mathbf{k}$ in the Brillouin zone and to the component ν of a Kramers doublet; we have a Luttinger-sum rule:

$$N = 2\sum_{n,\mathbf{k}} n(\xi_{n,\mathbf{k}}) \,, \tag{3}$$

where $n(\xi) = 1, \xi < 0; n(\xi) = 0, \xi > 0$. The main consequence of (3) is the existence of the Fermi surface if the number of electrons per unit cell is not even, the volume of the Fermi surface being independent of interaction. The Fermi surface may disappear due to certain changes of the lattice symmetry, when the sum rule (3) has to be reformulated in terms of an appropriate spectrum. But there exists the possibility that (2) doesn't work at all. It seems that it may happen only in case of some peculiar symmetry breaking. Otherwise it will be most probably an artefact of the model calculations. I was able to find only one type of broken symmetry which prevents Luttinger-Ward derivation – the noncenservation of the total number of particles (the gauge symmetry breaking). Therefore (3) is invalid in the superconducting state (probably, not only in this case [7]).

3. Duality of electron spectrum

The self-energy $\Sigma(\epsilon)$ does not depend on ϵ in a Hartree-Fock approximation, and therefore its ϵ-dependence is characteristic of correlation effects. There is, however, some complication for electrons in a crystal lattice: the spectral density operator

$$\hat{N}_{\mathbf{k}}(\epsilon) = \frac{1}{2\pi i}[G^R_{\mathbf{k}}(\epsilon) - G^A_{\mathbf{k}}(\epsilon)] \tag{4}$$

is nondiagonal with respect to the band index in the basis of Sec.2 and cannot be diagonalized simultaneously at all ϵ. To simplify the discussion we consider the one-band case. Essential phyiscs in which we are interested here is, in fact, model independent.

The Green function $G^R_k(\epsilon)$ may be expressed in terms of the kinematic spectrum $\xi_{\mathbf{k}} = G^{-1}_{\mathbf{k}}(0)$:

$$G^R_{\mathbf{k}}(\epsilon) = \frac{1}{\xi_{\mathbf{k}} - \epsilon - \tilde{\Sigma}^R_k(\epsilon)} \,, \tag{5}$$

where $\tilde{\Sigma} = \Sigma(\epsilon) - \Sigma(0)$ and $\xi_{\mathbf{k}} = 0$ on the Fermi surface. For small ϵ (as by usual derivation of Fermi-liquid theory)

$$\tilde{\Sigma}(\epsilon) \simeq \lambda\epsilon + i\gamma(\epsilon)$$

and we suppose that $\gamma(\epsilon)$ decreases faster than ϵ. In the vicinity of Fermi surface $N_k(\epsilon)$, defined by (4), is:

$$N_{\mathbf{k}}^F(\epsilon) = \frac{1}{\pi}\frac{\gamma}{[1(1+\lambda)\epsilon - \xi_{\mathbf{k}}]^2 + \gamma^2}\,, \int_{-\infty}^{\infty} N_{\mathbf{k}}^F(\epsilon)d\epsilon \simeq \frac{1}{1+\lambda}\,.$$

But there exists the exact relation:

$$\int_{-\infty}^{\infty} N_{\mathbf{k}}(\epsilon)d\epsilon = 1\,.$$

It means that only a part of the total density of states at a given $\mathbf{k}$ belongs to a Fermi spectrum $\xi_{\mathbf{k}}$ and is in the vicinity of the Fermi level. Having in mind a Hubbard-like picture (not neccessary exactly the Hubbard model) discussed in Sec. 1 we understand that at the same $\mathbf{k}$ there exists another part of $N_k(\epsilon)$, say $N_k^H(\epsilon) = (\lambda/1+\lambda)$, which is in the region of the Hubbard subbands. (In another context this picture was already discussed by Ruckenstein and Varma [8]). The parameter a, sec. 1, has therefore a very natural interpretation in terms of the Green function:

$$a = \frac{1}{1+\lambda}\,.$$

As it follows from the microscopic derivation of Fermi liquid theory [4] it can be excluded from the final formulation by means of renormalization of scattering amplitudes. Therefore it is impossible to extract the information on λ from low temperature thermodynamics or transport phenomena, which are consistently described in the framework of Landau theory. But it is, of course, a measureable parameter: $N_{\mathbf{k}}(\epsilon)$ is just the spectral characteristic measured by means of angle-resolved photoemission and inverse photoemission spectroscopy, and λ is simply a ratio of two mentioned parts of spectral density. Introducing it explicitly in a Fermi-liquid phenomenology we come to a peculiar picture of an electron spectrum, in which we have two different velocities for the same Fermi excitation, both being measruable:

$$v_F = \left(\frac{d\xi_{\mathbf{k}}}{dk}\right)_{k=k_F}\,, \quad \tilde{v}_F = \frac{v_F}{1+\lambda}\,. \tag{6}$$

Low temperature heat capacity is expressed in terms of $\tilde{v}_F$, and here is an interesting possibility to discuss a heavy fermion problem. We can expect here a very small density of states transfer from f-electrons to the Fermi level and therefore a large value of λ. All the entropy will be in this case due to Fermi excitations, although the charge remains mostly on the f-shell. Nevertheless the excitations will still be current carriers: this is clearly seen from the conductivity, which may be expressed only in terms of the larger velocity $v_{\mathbf{k}}$, (6). It means that excitations in highly correlated systems are connected with certain phase relations between almost localized electron states, rather than charge fluctuations between them. The latter are strongly suppressed by the Coulomb forces.

This picture has a direct relation to high-T_c superconductivity. Suppression of charge fluctuations connected with the Fermi-excitations means that the residual Coulomb repulsion between the latter will be reduced. This effect can be seen if we consider the simplest ladder diagram for the socalled Cooper channel: we have here $(1 + \lambda)$ in the denominator. An additional source for this reduction may be connected with the velocity v_F: the simple 2-site Hubbard model shows that a "band width" for $\xi_{\mathbf{k}}$ (kinematic spectrum) which is the difference between two eigenvalues of $G^{-1}(0)$ (see Sec.2) is equal to $V^2/6t$. Therefore we can expect an enhancement of v_F with increasing correlation strength.

4. Conclusions

The short-ranged Coulomb correlations manifests themself in a redistribution of the total one electron density of states between the dispersive Fermi-liquid like excitations and a higher energy Hubbard-like states which correspond to the "localized" part of the charge density. It is possible to describe this correlated state consistently in the framework of a slightly reformulated Fermi-liquid theory. In presence of sufficiently strong correlations only a small part of the density of states belong to the Fermi spectrum and the net repulsion between the excitations will be reduced. Such a state has to be sensitive to any change of crystal symmetry: the residual density of states at the Fermi level may be removed due to (energetically not very strong) antiferromagnetic ordering, lattice rearrangement, disorder etc. By the same reasons an enhanced interaction between Fermi excitations and phonons is expected here. It seems that we have here a clue to the qualitative understanding of high-T_c in correlated metals.

Acknowledgements. I'm very grateful to D. van der Marel, P. Horsch. D. Rainer, D. Einzel, P. Fulde, A. Aronov, A. Larkin, Yu. Ovchinnicov, U. Eckern J. Fink, H. Capellmann, and C. Varma for many useful discussions.

References

[1] J. G. Bednorz and K. A. Müller, Z. Phys. **B64**, 189 (1986).

[2] P. W. Anderson (unpublished).

[3] J. M. Luttinger, Phys. Rev. **119**, 1153 (1960).

[4] A. A. Abricosov, L. P. Gor'kov and I. Ye. Dzyaloshinskii, "Quantum Field Theoretical Methods in Statistical Physics", Ch IV, Pergamon Press 1965.

[5] J. M. Luttinger and J. C. Ward, Phys. Rev. **118**, 1417 (1960).

[6] L. D. Landau, Zh.l Eksp. Teor. Fiz. **30**, 1058 (1956); **32**, 59 (1957).

[7] P. Lederer, D. Poilblanc and T. M. Rice, Physica **C162-164**, 587 (1989).

[8] A. E. Ruckenstein, C. M. Varma, Physica **C185 - 189**, 134 (1991).

Electronic Structure and Superconductivity in $YBa_2Cu_3O_7/PrBa_2Cu_3O_7$ Superlattices

R. Fehrenbacher and T.M. Rice

Theoretische Physik, ETH-Hönggerberg, CH-8093 Zürich, Switzerland

Abstract. The antiferromagnetic insulator $PrBa_2Cu_3O_7$ contrasts with the superconductivity in the other rare earth systems. We show that the eight-fold Pr-O coordination stabilizes a Pr^{IV} oxidation state rather than a trivalent Pr^{3+}state through a strong admixture of $4f^1$ into $4f^2$ plus ligand hole configurations. This resolves the experimental controversy about the Pr valence. In $(YBa_2Cu_3O_7)_M(PrBa_2Cu_3O_7)_N$ superlattices, the change of oxidation state leads to an inhomogeneous hole distribution among inequivalent CuO_2-planes and -chains, which accounts reasonably for the observed dependence of T_c on M and N.

There has been a considerable debate over the electronic structure of $PrBa_2Cu_3O_7$ (Pr-O_7), and superlattices formed from alternate blocks of $YBa_2Cu_3O_7$ (Y-O_7) and Pr-O_7. In a recent article [1], we proposed a microscopic model for the electronic structure of Pr-O_7 which allows for a consistent interpretation of the known experimental results obtained for this system, and we discussed the resulting consequences for the Y-O_7/Pr-O_7 superlattices. The present contribution will therefore be restricted to a brief summary of the previously stated results, an extended discussion on the experimental consequences of our approach, and some open questions.

Our premise is that Pr in this compound takes an oxidation state Pr^{IV} [2] in contrast to Y and other rare earths (RE) which are trivalent (with the probable exception of Ce [3]). Only in this way, can we possibly account for the insulating antiferromagnetic (AF) CuO_2-planes in Pr-O_7 with a Néel-temperature T_N comparable to Y-O_6 [4]. Indeed, from the assignment of Cu^{II}, which this fact requires, it follows at once that Pr must be in this oxidation state.

The electronic structure of Pr^{IV} was shown [1] to be governed by the eight-fold almost cubic Pr-O coordination which allows the formation of a low energy hole state which is a superposition of $2p_\pi$-O orbitals with *f-symmetry* w.r.t. the central Pr-ion. The strong hybridization of $4f^2\underline{L}$ and $4f^1$ configurations, where $\underline{L}$ denotes a ligand hole on the O-neighbours was identified as the dominant electronic process being competitive in energy to the planar singlet [5] made from hybridized $3d_{x^2-y^2}$-Cu, and $2p_\sigma$-O orbitals. The essential difference between Pr and the other RE was proposed to be a crossing of these two levels, resolving the controversial issue about the Pr valence. As previously stated, the present Pr^{IV} configuration has a similar electronic structure to the one encountered in CeO_2, and PrO_2 [6], in which the RE-O coordination is in fact identical, and where the RE valence state also gave rise to a controversial debate.

Concerning the Y/Pr-O_7 superlattices [7], we showed that the assignment of the doped holes to Pr^{IV} in Pr-O_7, and to the CuO_2-chains and -planes in Y-O_7 leads to a charge rearrangement when superlattices are formed. The resulting drop in the hole density

Springer Series in Solid-State Sciences, Vol. 113 **Electronic Properties of High-T_c Superconductors**
Editors: H. Kuzmany, M. Mehring, J. Fink

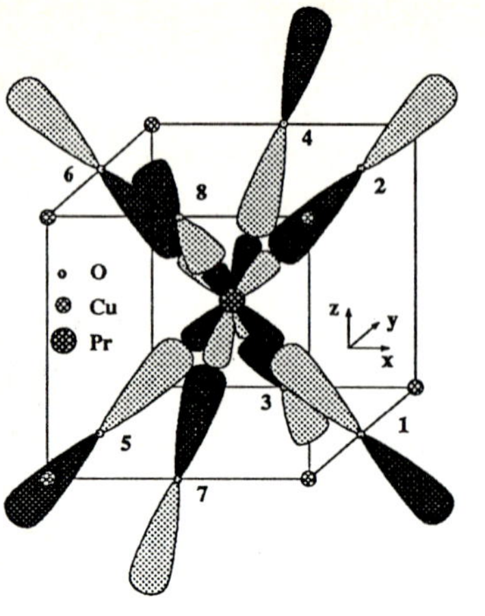

FIGURE 1: Schematic diagram of the eight $2p_\pi$-O orbitals pointing towards Pr site m, and the $4f_{z(x^2-y^2)}$-Pr orbital. The superposition

$$ {}^{2}_{f}\pi_{ms} = \frac{1}{\sqrt{8}} \sum_{\zeta_{mi}} (-1)^{M_{mi}} \pi_{mis}, $$

where ζ_{mi} is the vector connecting Pr site m with the neighbouring O site i, $M_{mi} = 1$, for $i \in \{2,3,6,7\}$, $M_{mi} = 2$, for $i \in \{1,4,5,8\}$, has $f_{z(x^2-y^2)}$-symmetry, and hence its overlap with all f-states apart from $4f_{z(x^2-y^2)}$ vanishes. Its phase coherence is indicated by dark (+), and light shading (-), as for the $4f_{z(x^2-y^2)}$-Pr orbital.

on the CuO_2-planes can plausibly account for the variation in T_c between different superlattices.

We describe the low energy electronic properties of Pr-O_7 by the model Hamiltonian

$$ \begin{aligned} H = & \sum_{ijs} \epsilon_{ij} c^\dagger_{is} c_{js} + \sum_{iss'} U_i c^\dagger_{is} c_{is} c^\dagger_{is'} c_{is'} + \epsilon_f \sum_{m,s,\nu} {}^{\nu}f^\dagger_{ms} {}^{\nu}f_{ms} + \\ & \sum_{\langle m,i \rangle \nu s} t^\nu_{mi} ({}^{\nu}f^\dagger_{ms} c^\dagger_{is} + \text{h.c.}) + U_f \sum_{m,\nu,\nu',s,s'} {}^{\nu}f^\dagger_{ms} {}^{\nu}f_{ms} {}^{\nu'}f^\dagger_{ms'} {}^{\nu'}f_{ms'} + \sum_m H^{\text{at}}_m \, , \end{aligned} \tag{1} $$

where i, j label planar Cu and O sites, m Pr sites, $c^\dagger_{is}$ create $3d_{x^2-y^2}$-Cu and $2p_{\sigma,\pi}$-O *holes*, ${}^{\nu}f^\dagger_{ms}$ create Pr $(4f, l_z{=}\nu)$ *electrons*, and s is the spin index. We use $2p_\pi$ orbitals which make an angle of 45° with the CuO_2 (ab) plane, hence point towards a Pr site. The ϵ_{ij} include the usual on-site energies $\epsilon_d = 0$ (by convention), $\epsilon_{p\sigma} = 3.6$, $\epsilon_{p\pi}$, and the nearest neighbour (n.n) hopping integrals $t_{pd} = 1.2$, $t_{p\sigma} = 0.62$, $t_{p\pi} = 0.46$, $t^\perp_{p\pi} = 0.5$, where $t^\perp_{p\pi}$ describes hopping in the c-direction ($\epsilon_{p\pi}$ will be discussed later). The on-site Coulomb repulsions are $U_d = 10.5$, $U_p = 4$. The f-parameters include the on-site energy $\epsilon_f - \epsilon_{p\pi}$ = -10, the t^ν_{pf} between $2p_\pi$, and $4f_\nu$ orbitals (all other t^ν_{mi} are negligible), and the on-site Coulomb repulsion $U_f = 10.5$ (t^ν_{pf} will be discussed below). Finally, H^{at}_m describes the *atomic* Coulomb, exchange, and spin-orbit interactions on the Pr-sites. All parameters are in eV (for the origin of their values refer to [1]). The vacuum $|\rangle$ is defined as *filled* Cu $3d^{10}$, O $2p^6$, and *empty* Pr $4f^0$ shells. H^{at}_m is taken into account, by restricting the Hilbert space to include only the $4f$ Hund's rule multiplet ground states.

Among the possible hole states on the 8 O atoms surrounding a Pr site (see Fig. 1), there exists a *unique* linear combination ${}^{2}_{f}\pi_{ms}$ of $2p_\pi$-O orbitals for which the O-O (at $-2t_{p\pi} - t^\perp_{p\pi}$), *and* the Pr-O hopping energy are minimized at the same time. Due to the $f_{z(x^2-y^2)}$-symmetry of ${}^{2}_{f}\pi_{ms}$ around Pr-site m, hybridization occurs *only* with ${}^{\pm 2}f_{ms}$, the matrix element $V = \sqrt{8}\, t_{pf}$ ($t_{pf} := t^\nu_{pf}$, $\nu = 2$) being enhanced by phase coherence.

The Pr^{IV} state can be written as a mixture of Pr^{4+}, and Pr^{3+}+ *ligand hole*

$$ |G_m\rangle = \sum_{\nu,s} \lambda^s_\nu \, {}^{\nu}f^\dagger_{ms} |\rangle + \sum_{\nu,\nu',s,s',s''} \kappa^{ss's''}_{\nu\nu'} \, {}^{\nu}f^\dagger_{ms} \, {}^{\nu'}f^\dagger_{ms'} \, {}^{2}_{f}\pi^\dagger_{ms''} |\rangle \; . \tag{2} $$

TABLE I: The energy difference Δ_1 in eV between the planar singlet ($E_o(\mathrm{Cu}^{III}) = -0.43\mathrm{eV}$, $\epsilon_d = 0$), and the Pr^{IV} state, together with the corresponding $4f$-occupation n_f as a function of t_{pf}, for $\Delta_{\sigma\pi} = 1.0\mathrm{eV}$. Note that $\Delta_1(\Delta_{\sigma\pi}) = \Delta_1(\Delta_{\sigma\pi} = 0) + \Delta_{\sigma\pi}$

	$t_{pf} = 0.2$	$t_{pf} = 0.3$	$t_{pf} = 0.4$	$t_{pf} = 0.5$
Δ_1	-0.13	0.12	0.38	0.65
n_f	1.73	1.66	1.63	1.60

The coefficients $\lambda^s_\nu, \kappa^{ss's''}_{\nu\nu'}$ are obtained by diagonalizing (1) in the subspace $\mathfrak{H}_m$ which contains the $J = 5/2$ multiplet, and product states combining the $J = 4$ multiplet with the two hole states ${}^2_f\pi_{ms}$. The relevant part of (1) then becomes

$$
\begin{aligned}
H_m = {} & \widetilde{\epsilon}_\pi \sum_s {}^2_f\pi^\dagger_{ms}\, {}^2_f\pi_{ms} + \epsilon_f \sum_{\nu,s} {}^\nu f^\dagger_{ms}\, {}^\nu f_{ms} + \\
& V \sum_{\nu\in\{2,-2\} s} \left({}^\nu f^\dagger_{ms}\, {}^2_f\pi^\dagger_{m-s} + \mathrm{h.c.} \right) + U_f \sum_{m,\nu,\nu',s,s'} {}^\nu f^\dagger_{ms}\, {}^\nu f_{ms}\, {}^{\nu'} f^\dagger_{ms'}\, {}^{\nu'} f_{ms'} ,
\end{aligned}
\tag{3}
$$

where $\widetilde{\epsilon}_\pi = \epsilon_{p\pi} - 2t_{p\pi} - t^\perp_{p\pi}$. H_m splits $\mathfrak{H}_m$ into four decoupled subspaces, $\mathfrak{H}^{\pm 5/2}_m$ containing the states coupled to $|4f^1; J_z = \pm 5/2\rangle$, $|4f^1; J_z = \mp 3/2\rangle$, and $\mathfrak{H}^{\pm 1/2}_m$ containing the states coupled to $|4f^1; J_z = \pm 1/2\rangle$. The diagonalization of (3) yields a four-fold degenerate ground state belonging to the (double cubic group O^+) representation Γ_8, and the first excited states belonging to the doublet Γ_7.

An alternative state for the hole is the planar singlet formed from hybridized $3d_{x^2-y^2}$-Cu, and $2p_\sigma$-O orbitals [5]. Neglecting delocalization of the singlet, the energy $E_0(\mathrm{Cu}^{III})$ of a hole in this state was calculated from (1). In table I, we quote the average $4f$-occupation n_f, and the energy differences $\Delta_1 = E_0(\mathrm{Cu}^{III}) - E_0(\mathrm{Pr}^{IV})$ as a function of the hybridization matrix element t_{pf}, and the O-site energy difference $\Delta_{\sigma\pi} = \epsilon_{p\sigma} - \epsilon_{p\pi}$. The Pr^{IV} oxidation state is stabilized for values $\Delta_{\sigma\pi} \geq 1\mathrm{eV}$, and $t_{pf} > 0.3\mathrm{eV}$.

In view of the uncertainty of the parameter values and the crudeness of our model, a definite answer on the stabilty of the two oxidation states cannot be given. In the following, we shall compare the properties of the Pr^{IV} state with experimental results, and also raise some open questions:

(a) The insulating behaviour of Pr-O_7 is readily understood, since then each Pr^{IV} state is singly occupied. Double occupancy costs large Coulomb *and* hybridization energy, leading to a Mott-insulator. A remaining uncertainty concerns the role of the Cu-O chains. In Pr-O_7, the chain Cu^{II}moments do not seem to order AF which seems unexpected. Whether this simply arises as a consequence of the chains 1D character, or whether it is due to a small number of holes being transferred from Pr^{IV} states to the chains (also leading to a small deviation from a half filled Pr^{IV} 'band') cannot be decided from our calculations. Another mysterious property is the huge increase in resistivity [8] which occurs in oxygen deficient Pr-O_7, since upon (electron) doping the Pr^{IV} state, one would expect an enhanced conductivity. A possible explanation for this is that the conductivity in Pr-O_7 is dominated by the chains which upon reducing oxygen become disordered thus increasing resistivity. This indicates once again that one has to take into account the role of the chain oxygen disorder when interpreting experiments.

(b) The average ground state $4f$-occupation is $n_f \approx 1.65$, explaining the spectroscopic results [9, 10, 11] which revealed a valence close to +3. Furthermore, a recent neutron scattering study [12] showed that the RE-O bond lengths in RE-O_7 are different for O(2) and O(3), with the exception of Pr-O_7 (equal Pr-O(2) and Pr-O(3) distances favour the O $^2_f\pi_{ms}$-Pr $4f$ hybridization), and that they scale linearly with the corresponding RE^{3+} ionic radii, the only exception again being Pr, for which an average valence of $\sim +3.3$ was extracted.

(c) The magnetic moment of the Pr^{IV} state cannot be exactly determined from our model, since the Coulomb crystal field is not included. However, one would expect a value close to that of a free $J = 5/2$ ion with a ground state belonging to Γ_8. This is consistent with high temperature susceptibility data revealing an effective Pr magnetic moment of $\sim 2.8\mu_B$ [13]. In order to understand the origin of the small ($\sim 0.74\mu_B$ [14]) AF ordered Pr moment, and the nature of the AF structure in general, the interaction of neighbouring Pr^{IV} states needs to be included in our model (see (d)).

(d) The anomalously large $T_N \sim$17K of the Pr-moments [15] is due to an enhanced superexchange process as a result of moderate overlap between $2p_\pi$-orbitals from neighbouring PrO_8 cubes. Due to the strong spin-orbit coupling the detailed nature of the superexchange is rather complicated (work to elucidate it is in progress). The superexchange is absent in the other RE-O_7 systems ($T_N \leq$2K) [14].

(e) The sensitivity of the energy difference Δ_1 on $t_{pf}, \Delta_{\sigma\pi}$ indicates that the RE contraction, reducing t_{pf}, combined with large RE^{4+} ionization energies (which is also reflected in the non-existence of REO_2, RE $\neq$ Ce, Pr, Tb) is responsible for the absence of general RE^{IV} hole binding for RE with atomic number $Z > 59$.

(f) In the alloy $Y_{1-x}Pr_x$-O_7, the Pr^{IV} state not only absorbs holes [16, 17], it can also act as a pair breaker, due to a small exchange coupling to the $2p_\sigma$-O orbitals.

The oxidation state Pr^{IV} in Pr-O_7 has direct consequences when $(\text{Y-O}_7)_M(\text{Pr-O}_7)_N$ superlattices are formed: The substitution of a complete plane of Pr^{IV} by Y^{III}, results in a homogeneous negative charge distribution on the Y-plane relative to pure Pr-O_7, and hence an electrostatic potential gradient along the c-axis. The compensating holes are then inhomogeneously distributed among the different CuO_2 planes and chains, such that the electrochemical potential μ^{el} is constant everywhere. We can determine the equilibrium hole distribution as a function of the superlattice parameters M, N from a simplified Hartree calculation, and finally relate the obtained hole counts to the measured T_c values using an empirical $T_c(\delta_{\text{pl}})$ relation.

Labeling the CuO_2 chains and planes in a superlattice unit cell according to their c-axis coordinate z_q ($q = 1, \ldots, 3(M+N)$), the condition for equilibrium is $\mu^{\text{el}}_q = \mu^{\text{el}}_r$ for any pair q, r, where $\mu^{\text{el}}_q = \mu_q(\delta_q) + e\Phi_q$ ($\mu_q(\delta_q)$ electronic chemical potential, δ_q number of holes/Cu, Φ_q the electrostatic potential at position z_q). Taking $\mu_q(\delta_q) = \epsilon_0 + b_t\delta_q$, *i. e.*, constant DOS characterized by a bandwidth $b_t = 8t$ ($t = 0.5eV$) for planes, and $\mu_q(\delta_q) = \alpha(\delta_q^2 + \gamma\delta_q)$, *i. e.*, a one-dimensional (1d) form ($\mu \propto \delta^2$) with small ($\gamma \ll 1$) 2d corrections for chains, the shift ϵ_0 can be estimated from experimental values

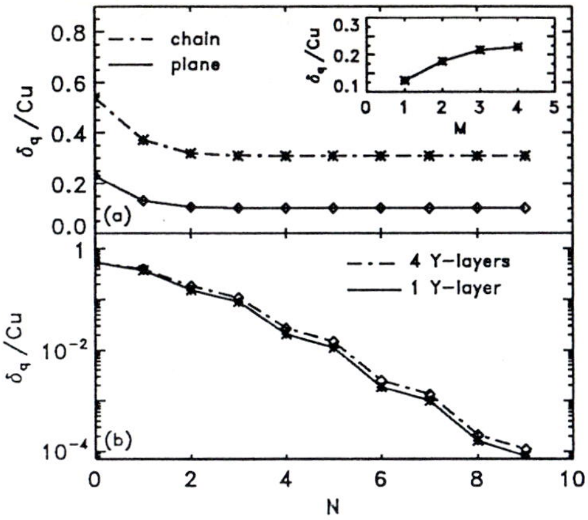

FIGURE 2: (a) The hole concentration δ_q of the plane and the chain lying closest to the Y for $M = 1$ as a function of the Pr thickness N. δ_q initially decreases, but then it saturates at $N = 3$. The inset shows the maximum planar hole distribution, $\delta_{\rm pl}^{\rm max}$ for varying Y-layer thickness M, and constant $N = 1$. One finds a monotonic increase, approaching the asymptotic value $\delta_{\rm pl}$ (Y-O_7), for $M \geq 4$. (b) The hole density $\delta_{\rm ch}^{\rm min}$ of the chains furthest from the Y-block for $M = 1, 4$ as a function of N. $\delta_{\rm ch}^{\rm min}$ drops exponentially for $N > 4$.

$\delta_{\rm pl} \approx 0.23, \delta_{\rm ch} = 1-2\delta_{\rm pl}$ in Y-O_7 as a function of the parameters α, γ. The potential has the form $\Phi(z) = \Phi_q - E_q(z-z_q)$ $(z_q < z < z_{q+1})$, and the electric field E is discontinuous at z_{q+1}, $E_{q+1}-E_q = 4\pi e\delta_{q+1}n_{\rm Cu}/\epsilon$, ($\epsilon$ static dielectric constant, $n_{\rm Cu} = (ab)^{-1}$, a, b lattice parameters). Using reflection symmetry, the equilibrium condition yields $3(M+N)/2-1$ independent equations fixing the hole counts δ_q.

We calculated the δ_q for all combinations of $M \leq 4, N \leq 9$ using different α, γ, ϵ, and Fig. 2(a) shows δ_q of the chain and plane closest to the Y-plane for $M = 1$ (for the figures we used $\alpha = 6t, \gamma = 0.13, \epsilon = 35$ resulting in $\epsilon_0 = 0.6$eV). One observes rapid saturation for increasing N, setting in at $N = 3$ (this also occurs for other M). For smaller values of ϵ, and (or) $\gamma = 0$, the saturation sets in even faster (a large ϵ could arise from screening by optical phonons, and the Pr-O_7-blocks). Another general feature is that only the planes closest (and inside) the Y-layers have nonvanishing δ_q (due to $\epsilon_0 > 0$). The inset of Fig. 2(a) displays $\delta_{\rm pl}^{\rm max}$, the maximum hole concentration in any pair of planes, for $N = 1$, showing that $\delta_{\rm pl}^{\rm max}$ approaches $\delta_{\rm pl}$(Y-O_7) as $M \geq 4$. Fig. 2(b) shows δ_q for the chains furthest from Y. There is an exponential fall-off for $N > 4$, as expected from solutions obtained in a continuum approximation by integrating $d^2/dz^2\mu_{\rm ch}(\delta(z)) = 4\pi e^2 n_{\rm Cu}/(\epsilon c)\delta(z)$, ($c$ lattice parameter).

Under the assumption that the mean-field T_c of the superlattice is entirely determined by the maximum hole concentration $\delta_{\rm pl}^{\rm max}$ in any pair of CuO_2 planes, one can use the empirical curve $T_c(\delta_{\rm pl}) = 92-\eta(\delta_{\rm pl}-\delta_o)^2$, ($\delta_o = 0.23$, η determined by $T_c(0.07) = 0$) [18] to estimate $T_c(M, N)$ (see Fig. 3). Comparing with the experimental values [7, 19], we note that while the variation of the asymptotic T_c ($N \geq 8$) with M is reasonably well described by our model, the saturation with Pr thickness occurs too fast (at $N = 3$ in the calculation compared to $N = 8$ from experiment). Note that the effect of hole transfer from Y- to Pr-blocks on T_c was analyzed previously [20] within a simpler model (not distinguishing between CuO_2 planes and chains), and found to be less important.

In conclusion, we presented a consistent description of the electronic structure of pure Pr-O_7, and Y/Pr-O_7 superlattices. The T_c suppression in Pr-O_7 was explained by the existence of a local Pr $4f$-$2p_\pi$ hybridized state which binds doped holes to Pr-sites, *i. e.*, an oxidation state Pr^{IV}. For the Y/Pr-O_7 superlattices, we demonstrated that

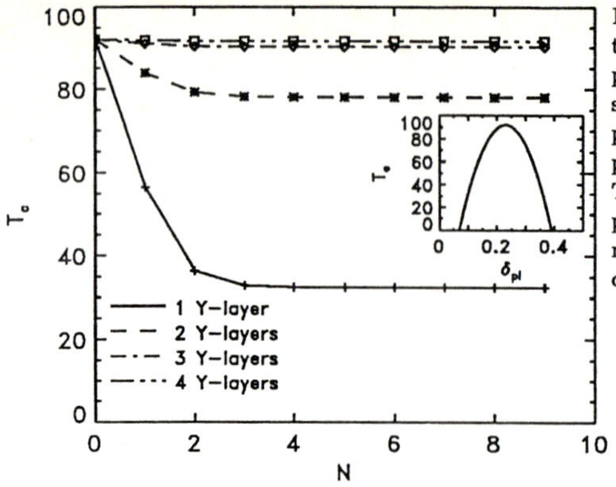

FIGURE 3: The dependence of T_c on superlattice parameters M, N calculated from the empirical form $T_c(\delta_{\rm pl}) = 92 - \eta(\delta_{\rm pl} - \delta_o)^2$ (see inset) under the assumption that the T_c of the superlattice is determined by the T_c of the CuO_2 planes with highest hole concentration ($\delta_{\rm pl}^{\rm max}$). The asymptotic values agree well with the experimental ones, whereas the saturation occurs much faster in the calculated curve (at $N = 3$ compared to $N = 8$ from experiment).

the different oxidation Pr^{IV} versus Y^{III} gives rise to an inhomogeneous distribution of itinerant holes among different CuO_2 planes and chains in the superlattice unit cell. The mean-field values of T_c determined by the maximum hole counts in a CuO_2 plane show fair agreement with the measured values of T_c.

We acknowledge useful discussions with H. Adrian, N. Bonesteel, Ø. Fischer, M. Guillaume, and U. Staub. In particular, we would like to thank F. Mila for many helpful comments and discussions. One of us (R.F.) was supported by the Swiss National Science Foundation.

References

[1] R. Fehrenbacher and T. M. Rice, ETH-preprint ETH-TH/92-8.
[2] A. W. Sleight, in *Proceedings of the 39. Scottish Universities Summer School in Physics*, page 97, St. Andrews, UK, 1991, Adam Hilger.
[3] C. R. Fincher, Jr. and G. B. Blanchet, Phys. Rev. Lett. **67**, 2902 (1991).
[4] D. W. Cooke et al., Phys. Rev. B **41**, 4801 (1990).
[5] F. C. Zhang and T. M. Rice, Phys. Rev. B **37**, 3759 (1988).
[6] H. Ogasawara et al., Phys. Rev. B **43**, 854 (1991).
[7] J. M. Triscone et al., Phys. Rev. Lett. **64**, 804 (1990).
[8] M. E. López-Morales et al., Phys. Rev. B **41**, 6655 (1990).
[9] U. Neukirch et al., Europhys. Lett. **5**, 567 (1988).
[10] J.-S. Kang et al., J. Less Comm. Met. **148**, 121 (1989).
[11] J. Fink et al., Phys. Rev. B **42**, 4823 (1990).
[12] M. Guillaume, U. Staub, and A. Furrer, private communication.
[13] J. L. Peng et al., Phys. Rev. B **40**, 4517 (1989).
[14] W.-H. Li et al., Phys. Rev. B **40**, 5300 (1989).
[15] A. Kebede et al., Phys. Rev. B **40**, 4453 (1989).
[16] A. P. Reyes et al., Phys. Rev. B **43**, 2989 (1991).
[17] D. P. Norton et al., Phys. Rev. Lett. **66**, 1537 (1991).
[18] W. A. Groen, D. M. de Leeuw, and L. F. Feiner, Physica C **165**, 55 (1990).
[19] G. Jakob et al., in *Proceedings of the International Conference on Mat. and Mech. of Superconductivity*, page 2087, Kanazawa, 1991, North-Holland.
[20] M. Rasolt, T. Edis, and Z. Tĕsanović, Phys. Rev. Lett. **66**, 2927 (1991).

Intermediate Range Order in the Possibility of Nonlinear Excitations in the Doping Subsystems of Cuprates*

H. Eschrig[1], *S.-L. Drechsler*[1], and *J. Malek*[1,2]

[1]Institut für Festkörper- und Werkstofforschung Dresden e.V., O-8027 Dresden, Fed. Rep. of Germany
[2]Institute of Physics, Czechoslovak Academy of Sciences, 180 40 Prague 8, Czechoslovakia

Abstract. A remarkable rich variety of nonlinear objects as bipolarons, polarons and polarexcitons is discussed for a quasi-onedimensional doping subsystem, possibly generic for all hole doped HTSC's. Based on LCAO-deformational studies of CuO_3 chains in $YBa_2Cu_3O_7$ and on known phonon frequencies, an effective two band Hamiltonian with two degrees of freedom, including both intra- and intersite electron-lattice interaction, has been proposed and examined in detail for various commensurate band filling ratios ($\nu = 1/2, 1/3$, and $1/4$ for the antibonding chain band). Well localized stable bipolarons with negative formation energies have been found in accord with a microscopic scenario for a boson-fermion (s-channel) approach to HTSC proposed in ref. [1].

1. Introduction

In [1] we proposed a microscopic scenario of s-channel HTSC, based on (i) the existence of a Peierls phase in the polarizable structural units, sandwiched between the CuO_2-planes, and (ii) on bipolaronic charge transfer excitations from the planes into the Peierls phase. This scenario is most easily illustrated for the cases of $YBa_2Cu_3O_7$ and $YBa_2Cu_4O_8$ where the chain structure of the doping subsystem is well known. For the most other hole doped superconductors, a chain-like *local* structure arises from a misfit between the cuprate planes and the doping subsystem. The elucidation of details of this local structure is hampered by the presence of vacancies and interstitial oxygen ions. In general we expect a M_xO_y chain-like structure of the doping subsystem, where M = Cu, Bi, Tl, etc. . The generalization of the model presented below, e.g. to TlO_x or BiO_x chains, is straightforward. However, at present no complete set of microscopic electronic parameters for these cases is available in contrast to $YBa_2Cu_3O_7$.

2. The Model and the Method

The electronic structure related to CuO_3-chains in $YBa_2Cu_3O_7$ can be modelled by a structure of single chains with alternating O-ions and CuO_2-molecules and effective interaction parameters. The chain bands are formed of $p\sigma$-states at the O-sites and antibonding molecular $dp\sigma$-states at the CuO_2-sites. Their Hamiltonian matrix consists of two on-site energies ε_A and ε_B (of the molecular site and the O-site, respectively) and one transfer integral t. Here, two kinds of deformation are considered: symmetric z-displacements $u = z_2 - z_1$ of the two molecular O-ions, and longitudinal displacements y of all chain

*This work was supported by the Deutsche Forschungsgemeinschaft under Project Es 85/1-1.

sites m; $v_m = y_{m+1} - y_m$. Thus, we adopt the effective AB-Hamiltonian

$$H = \sum_{n,s} \varepsilon_n c^\dagger_{n,s} c_{n,s} - t_{n,n+1} \left(c^\dagger_{n+1,s} c_{n,s} + h.c. \right) + \frac{K_u}{2} \sum_{m \epsilon A} u_m^2 + \frac{K_v}{2} \sum_m v_m^2,$$

where the off-site and on-site terms read for A and B-sites, respectively

$$t_{m,m+1} = \begin{cases} - & [t_0 - \gamma_1 u_m - \gamma_2 v_m] \\ & t_0 - \gamma_1 u_{m+1} - \gamma_2 v_m \end{cases}, \quad \varepsilon_m = \begin{cases} \varepsilon_A & - \ \alpha_A u_m - \beta_A (v_m + v_{m-1}) \\ \varepsilon_B & - \ \alpha_B (u_{m+1} + u_{m-1}) - \beta_B (v_m + v_{m-1}). \end{cases}$$

The LCAO-deformational study, presuming an elongation of apical oxygens by 0.1Å in z-direction [3], yields $t_0 = 1.67$ eV, $\gamma_1 = 1.32$ eV/Å, $\varepsilon_A = -3.59$ eV, $\varepsilon_B = -5.3$ eV, 2 $\alpha_B = \alpha_A = -0.816$ eV/Å , and from phonon modes at 505 cm^{-1} and 400 cm^{-1} we get $K_u = 7.78$ eV/Å^2 and $K_y = 4.87$ eV/Å^2. For $\beta_{A,B}$ we adopt values somewhat smaller than the analogous values used in [2] for the related M-X-chains (see below). Finally, due to the approximate "symmetry" of a CuO_4 plaquette we expect $\gamma_2 \approx \gamma_1$. The Hamiltonian under consideration is a two-component generalization of the two-band (one-component) Hamiltonian proposed by Bishop et al. for the M-X chains [2] . Two self-consistency equations for the displacement patterns are obtained from the variation of the total energy functional with respect to u_m and v_m , i.e. to the changes of the Cu(1)-O(4) and Cu(1)-O(1) bond lengths, respectively:

$$\begin{aligned} u_m &= \frac{1}{K_u} \left[\Lambda_u + \alpha_A P_{m,m} + \alpha_B (P_{m-1,m-1} + P_{m+1,m+1}) + 2\gamma_1 (P_{m,m+1} - P_{m-1,m}) \right], \\ v_m &= \frac{1}{K_v} \left[\Lambda_v + \begin{Bmatrix} \beta_A \\ \beta_B \end{Bmatrix} (P_{m,m} + P_{m+1,m+1}) - 2\gamma_2 (-1)^m P_{m,m+1} \right], \end{aligned}$$

where

$$\begin{aligned} \Lambda_u &= \frac{-2}{N} \sum_{m \epsilon A} \left[2\gamma_1 (P_{m,m+1} - P_{m,-1m}) + \alpha_A P_{m,m} + \alpha_B (P_{m-1,m-1} + P_{m+1,m+1}) \right], \\ \Lambda_v &= \frac{-1}{N} \left[(\beta_A + \beta_B) N_{el} - 2\gamma_2 \sum_m (-1)^m P_{m,m+1} \right], \\ P_{m,m'} &= \sum_\mu^{occ} \psi_\mu^*(m) \psi_\mu(m'). \end{aligned}$$

$P_{m,m'}$ denotes the density matrix, N stands for the chain site number, and N_{el} is the total number of electrons on the chain. The Lagrange multiplier Λ_v reflects the fixed chain length requirement $\sum_m v_m = 0$. The condition $\sum_m u_m = 0$, expressed by Λ_u, is presumed for the sake of simplicity in order to avoid an additional charge transfer between planes and chains. Finally, from the variation of the total energy functional with respect to the wave functions one gets the discrete Schrödinger's equation

$$E_\mu \psi_\mu(m) = \varepsilon_m \psi_\mu(m) - t_{m-1,m} \psi_\mu(m-1) - t_{m,m+1} \psi_\mu(m+1),$$

from which the eigenvalues E_μ and eigenstates $\psi_\mu(m)$ are obtained for finite N-membered rings (or open chains). The quantum number μ includes the spin index s. Since the displacement set $\{u, v\}$ depends on the density matrix, the problem becomes highly non-linear and the eqs. of Sect. 2 have to be solved self-consistently by iterations. In the calculations reported below we examined periodic chains with about 120 sites, i.e. the chain length is much larger than the size of defect states. In addition to the constraint condition $\sum_m v_m = 0$ mentioned above, we considered also the case where all A-sites are fixed. The modification of the self-consistency equations is straightforward.

3. Results

Experimentally, the band filling ratio of the antibonding chain band ν is not precisely known, because the interpretation of the Hall or optical data of strongly correlated systems like the cuprates is nontrivial. However, for a commensurate band filling a local minimum (cusp) of the total energy for Peierls distorted chains is expected. Therefore, we consider several values, $\nu = 1/2, 1/3$ and $1/4$. A rich variety of nonlinear defect states as various polarons and solitons have been found. Here, for the limited space, we restrict ourselves to a brief discussion of bipolarons and (bi)polarexcitons due to their possible direct relavance to the mechanism of high temperature superconductivity. For all band filling ratios and the reasonable parameters γ_2, $\beta_{A,B} \gtrsim 1$ eV/Å, a two mode bipolaron has been found self-consistently. We emphasize that it is stable with respect to a decay into two singly charged polarons as well as into a doubly charged soliton-antisoliton pair. The bipolaron is confined only to few lattice sites ($2b \approx 3.88$ Å) (s. Fig.), i.e. its width is smaller than the superconducting coherence length $\xi_{ab} \approx 15\div 20$ Å. Essentially, for all band filling ratios considered here, there are solutions for which the bipolaronic excess charge is confined to one CuO_4-plaquette only, thereby $65 - 80\%$ of the charge is located at an A-site and the remaining part at the neigbouring O(1) oxygens. The formation energy of a bipolaron E_f is typically of the order $-0.5 \div +1.5$ eV (see TABLE).
The formation energies of charged defect states depend sensitively on the parameter set and on the constraints on the lattice displacements (compare e.g. the first and the second row of the TABLE). For fixed A-sites and the adopted parameter set, the formation energies of electron and hole bipolarons are *positive*, i.e. they are truly resonance states. Contrarily, when all sites are allowed to be displaced, there is a strong electron-hole asymmetry and an unexpected strong influence of the band filling ratio with respect to their formation energies. For the half-filled antibonding band the formation energy of *electron* bipolarons becomes *negative*, whereas for one third or quarter filled band it becomes negative for *hole* bipolarons.

Furthermore, we have investigated excitonic and biexcitonic excitations. In the present simple approach, the electron and holes are bound by the strong electron-lattice

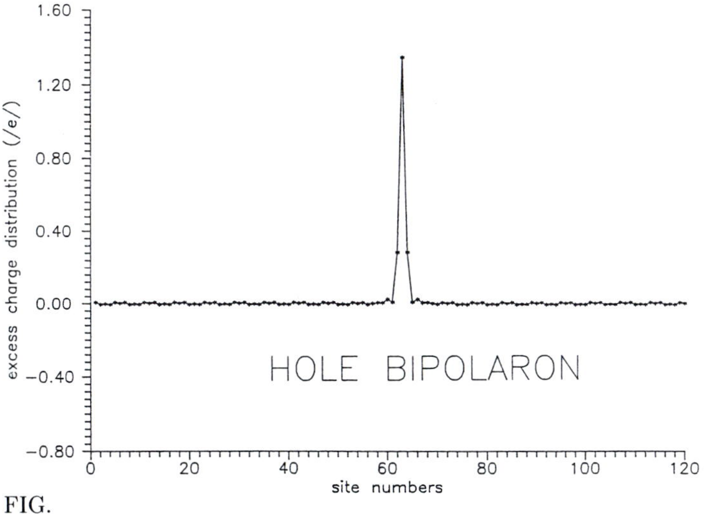

FIG.
Excess charge distribution of a hole bipolaron vs. site number m for a $N = 120$ membered periodic chain and the band filling ratio $\nu = 1/3$.

TABLE

Ground state properties and formation energies of polaronic states

The following abbreviations are used: ν - band filling ratio, $u_0(v_0)$ - amplitudes of the internal (inchain) component of the superstructure, E_{gap} - Peierls gap, $P_\pm$ - $\pm$ charged polaron, $P_{\pm 2}$ - $\pm$ charged bipolaron, P_0 - polarexciton, B_0 - biexciton; *) A-sites fixed.

ν	$\beta_{A,B}$ [eV/Å]	u_0 [Å]	v_0 [Å]	E_{gap} [eV]	$E_{P_{-2}}$ [eV]	E_{P_-} [eV]	E_{P_0} [eV]	$E_{P_{+2}}$ [eV]	E_{B_0} [eV]
1/2 *)	1.0	0.11	0.24	1.77	1.023	0.76	0.96	1.1	–
1/2	1.0	0.11	0.24	1.77	-0.403	0.37	0.94	0.704	0.116
1/3	1.5	0.14	0.49	2.36	0.314	0.64	1.11	-0.212	0...0.1
1/4	1.75	0.16	0.69	2.68	0.819	1.04	1.33	-0.665	0...0.154

interaction only. Thus, the neglected Coulomb interaction is expected to lower further their formation energy.

4. Discussion and Outlook

The negative formation energy and strong localization of hole bipolarons for the band filling ratios $\nu = 1/3$ or $1/4$ suggests an "backward" electronic charge transfer from the chains to the planes. Due to the "loss" of Madelung energy it will be stopped at a finite concentration of bipolarons. In this new equilibrium state the formation energy of bipolarons will be zero. Thus, the basic assumption of some phenomenological boson-fermion models (s. e.g. [9-11]) on the pinning of the bosonic level to the Fermi energy is fulfilled. For the case $\nu = 1/3$ $(1/4)$ the experimental value of 0.25 (0.2) holes per CuO_2 unit can be reproduced provided that at every sixth (tenth) A-place only a bipolaron is located. The existence of *single* hole bipolarons with negative formation energies for realistic band filling ratios seems to be a necessary condition for the applicability of the s-channel model to the cuprates, since the fermions in the planes are holes.

The formation energy of polarons agrees well with new optical data of Dewing et al. [4] showing a broad absorption region between 0.5 eV and 1.1 eV with a maximum near 0.7 eV. Within our model the formation of *chain* electron and hole polarons as well as polarexcitons should be expected to contribute sufficiently to the broad absorption curve due to their different formation energies (see TABLE).

The usual t-channel (exchange of neutral bosons, e.g. phonons) could possibly be enhanced by the biexcitons or polarexcitons considered above. The low energy of the bi(polar)exciton and its high metastability suggests a strong interaction with high-frequency phonons giving rise to their so far unexplained Fano-line shape. Since the formation energy of a biexciton is within the same range as the midinfrared absorption, a sizable contribution could be expected from its creation.

Recent structural data [5] claiming different positions of the apical oxygens $\Delta u = 0.13$Å $\propto u_0$ can be explained by our model simply as the superstructure induced due to the Peierls transition, i.e. no strong anharmonicity of double-well character for the apical oxygens is required. Similarly, different positions of apical oxygens reported for the Tl- and Bi-based cuprate superconductors could be intepreted as the result of a further structural instability of corresponding chain fragments mentioned in Sect.1. Large displacements of inchain oxygens were deduced from electron thermal diffuse scattering data [6]. Quite interestingly, hints for a local charge density wave and a pseudogap manifesting theirselves in two different Bi-O bond lengths (analogously to different Cu-O bond lengths for the CuO_3 chains) even for the nominal metallic and superconducting cubic phase $BaBi_{0.25}Pb_{0.75}$ were reported in [7]. A commensurate phase modulation for the other cubic oxide superconductor $Ba_{0.6}K_{0.6}BiO_3$ was found in [8].

Basic assumptions of several phenomenological boson-fermion (local pair) and negative U-models [9-11] can be approximately justified by our microscopic approach. Since peculiar experimental findings as marginal Fermi liquid behaviour, linear resistivity and suppressed isotope effects can be described by these models, we believe that there might also be a microscopic foundation by the present model. However, more detailed investigations with respect to a quantitative comparison with experimental data are necessary.

5. Literature References

[1] H. Eschrig and S.-L. Drechsler, Physica C**173**, 80(1991);
H. Eschrig, S.-L. Drechsler, and J. Malek Physica C**185-189**, 3597(1991).

[2] A.R. Bishop, J.T. Gammel, and S.R. Phillpot, Synthetic Metals **29**, F151(1989).

[3] H. Eschrig, R. Monnier, G. Schadler , and D. Schmicker, to be published.

[4] H.L. Dewing, E.K. Salje, K. Scott, and A.P. Mackenzie, J. Phys.: Cond. Matter **4**, L109(1992).

[5] J. Mustre de Leon, S.D. Conradson, I. Batistić *et al.*, Phys. Rev. B **44**, 2422(1991); P.G. Allen, J. Mustre de Leon, S. Conradson, and A.R. Bishop, Phys. Rev. B**44**, 9480 (1991).

[6] Y.Koyama and Y. Hasebe, Phys. Rev. B **37**, 5831(1988).

[7] J.B. Boyce, F.G. Bridges, T. Claeson, T.H. Geballe, G.G. Li, and A.W.Sleight, Phys.Rev.B **44**, 6961(1991).

[8] M. Verwerft, G. van Tendeloo, D.G. Hinks, B.Dabrowski, D.R. Richards, A.W. Mitchell, T.D. Marx, Shiyou Pei, and J.D. Jorgensen, Phys. Rev. B**44**, 9547(1991).

[9] Y. Bar-Yam, Phys.Rev. B**43**, 359, 2601(1991).

[10] R.I. Shekhter, G. Wendin, and I.O. Kulik, Phys.Rev. B**44**, 10215(1991).

[11] B.R. Alascio, R. Allub, C.R.Proetto, and C.I. Ventura, Solid State Commun. **77**, 949 (1991).

Phase Separation and High-T_c Superconductivity

E. Sigmund[1] *and V. Hizhnyakov*[2]

[1]Institut für Theoretische Physik, Universität Stuttgart, Pfaffenwaldring 57, W-7000 Stuttgart 80, Fed. Rep. of Germany

[2]Institute of Physics, Estonian Academy of Sciences, Riia 142, Tartu, Estonia

When doping the antiferromagnetically (AF) ordered high-T_c cuprates with holes magnetic polarons (spinpolarized clusters) are formed. At higher hole concentrations and due to cluster diffusion a phase separation is formed by establishing large fractal or percolative clusters. This percolation picture allows to understand experimentally obtained results for phase separation as well as magnetic and conductive phase diagrams.

1. Introduction

Doping or oxidation of high-T_c materials creates holes in antiferromagnetically ordered CuO_2 planes. Due to strong correlation effects a hole in the CuO_2 plane rearranges the antiferromagnetic (AF) order in its nearest vicinity forming a spin-polarized cluster (magnetic polaron or ferron)[1]. The cluster has only low mobility whereas the hole inside the cluster can move freely. As a result, when increasing the hole concentration and due to cluster diffusion a phase separation is formed by building up a (hole-rich) large fractal percolation net leading to destruction of AF order and to appearance of a metallic-like conductivity [2,3].

2. Hole dynamics in CuO_2 planes

Our considerations are based on the two-band Hubbard model (see e.g. Emery [4]), the effect of the strong particle-particle (Hubbard) repulsion is treated by two different approaches:

I.) The first approach makes use of the small value of the difference ε between the Cu and the O electronic on-site energies

Springer Series in Solid-State Sciences, Vol. 113 Electronic Properties of High-T_c Superconductors
Editors: H. Kuzmany, M. Mehring, J. Fink

compared with the on-site Hubbard repulsion energy U on Cu sites (see e.g. [5], where the ratio ε/U is found to be ≈ 0.3). A modified Schrieffer - Wolff transformation [6] is applied to the Hamiltonian allowing to eliminate those oxygen - copper hybridization terms, which change the double occupancy of the Cu ions. The transformed Hamiltonian is treated in Hartree-Fock approximation.

For the undoped case the structure of the bands and the ground state energy are calculated a) for the paramagnetically (non-spin-ordered) and b) for the antiferromagnetically ordered structure. The case (b) yields a lower energy.

When an extra hole is added to the system two different situations have to be considered: (i) the hole will occupy the top of the highest filled band and AF order persists. (ii) the hole forms a localized spin-polarized state (magnetic polaron); in the vicinity of the hole the spins are allowed to differ from the spin values of the AF ordered structure.

For the considered parameter range (ii) leads to the lower energy. In this situation due to the local spin-deviation from the AF order the hole can move rather freely inside the cluster gaining hybridization energy $\sim$T. This energy E can be calculated by Green's functions from the secular equation

$$\det \left| (E-\varepsilon)I - \sum_{m,n} V(\vec{M},\vec{m})\, G(\vec{m}-\vec{n},E)\, V(\vec{n},\vec{N}) \right| = 0,$$

where G(E) is the Green function of electron states in the AF ordered lattice, $V(M,m) \sim T$ specifies the Cu-O hybridization interaction in dependence of the Cu spin polarization, M and N refers to the positions of the disturbed spins, while m and n to the positions and the orbitals of the surrounding oxygen atoms. The value of the local (disturbed) spin polarization $\langle n_\alpha \rangle$ is estimated selfconsistently. For one disturbed spin the equation reads ($\alpha=\downarrow,\uparrow$)

$$\langle n_\alpha \rangle = \frac{1}{\pi} \int_0^{E_F} dE\, \mathrm{Im} G_\alpha(E) + \sum_i \frac{1}{\pi} \mathrm{Im}\, G_\alpha(E_i) \,.$$

Here $G_\alpha(E)$ depends on both $\langle n_\uparrow \rangle$ and $\langle n_\downarrow \rangle$, i counts the local states. In the limit $(U-\varepsilon)/T \gg 1$ the clusters are totally spin-polarized (ferron-type hole clusters). For $U/T \sim 6$ and $\varepsilon \sim 2$ the most stable clusters contain 2 to 4 turned Cu spins.

II.) The second approach is based on a Hartree-Fock (mean-field) approximation of the original two-band Hubbard Hamiltonian. Here the Hubbard repulsion is given in the form

$$U \sum_m n^d_{m\uparrow} n^d_{m\downarrow} = U \sum_m \left(n^d_{m\uparrow} \langle n^d_{m\downarrow} \rangle + n^d_{m\downarrow} \langle n^d_{m\uparrow} \rangle \right)$$

$$- U \sum_m \langle n^d_{m\uparrow} \rangle \langle n^d_{m\downarrow} \rangle + H'$$

The fluctuation term $H' = U \sum_m (n_{m\uparrow} - \langle n_{m\uparrow} \rangle)(n_{m\downarrow} - \langle n_{m\downarrow} \rangle)$ is neglected. Again, when adding an extra hole the local spin disturbance is calculated selfconsistently. As before the energy of the ferromagnetically ordered cluster is smaller than the unpolarized free hole state. For different parameter sets this energy difference is listed below (see tab.1).

Table 1 The binding energy and the Cu-spin polarization for the undoped $\langle n_\uparrow \rangle$, $\langle n_\downarrow \rangle$ and doped $\langle n'_\uparrow \rangle$, $\langle n'_\downarrow \rangle$ cases in dependence of U and ε.

U	ε	$\langle n_\uparrow \rangle$	$\langle n_\downarrow \rangle$	$\langle n'_\uparrow \rangle$	$\langle n'_\downarrow \rangle$	$-\Delta E$
4	2	0.67	0.03	0.31	0.57	0.48
5	2	0.77	0.02	0.30	0.68	0.43
6	2	0.84	0.005	0.29	0.75	0.42
7	2	0.89	0.003	0.28	0.81	0.44
8	2	0.94	0.002	0.28	0.85	0.45
9	2	0.96	0.001	0.26	0.88	0.46
10	2	0.97	0.0005	0.25	0.91	0.46
4	3	0.53	0.05	0.29	0.41	0.63
5	3	0.68	0.02	0.28	0.56	0.44
6	3	0.78	0.008	0.26	0.68	0.36
7	3	0.85	0.004	0.23	0.76	0.36
8	3	0.89	0.002	0.21	0.83	0.36
9	3	0.94	0.001	0.2	0.87	0.37
10	3	0.96	0.0007	0.19	0.89	0.38

3. Experimental evidences for percolative phase separation

Field dependent magnetization measurements in slightly doped (oxygen enriched as well as Sr doped) La_2CuO_4 samples show the formation of conducting phases by the existence of a percolative phase separation [7]. The essential results are summarized in Fig. 1. Below 37 K, the sample of $La_2CuO_{4+\delta}$ exhibits a sharp transition from the paramagnetic to a diamagnetic magnetization indicating the presence of superconductivity. The diamagnetic fraction in the magnetization strongly depends on the temperature T_S to which the

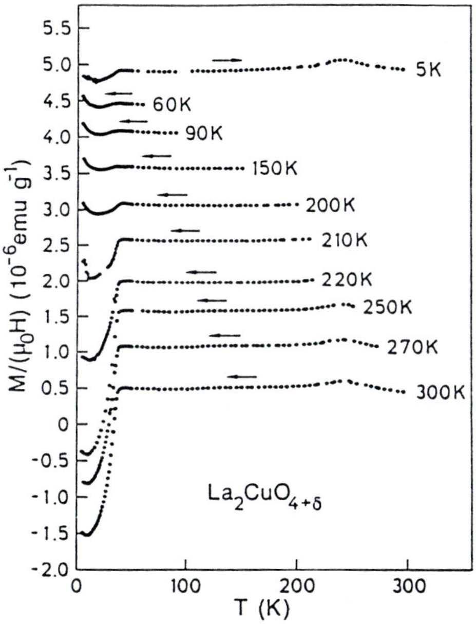

Fig.1 Magnetization of a $La_2CuO_{4+\delta}$ sample as a function of the temperature. The starting temperature T_S to which the sample was quenched from room temperature are indicated. The uppermost curve was obtained after quenching the sample to 5K and slowly heating to room temperature. Beginning from the lowest data set each curve was shifted upwards by a value of 5×10-7emu g^{-1} compared to the preceeding one. The measuring field was 90G, arrows indicate the direction of temperature change during the measurements.

sample was rapidly quenched. Below T_S magnetization data were acquired during slow cooling temperature scans. Note that a sudden decrease of the diamagnetic fraction occurs at values of T_S in the range of 200 - 250 K. Surprisingly, the sample quenched to 5 K (Fig. 1, uppermost curve) shows a very small diamagnetic fraction only. This clearly proves that superconductivity can almost completely be suppressed by rapid temperature quenching of the sample. If, however, cooling was performed *slowly* the diamagnetic shielding signal became maximal. As shown in [8] the formation of superconducting phases can also be initiated by application of sizeable magnetic fields.

The results obtained for the Sr doped samples can be seen in Fig. 2 showing an increasing diamagnetic fraction with higher Sr contents. The most obvious feature is the distinct separation between the field cooled (applied measuring field of 90G) and the zero-field cooled magnetization both for the $La_2CuO_{4+\delta}$ and the Sr doped samples in the same temperature range. It is important to note that this temperature range is well above any of the Neel temperatures in the Sr doped samples. We find that the $La_2CuO_{4+\delta}$ sample shows quantitatively similar behaviour as the $La_{1.98}Sr_{0.02}CuO_4$ sample.

All these measurements clearly prove that in the investigated samples diffusion processes of magnetic quasiparticles take place which can be influenced either by thermal treatment (fast and slow cooling) or by magnetic fields. Not all the quasiparticles, however, contribute to the conducting phase which is of fractal nature but rather coexist with single magnetic quasiparticles which give rise to the observed paramagnetic behaviour. The equilibrium between these two subsystems can be shifted by thermal treatment of the samples. With increasing temperature thermal fluctuations gradually destroy the conducting (superconducting) phase breaking it up into magnetic quasiparticles as can be seen by the monotonic increase in the paramagnetic signal (Fig. 2c and d, lower curves).

A clustering or percolation of this type, however, can only take place when the subunit i.e. the magnetic quasiparticle has a considerable size (several lattice units). In such a diffusion controlled

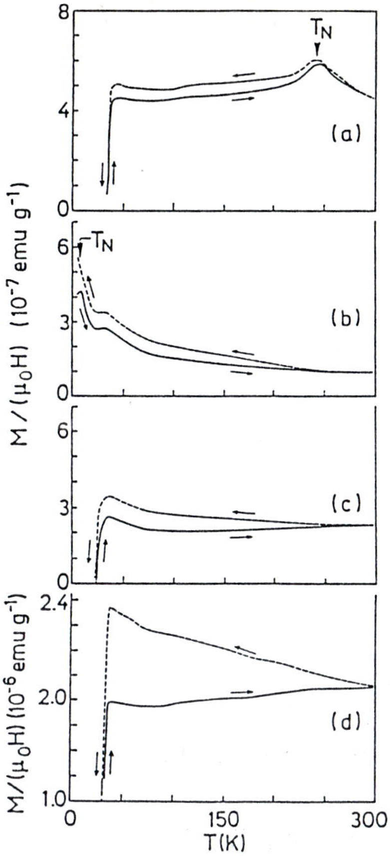

Fig. 2 fc and zfc magnetizations of the $La_2CuO_{4+\delta}$ sample and moderately Sr doped samples $La_{2-x}Sr_xCuO_4$ as a function of the temperature. Arrows indicate the direction of the temperature variation. The zfc magnetisation curve was measured after the sample had been cooled slowly from room temperature to 5K by using the same temperature interval step sequence, including equilibriation, as in the subsequent heating (or cooling) cycles and with applied magnetic field. The Neel temperatures T_N for the $La_2CuO_{4+\delta}$ samples and for $La_{1.94}\ Sr_{0.06}CuO_4$ are indicated. Note : the zero of ordinate for $La_{1.94}\ Sr_{0.06}CuO_4$ has been suppressed.

clustering process there is no critical phase transition temperature, but merely a temperature region wherein the conducting phase (delocalized holes) coexists with a noncondensed phase consisting of separated magnetic quasiparticles. Holes can also be created optically [8] (see also [9], where photoinduced conductivity and superconductivity has been observed in high-T_c cuprates). Hereby, first free (non-polaronic) holes are created, which subsequently relax to a ferron-type (polaronic) state [10]. This relaxation process is of activative nature: the free- and the ferron-type hole states are separated by an activation barrier [10].

References:

[1] Hizhnyakov, V., Sigmund, E., Physica C **156**, 655 (1988)

[2] Hizhnyakov, V., Kristoffel, V., Sigmund, E., Physica C **161**, 435 (1989)

[3] Hizhnyakov, V., Sigmund, E., Materials Letters 9, 425 (1990)

[4] Emery, V.J., Phys.Rev.Lett. **58**, 2794 (1987)

[5] Dopf, G., Muramatsu, A., Hanke, W., Phys.Rev.Lett. **68**, 353 (1992)

[6] Hizhnyakov, V., Sigmund, E., Schneider, M., Phys.Rev.B **44**, 795 (1991)

[7] Kremer, R.K., Sigmund, E., Hizhnyakov, V., Hentsch, F., Simon, A., Müller, K.A., Mehring, M., Z.Phys.B Cond. Matter **86**, 319 (1992)

[8] Taliani, C., Pal, A., Ruani, G., Zamboni, R., Wei, X., and Vardeny, Z.V., in Electronic properties of High-T superconductors and related compounds, ed. by H. Kuzmany, M. Mehring and J. Fink, Springer Series of Solid State Science, Vol. **99** (Springer Berlin)

[9] Yu, G., Lee, C.H., and Heeger, A.J., Physica C**90**, 563 (1992)

[10] Hizhnyakov, V., Sigmund, E., Zavt, G., Phys. Rev. B**44**, 12639 (1991)

Temperature-Dependent Phase Separation in the Emery Model

K. Dichtel and J. Carstensen

Institut für Theoretische Physik der Universität Kiel,
W-2300 Kiel, Fed. Rep. of Germany

Abstract: The variational principle of Bogoljubov is used to derive the temperature and parameter dependent phase diagram of carriers in hole doped HTSC cuprates.

1 Introduction

The understanding of the properties of the HTSC cuprates not only in the superconducting, but also in the normal state seems to be related intimately to the understanding of highly correlated models for the carriers in the copper oxygen planes. Despite of the fact that Hubbard and extended Hubbard models are known for decades there is still considerable lack of adequate calculation methods especially in the experimentally interesting intermediate coupling regime. Exact diagonalization studies are still restricted to few lattice units, Monte Carlo calculations become inefficient in the interesting parameter regions and analytic approximations apply only in special limiting cases. Thus it seems reasonable to perform a standard variational approach to obtain upper limits for the thermodynamical functions.

2 The Model and the Method

We start with the standard Emery Model [1] for the Cu–O Planes

$$\begin{aligned}\mathbf{H} &= \frac{U_d}{2}\sum_{n,\sigma} \mathbf{x}_{n,\sigma}^{1+}\mathbf{x}_{n,\sigma}^{1}\mathbf{x}_{n,-\sigma}^{1+}\mathbf{x}_{n,-\sigma}^{1} - \epsilon_0 \sum_{n,\sigma}\mathbf{x}_{n,\sigma}^{1+}\mathbf{x}_{n,\sigma}^{1} \\ &+ \gamma \sum_{\substack{\langle n,(m,j)\rangle \\ \sigma}} t_{n,(m,j)}\mathbf{x}_{n,\sigma}^{1+}\mathbf{x}_{m,\sigma}^{j} + \text{h.c.} \qquad ,\end{aligned}$$

where $\mathbf{x}_{n,\sigma}^{j+}$ creates holes on copper sites n for $j = 1$ and holes on adjacent oxygen sites m for $j = 2, 3$. The constant U_d denotes the on site

Coulomb correlation on copper places, γ denotes the absolute value of the transfer integral and ϵ_0 denotes the charge transfer energy. We use the thermodynamic variational principle of Bogoljubov in a form given by Koppe [2] extended to the grand canonical ensemble

$$\Omega - \Omega_0(\mathbf{U}) = \Omega_T + \left\langle \mathbf{U}^{+}\mathbf{H}\mathbf{U} \right\rangle_T - \left\langle \mathbf{H}_T + \mu \mathbf{N} \right\rangle_T \quad ,$$

where the test–Hamiltonian $\mathbf{H}_T$ and the canonical transformation $\mathbf{U}$ can be chosen arbitrarily with some variational parameters. $\left\langle ... \right\rangle_T$ means the thermodynamic average with $\mathbf{H}_T$

$$\mathbf{H}_T := \sum_{c_1,c_3} \tilde{u}_{c_1c_3} \frac{1}{2} \sum_{\sigma,n} \mathbf{x}_{n,\sigma}^{c_1+} \mathbf{x}_{n,\sigma}^{c_1} \mathbf{x}_{n,-\sigma}^{c_3+} \mathbf{x}_{n,-\sigma}^{c_3} - \tilde{\epsilon}_0 \sum_{n,\sigma} \mathbf{x}_{n,\sigma}^{1+} \mathbf{x}_{n,\sigma}^{1}$$
$$+ \sum_{n,c_1} h_n^{c_1} \mathbf{s}_{z,n}^{c_1} - \lambda \sum_{n,\sigma,c_1} \mathbf{x}_{n,\sigma}^{c_1+} \mathbf{x}_{n,\sigma}^{c_1} \quad ,$$

where $\tilde{u}_{c_1c_3}$, $h_n^{c_1}$, $\tilde{\epsilon}_0$ and λ are variational parameters.
The choice of a simple local operator in the strong coupling limit is improved by the introduction of a canonical transformation $\mathbf{U}$ which is optimized by an expansion to second order of γ. The procedure is strictly analogous to the one proposed by Jelitto and Heise [3] for the one–band–Hubbard–Model. The details of the calculation of the expectation values with this canonical transformation, first in lattice–, then in k–space will be published elsewhere.

3 Results for the Paramagnetic Case

Fig. 1 shows the resulting curves free energy F_0 versus hole concentration n_h for a) the atomic limit, b) the strong coupling variational approximation for $\gamma = 1eV$ and c) the standard paramagnetic Hartree Fock approximation for the same value of γ. For hole concentrations $n_h \gtrsim n_h^{\star}$ Hartree Fock yields a deeper (better) free energy than the strong coupling limit and Fermi liquid behaviour occurs.
Fig. 2 shows the chemical potential μ versus doping n_h with the "charge transfer" discontinuity at $n_h = 1.0$. One sees that the effective charge transfer constant ϵ_0 is increased in our solution.
Fig. 3 shows an enlarged portion of the roughly constant chemical potential in the interval $n_h > 1$ thus unrevealing the most important feature that there is a region of negative slope of μ, that means thermodynamical instability. The system separates spatially into nearly neutral regions and regions of high carrier concentration as proposed by [4]. The Maxwell

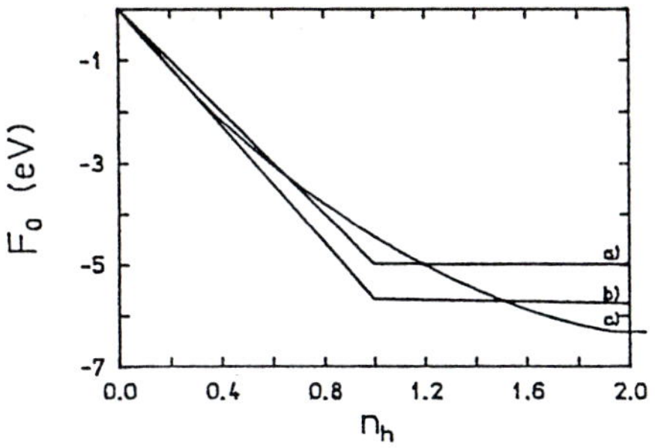

Fig. 1: Free energy F_0 versus hole concentration n_h for $U_d = 10eV$, $\gamma = 1eV$ and $\epsilon_0 = 5eV$

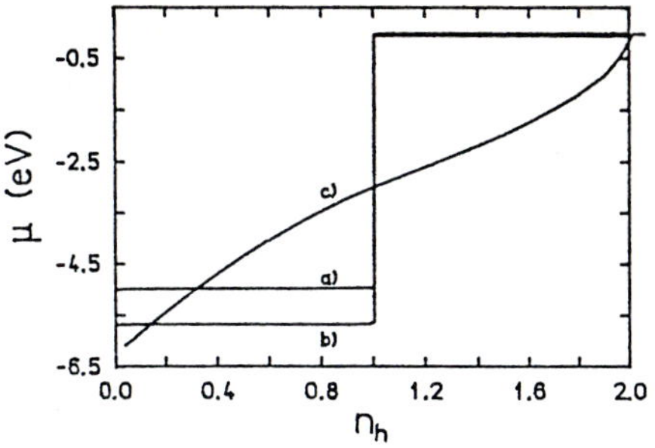

Fig. 2: chemical potential μ versus doping values n_h

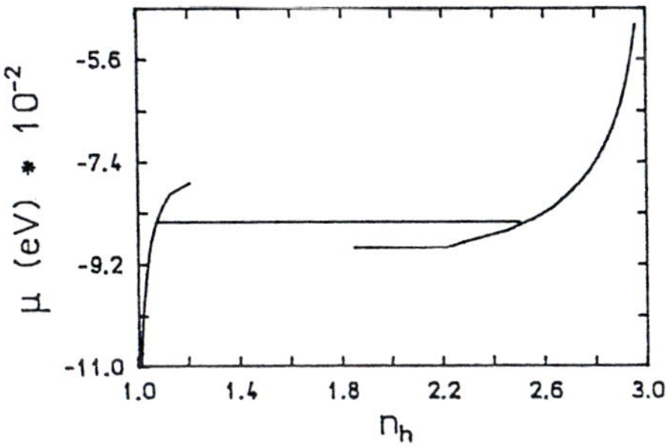

Fig. 3: Enlarged part of the constant chemical potential μ versus n_h in Fig. 2 with negative slope and Maxwell construction

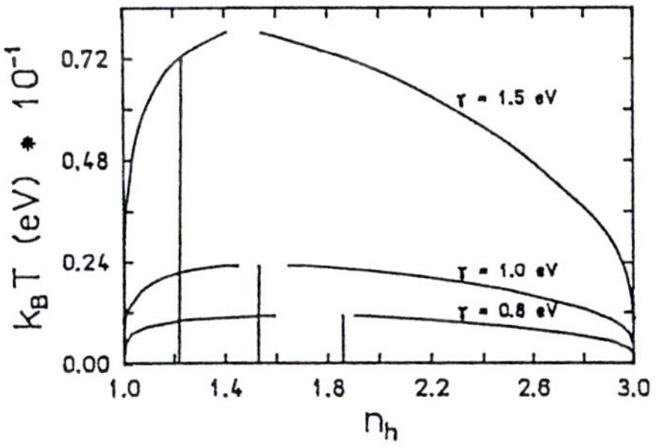

Fig. 4 : Dependence on γ of the paramagnetic phase diagram

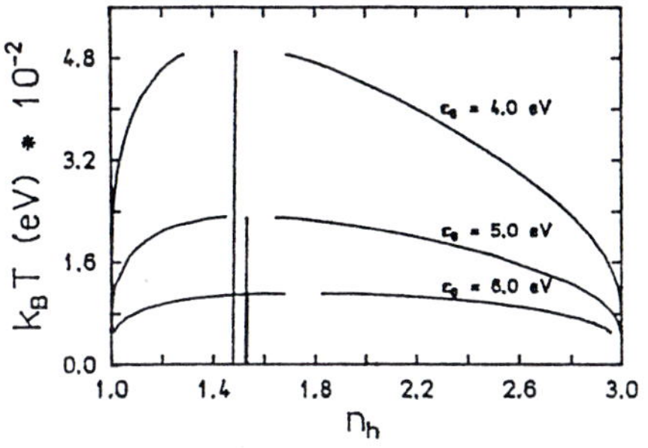

Fig. 5: Dependence on ϵ_0 of the paramagnetic phase diagram

construction in the free energy allows to determine the coexistence regions in the temperature dependent phase diagrams in Figs. 4 and 5. In the regions left to the nearly vertical line at n_h^* which limits the validity of the strong coupling solution this separation occurs whereas right to this line the standard homogeneous (paramagnetic) HF regime extends. Fig. 4 shows that the maximum temperature of this coexistence region increases with increasing γ, but then also the HF line goes to the left thus arriving at some critical value where phase separation disappears. Fig. 5

gives the phase separation regions for different values ot the charge transfer energy ϵ_0. Within this interval of numerical values ϵ_0 the maximum attainable temperature of phase separation goes up with decreasing ϵ_0, whereas the Hartree limiting curve does not change much with ϵ_0.

4 Magnetic Order

At low temperatures the variational solutions with nonvanishing molecular fields are the lower ones. Pure antiferromagnetism occurs as a phenomenon of order γ^4 in the nearly neutral regime up to $n_h \simeq 1.01$ with a Neèl temperature $T_N \approx 290^o K$ for $\gamma = 1eV$. Ferromagnetism is for large n_h the phase with lowest energy. Fig. 6 shows the phase diagram of separation between antiferro– (para)– and ferromagnetic phases with the coexistence regions rather enlarged compared to the paramegnetic ones. But contrary to early suggestions with phase separation caused by competing energies for phases of different magnetic order our result indicates phase separation independent of magnetic order as a result of strong coupling solutions.

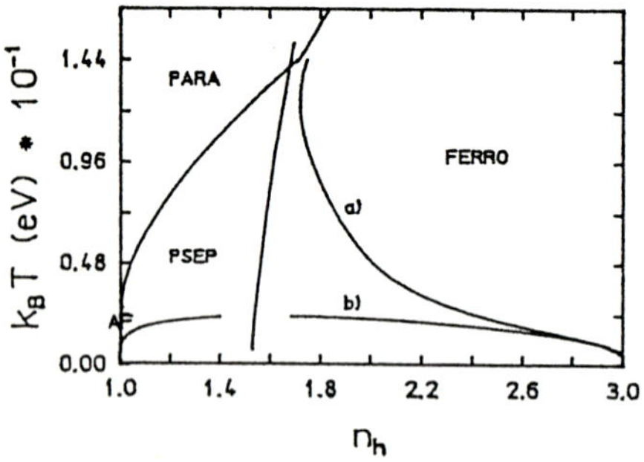

Fig. 6 : Phase diagram between antiferromagnetic (paramagnetic for higher temperature) and ferromagnetic phases

References

[1] V.J. Emery, Phys. Rev. Lett. 58 (1987) 2794

[2] H. Koppe in: "Werner Heisenberg und die Physik unserer Zeit", Vieweg 1956

[3] M. Heise, R.J. Jelitto Z. Phys. B 25 (1976) 381 and B 26 (1977) 177

[4] V.J. Emery, S.A. Kivelson, H.Q. Lin Phys. Rev. Lett 64 (1990) 475

Pairing Interaction Induced by Distortive Electron–Lattice Coupling

A. Bill, E. Sigmund, V. Hizhnyakov, and M. Schneider

Institut für Theoretische Physik, Universität Stuttgart,
Pfaffenwaldring 57, W-7000 Stuttgart 80, Fed. Rep. of Germany

Abstract. For systems with at least two atoms in the unit cell, it is shown that local distortive electron-lattice interactions induce a new type of Cooper pair formation. These interactions lead to a non-retarded coupling which is attractive for charge-carriers (holes) over the whole Brillouin zone. Further, consequences of this new pairing interaction for the gap Δ and the critical temperature T_c are considered. The gap equation is solved for an isotropic model with arbitrary dimension d. In this way, the dependence of T_c on the hole concentration can be obtained and comparison with experimental data allows to obtain the effective dimension of the electronic subsystem $d \approx 1.5$.

1. Introduction

The pairing mechanism considered in the weak-coupling BCS description of conventional superconductors has two main features. Firstly, the effective interaction between charge carriers is mediated by virtual phonon exchanges. This expresses itself in the presence of phonon energies in the analytical form of the coupling. Secondly, due to this mediation, the resulting effective interaction is only attractive for charge carriers with energies near the Fermi energy; the range being characterized by a mean phonon frequency.

Beside the usual electron-phonon interaction which is the origin of this pairing mechanism, there exists another type of electron-lattice coupling, which can lead to a new kind of Cooper pair formation [1]. Namely, the interaction of charge carriers with local static distortions of the lattice. For such a local coupling to be effective it is necessary to have at least two atoms in the unit cell.

To show this we consider the system described by the Hamiltonian

$$\begin{aligned} H &= H_e + H_L + H_{eL} \ , \\ H_e + H_L &= \sum_k \epsilon(k) c_k^+ c_k + \sum_{q\nu} \hbar\omega_{q\nu} (b_{q\nu}^+ b_{q\nu} + \frac{1}{2}) \ , \\ H_{eL} &= W \sum_{n\sigma} c_{n\sigma}^+ c_{n\sigma} Q_n^I + V \sum_{n\sigma} c_{n\sigma}^+ c_{n\sigma} Q_n^{II} \ . \end{aligned}$$

For simplicity we restrict our present discussion to a single electronic band and to a local, i.e. diagonal, electron-lattice coupling.

We have splitted the local electron(hole)-lattice coupling in two parts. The peculiarity of the first part is that the lattice coordinates Q_n^I can be written as a derivative of the potential energy of the vibrating system. This is not the case of the second part Q_n^{II}. This separation can in principle always be done for a system with a many atomic unit cell. The presence of one or the other (or both) depend on the specific system studied. For example, if we consider one CuO_2 plane in the orthorhombic phase(tilted octahedra), the interaction of the charge-carriers with out-of-plane distortions belongs to the first part of the electron-lattice coupling whereas the interaction with in-plane distortions belongs to the second part [2]. In the present description of the CuO_2 we suppose, according to [3], that the Coulomb repulsion is taken into account in the renormalization of the parameters of H.

2. Pairing mechanism

The derivation of the pairing mechanism is done with the help of unitary transformations. Within this method one eliminates the linear electron-lattice coupling with a transformation U and replace it by a series of electron-electron and higher order electron-lattice coupling terms. In the spirit of a perturbation theory in the hole-lattice coupling, one restrict the series obtained up to order $(W+V)^2$. Usually this is done in k-space with a Fröhlich-type transformation [4]. For the local distortive coupling introduced in the precedent section it is however more suitable to use a local transformation U_1 which removes partly the interaction H_{eL}^I. This displacement transformation is written in site representation and has the effect of shifting the equilibrium positions of the atoms in the unit cell in which the particle is present. The transformed H thus describes the motion of particles interacting with a distorted lattice.

In a second step we get rid of the residual hole-lattice interaction by means of a Fröhlich-type transformation U_2 that is non-local and so, is adequately written in k-space.

One finally obtains an expression for the effective coupling between the charge-carriers. If we restrict ourselves to the scattering of Copper pairs ($k\uparrow$, $-k\downarrow$), one obtains two contributions which have a very different structure. This can be seen on the example of the CuO_2 plane were the expressions are particularly simple (K is the Cu-O restoring force constant)

$$H_{ee} = \sum_{k,k'} (V_{ee}^a + V_{ee}^b) c_{k\uparrow}^+ c_{-k\downarrow}^+ c_{-k'\downarrow} c_{k'\downarrow} ,$$

$$V_{ee}^a = -\frac{4W^2}{K} ,$$

$$V_{ee}^b = V \sum_{\nu} \frac{V N_\nu(k,k') + W M_\nu(k,k')}{(\epsilon(k)-\epsilon(k'))^2 - (\hbar\omega_{k-k',\nu})^2} .$$

At this point two important remarks have to be done. Since we consider only terms up to order $(W+V)^2$, we are working in the framework of a *weak* electron (hole)-lattice coupling theory. This means that we cannot have self-trapped polarons in the regime studied in this model. Secondly, the new term V^a appearing in the pairing interaction is ***not*** an on-site negative Hubbard-type term but takes this form only for $(k \uparrow, -k \downarrow)$ pairs. It describes in k-space, a scattering of particles moving in a distorted crystal.

As one can see, the first, non retarded, interaction is attractive for all charge-carriers of the Fermi sea. Furthermore, it does not depend on the ionic masses and therefore will give no isotope effect. Finally, because of the dependence on $1/K$, soft modes will enlarge the contribution of this term. These are general assertions about this term that are independent of the particular model (the CuO_2 plane) considered here. A special feature of the model is that V^a arises from the coupling of the holes with out-of-plane local distortions. If the crystal would be in the tetragonal phase, this term would disappear because the linear W coupling is then forbidden by grouptheoretical arguments.

The second term of the pairing interaction has the usual Fröhlich-type denominator. Thus, only those holes which are close to the Fermi surface (the energy range being given by a mean phonon frequency) will attract each other. In addition, it will give a contribution to the isotope effect. In general, the interplay of the two contributions to the pairing interaction will depend on the system considered.

3. The gap equation

We study here the effect of the new term V^a appearing in the pairing interaction. To this aim we set $V = 0$, which means that we consider only the interaction of holes with local out-of-plane distortions. In particular, we want to determine the dependence of the gap Δ and T_c on the hole concentration and the dimension d of the hole subsystem. The self-consistency equation for the gap Δ has the same structure as in the BCS theory but the pairing term is here given by V^a. This effective interaction is independent of the vector k, thus also the gap. Consequently one can go from the sum over k' appearing in the equation to the integral over the energy. The resolution of this equation has now to differ from the usual BCS treatment. As a matter of fact, the pairing interaction being attractive for all particles of the system, one cannot restrict the integration to a small range defined by the mean phonon energy about the Fermi surface. The integration has to be performed over the whole band. This further implies that it is not possible to take only the DOS $\rho(E)$ at the Fermi energy; its structure becomes important.

The dimension d of the electronic subsystem only appears in the DOS. To perform calculations for arbitrary dimensions, we have replaced the tight-binding DOS by the one of a free hole gas [2]

$$\rho_d(E) \quad \sim \quad \left(\frac{E_f}{E + E_f}\right)^{\frac{d}{2}-1}.$$

We, however, still take into account the finite bandwidth B of the dispersion.

For $d = 2$ it is possible to obtain the result analytically

$$T_c, \Delta \sim \sqrt{BE_f} exp(\frac{1}{\rho(0)V^a}).$$

As one can see, T_c is now proportional to the bandwidth times the Fermi energy instead of a mean phonon energy. Since we have considered no band reduction for the weak coupling case and since the Fermi energy, although small, is still greater than the phonon energies, one can obtain values of T_c that are much greater than in the BCS theory. In the case $d < 2$, the calculations have to be done numerically. Fitting the results, and knowing the relation between the Fermi energy and the hole concentration n in our simple model, one obtains the following relation

$$\Delta, T_c \sim n^{\frac{3}{d}-1}.$$

Uemura et al. [5] have shown, that for low carrier concentrations n, the relation $T_c \sim n$ holds for a wide group of superconducting materials. Based on the percolation model [3], we are now able from our last expression to deduce the dimension of the underlying fractal system. If Uemura's relation holds, we find $d = 1.5$. This is in quite good agreement with the numerical determination of the fractal dimension of such a network at the percolation threshold $d^* = 1.42$ [6]. In this last paragraph, we have considered $V = 0$ as a special case. If $V \neq 0$, the two parts of the hole-hole interaction compete and one can show that for reasonable values of W and V, the ratio $2\Delta/k_BT_c$ can take values up to 5.

References

[1]V.Hizhnyakov, E.Sigmund, Proc. Estonian Acad. Sci. Phys. Mat., **40**,337 (1991); Philosophical Magazin, in press.

[2]A.Bill,M.Schneider,V.Hizhnyakov,E.Sigmund, to be published

[3]V.Hizhnyakov, E.Sigmund, Physica **C156**,655(1988), and this volume

[4]H.Fröhlich, Proc.Roy.Soc.Lond., **A223**,296(1954)

[5]Y.J.Uemura, L.P.Le, G.M.Luke, B.J.Sternlieb, W.D.Wu, J.H.Brewer, T.M.Riseman, C.L.Seaman, M.B.Maple, M.Ishikawa, D.G.Hinks, J.D.Jorgensen, G.Saito, and H. Yamochi, Phys.Rev.Lett. **66**(20), 2665(1991)

[6]B.M.Sminov, Sov.Phys.Usp.**29**, 482(1986)

Cooperative Electronic Phenomena in High-T_c Superconductors

W. Winkler

Hahn-Meitner-Institut GmbH,
Glienicker Str. 100, W-1000 Berlin 39, Fed. Rep. of Germany

The general existence of a quadrupolar induced hole pairing in high-T_c superconductors is established, as well as, the occurence of valence fluctuations. A model of the electrical conductivity in high-T_c materials has been developed. It is mainly based on a new bosonic conductivity mechanism which permits the understanding of the normal and superconducting state. An excellent agreement is achieved with respect to the experimentally determined T_c-charge carrier relation, the resistivity and Hall effect data.

1. Introduction

In analysing the electronic situation in the new copper oxides, we proceed basically from an electronic reorganization principle in covalently bonded systems which we have termed "detailed momentum balance" [1]. This is to say that the response of the electronic system to perturbations is analysed first in terms of an independent multipole representation. Then, the possible interactions between these distributions are determined through minimum total energy arguments. In relation to this point of view, the situation is very pronounced in the new copper oxides. Highly negatively charged $Cu(II)O_2$ planes, with well separated charges on the copper and oxygen atoms and highly charged cations, give rise to a pronounced situation with respect to the coulombic multipole interactions.

Hence, we proceed primarily from pure electronic mechanisms, as the basis of the cooperative electronic phenomena in the high T_c superconductors, which are accompanied by magnetic interactions, which are, however, not the driving force. This is supported especially by the inelastic neutron scattering experiments which give energetic low laying spin excitations and higher collective excitations through the superconducting gap [2]. Based on the high polarizability of the copper and oxygen atoms, we proceed basically from a pure electronic response on a electronic perturbation and neglect structural or phononic interactions at this time. The results outlined here are based on Hartree-Fock MO cluster calculations.

2. Hole pairing

As experimentally evidenced by X-ray absorbtion studies, XPS as well as by high-energy electron energy-loss spectroscopy, the creation of holes occurs at the oxygen site of the superconducting cuprates [3-7].

Hence, the first question of interest is the spatial extension of the holes in the oxygen bands. In a O^{2-} ion, the doping of one hole gives only a small deviation from a linear energy ($\mathscr{E}$)-hole relation. If we place the oxygen atom additionally in a low dimensional ligand field, as realized in the $Cu(II)O_2$ planes, the energy is lowered, with a corresponding increase in ligand field strength and hole density [8]. Therefore, the

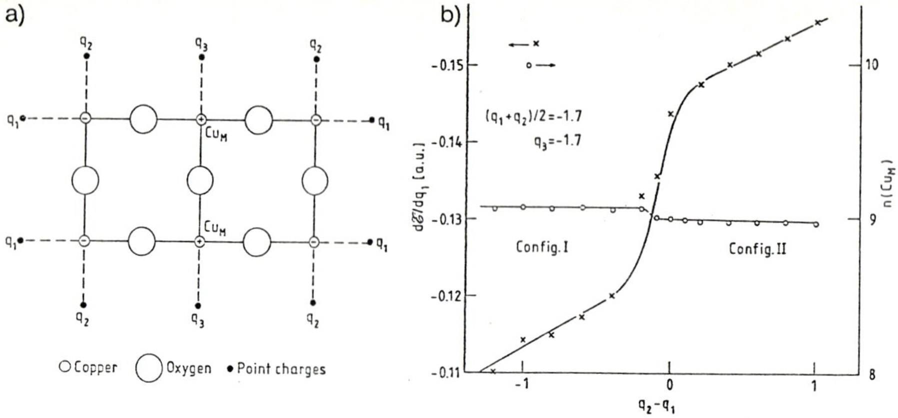

Fig. 1 a) Cluster representing a part of the CuO_2 plane and additional charges q_1,q_2,q_3 located at the Cu-O bonding distance. The signs on the copper atoms indicate the valence fluctuation state. b) Dependence of the derivative of the electronic energy on the charge difference q_2-q_1 with q_3=-1.7=const.. The jump at q_2-$q_1 \approx 0$ indicates the pairing-antipairing transition.

state is favoured for which the holes are more localized at the oxygen atoms and stabilized by the surrounding, more negativelly charged oxygens, thereby producing an intense quadrupolar polarization, i.e. giving an electronic polaron or exitonic state.

In a similar way, the situation concerning the Cu-valences can be analysed. The mean copper valence is about 9.5, as we have shown. Concerning the copper atoms, the correlation energy

$$U(\delta n,\phi_i)=\mathscr{E}_{Cu}(9.5+\delta n,\phi_o,\phi_i)+\mathscr{E}_{Cu}(9.5-\delta n,\phi_o,\phi_i)-2\mathscr{E}_{Cu}(9.5,\phi_o,\phi_i) \quad (1)$$

is always positive. But, if we assume an alternating valence fluctuation state, as depicted in Figs. 1a,2a,3, an effective negative correlation energy

$$U_{eff}(\delta n,\Delta\phi_o,\phi_i)=[\alpha(n+\delta n)-\alpha(n-\delta n)]\Delta\phi_o+U(\delta n,\phi_i) \quad (2)$$

can be obtained, with $\Delta\phi_o$ the changed monopole potential. Therefore, a fluctuating valence state, with respect to the copper valences already seems possible proceeding from these atomic considerations. Under the condition of strong low dimensional ligand fields, the remarkable s-d_z excitations give rise to the possible existence of such static, as well as, dynamic valence fluctuations. Indeed, we have always found fluctuating copper valences in our cluster calculations.

Equally important is the consistent decreasing of energy with lowering symmetry, as we have show [8]. This favours supplementary small spatial extended hole states. Therefore, we have to include strong quadrupolar polarizations by the holes. If the hole location coincides with the valence fluctuation wave length, we can find attractive and repulsive hole-hole interactions, depending on the hole topology and the charge fluctuation sequence (Fig. 1,2).

Bearing this in mind, it is evident that the equallized hole distribution, as in Fig. 2a, is not the most stable one. Rather, it is the state where only attractive hole pairings are existent (bosons). Therefore, we can proceed from a definite boson(n_b)-fermion(n_f)

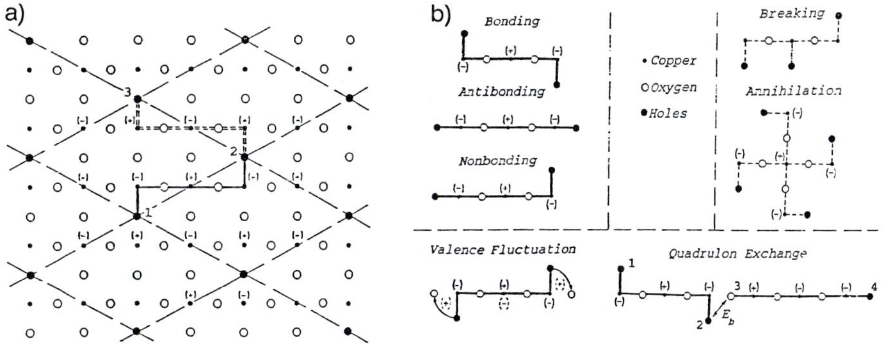

Fig. 2 a) Equalized hole distribution for $n_h=0.1$. Full line means bonding (1-2) dotted line antibonding (2-3). The +,- signs indicate the valence fluctuation state. b) Quadrupolar induced hole-hole interactions depending on the hole topology and the valence fluctuation state. E_b means the hole pairing (quadrulon) energy.

distribution ($n_h=2n_b+n_f$). These hole pairings are balanced by the changed coulombic monopole interaction. From this, the specific quadrupolar polarizations and, the presuposition that $T_c \propto n_b$, the experimentally found T_c-n_h relation can be explained, as well as, the short coherence length [8,9]. Therefore, these results establish the quadrupolar-polarization induced hole pairings as the preexistence for the superconducting state.

3. Hole kinematics

The inelastic neutron scattering experiments indicate the persistence of a pseudo gap well above T_c which can also explain the unusual temperature dependence of the NMR relaxation rates. This supports our result on the preformation of superconducting pairs well above T_c [2,10]. Similarly, the observed slowly frequence dependent infrared conductivity also supports such coulombic induced hole pairing above T_c, such as reported here [11].

The type of coupling between the holes depends strongly on their topology in relation to each other and to the existing valence fluctuation state. Proceeding from a static valence fluctuation regime, we obtain bonding, antibonding and nonbonding hole-hole couplings for a specific charge density sequence , e.g. (-,+,-) in Fig. 2. In the opposite case (+,-,+) the relations are inverted. If we delocalize some holes in Fig. 2a, in an appropriate manner, so that the antibonding couplings are broken, a net energy lowering can be attained. In consequence, the state depicted in Fig. 3, is energetically favourable, where a certain number of holes stays in a bonding bosonic state and the remaining fraction are free fermionic holes.

Turning now to the kinematics of the charge carriers above T_c we can distinguish three possible kinds of movements. First, there exists a free uncorrelated movement of the fermions. Secondly, the bosons, when alone, are rigidly fixed at the lattice, hence are immobile. But, we have to proceed from intense temperature dependent charge density fluctuations. As a result a correlated movement of the bosonic paired holes is possible (Fig.2b). The most crucial kind of movement is the nonadiabatic bosonic exchange (Fig. 2b). In this case the coupling between the holes 1-2 is transfered to 3-4 and vice versa through the displacement of hole 2. We have termed this exchange of the quadrupolar-polarization based energy quantum: "quadrulon".

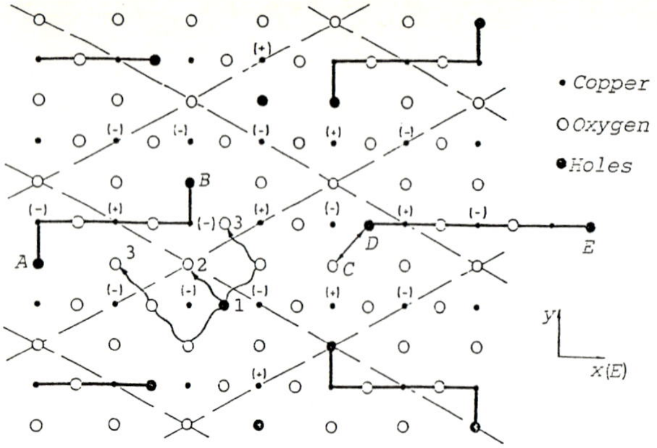

Fig. 3 . Boson-fermion configuration with the electric field placed in x direction. The bosonic chains, the quadrulon exchange and the scattering processes are depicted.

Besides the normal fermion conductivity a more effective mechanism of conductivity is possible along the bosonic lines. If the bosonic density is high enough, an efficient bosonic exchange can occur, e.g. if the hole D moves to C a quadrulon is transferred from D-E to B-C (Fig. 3). In this way an electric conductivity along such bosonic chains is possible, in the manner of a "quadrulon wave".

Two effects are very important with respect to the Hall effect. First, in minimizing the internal energy, the alignment of the Bosons in direction of the electric field prevents chains in y direction (i.e. a quadrulon wave in y direction cannot occur). This is equivalent to a bosonic mobility in the y direction of zero ($\mu_{b_y}=0$). The most crucial process in limiting the fermion mobility μ_f is the fermion-Boson (quadrulon wave) scattering leading to $\mu_f \sim 1/T^2$. With $\mu_{b_x} \sim 1/T$ results

$$R_H = \frac{\mu_{f_x}(n_b)}{e(2n_b\mu_{b_x} + \mu_{f_x}(n_b)\,n_f)} \tag{3}$$

for the Hall constant and

$$\cot\theta = \frac{1}{\mu_{f_x}} \cdot \frac{1}{\omega_c m_f} \tag{4}$$

for the Hall angle, and therefrom the experimentally found $1/R_H \sim T$ and $\cot\theta \sim T^2$ dependence results immediately. Furthermore, specific Hall effect measurements can be explained [12,13,14].

The transition from the normal to the superconducting state is mainly charcterized by the quadrulon waves of the single bosonic chains moving phase rigidly to each other. Therefore, we can conclude that the transition temperature depends on n_b,

$$T_c \propto n_b, \tag{5}$$

on the hole pairing energy E_b,

$$T_c \propto E_b, \tag{6}$$

and on the correlation energy of the valence fluctuations,

$$T_c \propto |U_{eff}| . \tag{7}$$

The substance specific influences are mainly reflected by U_{eff}.

References

[1] W. Winkler, R. Vetter, Chem. Phys. 144, 7, 29 (1990).
[2] J. Rossat-Mignod et al., this volume.
[3] J.M. Tranquada et al., Phys. Rev. B 35, 7187 (1987).
[4] A. Biaconi et al., Solid State Communications 63, 1009 (1987).
[5] N. Nücker et al, Z. Phys. B 67, 9 (1987).
[6] D. van der Marel, J. van Elp, G.M. Sawatzky and D. Heitmann, Phys. Rev. B 37, 5136 (1988).
[7] N. Nücker et al, Phys. Rev. B 37, 5158 (1988).
[8] W. Winkler, Phys. Rev. B1, submitted.
[9] J.B. Torrance et al., Phys. Rev. Lett. 62, 2317 (1988).
[10] M. Mehring et al., this volume.
[11] Z. Schlesinger et al., this volume.
[12] T.R. Chien et al., Phys. Rev. B 43, 6242 (1991).
[13] T.R. Chien et al., Phys. Rev. Lett. 67, 2088 (1991)
[14] W. Winkler, Phys. Rev. Lett., submitted.

Calculation of Electronic Excitation and Ionization Process in High-T_c Superconductors

Z. Crljen[1,2], *G. Wendin*[2], *and Z.H. Levine*[3]

[1]Institute of Theoretical Physics, Chalmers University of Technlogy, S-412 96 Göteborg, Sweden
[2]Rudjer Boskovic Institute, P.O. Box 1016, 41001 Zagreb, Croatia
[3]Department of Physics, The Ohio State University, Columbus, OH 43210-1368, USA

In order to calculate the optical conductivity of HTSC, we first consider the optical response of related small clusters. In this way, the photoabsorption cross section of a CuO_2 molecule is calculated in the TDLDA via one-centre expansion around the Cu site. The resulting absorption shows strong oscillations due to molecular structure.

We are engaged in a study of the many-electron response of high-T_c superconductors and related systems. So far, we have made some general studies of high-energy and optical spectra [1], and calculated optical conductivity, PES and EELS for a simple model of $YBa_2Cu_3O_7$ [2-4]. In this model the 13-atom unit cell is considered as an atomic effective medium with a polarizability equal to the sum of the atomic polarizabilities, calculated in the LDRPA, local-density random phase approximation, to incorporate collective effects within the unit cell.

We are presently extending the work to *cluster descriptions of the unit cell*, to model the local environment and to include charge transfer within the unit cell. The method involves one-centre angular momentum expansion of the cluster potential and wave functions [5-7]. This is a "brute force" method in the sense that very high angular momenta are needed to describe the ligand atoms with reasonable accuracy. The advantage is that, when the expansion works, the Coulomb interaction can be calculated in straightforward manner. This means that electron-electron correlation and many-particle dynamics in the cluster can be studied using well established many-body techniques for atomic systems.

A single-cluster description of the unit cell will not be possible with the present method. A realistic approach may be to model basic subunits of the unit cell, like square-planar CuO_4 and BaO_4 plaquettes or CuO_6 octahedra, etc. We are presently testing the method by calculating the polarizability of the linear molecules Cu-O, O-Cu-O and Ba-O.

In this paper we present preliminary results for the polarizability and optical absorption spectrum of the linear O-Cu-O cluster (Cu-O distance 1.8 Å, from YBaCuO) in the frequency range 0-50 eV. In these first calculations we model the O-Cu-O cluster using overlapping atomic potentials and use this non-self-consistent cluster potential to calculate bound and continuum states and Greenfunctions. This describes basic effects of charge delocalization, charge transfer and covalency, and the resulting optical absorption shows characteristic oscillations due to molecular structure.

Springer Series in Solid-State Sciences, Vol. 113 **Electronic Properties of High-T_c Superconductors**
Editors: H. Kuzmany, M. Mehring, J. Fink

To calculate the electronic structure of the CuO_2 molecule we expand the initial bound state wave functions and the final continuum state Green functions in a spherical-harmonics angular-momentum expansion

$$\psi(\mathbf{r}) = \frac{1}{r} \sum_L u_L(r)\, Y_L(\Omega)\,, \tag{1}$$

$$G(\mathbf{r},\mathbf{r}';E) = \sum_{L,L'} Y_L(\Omega)\, G_{LL'}(r,r';E)\, Y^*_{L'}(\Omega')\;, \tag{2}$$

arriving at coupled set of Schrödinger equations

$$\left(\frac{d^2}{dr^2} + E - \frac{l(l+1)}{r^2}\right) u_L(r) - \sum_{L'} V_{LL'}(r)\, u_{L'}(r) = 0\;, \tag{3}$$

$$\left(\frac{d^2}{dr^2} + E - \frac{l(l+1)}{r^2}\right) G_{LL'}(r,r';E) - \sum_{L''} V_{LL''}(r)\, G_{L''L'}(r,r';E) = \frac{1}{rr'}\,\delta(r-r')\,\delta_{LL'}\;, \tag{4}$$

involving angular momentum expansion of the non-spherical potential $V(\mathbf{r})$,

$$V_{LL'}(r) = \sum_{L''} C_{LL'L''} \int V(\mathbf{r})\, Y_{L''}(\Omega)\, d\Omega \tag{5}$$

($C_{LL'L''} = \int Y_L Y_{L'} Y^*_{L''} d\Omega$ are Gaunt integrals). These equations are solved by procedures described in refs. [5-7]. In the present calculation we truncate the l-expansion, Eq. (1), of the wave function at l=13 (which implies including potential l-components $V_{LL'}(r)$ up to l=26), dictated by the accuracy of the computer (64 bit word).

From the initial state wave functions and the final state Green functions we then construct the dielectric susceptibility

$$\chi_0\,(\mathbf{r},\mathbf{r}';\omega) = \sum_i \psi^*(\mathbf{r})\,\psi(\mathbf{r}')\,G(\mathbf{r},\mathbf{r}';\varepsilon_i+\omega) + \sum_i \psi(\mathbf{r})\,\psi^*(\mathbf{r}')\,G^*(\mathbf{r},\mathbf{r}';\varepsilon_i-\omega), \tag{6}$$

and calculate the induced charge in a self-consistent manner in the usual TDLDA (time dependent local density approximation) manner,

$$\delta n(\mathbf{r};\omega) = \int \chi_0\,(\mathbf{r},\mathbf{r}';\omega)\,\phi^{scf}(\mathbf{r}';\omega)\,d\mathbf{r}'\;, \tag{7}$$

$$\phi^{scf}(\mathbf{r};\omega) = \phi^{ext}(\mathbf{r};\omega) + \int \frac{\delta n(\mathbf{r}';\omega)\,d\mathbf{r}'}{|\mathbf{r}-\mathbf{r}'|} + \delta V_{xc}(\mathbf{r};\omega)\,; \tag{8}$$

and where $\delta V_{xc}(\mathbf{r};\omega)$ is the induced exchange potential (see ref. [5] for details).

The photoabsorption cross section is finally given by

$$\sigma(\omega) = -\,4\pi\,\alpha\,a_0\,\omega\,\mathrm{Im}\int z\,\delta n(\mathbf{r};\omega)\,d\mathbf{r}\;, \tag{9}$$

where $z=r\cos\theta$ is the component of the electric dipole operator along the O-Cu-O axis, α is the fine structure constant (1/137) and a_0 is the Bohr radius.

Figure 1 shows the result of a recent calculation of the conductivity of YBaCuO using a superposition of atomic LDRPA cross sections [4]. In this figure we have specially indicated the contribution from Cu_3O_7 (i.e. 3Cu + 7O).

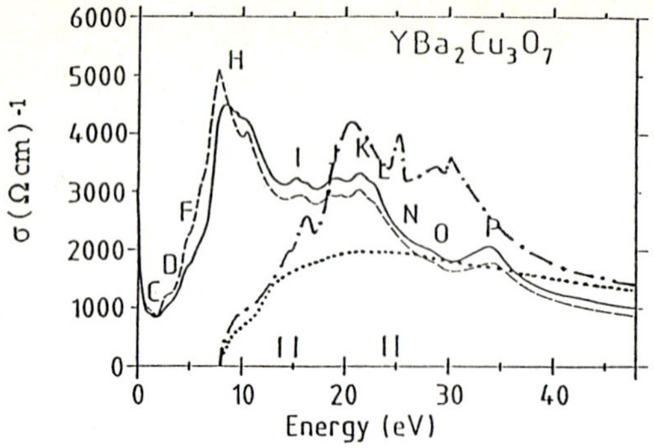

Fig. 1. Experimental optical conductivity of $YBa_2Cu_3O_7$ [8] (full and dashed lines) compared with theory [4] (dashed-dotted line). The dotted line gives the contribution due to Cu_3O_7.

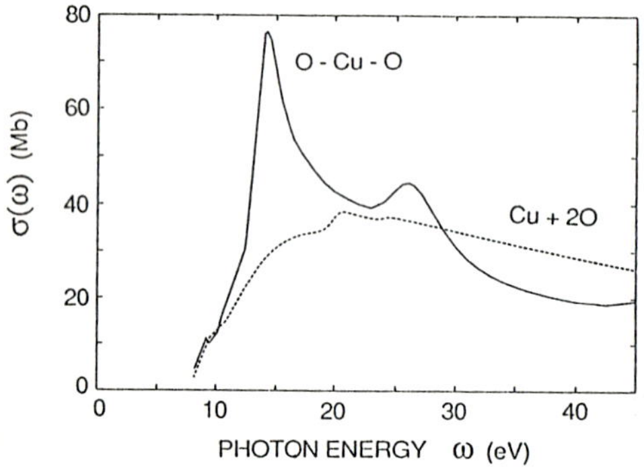

Fig. 2. Theoretical cross sections (~ optical conductivity) of molecular CuO_2.

Figure 2 shows our present result for the O-Cu-O molecule together with the result for superposed atoms. The effect of the molecular structure is to shift intensity from higher to lower excitation energies and to induce structure. The structure can be understood in terms of resonances or multiple scattering, and the shift of intensity in terms of delocalization of valence charge.

It should be mentioned that our results are not well converged. Including up to l=13 is not enough for properly describing the deep Coulomb part of the oxygen potential. As a consequence, there is no clear separation between the O 2p and 2s levels and the energies and wave functions of molecular levels centred on oxygen do not correspond to the real system but have rather a character of pseudostates.

Nevertheless, the total photoabsorption cross section in Fig. 2 should be reasonably well described because it involves a sum over initial levels. The result makes sense since the sum rule seems to be fulfilled.

Finally, in comparison with the superposed-atom result in Fig. 2, two things should be noted. Firstly, the the molecular cluster result in Fig. 2 suggests that the superposed-atom absorption intensity (conductivity) is too high above 30 eV. This will reduce the conductivity in Fig. 1 above 35 eV and lead to good agreement with experiment. Secondly, the conductivity will be considerably enhanced in the 10-15 eV region, basically leaving only the structure H as the major peak that remains to be accounted for. There are good reasons for ascribing this to O2p->Ba5d type of transitions, and we therefore plan to investigate a BaO cluster in the near future.

This work has been supported by the Swedish Natural Science Research Council, by NUTEK, and by the Swedish Institute. ZHL was supported in part by the US DOE -- Basic Energy Sciences, Division of Materials Research.

References:

1. G. Wendin, J. Physique (France) 48, C9-1157 (1987); Physica Scripta **T27**, 31 (1989).
2. G. Wendin and Z. Crljen, Physica C 162-164, 1327 (1989).
3. G. Wendin and Z. Crljen, in Electronic Properties of High-T_c Superconductors and Related Compounds, eds. H. Kuzmany, M. Mehring and J. Fink, Springer Series in Solid State Sciences, vol 99, Springer Verlag, 1990, pp. 147-151.
4. G. Wendin and Z. Crljen, to be published.
5. Z. Levine and P. Soven, Phys. Rev. Lett. **50**, 2074 (1983).
6. Z. Levine and P. Soven, Phys. Rev. A **29**, 625 (1984); erratum, Phys. Rev. A **35**, 3964 (1987).
7. Z. Levine, Phys. Rev. A **30**, 1120 (1984).
8. H. Romberg, N. Nücker, J. Fink, Th. Wolf, X.X. Li, B. Koch, H.P. Geserich, M. Dürrler, W. Assmus and B. Gegenheimer, Z. Phys. B **78**, 367 (1990).

Investigation of Tunneling, Linear and Nonlinear Optical Properties of Negative-U Local-Pair Model for Oxide High-T_c Superconductors

Z. Crljen, M. Hurd, L. Jönsson, R.I. Shekhter, V. Shumeiko+, and G. Wendin*

Institute of Theoretical Physics, Chalmers University of Technology, S-412 96 Göteborg, Sweden
*Permanent address: "R. Bošković" Institute, P.O. Box 1016, 41001 Zagreb, Croatia
+Permanent address: Institute for Low Temperature Physics and Engineering, Ukrainian Academy of Sciences, 47 Lenin Ave., 310164 Kharkov, Ukraine

The linear and nonlinear optical absorption as well as normal state tunneling is investigated within the local-pair model for high Tc materials. Doping dependence of absorption peaks and linear voltage dependence of tunneling conductance is obtained in a qualitative agreement with experiments.

The problem of electronic correlation effects in metallic oxides is a central one in theoretical considerations of high T_c superconductivity. Among other special features of high Tc materials is the small coherence length of the order of 10 Å. That means that superconductivity pairing should be strongly localized within distances comparable with interatomic spacing leading to an old Shafroth idea of pairing in real space [1], possible only in the case of net attraction betwen electrons. Experimental results from infrared spectroscopy reveal gap structrure, still seen above the critical temperature. This has inspired further ideas about preformed pairs being central for explanation of normal and superconducting properties of high Tc materials [2]. Spectroscopic observation of such pairs could give an independent confirmation on mechanism of superconductivity.

In this paper we investigate some consequences of a model which asumes the existance of two particle states caused by negative correlation energy between localized electrons. The very high sensitivity of normal and superconducting properties on carrier doping leads to an assumption for the energy of two particle state to be close to the Fermi energy of the system. Excitation and transport processes at threshold involving those states then have to be two particle processes. That naturally gives rise to nonlinear optical properties, but we shall show that , due to a hybridization of wide band states with these local states, a single photon absorption can give rise to two particle transitions, i.e. to a linear processes.

Our starting point is the periodically extended Anderson model:

$$H_C = \sum_{\kappa\sigma} \varepsilon_{\kappa\sigma} a_{\kappa\sigma}{}^{+} a_{\kappa\sigma} + E_1 \sum_{i\sigma} c_{i\sigma}{}^{+} c_{i\sigma} + U \sum_{i\sigma} n_{i\sigma} n_{i\sigma}$$
$$+ 1/\sqrt{N} \sum_{i\kappa\sigma} \left(t_\kappa e^{-i\kappa R_i} c_{i\sigma}{}^{+} a_{\kappa\sigma} + \text{h.c.} \right), \qquad (1)$$

where $a_{\kappa\sigma}{}^{+}$ and $a_{\kappa\sigma}$ are band-states operators, $c_{i\sigma}{}^{+}$ and $c_{i\sigma}$ localized-states operators at site R_i with intrasite interaction U, and t_κ hybridization between band states and localized states.

Springer Series in Solid-State Sciences, Vol. 113 **Electronic Properties of High-T_c Superconductors**
Editors: H. Kuzmany, M. Mehring, J. Fink

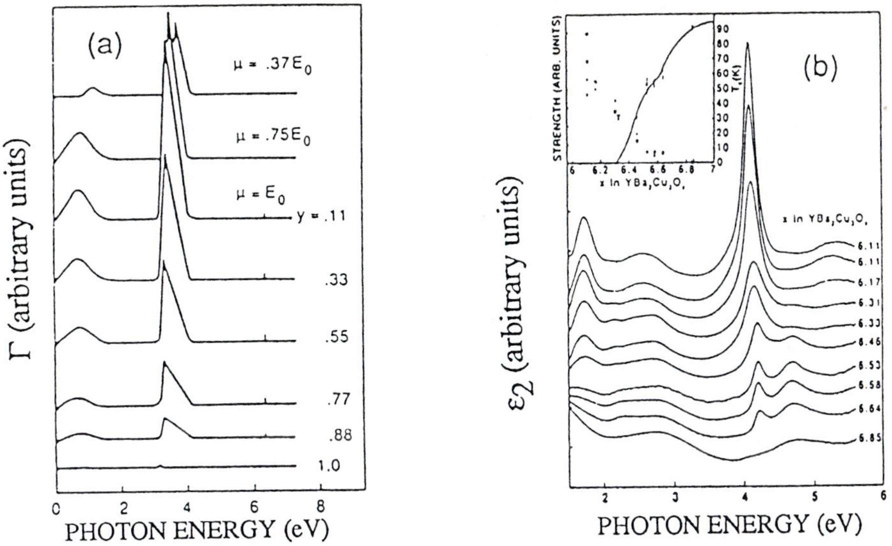

Fig. 1. a) Model calculation of optical absorption. (Parameters: ω_1=4.1eV, ω_2=1.7eV, t_K=1.27eV for all k, E_0=E_2/2) . b) Experimentally observed absorption in ceramic $YBa_2Cu_3O_{6+x}$ from Kelly et al. [4].

In the case of a relatively weak hybridization, in normal phase (T>Tc), the optical absorption Γ exibits two peaks, corresponding to single and double electron transitions with energies ω_1 and ω_2, respectively [3]. Double-electron transition is only due to hybridization t_K and therefore smaller in amplitude than the single-electron transition. The difference between absorption peak positions and intensities enable us to determine directly the magnitude and sign of the local site correlation energy U through the relation $U=\omega_2-2\omega_1$. The essential aspect of the doping dependence is that the transitions shift down in energy and increase in strenght, until the Fermi level becomes pinned at the local pair level E_0, as seen from Fig. 1a. For increased doping, the local level gradually fills up, keeping the Fermi level fixed, and peaks lose intensity and finally disappear.The same behaviour as in our model one finds in $YBa_2Cu_3O_{6-x}$ [4], shown in Fig.1b. Simply associating the experimentally observed peaks with our ω_1 and ω_2 we get a correlation energy U=-6.5 eV. That looks a bit large value for correlation energy, what makes this identification probably unlikely.

In the superconducting phase (T<Tc) our periodically extended Anderson model in BCS approximation leads to the Hamiltonian:

$$H = \sum_{\kappa\sigma} \varepsilon_{\kappa\sigma} a_{\kappa\sigma}{}^{+} a_{\kappa\sigma} + E_1 \sum_{i\sigma} c_{i\sigma}{}^{+} c_{i\sigma} + U \sum_{i\sigma} n_{i\sigma} n_{i\bar{\sigma}}$$
$$+ \{ \sum_{\kappa} \Delta\, a_{\kappa\sigma}{}^{+} a_{-\kappa\bar{\sigma}}{}^{+} + \sum_{i} \Delta_0\, c_{i\sigma}{}^{+} c_{i\bar{\sigma}}{}^{+} + \text{h.c.} \} \qquad (2)$$

with superconducting parameters Δ and Δ_0 taken to be independent of wave number for simplicity. The superconductivity steams from the second order of the hybridization Hamiltonian (last term in Eq. (1)). Assuming negative U and that the single occupied states of LS are well above the Fermi level the localized excitations

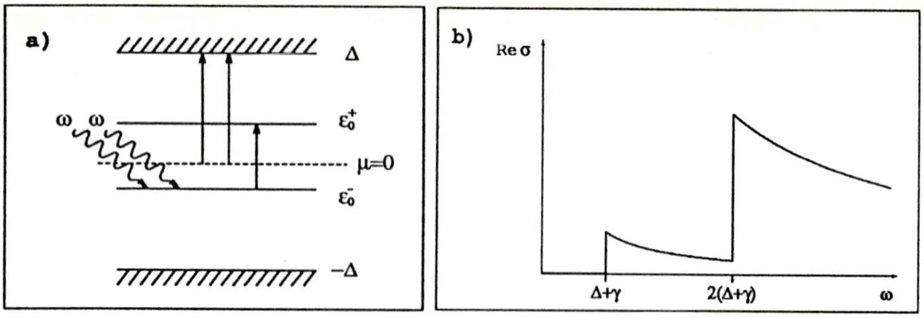

Fig. 2. a) Level diagram for the two-photon absorption from the lower branch of the localized state to the upper branch of the wide band. b) Interband threshold absorption at zero temperature, ($\gamma = (\varepsilon_1^2 + \Delta_0^2)^{1/2}$).

are a two-level system with one and only one state occupied (see Fig. 2a). The local state spectrum is $\varepsilon_0^{\pm} = \varepsilon_1 \pm (\varepsilon_1^2 + \Delta_0^2)^{1/2}$ with $\varepsilon_1 = E_1 - U/2$, while the wide band spectrum is the same as for the ordinary BCS band [5]. At zero temperature the lower branches in both bands are fully occupied while the upper branches are empty.

To calculate the optical absorption we use the Golden rule and obtain the interband threshold absorption spectrum as presented in Fig. 2b. One can see two thresholds, one at $\omega = \Delta + \gamma$, due to direct two photon absorption and another one due to hybridization induced one-photon absorption at twice the energy of lower threshold. However, the lower threshold at normal intensities is a weaker effect than a one-photon process.

Let us now turn to yet another interesting effect coused by local pairs. In sandwich type tunnel junctin of ordinary metal with high Tc material Bi-Sr-Ca-Cu-O the condactance shows large zero-bias value and a linear voltage dependance at low temperature [6] (Fig. 3a). Assumption that high Tc material is a strongly correlated system (CS) with local pair sites opens a possibility for a single electron tunneling between a band in ordinary metal (M) and the local pair sites in CS [7], besides the conventional band to band tunneling, as shown in Fig. 3b. In terms of Hamiltonian system is :

$$H = H_c + \sum_{\kappa\sigma} (\varepsilon_{\kappa\sigma} + eV) b_{\kappa\sigma}^{+} b_{\kappa\sigma}$$

$$+ \sum_{\kappa p \sigma} ta_{\kappa p}\, b_{\kappa\sigma} a_{p\sigma}^{+} + 1/\sqrt{N_2} \sum_{i\kappa\sigma} tc_{\kappa i}\, b_{\kappa\sigma} c_{i\sigma}^{+} + \text{h.c.}\,. \qquad (3)$$

The first term represents the CS band, localized states and the hybridization between CS band and localized states and the second represent the M band. The last two terms are two tunneling channels, band to band (ta) and band to LS levels (tb). At low voltages ($eV<E_0-U/2$, $U<0$) the simple one electron tunneling process from M side into LS state is energetically forbiden, as the LS state can be only occupied with two electrons. A double occupation of LS state is possible if we combine single-electron tunneling with transition, due to hybridization, from wide band in CM into the same LS state. That leads to a threshold $eV>2E_0$ for single electron tunneling and to a steplike voltage dependance of tunnel conductance. It is important to assume a random distribution of LS energies over a large area contacts. The averaging of tunnel conductance over distribution of energy levels results in a linear voltage dependance of the conductance, shown in Fig.3b is in a qualitative agreement with experiment (Fig. 3c).

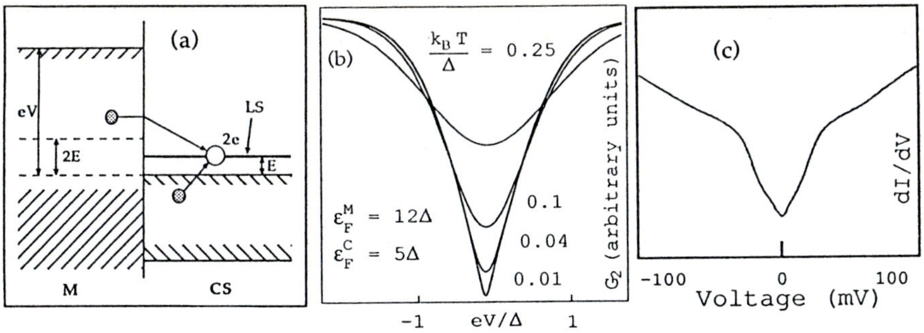

Fig 3. a) Diagram of electron tunneling into local-pair states. b) Voltage dependence of tunnel conductance G(V) calculated within present theory. 2Δ is the width of the LS energy distribution. c) Experimentaly observed G(V) curve, from Ikuta et al. [6].

To conclude, we have shown that the existance of local pair sites with negative U can give an explanation of some of the unusual spectroscopic features of high Tc materials.

References:

1. M.R. Schafroth, Phys. Rev. 96,1442 (1954).
2. I.O. Kulik, Int. J. Mod. Phys. 1, 851 (1988); A.S. Alexandrov, I. Ranninger and S. Robaszkiewicz, Phys. Rev. B 33, 4526 (1986), N.F. Mott, Adv. in Phys. 39, 55 (1990).
3. R. Shekhter, Z. Crljen and G. Wendin, to appear in Physica Scripta.
4. M.K. Kelly, P. Barboux, J.-M. Tarascon, D.E. Aspnes, W.A. Bonner, and P.A. Morris, Phys.Rev B 38, 870 (1988).
5. V. Shumeiko, L. Jönsson, R. Shekhter and G. Wendin, to appear in Physica Scripta
6. H. Ikuta, A. Maeda, K. Uchinokura and S. Tanaka, Jpn. J. Appl. Phys. 27, L1038 (1988).
7. M. Hurd, R. Shekhter and G. Wendin, submitted to Phys. Rev. B.

Electric Field Gradient Calculations of $PrBa_2Cu_3O_7$

C. Ambrosch-Draxl[1], *P. Blaha*[2], *and K. Schwarz*[2]

[1]Institut für Theoretische Physik, Universität Graz, Universitätsplatz 5, A-8010 Graz, Austria

[2]Institut für Technische Elektrochemie, Technische Universität Wien, Getreidemarkt 9/158, A-1060 Wien, Austria

Abstract. We have performed full potential LAPW band structure calculations for $PrBa_2Cu_3O_7$, where the Pr atoms are allowed to order antiferromagnetically. The Pr-4f electrons are treated either as band states or as core states according to a Pr valency of 3+ and 4+ with a fixed f-occupancy of 2 and 1, respectively. Total energy calculations find the itinerant case most stable, but would favor the Pr^{3+} over Pr^{4+}. The electric field gradient tensors differ for these 3 cases not only for the Pr but for some other sites too.

1. Introduction

In the high temperature superconductor $YBa_2Cu_3O_7$ Yttrium may be replaced by other rare earth elements with nearly no effect on the critical temperature. By doping $YBa_2Cu_3O_7$ with Pr, however, superconductivity is lost. The observed antiferromagnetic moment at the Pr site cannot be the only reason for this effect, since replacing Y by other magnetic rare earth atoms does not affect superconductivity. One possible explanation might come from the valency of Pr: when the trivalent Y is replaced by a tetravalent Pr the additional electron fills up the hole in the copper-oxygen-plane, which is responsible for superconductivity in $YBa_2Cu_3O_7$.

In this paper we want to investigate the role of the Pr-4f-electrons. If these electrons are localized, the trivalent (tetravalent) Pr would have 2 (1) f-electrons, but if they are itinerant and hybridize noninteger f-occupation numbers would occur.

The electric field gradient tensor (EFG) is a very sensitive tool for investigating the non-spherical charge distribution [1], so that a comparison of theoretical EFGs with experimental data could help to determine the actual Pr valency in this system. So far experimental EFG values are available for copper only [2].

2. Results and Discussion

In order to investigate the 3 models mentioned above, we have performed full potential LAPW band structure calculations for $PrBa_2Cu_3O_7$, where the Pr atoms are allowed to order antiferromagnetically (Fig. 1), while the Cu sites were assumed to be non-magnetic for computational reasons. The *"itinerant"* calculation utilizes a standard spin-polarized band calculation, including the Pr-4f electrons as band states. In order to simulate *"loca-*

Springer Series in Solid-State Sciences, Vol. 113 **Electronic Properties of High-T_c Superconductors**
Editors: H. Kuzmany, M. Mehring, J. Fink

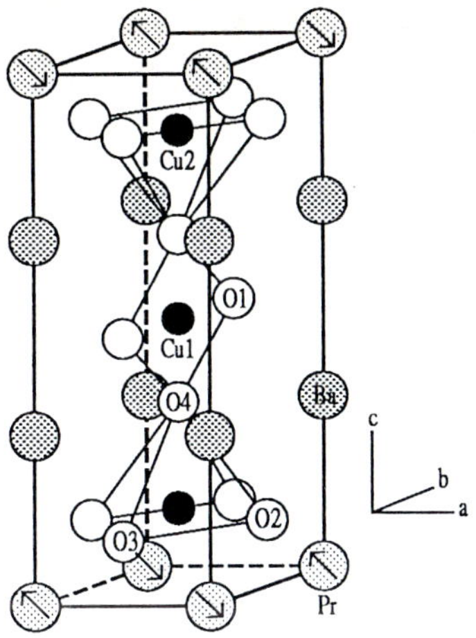

Fig.1 Crystal structure of $PrBa_2Cu_3O_7$. The antiferromagnetic order of the Pr atoms causes a doubling of all three lattice constants. The antiferromagnetism of the Cu(2) atoms is neglected for computational reasons.

lized" 4f states, we turn off the hybridization between them and all the other valence electrons and treat the 4f states in the spherical part of the potential as atomic core-like states. The calculation with a 4f occupancy of 2 and 1 is denoted by Pr^{3+} and Pr^{4+}, respectively. A similar set of calculations has been performed by Guo and Temmerman [3] but without allowing for the antiferromagnetic ordering in the Pr sublattice.

In the "itinerant" case the Pr-4f states are exchange split by about 1 eV and form two narrow bands. The Fermi energy is pinned to the lower f-bands which are partly occupied at one Pr but almost unoccupied at the other Pr for spin-up and vice versa for spin-down electrons leading to the antiferromagnetic moment of about 1.5 μ_B in the Pr sublattice (Table 1).

In the "localized" cases the f occupation is constraint to integer values (of 1 or 2) which cause the corresponding magnetic moments (Table 1). The itinerant magnetic moment falls half-way between the Pr^{3+} and Pr^{4+}, while the total charge Q inside the atomic sphere of Pr is very similar for the

Table 1: Total charge Q, 4f-charge q^{4f} (decomposed into spin-up and spin-down) and magnetic moment M corresponding to the atomic sphere of Pr in the three models (localized Pr^{3+} and Pr^{4+} or itinerant).

		3+	itinerant	4+
Q		56.9 e	56.9 e	56.5 e
q^{4f}	↑	2.1 e	1.8 e	1.1 e
	↓	0.1 e	0.3 e	0.1 e
M		2.0 μ_B	1.5 μ_B	1.0 μ_B

Table 2: Electric field gradients are specified with principal component (EFG, in units of 10^{21} V/m^2), asymmetry parameter η, and direction of the principal axis, when the Pr-4f states are treated in one of the three cases: Pr^{3+}, itinerant 4f or Pr^{4+} in comparison with experiment [2].

		3+	itinerant	4+	experiment
Pr	EFG	-5.7	-4.2	4.2	
	η	0.9	0.8	0.9	
	direction	c	c	a	
Ba	EFG	-8.0	-8.6	-8.7	
	η	0.7	0.8	1.0	
	direction	a	a	a	
Cu(1)	EFG	7.4	6.9	6.5	±8.2
	η	0.7	0.7	0.6	
	direction	b	b	b	
Cu(2)	EFG	-5.9	-3.0	1.0	∓6.7
	η	0.1	0.3	0.4	0.0
	direction	c	c	c	
O(1)	EFG	17.7	17.7	17.1	
	η	0.3	0.4	0.3	
	direction	b	b	b	
O(2)	EFG	13.1	9.7	8.3	
	η	0.3	0.2	0.2	
	direction	a	a	a	
O(3)	EFG	13.8	10.0	8.3	
	η	0.3	0.2	0.3	
	direction	b	b	b	
O(4)	EFG	11.7	12.0	11.6	
	η	0.1	0.2	0.2	
	direction	c	c	c	

itinerant and the Pr^{3+} case. Note that, although one f-electron has been removed in Pr^{4+}, Q is reduced by only 0.4 e, showing that this extra charge is screened by other electrons (with 0.6 e). This reduced effective charge Q would affect the position of all Pr (core) levels. Such an argument was used by Kircher et al [4] to rule out Pr^{4+}, since they did not find optical transitions into empty Pr-5d states, which (according to Guo et al [3]) should be at sufficiently low energy to be observed in Pr^{4+} in contrast to Pr^{3+}. Our total energy calculations for the constraint localized cases yield the Pr^{3+} to be more stable than Pr^{4+} by about 0.1 Ry per formula unit. (Of course, the itinerant case has an even lower total energy).

In $YBa_2Cu_3O_7$ [1] all calculated EFGs agreed well with experiment except the EFG of Cu(2), where theory predicted only half the experimental value. In $PrBa_2Cu_3O_7$ (Table 2) the EFG at Cu(1) is close to experiment (in all 3 models), while for Cu(2) the Pr^{4+} calculation is far from experiment; the itinerant model finds about half the EFG (as in other high Tc materials [1]), but the Pr^{3+} result is close to experiment. The EFGs at Ba, Cu(1), O(1) and O(4) are not very sensitive to the 3 models, while for Pr, Cu(2), and the oxygens in the Cu-O plane, O(2) and O(3), the EFG varies sufficiently, so that EFG experiments might be able to distinguish between the Pr^{3+}, the itinerant and the Pr^{4+} case.

The EFG comes from the non-spherical charge distribution near the nucleus, so that f-states do not contribute to the Pr-EFG when treated as (core-like) localized states with a spherical density. One can, however, estimate that an occupation according to Hund's rule would lead to an EFG of about 25 10^{21} V/m^2, dominating all other contributions. The itinerant and both localized cases (with spherical f) yield an Pr-EFG about a factor of 5 smaller (ignoring sign) than Hund's rule (Table 2).

Acknowledgment This project has been supported by the *Fonds zur Förderung der wissenschaftlichen Forschung*, Project Numbers P7063 and P8176.

References

[1] K. Schwarz, C. Ambrosch-Draxl, and P. Blaha, Phys. Rev. B 42, 2051 (1990)

[2] A.P. Reyes, D.E. MacLaughlin, M. Takigawa, P.C. Hammel, R.H. Heffner, J.D. Thompson, J.E. Crow, Phys. Rev. B 43, 2688 (1990)

[3] G.Y. Guo, and W.M. Temmerman, Phys. Rev. B 41, 6372 (1990)

[4] J. Kircher, M. Cardona, S. Gopalan, H.-U. Habermeier, and D. Fuchs, Phys. Rev. B 44, 2410 (1991)

Are There Ordering Effects in $Ba(Pb,Bi)O_3$ and $(Ba,K)BiO_3$?

U. Hahn, G. Vielsack, and W. Weber

Institut für Physik, Universität Dortmund,
W-4600 Dortmund, Fed. Rep. of Germany

Abstract. A simple model is presented for the origin of the wide nonmetallic ranges in the $(Ba, K)(Bi, Pb)O_3$ alloy phase diagram, proposing that the semiconducting behaviour is caused by the presence of incommensurate oxygen breathing-type charge density waves as well as Bi/Pb ordering waves. The model is studied for large variety of supercell configurations using a simple, yet realistic tight-binding Hamiltonian. Good agreement with experiment is found. Crucial predictions of the model can be tested by diffuse elastic scattering experiments.

1. Introduction

Apart from the superconducting properties, the most puzzling feature of the perovskite-type alloy system $(Ba, K)(Bi, Pb)O_3$ appear to be the wide nonmetallic regions in the respective phase diagrams. For $Ba_{1-x}K_xBiO_3$ semiconducting behaviour is found up to $x \approx 0.3$, while for $BaBi_{1-x}Pb_xO_3$ this region extends even up to $x \approx 0.65$. Pure $BaBiO_3$ exhibits a commensurate charge density wave (CDW) with alternating breathing-type distortions of the O octahedra, leading to two inequivalent Bi sites (charge disproportionation). The crystallographic data for the doped material yield only one Bi(Pb) site /1,2/.

Energy band calculations /3/ predict the existence of a simple, almost free-electron-like conduction band, which is the antibonding part of a wide $Bi(Pb) - s$ and $O - p_\sigma$ hybrid band complex. Approximately, a rigid-band model holds, so that the band filling is given by 1-x. At half filling (i.e. x=0, $BaBiO_3$), the O breathing distortions induce the opening of a large gap at the Fermi energy E_F, leading to a Peierls instability with a commensurate CDW with wavevector $\vec{Q} = \frac{\pi}{a}(1,1,1) = 2\vec{k_F}$. In a previous note /4/, a model for the nonmetallic behaviour of $BaBi_{1-x}Pb_xO_3$ was presented, suggesting that it is caused by the presence of coupled, incommensurate CDW and Bi/Pb ordering waves. Here we report more detailed results of this model and propose an extension to include the $(Ba, K)BiO_3$ system.

Springer Series in Solid-State Sciences, Vol. 113 Electronic Properties of High-T_c Superconductors
Editors: H. Kuzmany, M. Mehring, J. Fink

2. The model

Generalizing the $BaBiO_3$ case waves of static O distortions

$$d_{lj}(\vec{Q},\phi_{\vec{Q}}) = \hat{Q}_j\, cos[\vec{Q}(\vec{R}_l + \vec{r}_j) + \phi_{\vec{Q}}]$$

with $\vec{R}_l$ being the lattice vector to cell l (center is the Bi site) and $\vec{r}_j$ being the vector to the O site j (bonding along the Cartesian axis j) are superposed. We choose $\vec{Q} \approx 2\vec{k}_F$, yet allow different values of $\vec{Q}$ (usually members of the star of $\vec{Q}$, sometimes also 'adjacent' $\mid \vec{Q} \mid$ values) and allow further to vary the phases $\phi_{\vec{Q}}$. For simplicity , equal amplitudes of the waves are used (relaxed for the $(Ba,K)BiO_3$ case) and the resulting displacements

$$\delta_{lj} = sign\,[\sum_{\vec{Q}} d_{lj}(\vec{Q},\phi_{\vec{Q}})\,]$$

are digitalized. The resulting configurations $\delta_{lj}\{\vec{Q},\phi_{\vec{Q}}\}$ are then analysed for their 'breathing' character c_{br} of the sites l, with c_{br} ranging from 0 to $+/-6$ (maximum breathing in/out). The Bi/Pb order wave is implemented by placing the available Bi atoms on those sites l with the largest $\mid c_{br} \mid$ values and the Pb atoms on the remaining sites.
We have investigated a variety of configurations δ_{lj} in supercell geometries up to 6^3 and 2×8^2 simple cells. For the 6^3 case this choice allows values of $\vec{Q}(x) = \frac{1}{3}\frac{\pi}{a}(n_1,n_2,n_3)$ with $n_\alpha = 0,1,2,3$ so that the $\vec{Q}(x)$ values span the whole doping range.
The δ_{lj} configurations were studied using a simple tight-binding Hamiltonian /3/ with $\varepsilon_{Bi} = -6eV$, $\varepsilon_{Pb} = -2eV$, $\varepsilon_O = 0$, and $t_{sp\sigma} = (2.2 + 0.2\delta_{lj})eV$ to calculate the electronic density of states N(E). All configurations with finite $N(E_F)$ were rejected. The model is extended to $(Ba,K)BiO_3$ by allowing a modulation of ε_{Bi} according to the breathing character of the respective site l /5/:

$$\varepsilon_{Bi} = (-4.9 + 0.17\, c_{br})eV$$

3. Results for $BaBi_{1-x}Pb_xO_3$

A large variety of configurations δ_{lj} has been investigated, and nonmetallic configurations have been found over a doping range $0 < x < 0.9$. In all cases, the aforementioned rules to place the Bi and Pb atoms had to be fulfilled to avoid finite $N(E_F)$. The $Q(x)$ values agree very well with the $2k_F(x)$ line (see fig. 1). A simple, yet typical configuration for $x = 0.5$ is shown in fig.2 . One feature is the presence of Pb chains, which

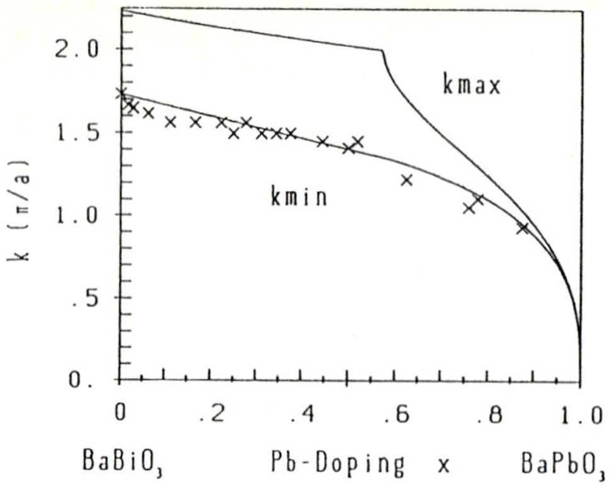

fig.1: Q-vectors of semiconducting configurations compared with the minimum / maximum Fermi surface diameter.

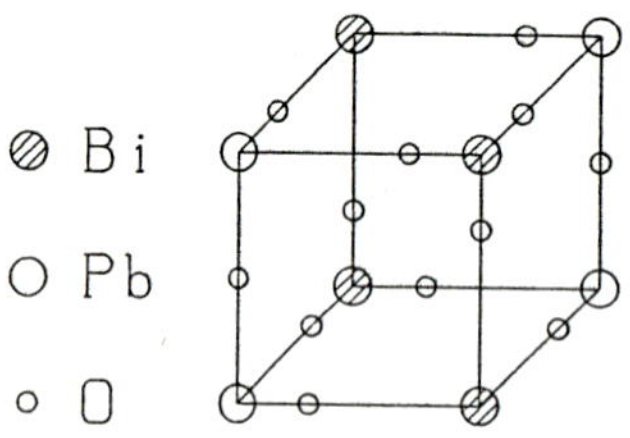

fig.2: Semiconducting configuration with 50% Pb content.

is typical for smaller doping, especially in the limit $x \to 0$. For larger x, the real space structures become increasingly more complicated; in particular, the smaller values of $2k_F$ require the absence of any 1NN Bi-Bi bonds.

4. Results for $(Ba, K)BiO_3$

The nonmetallic configurations were found in a similar way, yet a stronger mixing of waves with different $|\vec{Q}|$ and different amplitudes was required. All nonmetallic $\delta_{lj}(\vec{Q}, \phi_{\vec{Q}})$ configurations belong to supercells of the size $2 \times n^2$ with $n = 4, 6, 8$ pointing along the c direction like the Pb chains for $x \to 0$ in $BaBi_{1-x}Pb_xO_3$. The range of nonmetallic configurations is limited to $x \lesssim 0.35$. We note that an implementation of the more general $Ba(Bi, Pb)O_3$ model with its ε_{Bi} breathing modulation to the previously investigated $Ba(Bi, Pb)O_3$ configurations always resulted in even bigger gaps at E_F.

5. Concluding remarks

Our model provides a simple explanation for the wide nonmetallic ranges in the $(Ba, K)(Bi, Pb)O_3$ alloy systems. We have found many different nonmetallic configurations, very often more than one for the same x value. Thus we do not believe that, for a specific x value, a single configuration is energetically much more stable than others. Consequently, we expect the real alloy crystal to consist of small domains of slightly different incommensurate configurations - not detectable by standard crystallography. We note that a full gap probably is a too strong requirement for nonmetallic behaviour. A deep $N(E)$ minimum near E_F should be sufficient to localize the states at E_F – thus long range ordered superstructures need not be required. However we expect that, in the diffuse elastic scattering, intensity maxima should show up near $2k_F(x)$. In addition, our model predicts for the $Ba(Bi, Pb)O_3$ alloy system that a bimodal distribution of Bi-O bond lengths exists, yet a unimodal one for the Pb-O bond. This result has been confirmed by EXAFS studies /6/ which also report that the bimodal Bi-O bond length distribution exists even in the metallic range of $Ba(Bi, Pb)O_3$.

Acknowledgements: This work has been supported by Deutsche Forschungsgemeinschaft (Graduiertenkolleg Festkörperspektroskopie) and by the Minister für Wissenschaft und Forschung des Landes Nordrhein-Westfalen.

References

/1/ D.E. Cox and A.W. Sleight, Solid State Commun. 19, 969 (1976)
/2/ Shiyou Pei et al, Phys. Rev. B 41, 4126 (1989)
/3/ L.F. Mattheiss and D.R. Hamann, Phys. Rev. B 28, 4227 (1983)
/4/ W. Weber, Jpn. J. Appl.Phys. 26, Suppl. 3, 981 (1987)
/5/ G.Vielsack et al, this volume
/6/ J.B. Boyce et al, Phys. Rev. B 41, 6306 (1990)

Constraint-FLAPW Calculations and Determination of Hubbard Model-Parameters for $BaBiO_3$

G. Vielsack[1], W. Weber[1], P. Blaha[2], and K. Schwarz[2]

[1]Institut für Physik, Universität Dortmund,
W-4600 Dortmund, Fed. Rep. of Germany
[2]Institut für Technische Elektrochemie, Technische Universität Wien,
Getreidemarkt 9/158, A-1060 Wien, Austria

Abstract. The origin of the breathing distortions of $BaBiO_3$ could either be a Peierls distortion or a Bi^{4+} valence instability, discribable by a "negative U" effect in a Hubbard model. We have performed constraint-FLAPW calculations for the ideal and the breathing distorted $BaBiO_3$. Analysing both the energy bands and the total energy results for the parameters of multiband Hubbard models, we always find positive U.

1 Introduction

$(Ba,K)BiO_3$ and $Ba(Bi,Pb)O_3$ are the only known oxide high temperature superconductors without copper. Unlike the cuprates, these materials are cubic perovskites and have no two-dimensional properties[1, 2]. As in the cuprates, undoped $BaBiO_3$ is a semiconductor, yet there is no antiferromagnetism, but a breathing-like distortion of the oxygen octahedra, leading to two inequivalent Bi valences. According to band structure calculations[3, 4], one finds a splitting of the energy bands at the Fermi energy, which suggests the breathing distortion to be a Peierl instability. Alternatively, the distortion could be interpreted as an intrinsic valence instability of the Bi^{4+} ion, which is unstable in the open $6s^1$ configuration[5]. The missing valence state could be described in a negative U Hubbard model (HM).

Another argument for a negative U situation is, that standard electron-phonon coupling does not seem to provide a satisfactory description for the doping dependence of T_c in the two alloy systems[6, 7], suggesting an additional purly electronic contribution.

2 Constraint-Density-Functional approach

Our constraint-density-functional approach is quite similar to that of Hybertsen et.al.[8]. The total energy has to be minimized with the constraint

$$\int d^3r \hat{P} n(\vec{r}) = N_{\hat{P}} \tag{1}$$

for the electronic density $n(\vec{r})$, where $\hat{P}$ projects charge of specified symmetry. The constraint (1) leads to modified Kohn-Sham equations:

Springer Series in Solid-State Sciences, Vol. 113 Electronic Properties of High-T_c Superconductors
Editors: H. Kuzmany, M. Mehring, J. Fink

$$\left[\hat{T} + V_{SC}(\lambda) - \lambda\hat{P}\right] \phi^{\lambda}_{n\vec{k}}(\vec{r}) = \epsilon^{\lambda}_{n\vec{k}}\phi^{\lambda}_{n\vec{k}}(\vec{r}) \quad (2)$$

Here $V_{SC}(\lambda) = v^{\lambda}_{H} + v^{\lambda}_{xc}$, the sum of Hartree and exchange-correlation potential, has to be obtained selfconsistently. As in ref. [8], we choose $\hat{P}$ to be a combination of angular momentum projectors $\hat{P}^{i}_{l}$ inside the relevant atomic muffin-tin (MT) spheres (site i) and zero outside. This procedure yields the total energy $E[N^{i}_{l}]$ as a function of MT charges N^{i}_{l}, selfconsistent energy bands $\epsilon^{\lambda}_{n\vec{k}}$, and also energy bands $\tilde{\epsilon}^{\lambda}_{n\vec{k}}$ of the "screening-potential" defined by

$$\left[\hat{T} + V_{SC}(\lambda)\right] \tilde{\phi}^{\lambda}_{n\vec{k}}(\vec{r}) = \tilde{\epsilon}^{\lambda}_{n\vec{k}}\tilde{\phi}^{\lambda}_{n\vec{k}}(\vec{r}). \quad (3)$$

We note, that eqn. (3) *must* not be solved selfconsistently—$V_{SC}(\lambda)$ is the selfconsistent solution of equation (2).

All our calculations are carried out for a fcc unit cell with two inequivalent Bi sites (Bi^{I} and Bi^{II}). Only constraints antisymmetrically for the two Bi sites are applied (e.g. $\hat{P} = \hat{P}^{I}_{s} - \hat{P}^{II}_{s}$). This choise leads to a significant charge transfer $\Delta n_l = n^{II}_{l} - n^{I}_{l}$ between Bi sites, but leaves the oxygen charge practically unchanged. Our analysis thus allows to detect U^{Bi}_{s}, U^{Bi}_{p} and U^{Bi}_{sp}, with $U_p = 1/5U^{xx}_{p} + 4/5U^{xy}_{p}$.

2.1 Total energy analysis

In analogy to ref. [8] the DFT total energy as a function of "charge displacements", induced by various constraints, is fitted to the following form:

$$\delta E[\Delta n_s, \Delta n_p] = \tilde{U}_s \cdot \Delta n_s^2 + \tilde{U}_p \cdot \Delta n_p^2 + \tilde{U}_{sp} \cdot \Delta n_s \cdot \Delta n_p \quad . \quad (4)$$

We obtain $\tilde{U}_s = 4.5$ eV, $\tilde{U}_p = 8.3$ eV, $\tilde{U}_{sp} = 4.9$ eV, with an rms fitting error of about 3 meV. Now an extended HM with parameters U_s, U_p and U_{sp} is solved in mean-field (MF) approximation. We used a basis set of Bi s, p and O p orbitals and employ the standard tight binding (TB) matrix elements. The hopping and MF on-site energies are an optimum choice for the unconstrained case and are kept constant during the analysis. Charge displacements are induced by shifts of Bi orbital energies ϵ_s and ϵ_p. The final U parameters are choosen to give the same total energy curvatures as above. We obtain: $U_s = 3.1$ eV $\pm$ 1 eV, $U_p = 1.7$ eV$\pm$1 eV and $U_{sp} = 1.2$ eV$\pm$0.5 eV. We note, that a delicate scaling, concerning the ratio of TB and MT partial charges, is required (details will be published elsewhere). The scaling causes the big error bars in the resulting U parameters.

2.2 Energy band analysis

Analysing the energy bands $\epsilon^{\lambda}_{n\vec{k}}$ (of $\hat{T} + V_{SC}(\lambda) - \lambda\hat{P}$) and $\tilde{\epsilon}^{\lambda}_{n\vec{k}}$ (of $\hat{T} + V_{SC}(\lambda)$), provides a simple and undelicate methode to evaluate the U parameters. Fitting $\tilde{\epsilon}^{\lambda}$ yields TB on-site energies $\tilde{\epsilon}^{TB}_{s/p}$, while fitting ϵ^{λ} yields TB partial charges $n^{TB}_{s,p}$. Now the changes in the on-site energies $\delta\tilde{\epsilon}^{TB}_{s,p}$ are simply caused by the

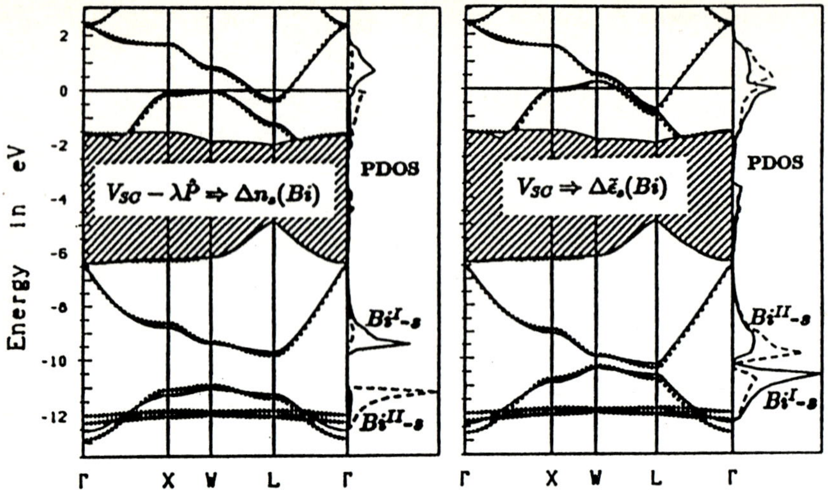

Figure 1: The dotted lines show the LAPW results and the full lines the appropriate TB fits. The PDOS are calculated from the TB results. Left: Selfconsistent energy bands ϵ^{λ} of $V_{SC}(\lambda) - \lambda\hat{P}$, with $\lambda = 0.2$ Ryd. and $\hat{P} = \hat{P}_s^{I} - \hat{P}_s^{II}$ (see eqn. (2)), giving $\Delta n_s^{TB} = 0.57$. Right: Energy bands $\tilde{\epsilon}^{\lambda}$ of the "screening-potential" $V_{SC}(\lambda)$ (see eqn. (3)), giving $\Delta\tilde{\epsilon}_s^{TB} =$ 0.84 eV. Now $\Delta\tilde{\epsilon}_s^{TB} \approx 1/2 U_s \cdot \Delta n_s^{TB}$ simply yields $U_s \approx 2.9$eV

renormalization due to the "screening-charges" $\delta n_{s,p}^{TB}$. Within a mean-field interpretation we get:

$$\Delta\tilde{\epsilon}_s^{TB} = \frac{1}{2}U_s \cdot \Delta n_s^{TB} + U_{sp} \cdot \Delta n_p^{TB} \quad \text{and}$$

$$\Delta\tilde{\epsilon}_p^{TB} = U_{sp} \cdot \Delta n_s^{TB} + \frac{5}{6}U_p \cdot \Delta n_p^{TB}.$$

As shown in figure (1) only one constraint calculation is necessary to get a reasonable estimate for U_s. The average values from fourteen constraint calculations are: $U_s = 3.1$ eV $\pm$ 0.4 eV, $U_p = 2.2$ eV $\pm$ 0.4 eV and $U_{sp} =$ 1.4 eV $\pm$ 0.2 eV.

3 Discussion

We do not find any negative value for the *Bi* U parameters in multi-band HMs for $BaBiO_3$. A negative U situation can be created, when we eliminate the oxygen distortions, thus describing the conduction band within an effective one-band model. A consistent set of parameters is: $t^{1NN} = -0.4$ eV, $t^{4NN} = 0.1$ eV and $U_s = -1.3$ eV. However such a model is *not* a purely electronic negative U model and does not yield additional contributions to an effective *e-e* attraction.

Further constraint analyses, including the oxygen breathing distortion do not yield any drastic changes in the U values. However they indicate that there are large gradients of the *Bi* crystal-field matrix elements due to oxygen motion. These large gradients give important contributions to the electron-phonon coupling. Further work along these lines is in progress.

Acknowledgment This project has been supported by the*Deutsche Physikalische Gesellschaft (Graduiertenkolleg Festkörperspektroskopie)*, by the *Minister für Wissenschaft und Forschung des Landes Nordrhein-Westfalen* and by the *Fonds zur Förderung der wissenschaftlichen Forschung*, Project Numbers P7063 and P8176

References

[1] D. E. Cox, and A. W. Sleight, Acta Cryst. **B35**, 1 (1979)

[2] S. Pei, J. D. Jorgensen, B. Dabrowki, D. G. Hinks, D. R. Richards, A. W. Mitchel, J. M. Newsam, S. K. Sinha, D. Vaknin, and A. J. Jacobson, Phys. Rev. **B41**, 4126 (1990)

[3] L. F. Mattheiss, and D. R. Hamann, Phys. Rev. **B28**, 4227 (1983)

[4] L. F. Mattheiss, and D. R. Hamann, Phys. Let. **60**, 2681 (1988)

[5] C. M. Varma, Phys. Rev. **B61**, 2713 (1988)

[6] M. Shirai, N. Suzuki, and K. Motizuki, J. Phys.: Condens. Matter **2**, 3553 (1990)

[7] A. W. Sleight, J. L. Gillson, and P. E. Bierstedt, Solid State Commun. **17**, 27 (1975)

[8] M. S. Hybertsen, M. Schlüter, and N. E. Christensen, Phys. Rev. **B39**, 9028 (1989)

Electronic Structure Aspects of the Pressure Dependence of T_c in High-T_c Superconductors

R.P. Gupta[1] *and M. Gupta*[2]

[1]Section de Recherches de Métallurgie Physique, Centre d'Etudes de Saclay, F-91191 Gif-sur-Yvette Cedex, France
[2]Institut des Sciences des Matériaux, UA 446 du CNRS, Bât. 415, Université de Paris-Sud, F-91405 Orsay, France

Abstract : The pressure dependence of T_c in high-T_c superconductors is quite complex. It shows a large variation from one compound to another, and further depends upon the stoichiometry in oxygen. The effect of a hydrostatic pressure on the crystal structures of these compounds can be quite complex, considering especially the rather anisotropic layered nature of these materials. This can in turn result in a modification of their electronic structure. The results of electronic structure calculations are presented in this paper which shed some light on the charge redistribution that occurs under pressure. These calculations show that in the doped Ln_2CuO_4 family of superconductors and in $YBa_2Cu_3O_7$ and $YBa_2Cu_3O_8$, the pressure induced charge transfer can account for the changes in T_c that occur under pressure. We find that the ionic elements Y, Ba, Ln, etc. the role of which has been ignored upto now, play a crucial role in the charge redistribution under pressure. There is an increase in the electronic charge at these sites under pressure. In the doped Ln_2CuO_4 family of superconductors this leads to a decrease in the electronic charge at the CuO_2 planes. This results in an increase in the carrier density in the hole-doped superconductors but a decrease in the electron-doped superconductors. In the $YBa_2Cu_3O_7$ and $YBa_2Cu_3O_8$ superconductors the change in the carrier density depends in a crucial manner on the response of the chains. In $YBa_2Cu_3O_8$ the chains accept additional electronic charge whereas in $YBa_2Cu_3O_7$ their behaviour is quite the opposite and they transfer the electrons. This difference in behaviour leads to practically no change in the carrier density under pressure in $YBa_2Cu_3O_7$ but a significant change in $YBa_2Cu_3O_8$, in good agreement with experiment.

1. Introduction

Recently, a considerable amount of attention has been devoted to the investigations of the pressure dependence [1-9] of T_c in high-T_c cuprate superconductors, due largely to the fact that a proper understanding of the pressure dependence could shed some light on the mechanisms responsible for the high-T_c superconductivity in these materials, and could also help in designing new and better materials. In the doped Ln_2CuO_4 (Ln = lanthanide) family of superconductors, two kinds of pressure dependences of T_c have been observed : a large pressure dependence ($dT_c/dP \sim 3$-4 K/GPa) in the hole-doped T-phase $La_{2-x}Sr_xCuO_4$ and T*-phase $Nd_{2-x-y}Ce_xSr_yCuO_4$ superconductors [4-6], and almost no pressure dependence or in fact a slight decrease in T_c in the electron-doped $Nd_{2-x}Ce_xCuO_4$ superconductors [4]. It has been suggested that the apical oxygens play a major role in determining

Springer Series in Solid-State Sciences, Vol. 113 Electronic Properties of High-T_c Superconductors
Editors: H. Kuzmany, M. Mehring, J. Fink

the pressure dependence of T_c and that it is in fact the absence of these apical oxygens in the T'-phase structure that leads to a T_c independent of pressure. The degree of the contraction of the planar Cu-apical oxygen bond length has been considered to be a bench-mark of the pressure dependence of T_c in the hole-doped superconductors. This is in analogy of the behaviour of this bond in $YBa_2Cu_3O_{6+x}$ family of superconductors as a function of stoichiometry x in oxygen. As x increases, this bond contracts and the T_c increases. It is true that this bond length does exhibit a distinctly pronounced contraction (significantly larger than the other Cu-O bond lengths) under pressure in the hole-doped superconductors, most of which have a large pressure dependence of T_c. However, a fundamental flaw in adopting the relationship between T_c and this bond length from the $YBa_2Cu_3O_{6+x}$ family of superconductors is that it turns a blind eye on the role that is played by the oxygen atom themselves in facilitating the electron transfer from the CuO_2 planes, and hence in enhancing the T_c. A flagrant violation of this relationship is observed in the pressure dependence of T_c of the fully stoichiometric compound $YBa_2Cu_3O_7$ where the contraction of the planar Cu-apical oxygen bond length is twice as large as the other Cu-O bond lengths and yet there is only a very minor increase [7] in the T_c ($dT_c/dP \sim$ 0.5-1 K/GPa). This is in contrast to the double chain compound $YBa_2Cu_4O_8$ where the increase [3, 7-9] in T_c is an order of magnitude larger ($dT_c/dP \sim$ 5-6 K/GPa).

The effect of a hydrostatic pressure on the crystal structures of these cuprate superconductors can be quite complex, especially considering the rather anisotropic layered nature of these materials. Structural changes that occur under pressure can result in a subtle modification of the electronic structure, which in turn can modify the carrier density in the two-dimensional CuO_2 planes which govern the T_c of these compounds. In this paper the results of our electronic structure calculations are presented which shed some light on the charge redistribution that occurs under pressure. These calculations show that it is difficult to correctly understand the pressure dependence of T_c without properly taking into account this charge redistribution.

2. Results

In Table I we have presented the change in the electronic charges that occurs under pressure (GPa) at different atomic sites in the doped T-, T*-, and T'-phase superconductors, the first two of which are hole-doped with 0.15 hole/formula while the last one is electron-doped with 0.15 electron/formula. The changes in the electronic charges are necessarily small since the changes in the atomic positions and bond lengths under pressure are quite small. The crystal structure data for the T-phase superconductor was taken from the work of Pei et al. [5] and for the T*-phase superconductor from the work of Izumi et al. [6]. Since no detailed structural measurements have been made for the T'-phase superconductor under pressure, a uniform compression of ~ 0.12% of all bond lengths was assumed at a pressure of 0.50 GPa which corresponds to the contraction observed in the T-phase superconductor at an equivalent pressure.

Table I shows that under pressure there is a considerable charge redistribution, and that in all three structures there is a reduction in the electronic charge of ~ 0.006-0.007/CuO_2 in the two-dimensional CuO_2 planes. This charge flows directly

Table I : Change in the electronic charges at different atomic sites at a given pressure (GPa) relative to their corresponding values at the atmospheric pressure in the hole-doped T-phase and T*-phase superconductors for a doping of 0.15 hole and the electron-doped T-phase superconductor for a doping of 0.15 electron. Also shown are the changes in the hole or the electron carrier density per CuO_2 in the two-dimensional CuO_2 planes.

Atomic site	T-phase P = 0.53	T*-phase P = 0.637	T'-phase P = 0.50
CuO_2 plane			
Copper	- 0.006	- 0.021	- 0.006
Oxygen	0.000	+ 0.007	0.000
Total CuO_2 plane	- 0.006	- 0.007	- 0.006
Hole change	+ 0.006	+ 0.007	
Electron change			- 0.006
Apical oxygen	- 0.001	- 0.002	
Face oxygen		- 0.002	- 0.001
Ln_1	+ 0.004	+ 0.006	
Ln_2		+ 0.005	+ 0.004

to the rare earth sites, where there is an increase of ~ 0.004-0.006 electron at each site. In fact the apical or the face site oxygens do not accept additional electronic charge under pressure, but instead transfer some charge towards the rare earth sites. Because of this behaviour, the electronic charge transfer from the CuO_2 planes is less than what it would have been without these oxygens. The decrease in the electronic charge at the CuO_2 planes translates into an *increase* in the hole carrier density in the T- and T*-phase hole-doped superconductors, but a *decrease* in the electron carrier density in the T'-phase electron-doped superconductor. Using the T_c versus the hole density relation [10], one obtains an increase in T_c ~ 2 K in the T-phase and ~ 1.5 K in the T*-phase superconductors, but a decrease of ~ 1 K in the T'-phase superconductor, in good agreement with experiment.

In Table II we have presented the changes in the electronic charges that occur under pressure (GPa) at different atomic sites in $YBa_2Cu_3O_7$ and $YBa_2Cu_4O_8$ superconductors. The crystal structure data for $YBa_2Cu_3O_7$ were taken from the work of Jorgensen et al. [7], and for $YBa_2Cu_4O_8$ from Yamada et al. [8] at atmospheric pressure and P = 0.632 GPa and from Nelmes et al. [9] at atmospheric pressure and P = 4.65 GPa. Again one sees a considerable charge redistribution under pressure. However, this charge rearrangement is such that it tends to increase substantially the hole density in the CuO_2 planes in $YBa_2Cu_4O_8$ at both pressures while in $YBa_2Cu_3O_7$ this increase is really very minor. With this change in the hole density one expects a considerable increase in T_c in $YBa_2Cu_4O_8$ but only rather modest increase in $YBa_2Cu_3O_7$.

In these two superconductors one can think in terms of three separate structural components which participate in the charge redistribution : CuO_2 planes, CuO chains and the apical oxygens, and the ionic elements Y, Ba. There is always an increase in the electronic charge at the ionic sites under pressure, as in the case of the doped Ln_2CuO_4 families of superconductors. This tends to increase the hole density in the CuO_2 planes. This effect is however compensated by an almost

Table II : Change in the electronic charges at different atomic sites at a given pressure (GPa) relative to their corresponding values at the atmospheric pressure in $YBa_2Cu_3O_7$ and $YBa_2Cu_4O_8$. Also shown is the change in the hole carrier density per CuO_2 in the two-dimensional CuO_2 planes.

	$YBa_2Cu_3O_7$	$YBa_2Cu_4O_8$	
Atomic site	P = 0.578	P = 0.632	P = 4.65
CuO_2 plane			
Copper	- 0.002	- 0.002	- 0.009
Oxygen (a-axis)	+ 0.002	- 0.003	- 0.010
Oxygen (b-axis)	- 0.001	0.000	0.000
Total CuO_2 plane	- 0.001	- 0.005	- 0.019
Hole change	+ 0.001	+ 0.005	+ 0.019
Chain unit			
Apical oxygen	- 0.001	- 0.003	- 0.015
Chain copper	+ 0.003	+ 0.002	+ 0.007
Chain oxygen	- 0.004	+ 0.002	+ 0.011
Total chain unit	- 0.003	+ 0.002	+ 0.006
Ionic elements			
Y	+ 0.003	+ 0.004	+ 0.014
Ba	+ 0.001	+ 0.002	+ 0.009
Total Y, Ba	+ 0.005	+ 0.008	+ 0.032

equivalent decrease in the electronic charge at the apical oxygen sites due to an increased coupling. This compensation is however not complete. The difference in behaviour under pressure in $YBa_2Cu_3O_7$ and $YBa_2Cu_4O_8$ arises due to the chains. While in $YBa_2Cu_4O_8$ they further accept the electronic charge, and hence further increase the hole density in the CuO_2 planes, their behaviour is quite the opposite in $YBa_2Cu_3O_7$ where they transfer back the electronic charge. The final result is that there is an extremely small increase in the hole density under pressure in $YBa_2Cu_3O_7$. The origin of this difference in behaviour of the chains in the two compounds is of structural origin, namely single chains versus double chains, which affects the densities of states in the vicinity of the Fermi level. The increase in the hole density of ~ 0.019/CuO_2 in $YBa_2Cu_4O_8$ at P = 4.65 GPa obtained in our work is of the correct order of magnitude. Assuming a linear relationship between T_c and the hole density in the region of interest this corresponds to an increase in T_c of ~ 20 K, in good agreement with experiment.

3. Conclusions

We have shown that a considerable charge redistribution occurs under pressure, and that the pressure-induced changes in the carrier density in the CuO_2 planes can account for the changes in T_c that occur under pressure. The rare earth sites play an important role in this charge redistribution, and that there is always an accumulation of the electronic charge at those sites. There is a reduction of the electron density at the apical oxygen sites due to an increased coupling. Overall, there is a reduction in the electronic charge in the CuO_2 planes. This leads to an increase in the hole carrier density in the T-, and T*-phase superconductors, but a decrease in the electron carrier density in the T'-phase superconductors. In the $YBa_2Cu_3O_7$ and $YBa_2Cu_4O_8$ superconductors it is the nature of the single versus double chain structure that contributes to the difference in the pressure dependence of T_c. The double chain structure, due to the chain-chain interaction, helps to increase the hole density in the CuO_2 planes.

References

[1] R. Griessen, Phys. Rev. B36, 5284 (1987).

[2] J.J. Scholtz, E.N. Van Eenige, R.J. Wijngaarden, and R. Griessen, Phys. Rev. B45, 3077 (1992).

[3] E.N. Van Eenige, R. Griessen, R.J. Wijngaarden, J. Karpinski, E. Kaldis, S. Rusiecki, and E. Jilek, Physica C 168, 482 (1990).

[4] C. Murayama, N. Mori, S. Yomo, H. Takagi, S. Uchida, and Y. Tokura, Nature 339, 293 (1989).

[5] S. Pei, J.D. Jorgensen, D.G. Hinks, B. Dabrowski, P. Lightfoot, and D.R. Richards, Physica C 169, 179 (1990).

[6] F. Izumi, J.D. Jorgensen, P. Lightfoot, S. Pei, Y. Yamada, E. Takayama-Muromachi, and T. Matsumota, Physica C 172, 166 (1990).

[7] J.D. Jorgensen, S. Pei, P. Lightfoot, D.G. Hinks, B.W. Veal, B. Dabrowski, A.P. Paulikas, R. Kleb, and I.D. Brown, Physica C 171, 93 (1990).

[8] Y. Yamada, J.D. Jorgensen, S. Pei, P. Lightfoot, Y. Kodama, T. Matsumoto, and F. Izumi, Physica C 173, 185 (1991).

[9] R.J. Nelmes, J.S. Loveday, E. Kaldis, and J. Karpinski, Physica C 172, 311 (1990).

[10] J.B. Torrance, Y. Tokura, and S.S.P. Parkin, Phys. Rev. Lett. 61, 1127 (1988).

Charge-Transfer Interplay Between Cu–O Planes in the $YBa_2Cu_3O_{7-\delta}$ Family of Superconductors: Its Dependence on Oxygen Ordering and Stoichiometry

M. Gupta[1] *and R.P. Gupta*[2]

[1]Institut des Sciences des Matériaux, UA 446 du CNRS, Bât. 415, Université de Paris-Sud, F-91405 Orsay, France
[2]Section de Recherches de Métallurgie Physique, Centre d'Etudes de Saclay, F-91191 Gif-sur-Yvette Cedex, France

Abstract : While it is well known that the critical temperature T_c in the $YBa_2Cu_3O_{7-\delta}$ family of superconductors depends strongly on the stoichiometry δ in oxygen, the role which the ordering of the oxygen atoms in the CuO planes plays in controlling the T_c is less well appreciated. Results of electronic structure calculations are presented in this paper which show that the electron transfer from the two-dimensional CuO_2 planes to the CuO plane, and hence the value of the hole density, depends in a crucial manner on the crystallographic characteristics and particularly on the local coordination geometry of the Cu(1) atom in the CuO plane. Our calculations show that twofold, threefold, and the non-square fourfold configurations of the Cu(1) atoms are not favourable for electron transfer from the CuO_2 planes to the CuO plane, independent of the stoichiometry in oxygen while a square planar fourfold configuration facilitates the creation of a significant hole density. These results help explain the metal-insulator transitions and the radiation-induced loss of superconductivity in these compounds. Finally, a tetragonal crystal structure for $YBa_2Cu_3O_7$ is proposed which, if it can be stabilized, should have the same T_c as the orthorhombic one.

1. Introduction

The superconducting transition temperature T_c in the $YBa_2Cu_3O_{7-\delta}$ family of superconductors depends very strongly on the stoichiometry δ in oxygen [1]. Some experiments suggest, however, that the stoichiometry in oxygen is not a sufficient condition for the occurrence of superconductivity in these compounds, and that the local ordering of the oxygen atoms in the CuO planes plays a vital role. We discuss two such experiments in this paper. The first one concerns the effect of ion irradiation [2] on the superconducting properties of $YBa_2Cu_3O_7$. Under low temperature ion irradiation this compound transforms into an insulator at relatively low doses ~ 0.04 displacement per atom. This degradation happens at much lower doses than in the Sr doped La_2CuO_4 superconductor or in the conventional superconductors. This change to the insulating state is accompanied by a crystallographic phase transition from the orthorhombic to the tetragonal symmetry. There is no loss of oxygen since the superconducting properties can be rapidly recovered by annealing in air at room temperature or a slightly higher temperature ~ 200°C.This indicates that there is simply a disordering of the oxygen atoms in the CuO planes under irradiation, and that this disordering is responsible for the destruction of superconductivity in this compound. It is true that all types of atoms are displaced under irradiation, but this displacement depends upon the mass of an atom and its location in the lattice. A lighter atom is easier to displace, and furthermore if the atom is loosely bound in the lattice and has vacant lattice sites nearby, it will be ejected rather easily from its lattice site. This makes the oxygen atoms along the chains in the $YBa_2Cu_3O_7$ superconductor the dominant source of atomic displacement under irradiation.

The second experiment we want to discuss is quite similar in nature and concerns the work of Jorgensen et al [3] on $YBa_2Cu_3O_{6.41}$. These authors show that this compound quenched from 520°C into liquid nitrogen is not superconducting down to 4.2 K. However, annealing it in air at room temperature for a few days results in a material which is superconducting with a $T_c \sim 20$ K although there is no change in the stoichiometry. This appearance from the non-superconducting to the superconducting state was attributed by these authors, based on the evolution of different bond lengths, to the local ordering of the oxygen atoms around the Cu(1) sites in the CuO plane from an initially disordered state.

In this paper the results of our electronic structure calculations are presented which shed some light on the role of ordering of the oxygen atoms around the Cu(1) atoms. These calculations show that the charge transfer from the CuO_2 planes, and hence the hole density, depends in a critical manner on the ordering of the oxygen atoms in the CuO plane. We also propose a fully ordered tetragonal structure for $YBa_2Cu_3O_7$ which has the potential to be superconducting with the same T_c value as the orthorhombic crystal structure.

2. Results

An important crystallographic property of the $YBa_2Cu_3O_{7-\delta}$ family of superconductors is that the planar copper-apical oxygen bond length is ~ 25% longer than the other Cu-O bond lengths in the crystal. This renders the interaction of the planar Cu(2) atom with the apical oxygen atom much weaker relative to its interaction with the oxygen atoms in its plane. Thus despite a square pyramidal coordination, the Cu(2) atom in reality retains a square planar coordination. In fact the chain Cu(1) atom forms a natural partner of the apical oxygen atom since the Cu(1)-apical oxygen bond length is the shortest. Actually, in these compounds the overall Cu-O bond lengths are such that the Cu(1) atom has a natural square planar coordination of its own in the bc-plane. This leads to the formation of two separate sets of antibonding band complexes in the vicinity of the Fermi level : (a) planar CuO_2 bands formed between the planar Cu(2) $d_{x^2-y^2}$ orbital and the planar p_x and p_y oxygen orbitals, and (b) the chain unit bands formed between the chain Cu(1) $d_{z^2-y^2}$ orbital and the apical oxygen p_z orbital and the chain oxygen p_y orbital. The charge transfer from the CuO_2 planes depends in a rather delicate manner on the relative position of the planar CuO_2 bands with respect to the chain unit bands, and the neglect of the hybridization between the two allows one to calculate this charge transfer. In $YBa_2Cu_3O_6$ the chain bands are below the Fermi level so that the planar CuO_2 bands are exactly half-filled, while in $YBa_2Cu_3O_7$ the presence of the oxygen atoms in the chains makes them nearly, but not completely, empty so that the planar CuO_2 bands are less than half-filled. The hole concentration can be

Table I : Effective charges (p at oxygen sites and d at other sites) at different atomic sites in $YBa_2Cu_3O_7$ in orthorhombic, irradiated, and ordered tetragonal crystal structures. The hole density is obtained by taking the total charge on a CuO_2 plane in $YBa_2Cu_3O_6$ corresponding to the half-filled band situation as a reference.

Site	Orthorhombic	Irradiated	Ordered Tetragonal
CuO_2 plane			
Copper	9.371	9.453	9.363
Oxygen (a-axis)	5.496	5.582	5.523
Oxygen (b-axis)	5.539	5.582	5.523
Total CuO_2 plane	20.406	20.617	20.409
Hole count	0.283	0.072	0.280
CuO_3 unit			
Apical oxygen	5.658	5.631	5.699
Copper	9.430	9.271	9.419
Oxygen	5.613	5.381	5.537
Total CuO_3 unit	26.359	25.914	26.354
Ionic Elements			
Y	0.425	0.425	0.425
Ba	0.202	0.214	0.202
Total Y, Ba	0.829	0.853	0.829

determined by comparing the total charge [4] on a CuO_2 plane with respect to its value in $YBa_2Cu_3O_6$.

In Table I we have presented the effective charges (total number of valence electrons) at different atomic sites in $YBa_2Cu_3O_7$ calculated by integrating the densities of states at these sites upto the Fermi level. The chain unit is labelled in this table as the CuO_3 unit which corresponds to the chemical formula of this complex. Taking the calculated charge [4] on a CuO_2 plane in $YBa_2Cu_3O_6$ as a reference we obtain a hole density of 0.283/CuO_2 in $YBa_2Cu_3O_7$, a result which is in good agreement with the available experimental data [5].

In order to investigate the effect of disorder of the oxygen atoms in the CuO plane caused by irradiation on the charge transfer from the CuO_2 planes, two models of the disordering of the oxygen atoms were considered [6]. The models differ slightly in so for as the local environment of the oxygen atoms in the CuO planes is concerned, but in each case an alternate oxygen atom from the chains along the b-axis is missing and is found at the originally vacant oxygen sites along the a-axis. This results in a complete destruction of the chains and an identical population of the oxygen atoms along both a-and b-axes. This also results in the destruction of the square planar fourfold coordination of the Cu(1) atom and its replacement by non-square planar fourfold coordination. The electronic charge distributions in the two models do not differ significantly from each other [6]. In Table I we have given the average values, and we see that there is a drastic drop in the hole density in the CuO_2 planes due to a change in the coordination geometry of the Cu(1) atom. The hole density of ~ 0.07/CuO_2 falls in the limit where electron localization is expected to occur, so that the irradiated compound loses metallicity and superconductivity simultaneously.

There has been a considerable debate in the literature concerning the role of crystal symmetry in the occurrence of superconductivity in the $YBa_2Cu_3O_{7-\delta}$

Table II : Effective charges (p at oxygen sites and d at other sites) at different atomic sites in $YBa_2Cu_3O_{6.5}$ in the three models of crystal structures. The hole density is obtained by taking the total charge on a CuO_2 plane in $YBa_2Cu_3O_6$ corresponding to the half-filled band situation as a reference.

Site	ACM	IBCM	Tetragonal
CuO_2 plane			
Copper	9.424	9.501	9.501
Oxygen (a-axis)	5.542	5.587	5.594
Oxygen (b-axis)	5.562	5.603	5.594
Total CuO_2 plane	20.528	20.691	20.689
Hole count	0.161	~ 0.0	0.000
$CuO_{2.5}$ unit			
Apical oxygen	5.795	5.712	5.735
Copper	9.749	9.603	9.591
Oxygen	5.616	5.528	5.483
Total $CuO_{2.5}$ unit	24.147	23.791	23.802
Ionic Elements			
Y	0.421	0.423	0.422
Ba	0.188	0.202	0.199
Total Y, Ba	0.797	0.827	0.820

family of superconductors. In fact, the crucial role is played by the coordination geometry of the Cu(1) atom as discussed above and not the crystal symmetry. We consider an ordered tetragonal crystal structure for $YBa_2Cu_3O_7$ in which an alternate chain along the b-axis in orthorhombic $YBa_2Cu_3O_7$ is removed and placed along the a-axis. This leads to the twofold, fourfold square planar, and sixfold octahedral configurations of the Cu(1) atom. The average charge distributions at different atomic sites for this structure are given in Table I. We obtain essentially the same hole density as in the orthorhombic case, and thus this ordered tetragonal crystal structure is a potential candidate for the high-T_c superconductivity.

The effect of oxygen ordering was also investigated in $YBa_2Cu_3O_{6.5}$ which is closest to the stoichiometry in oxygen used by Jorgensen et al [3]. Three models of crystal structures were considered for this purpose : (a) an alternate chain model (ACM), (b) an identical broken chain model (IBCM), and (c) a disordered pseudo tetragonal structure with equal occupancy of oxygens along both a- and b- axes. The detailed electronic charge distributions are given in Table II. We notice that only in the ACM, which has intact fourfold square planar coordinations of Cu(1) atom, is there a significant hole density in the CuO_2 planes. This hole density ~ $0.16/CuO_2$ corresponds to a T_c ~ 55 K, in good agreement with the value of T_c in the plateau region. The two other structures (IBCM and disordered tetragonal), which have twofold, threefold, and non-square planar fourfold coordinations, are not superconducting since the hole density in these structures is non-existent and the CuO_2 planes are insulating.

These results can qualitatively explain the results of Jorgensen et al [3]. Our results suggest that in their sample the oxygen atoms are originally randomly distributed so that the compound is non-metallic and non-superconducting due to the absence of a hole density in the CuO_2 planes. Annealing results in the formation of fourfold square planar coordinations around the Cu(1) atoms which allows significant charge transfer to occur from the CuO_2 planes. This makes the compound metallic and superconducting.

3. Conclusions

We have shown that the local coordination geometry around the Cu(1) atom plays a vital role in controlling the charge transfer from the CuO_2 planes, and that the stoichiometry in oxygen alone is not of sufficient value in predicting this charge transfer. The twofold, threefold, and non-square planar fourfold coordinations of the Cu(1) inhibit this charge transfer while the square planar fourfold and octahedral sixfold coordinations facilitate a significant amount of charge transfer.

References

[1] R.J. Cava, B. Bathogg, C.H. Chen, E.A. Rietman, S.M. Zahurak, and D. Werder, Phys. Rev. B36, 5719 (1987).

[2] O. Meyer, in *Studies of High Temperature Superconductors*, Edited by A.V. Narlikar (Nova Science, New York, (1989), Vol. 1, p. 139

[3] J.D. Jorgensen, S. Pei, P. Lightfoot, H. Shi, A.P. Paulikas, and B.W. Veal, Physica C167, 571 (1990)

[4] R.P. Gupta and M. Gupta, Phys. Rev. B44, 2739 (1991)

[5] M.W. Shafer and T. Penney, Europ. J. Solid State Inorg. Chem. 27, 191 (1990)

[6] R.P. Gupta and M. Gupta, Phys. Rev. B45, (1 May 1992)

Anharmonic Effects in the Apex O Phonon in Relation to the Background Continuum in High-T_c Cuprates

D. Mihailovic

Jozef Stefan Institute, University of Ljubljana, 61111 Ljubljana, Slovenia

The observed temperature dependence of the apex O phonon self-energy has been found to be described well by a static aharmonicity in the apex O vibrational potential in $YBa_2Cu_3O_{6.9}$, $TlBa_2CaCu_2O_7$ and $Tl_2Ba_2CaCu_2O_8$. The anharmonicity (of apex Os) thus appears to be present in all the cuprates investigated so far. The significant contribution from three- and four-phonon vorteces in the phonon self energy suggest that the asymmetric lineshape of the apex O lines, which is especially clearly visible in $TlBa_2CaCu_2O_7$, arises due to anharmonic coupling, rather than coupling of the phonon to an electronic continuum. Given that multi-phonon effects are strong, we can infer that scattering "continuum" consists not only of electronic scattering, but contains also a multi-phonon scattering background.

1. Introduction

The lattice properties in high-Tc superconductors and apex O ion's anharmonicity in particular are receiving significant attention partly because of the multitude of structural anomalies present in the cuprates, and partly also as a possible driving force, - or perhaps component - for the high-temperature superconductivity.

In this paper we focus on the anharmonicity of apex O phonons observed in Raman scattering and the relation of the anharmonicity to the different possible components of the Raman scattering "continuum", the origin of which has been (and possibly still is) somewhat controversial.

2.Experimental observations.

Previously it was found in Raman measurements [1,2,3,4] that whereas the apex O modes show a significant temperature dependence of the self-energy, phonons involving the motion of O ions in the planes as well as Cu and Ba vibrations show very little T-dependence. Analogous T-dependence of apex O phonons is seen in 1212 and 2212 structure Tl compounds as well as in La_2CuO_4 [4]. Because of the problem of O mobility outside the CuO_2 planes in metallic YBCO, we concentrate here in analyzing Tl-1212, where significant O motion has not been reported. To give the reader confidence that heating the material does not cause irreversible change in this material, we compare the "before" and "after" Raman spectra in Figure 1. (No significant changes with temperature cycling have also been shown in *insulating* $YBa_2Cu_3O_{6.2}$ [1]). The frequencies and linewidths for the apex O mode as a function of temperature

Springer Series in Solid-State Sciences, Vol. 113 **Electronic Properties of High-T_c Superconductors**
Editors: H. Kuzmany, M. Mehring, J. Fink

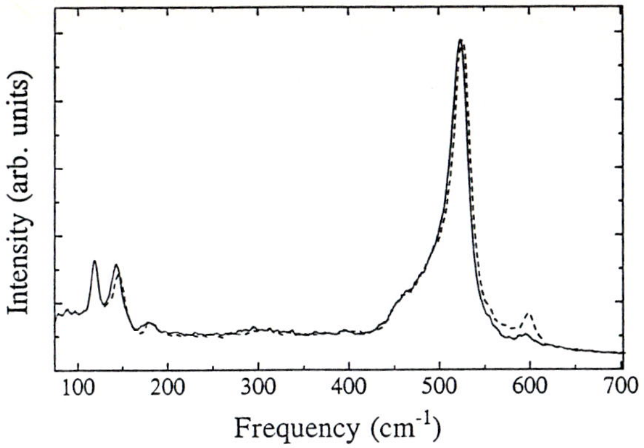

Figure 1. Raman spectra of Tl-1212 at room temperature before (dashed) and after (solid) heating to 1000K.

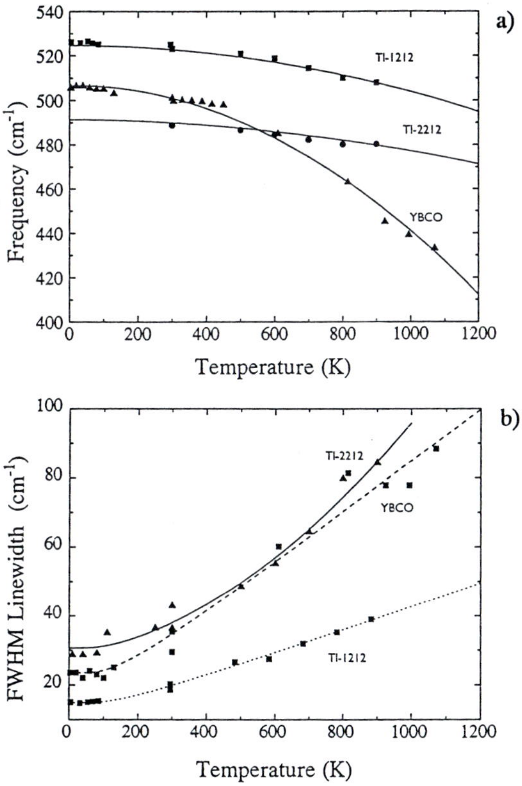

Figure 2. a) Temperature dependence of the apex O frequency for YBCO, Tl-1212 and Tl-2212; b) Temperature dependence of the apex O linewidth for the same three materials.

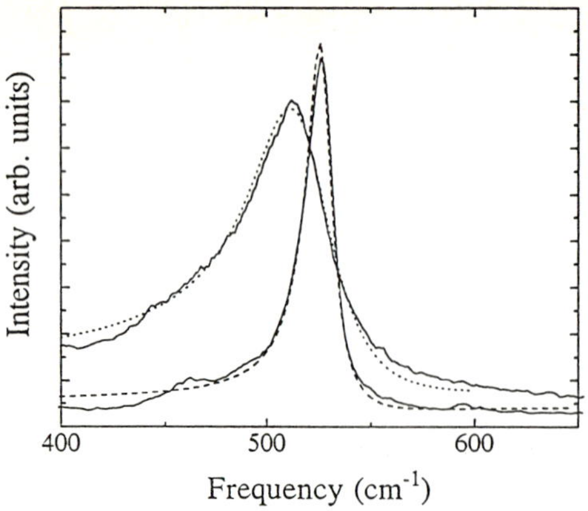

Figure 3. Fano fit to the 5K and 783 K spectra of Tl-1212 show significant change in asymmetry with temperature.

in 123, 1212 and 2212 structure materials are shown in Figure 2. The solid lines are fits to the data using a theoretical model for Raman scattering from anharmonic phonons including 3- and 4-phonon vorteces. (The details of the model and the fitting parameters used to fit the data are given elsewhere [5]). We note that the anharmonic effects are largest in YBCO, where the crystal potential also seems to allow the largest oxygen mobility - in the CuO chains. The fits show that the T-dependence apex O modes in the Raman spectra can be understood quite well in terms of simple anharmonicity.

So far there has been no evidence in Raman scattering that the $q=0$ apex O phonons are significantly coupled to electronic states in the cuprates, but lineshapes could not be properly analysed because of other phonons nearby (especially in YBCO). In Tl-1212, however, the "440 cm^{-1}" mode is very weak and there is no observed feature above the apex O line. A significant T-dependent asymmetry in the lineshape of the apex O of 1212 in the Raman spectra can now be observed and analysed in this material (Figure 3).

3.Discussion

From the anharmonicity of apical O phonons, we can infer the significant contribution from 3- and 4-phonon diagrams in the self-energy of these modes. We can thus also expect the presence of other multi-phonon processes (and especially 2-phonon processes) in Raman scattering: and in particular, a multi-phonon background in the range 0 - 1000 cm^{-1}, for example. Indeed, multi-phonon scattering (overtones) of the apex O vibration have been observed in insulating YBCO [6], independently confirm the existence of higher-order multi-phonon processes in the material.

In order to try and determine the origin of the asymmetry of the apex O phonons, we compare the behaviour of the in-plane 340 cm^{-1} O2/O3 asymmetric mode (visible well in YBCO) and the apex O modes in all three materials.

1) The apex O modes show significant temperature dependence, while the 340 cm^{-1} mode does not - apparently not being strongly anharmonic.

2) The 340 cm^{-1} mode (which also has an asymmetric lineshape), has been reasonably unambiguously shown to be coupled to an *electronic* background, especially convincingly by the renormalization of its self-energy below T_c [7]. Given that the linewidth of this mode is not strongly temperature-dependent, it is likely that the origin of the asymmetry is different for the 340 and 500 cm^{-1} modes.
3) The coupling between one and two-phonon processes is expected to be strongly T-dependent [8], while no such simple temperature dependence is expected in the coupling between one-phonon and electronic states.

The strong T-dependence of the asymmetry [5] thus suggests anharmonic coupling between one and two-phonon processes to be the origin of the asymmetry in the apex O phonons.

The presence of 2-phonon scattering, as suggested by the analysis above can have significant impact on the interpretation of the "continuum", which was so far assumed to be entirely electronic in origin. The Raman scattering from intra-gap states below T_c, has been a slight puzzle hitherto. Although the shape of the multi-phonon scattering cannot be easily analyzed, the temperature dependence of 2-phonon scattering is $(n+1)^2$, where n is the Bose factor, and so the present suggestion of the existence of a multi-phonon continuum can be verified independently.

4. Conclusions

There are three conclusions on the basis of the T-dependence of the Raman spectra:

1. Temperature cycling is shown to be reproducible in the sense that a comparison of Raman spectra in 1212 and 2212 before and after heating do not show significant differences. (The behaviour of insulating $YBa_2Cu_3O_6$ is similar, [1]).
2. The anharmonicity should not be considered independent to the susceptibilty to O hopping, O rearrangement and resulting disorder in the cuprates. The cause for both is presumably the form of the crystal potential.
3. Although the static anharmonicity of the apex O phonon as seen in Raman scattering is probably unlikely in itself to account for high T_cs in the cuprates, non-adiabatic behaviour appears to be a ubiquitous feature of the apex O vibrations in these materials.
4. The origin of the "continuum" in Raman scattering needs to be examined in still more detail. Importantly, since the multi-phonon scattering will remain visible even below the superconducting transition, it could be the origin of the temperature-dependent "remaining scattering below Tc" .

5. References

1. K.F.McCarty, J.C.Hamilton, R.N.Shelton and D.S.Ginley, PhysRev.B. **38**, 2914 (1988)
2. D.Mihailovic and C.M.Foster, Sol.Stat.Comm., **74**, 753 (1990)
3. D.Mihailovic, K.F.McCarty and D.S.Ginley, Ferroelectrics, in press (1992)
4. O'Hana et al Phys.Rev.B **40**, 2562 (1989)
5. D.Mihailovic, K.F.McCarty and D.S.Ginley, (to be published)

6. R.Zamboni, G.Ruani, A.J.Pal and C.Taliani, Sol.Stat.Comm. **70**, 813, (1989); also G.Ruani and C.Taliani, this proceedings.
7. E.T.Heyen, M.Cardona, J.Karpinski, E.Kaldis and S.Rusiecki, Phys.Rev.B 43, 12958 (1991), also S.L.Cooper, M.V.Klein, B.G.Basol, J.P.Rice and D.M.Ginsberg, Phys.Rev. B 37, 5920 (1988) and others.
8. R.A.Cowley in "The Raman Effect", p.148, Ed. A.Anderson, (Dekker, 1971)

Part VIII

Fullerenes

Fullerenes and Fullerites: New Forms of Carbon

W. Krätschmer

Max-Planck Institut für Kernphysik, P.O. Box 103980,
W-6900 Heidelberg, Fed. Rep. of Germany

When C_{60} and other fullerene molecules became available in bulk quantities, a new and rapidly developing field of research was opened. Here I describe the events leading to the discovery of our fullerene/fullerite production method, and try to give an overview of the most exciting developments in current fullerene/fullerite research.

Fullerenes and Fullerites

Diamond and graphite are the known "classical" forms of crystalline carbon. Theoretical chemists, probably challanged by the flatness of the graphitic structure, have been speculating for decades on the possibility of curved and closed cage carbon sp^2 arrangements. However, until quite recently, these ideas were never taken very seriously. Then the "fullerenes", a new class of carbon molecules, were discovered which have exactly these closed cage sp^2 carbon structures. Nowadays, the most stable fullerenes can be synthesized in bulk quantities, and solids can be produced consisting entirely of fullerene molecules. These are the "fullerites" which represent new forms of carbon. In contrast to diamond and graphite, which have dangling bonds at the crystal boundaries and which must be saturated by foreign atoms, the closed cage fullerene molecules have no such bonds. Fullerites are thus the only pure forms of elemental carbon. The names "fullerene" and "fullerite" are derived from Richard Buckminster Fuller, the designer of large dome constructions. His domes

Springer Series in Solid-State Sciences, Vol. 113 **Electronic Properties of High-T_c Superconductors**
Editors: H. Kuzmany, M. Mehring, J. Fink

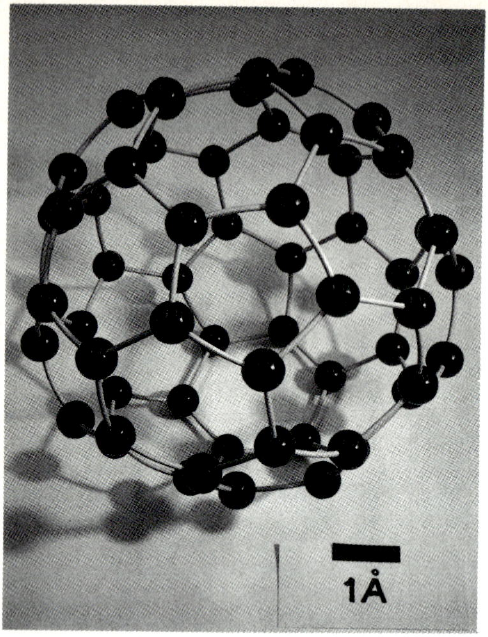

Figure 1: The structure of the soccer-ball shaped C_{60} molecule, consisting of 12 pentagonal and 20 hexagonal carbon rings. The carbon cage has a diameter of about 0.7 nm, the outside and the inside van der Waals diameter of the molecule is about 1 and 0.4 nm, respectively.

resemble in some respects the bond structure of fullerene molecules.

The most prominent fullerene is the C_{60} molecule. It was discovered by H.W. Kroto, R.E. Smalley, and co-workers in 1985 in the mass spectra of carbon clusters, i.e. molecules [1]. The clusters were produced by evaporating graphite with a powerful laser beam and quenching the carbon vapour with a helium jet. These researchers suggested the soccer ball-like cage structure for C_{60} (as shown in Fig. 1) and named it Buckminsterfullerene (in short Buckyball). They further assumed that the other molecules formed along with C_{60} (e.g. C_{70}) also exhibit closed cage fullerene structures. Results obtained a few years later fully confirmed their view.

In an attempt to produce interstellar dust analogue carbon soot in the laboratory, D.R. Huffman and the author evaporated graphite rods by resistive heating in a quenching atmosphere of helium. At elevated helium pressures, i.e. 100 torr and more, the UV and IR spectra of the soot exhibited unexpected features which could not be explained by graphitic soot particles alone. Together with K. Fostiropoulos and L.D. Lamb we could show in 1990 that these spectral features originate from C_{60} (and C_{70}) [2]. It turned out that the fullerene yield is surprising large: About 10% the soot mass produced is C_{60} (about 1% is C_{70}, and 0.1% are larger fullerenes). Such a high yield in such a chaotic formation process very probably points towards very specific chemical pathways for fullerene production. In the nucleating carbon vapour, the cyclic C_{10} cluster may play a key role as a precursor of C_{60} and C_{70} [3]. The lighter fullerenes, like e.g. C_{60} and C_{70} dissolve in non-polar solvents (e.g. benzene, toluene, hexane, CS_2) and can be extracted by flushing the soot with the solvent, e.g. by means of a soxhlet extractor. The solution assumes a deep red color (which is due to the small amounts of C_{70}). Drying the solvent yields crystals of fullerite material. Depending on crystallisation conditions, thin yellow to red flakes (see SEM picture of Fig. 2), or more metallic-looking rods are obtained. Such fullerites consist of a mixture of C_{60} and C_{70} and contain traces of the solvent as impurity. As an alternative to extraction by solvents, extraction by heat is also possible. Because the fullerenes sublime relatively easy, 500 to 600 ^{o}C are sufficient. Solvent-free crystals can be grown directly from the vapour phase [4].
In solution, C_{60} can be separated from C_{70} and the other fullerenes by chromatography (e.g. n-hexane solutions on neutral alumina). The benzene or toluene solution of pure C_{60} is purple (while thin coatings or flakes of pure C_{60}-fullerite are of yellow color), that of C_{70} is red (thin solid films of C_{70}-fullerite are red-brown) [5].

Figure 2: Scanning electron microscope picture of crystals of C_{60} (containing about 15% C_{70}) as grown from a benzene solution. Pictures of pure C_{60} crystals, where the buckyballs assume fcc structure, look rather similar. At interstical positions, solvent molecules are built into the lattice. The flat faces of the flake-like crystals are probably (111). (Photo by H.-U. Nissen, ETH Zürich).

Recent Developements

Only a brief overview of some of the many results obtained by numerous research groups can be given (for more details, see e.g. [6]):

Studies of the structures (mainly deduced from ^{13}C NMR spectra) and the physical characterisation of the fullernes C_{76}, C_{78}, C_{82}, C_{84}, and larger are in progress [7]. Because of the low yields of these species, such work is difficult to perform. In the mass range up to C_{330}, the fullerenes seem to stay more or less spherical [8]. Giant fullerenes have also been found in the soot. They form large nested cylinders, i.e. needle-like structures of a few micron length [9]. These "Buckytubes" may show interesting electrical properties depending on diameter and the degree of helical arrangement of the graphitic layers [10].

The chemistry of C_{60} and the other fullerenes can be naturally devided into three domains: the outside, the surface, and the inside (see, e.g. [11]). Hydrogen, fluor, metal-organic and other groups have been successfully attached onto the outside of the fullerene. Polymers involving C_{60} have also been reported. On the fullerene surface, a few of the carbon atoms can be replaced by others (e.g. by boron). The chemistry of the inside is still in its infancy. Some compounds, like e.g. He, Y, and La inside C_{60} and also Y, or La inside C_{82} have been reported, but have not yet been well characterised. It is hoped that a large range of new materials can be obtained by these so-called endohedral (inside) fullerene compounds (see e.g. [12]).

The pure C_{60} solid has been studied in greater detail [13]. The Buckyballs form a fcc lattice like that of closely packed spheres. They interact only weakly by van der Waals forces. At room temperature, the balls in the crystal rotate almost freely. At low temperatures, several phase transitions occur and the rotations freeze out [14]. As expected for such a weakly bound solid, the electronic and vibrational states are very much similar to that of the free molecule. Similar studies on the rotation of C_{70} molecules and phase transitions of C_{70}-fullerite are in progress.

Solid C_{60} is an electrical insolator (bandgap about 1.5 eV). In order to obtain a conductor, C_{60} can be doped with electron donators, like e.g. K, Rb, or Cs. It was found that the doped solid is not only electrically conducting, but even becomes superconducting at surprisingly high temperatures (18 K for K_3C_{60} and 33 K for Cs_2RbC_{60}) [15]. Attempts to dope C_{60} with electron acceptors (e.g. iodine) have, so far, not been successful.

The alkali-doped C_{60} compounds are - e.g. due to their high symmetry - comparatively simple systems which can be investigated and probably also understood much more easily than other types of superconductors. I thus feel that the real importance of these compounds lies not so much in the domain of technical application. They may better serve as materials from which more can be learned about superconductivity.

References

[1] H.W. Kroto, J.R. Heath, S.C. O'Brien, R.F. Curl, and R.E. Smalley, Nature 318, 162-163 (1985); for a review see: H. W. Kroto, A.W. Allaf, and S.P. Balm, Chem. Rev. 91, 1213-1235, (1991).

[2] W. Krätschmer, L.D. Lamb, K. Fostiropoulos, and D.R. Huffman, Nature 347, 354-358 (1990).

[3] A. Goeres und E. Sedlmayr, Chem Phys. Lett., 184, Nr. 4, 310 (1991)

[4] For C_{60}/C_{70} separation by sublimation see: D.M. Cox, R.D. Sherwood, P. Tindall, K.M. Creegan, W. Anderson, D. Martella, ACS Symposium Series 481, "Fullerenes", G.S. Hammond, V.J. Kuck eds., (1992), p. 117; for crystal growth, see: R.M. Fleming, T. Siegrist, P. M. Marsh, B. Hessen, A.R. Kortan, D.W. Murphy , R.C. Haddon, R. Tycko, G. Dabbagh, A.M. Mujsce, M.L. Kaplan, S.M. Zahurak, in "Clusters and Cluster-Assembled Materials", R.S. Averback, J. Bernholc, D.L. Nelson, eds., Symp. Proc. 206, Mater. Res. Soc., Pittsburgh, Pa. (1991), p. 691.

[5] R. Taylor, J.P. Hare, A.K. Abdul-Sada, H.W. Kroto, Chem. Soc., Chem. Commun. 1990, 1423; and also H. Ajie, M.M. Alvarez, S.J. Anz, R.D. Beck, F. Diederich, K. Fostiropoulos, D.R. Huffman, W. Krätschmer, Y. Rubin, K.E. Schriver, D. Sensharma, R.L. Whetten, J. Phys. Chem. 1990, 94, 8630.

[6] Accounts of Chemical Research 25, No. 3, March 1992, "Special Issue on Buckminsterfullerenes", American Chemical Society.

[7] F. Diederich, R.L. Whetten, C. Thilgen, R. Ettl, I. Chao, M. M. Alvarez, Science, 1991, 254, 1768; see also: K. Kikuchi, N. Nakahara, T. Wakabayashi, H. Matsumiya, T. Moriwaki, S. Suzuki, H. Shiromaru, K. Saito, K. Yamauchi, I. Ikemoto, Y. Achiba, Chem. Phys. Lett., 1992, Vol 188, No. 3,4, 177; see also the contribution by Y. Achiba in the proceedings of this winterschool.

[8] L.D. Lamb, D.R. Huffman, R.K. Workman, S. Howells, T. Chen, D. Sarid, R.F. Ziolo, Science, 255, 1413 (1992).

[9] S. Ijima, Nature 1991, 354, 56

[10] N. Hamada, S. Sawada, A. Oshiyama, Phys. Rev. Lett. 68, No. 10, 1579 (1992).

[11] H. Schwarz, Angew. Chem. Int. Ed. Engl. 31, No. 2, 183 (1992).

[12] R.F. Curl, R.E. Smalley, Scientific American, October 1991, 32.

[13] D.R. Huffman, Physics Today 44, 22-31 (1991).

[14] P.A. Heiney, J.E. Fischer, A.R. McGhie, W.J. Romanow, A.M. Denenstein, J.P. McCauley, A.B. Smith, Phys. Rev. Lett., 1991, 66, 2911.

[15] M.J. Rosseinsky, A.P. Ramirez, S.H. Glarum, D.W. Murphy, R.C. Haddon, A.F. Hebard, T.T.M. Palstra, A.R. Kortan, S.M. Zahurak, A.V. Makhija, Phys. Rev. Lett. 1991, 66, 2830.

Temperature- and Doping-Induced Phase Transitions in C_{60}

M. Matus, T. Pichler, M. Haluška, and H. Kuzmany

Institut für Festkörperphysik, Universität Wien, and
Ludwig-Boltzmann Institut für Festkörperphysik, A-1090 Vienna, Austria

Abstract. The Raman spectra of C_{60} were investigated as a function of temperature and K-doping between 320 K and 10 K. Relationships between features in these spectra, the first order rotational phase transition at 260 K, and the higher order phase transition at 90 K are shown. For the doped fullerenes a strict phase separation between C_{60}, K_3C_{60}, and K_6C_{60} was found.

1 Introduction

One of the reasons for the dramatic increase from interest of material scientists to the buckminsterfullerenes originates from the various kinds of phase transitions in the solid state [1]. At room temperature C_{60} forms a crystal with free rotating C_{60} molecules on an *fcc* Bravais lattice with space group $Fm\overline{3}m$ [2]. Below 260 K the crystal turnes to a *sc* structure with space group $Pa\overline{3}$. Since $Pa\overline{3}$ is not a direct subgroup of $Fm\overline{3}m$ the phase transition is first-order. Between the two temperatures the molecules rotate uniaxially around the [111] direction untill they finaly lock in completely below 90 K. Since the site symmetry and hence the selection rules in the two structures change, one would expect to observe the phase transition in vibrational spectra. We have performed temperature dependent Raman spectroscopy on single crystals to elucidate this point.

Beside the pristine material, also the alkali metal doping shows interesting phase transitions [3,4]. Several phases of A_xC_{60} have been identified by X-ray measurements [4]: for x=3 the structure is still *fcc* but with a modified lattice parameter and metallic state, x=4 has a *bct* and x=6 a *bcc* structure with a narrow semiconducting gap.

Raman experiments have been reported for the pristine material thin film in some detail [5]. From the 174 vibrational modes of the C_{60} molecule only the two A_g and the eight fivefold degenerated H_g modes of the icosahedral factor group are Raman active. The most characteristic A_g mode is the pinch mode. A resonance enhancement of a characteristic mode at 1467 cm^{-1} was reported recently [6]. This mode was originally identified with the pinch mode but recent investigations [7,8] showed that it is oxygen induced. In oxygenfree C_{60} it can be found at 1458 cm^{-1}. In a previous work [8] we suggested that the line at 1467 cm^{-1} is from an ionic carbonoxide of the form $[C_{60}]^{+2}O^{-2}$. Raman scattering proved to be very useful for monitoring the doping process [9] as was demonstrated already in the initial work by Haddon et al [10].

We report room temperature *in situ* Raman measurements during the potassium doping of pure C_{60} films. Doping was carried out continuously in the range of $0 \leq x \leq 6$ for K_xC_{60} in order to check on any intermediate states between the empty, half filled and completely filled conduction band.

Springer Series in Solid-State Sciences, Vol. 113 Electronic Properties of High-T_c Superconductors
Editors: H. Kuzmany, M. Mehring, J. Fink

2 Experimental

Measurements were performed on thin films and on single crystals, respectively. Fullerene filmes were prepared by evaporation of the purified material on silicon and quartz substrates. Single crystals of pure C_{60} with typical dimensions of 0.5–2 mm were grown using the vapour phase technique [11].

The crystals were embedded in an indium block on the cold finger of a closed cycle cryostat. A Dilor XY spectrometer was used for Raman measurements on the single crystals. The line of an Ar^+ laser at 514 nm with an intensity of 200 μW was used to excite the sample and a liquid N_2.cooled CCD detector was used to collect the spectrum.

The *in situ* doping measurements were carried out on fullerene films with typical thickness of 0.2–0.8 μm in front of a Spex double monochromator with a Peltier cooled photomultiplier. Simultaneously with the doping process the electrical resistance and the optical transparency were determined.

3 Results

Fig.1 shows Raman spectra of a C_{60} single crystal at 300 K and at 10 K, respectively. The room temperature spectrum shows clearly the features of the oxygen contaminated C_{60} material with the quasi pinch mode at 1467 cm^{-1}. It is noteworthy that the H_g modes are considerably broader than the two A_g lines. Besides the ten Raman alowed modes (in the free molecule) one can observe some weaker lines. The spectrum at 10 K of the same crystal shows more than 30 lines some of them obviously splitted. The pinch mode shows no frequency shift or broadening in the temperature range between 320 K and 10 K. This is in contrast to observations of other groups [12,13] which found an abrupt change of the pinch mode frequency from 1460 cm^{-1} to 1468 cm^{-1} around 250 K.

The temperature dependent peak heights of two Raman lines with different symmetries can be seen in Fig.2. Between 320 K and 260 K the peak height of the Raman line

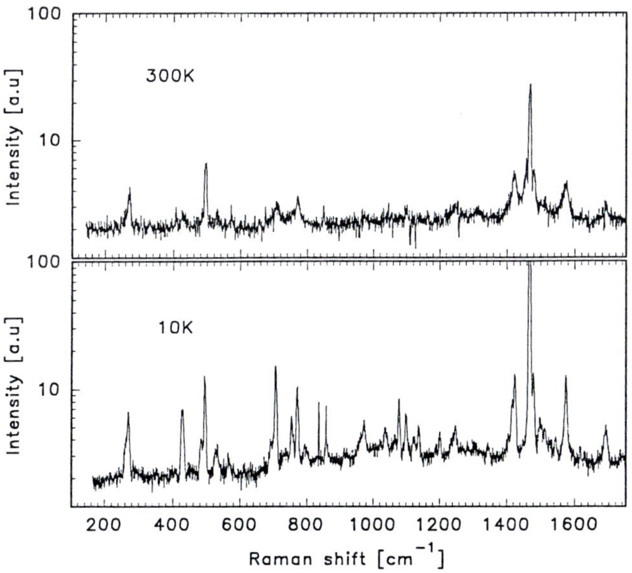

Fig.1: Raman spectra of a C_{60} single crystal at 300 K and at 10 K.

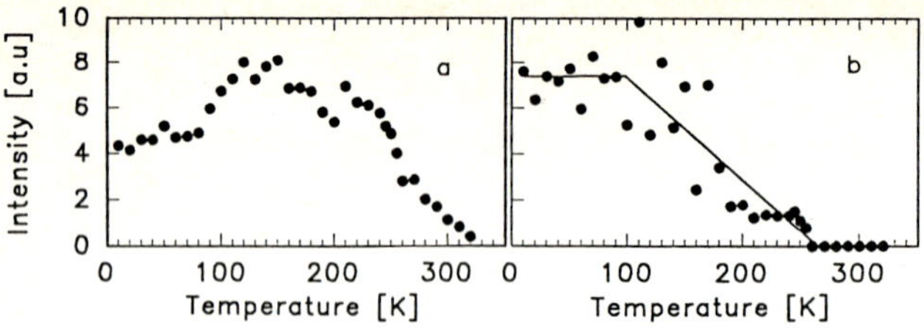

Fig.2: Intensities (peak height) two Raman lines of a C_{60} single crystal versus temperature. a: breathing mode at 495 cm^{-1}, b: 753 cm^{-1}.

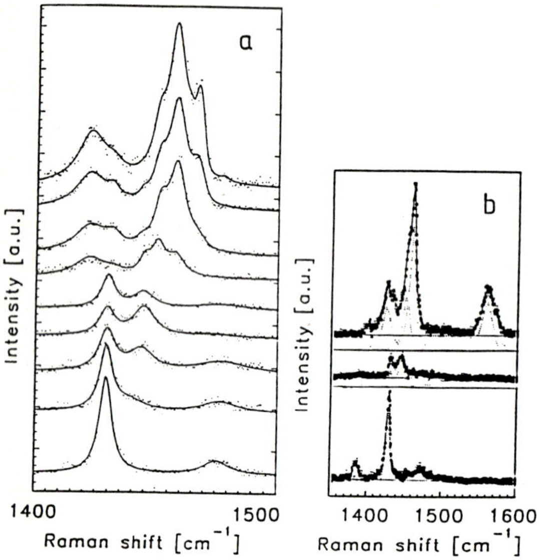

Fig.3: a) Raman spectra of a C_{60} film during *in situ* potassium doping. b) Raman spectra of C_{60}, of K_3C_{60} with some addition of K_6C_{60}, and of pure K_6C_{60} (from top to bottom).

at 495 cm^{-1} with A_g symmetry (breathing mode) increases strong with decreasing temperature. The intensity remains more or less unchanged until it drops abruptly at 100 K. The line at 753 cm^{-1} can not be observed in the high temperature phase. The intensity grows continuously below 260 K and stays constant below 100 K.

Raman spectra between 1400 cm^{-1} and 1500 cm^{-1} for the potassium doping experiment are shown in Fig.3a. The doping increases from top to bottom. The uppermost spectrum corresponds to undoped C_{60} which has lost most of its oxygen during the laser irradiation [8]. The spectrum at the bottomshows the pinch mode at 1430 cm^{-1} and an H_g mode at 1475 cm^{-1} which is characteristic for the K_6C_{60} compound [9]. The solid lines in Fig.3a are fits to the data with a linear superposition of the spectra for the C_{60}, K_3C_{60} and the K_6C_{60} material. No frequency shift of a Raman line could be observed. In Fig.3b the spectra for the three phases are ploted between 1350 cm^{-1} and 1600 cm^{-1}. The spectrum in the middle of the plot corresponds mainly to the metallic K_3C_{60} with a little addition of K_6C_{60}. In contrast to the two other phases the pinch mode at 1444 cm^{-1} is the only visible feature in the Raman spectrum of K_3C_{60}. In the two nonmetallic compounds two H_g lines can be observed besides the strong pinch mode.

4 Discussion

The different number of Raman lines in the spectra above and below the *fcc* to *sc* phase transition can be easily explained in terms of the different site symmetry in the two structures. According to a factor group analysis [13] one would expect 37 Raman allowed modes in the high temperature region and 145 lines in the low temperature region, respectively. The lines common to both spectra do not shift with temperature so one can conclude that the difference is mainly due to the symmetry change. It is tempting to assign the 753 cm^{-1} Raman line of Fig.2b to a mode which is forbidden in the $Fm\bar{3}m$ structure and is Raman active in the less symmetric low temperature phase.

The main result from Fig.3a is that independent of the overall doping concentration and doping time the spectra can always be deconvoluted into the respective spectra of the x=0,3,6 compounds. This result indicates a phase separation into this three phases at any time of the doping experiment. No contribution from an x=4 phase could be observed in the Raman experiments. The very fast increase of the Raman line for the pinch mode of K_6C_{60} towards the end of the doping process and the rapid decrease of the respective mode of K_3C_{60} is a consequence of the much higher absorption coefficient for the fully doped compound [14]. The absence of high frequency H_g modes in the metallic K_3C_{60} (Fig.3b) fits nicely into the picture of Varma et al. [15]. According to his calculations the high energy H_g modes should become very broad ($\approx$200 cm^{-1}) in the metallic state. This would make them indistinguishable from the background.

Acknowledgement. This work was supported by the the Fond zur Förderung der Wissenschaftlichen Forschung in Austria (grant P 8172). We acknowledge W. Krätschmer, J. Fink, and E. Sohmen for the donation of fullerene samples.

References

[1] P.A. Heiney, J.E. Fischer, A.R. McGhie, W.J. Romanow, A.M. Denenstein, J.P. McCauley Jr., and A.B. Smith III, Phys. Rev. Lett. **66** (1991), 2911.

[2] W.I.F David, R.M. Ibberson, T.J.S Dennis, J.P. Hare, and K. Prassides, Europhys. Lett. **18** (1992), 219.

[3] A.F. Hebard, M.J. Rosseinsky, R.C. Haddon, D.W. Murphy, S.H. Glarum, T.T.M. Palstra, A.P. Ramirez, and A.R. Kortan, Nature **350** (1991), 600.

[4] R.M. Fleming, T. Siegrist, P.M. March, B. Hessen, A.R. Kortan, D.W. Murphy, R.C. Haddon, R. Tycko, G. Dabbagh, A.M. Mujsce, M.L. Kaplan, and S.M. Zahurak, Mater. Res. Soc. Symp. Proc. **206** (1991), 691.

[5] D.S. Bethune, G. Meijer, W.C. Tang, H.J. Rosen, W.G. Golden, H. Seki, C.A. Brown, and M.S. de Vries, Chem. Phys. Lett. **179** (1991), 181.

[6] M. Matus, H. Kuzmany, and W. Krätschmer, Solid State Commun. **80** (1991), 839.

[7] S.J. Duclos, R.C. Haddon, S.H. Glarum, A.F. Hebard, and K.B. Lyons, Solid State Commun. **80** (1991), 481.

[8] T. Pichler, M. Matus, J. Kürti, and H. Kuzmany, Phys. Rev. **B**, submitted.

[9] S.J. Duclos, R.C. Haddon, S.H. Glarum, A.F. Hebard, and K.B. Lyons, Science **254** (1991), 1652.

[10] R.C. Haddon, A.F. Hebard, M.J. Rosseinsky, D.W. Murphy, S.J. Duclos, K.B. Lyons, B. Miller, J.M. Rosamilia, R.M. Fleming, A.R. Kortan, S.H. Glarum, A.V. Makhija, A.J. Muller, R.H. Eick, S.M. Zahurak, R. Tycko, G. Dabbagh, and F.A. Thiel, Nature **350** (1991), 320.

[11] M. Haluška, P. Rogl, and H. Kuzmany, in this volume.

[12] S.H. Tolbert, A.P. Alivisatos, H.E. Lorenzana, M.B. Kruger, and R. Jeanloz, Chem. Phys. Lett. **188** (1992), 163.

[13] P.H.M. van Loosdrecht, P.J.M. van Bentum, and G. Meijer, Phys. Rev. Lett. **68** (1992), 1176.

[14] T. Pichler, M. Matus, J. Kürti, and H. Kuzmany, Solid State Commun. **81** (1992), 859.

[15] C.M. Varma, J. Zaanen, and K. Raghavachari, Science **254** (1991), 989.

Preparation of Single-Crystal Buckminster Fullerenes from Transport Reactions

M. Haluška[1], *P. Rogl*[2], *and H. Kuzmany*[1]

[1]Institut für Festkörperphysik, Universität Wien, A-1090 Vienna, Austria
[2]Institut für Physikalische Chemie, Universität Wien, A-1090 Vienna, Austria

Abstract. Crystals of buckminsterfullerene were prepared from supersaturated solution in cyclohexane and by sublimation of powder. In both cases we obtained crystals with well expressed smooth and shiny faces. X-ray characterization showed that crystals prepared by sublimation were monocrystalline with long range order and crystals from solution were disordered. The crystals were further characterized by IR and Raman spectroscopy.

1. Introduction

The development of preparation methods for macroscopic quantities of fullerenes [1] allowed to stady the solid state phase of the materials, and led to a number of interesting discoveries. Most of the studies were made sofar on polycrystalline samples or on thin films obtained by vacuum deposition. Single crystals of C_{60} have been prepared from solution of fullerenes in suitable solvents by several methods [2,3] and by sublimation of powder in a temperature gradient [4]. We prepared C_{60}, C_{70}, C_{60}/C_{70} (ratio 8.5:1.5 in powder) single crystals with excellent facets by a sublimation method. X-ray, Raman and IR measurements confirmed that single crystals are really pure C_{60} or C_{70} and that a certain amount of C_{70} can be incorporated into the f.c.c. structure of C_{60}.

2. Experimental

Crystals of C_{60} were prepared by a thermo diffusion technique in solution and crystals of C_{60}, C_{70} and C_{60}/C_{70} by sublimation of powder. For crystal production from solution, we used a glass tube with a supersaturated solution of fullerene in cyclohexane. The bottom of the tube was heated to to $T_1 \sim 35^oC$. The other end was held at room temperature $T_2 \sim 25^oC$. After several days, shiny dark brown crystalline cubes with well expressed rectangular faces had grown.

Since fullerenes sublimate at relative low temperature, they can be grown with moderate technical effort by slow condensation from the vapor. Fullerene powder was stored in the glass tube, evacuated to $p \sim 10^{-6}$mbar and purified from solvents by heating to 250°C. Then, the temperature was increased to 600°C and the powder was two times sublimated as a fullerene film to the colder part of the glass tube. Finally the tube was sealed and deposited in a horizontal furnace with temperature gradient. The fullerene film was on the hot end at $T_1 \sim (560\text{-}620)^\circ C$. The end where the crystal was expected to grow was held a temperature $T_2 \sim (500\text{-}560)^\circ C$. The glass tube was 100-250 mm long with i.d. 3-8 mm.

3. Results and Discussion

From solution of C_{60}/C_{70} and from pure C_{60} in cyclohexane, we obtained cubes with well expressed faces (Fig. 1a) with typical dimension of 0.3 mm. The nice geometrical form indicates a highly crystalline structure of this material. However, the X-ray characterization showed, that the cubes are not single crystals. It is assumed that they contain solvent which is partially lost when the crystals were taken out from solution. This effect may destroy crystalline order. The cubes were very fragile and manipulation with them was difficult. The crystals grown from sublimation were very compact and relative hard with very smooth and shiny surfaces. They have sizes up to 3 mm in the long axis for C_{60} and up to 0.6 mm for C_{70}. Fig. 1 b,c shows the photographs of crystals of C_{60} and C_{70}. X-ray characterization confirmed that these crystals are really monocrystalline. For the C_{60} and C_{70} crystals X-ray diffraction showed reflection pattern out to a limit of $\sin(\theta)/\lambda = 3.1\ nm^{-1}$ which means $a^2/d^2 = 81$ for an f.c.c. lattice constant of 1.4 nm. This indicates well defined long range order. The crystals from the C_{60}/C_{70} compound gave also well expressed diffraction pattern, but the minimum observable d-values and a slight " arching" of the reflections indicated a lesser degree of long range order.
The crystals were further characterized by spectroscopic investigation. Fig. 2 shows IR reflection and transmision spectra for the crystals and for sublimated thin films. Whereas the film still show structures around 3000 cm^{-1} which originate from organic solvents no such features are seen in the single crystals. In Fig. 3 Raman spectra for the single crystals of C_{60} (a), C_{70} (b) and C_{60}/C_{70} compound (c) are shown. The last spectrum (d) is for a C_{60}/C_{70} film. The strong line at 1467 cm^{-1} for the C_{60} crystal indicates oxygen contamination since the crystals were handled at ambient condition. A comparison between

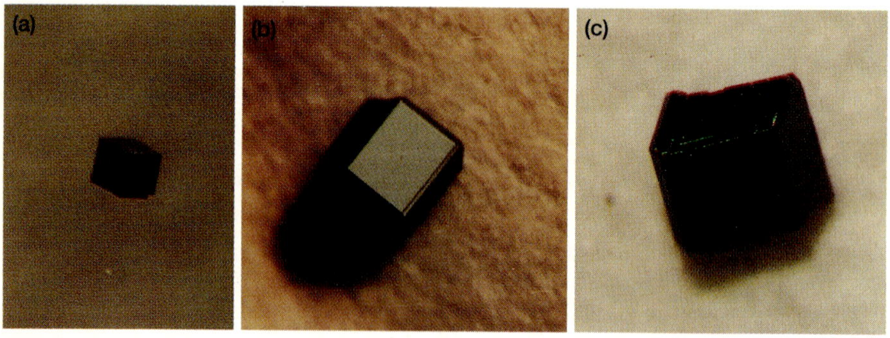

Fig. 1 Photographs of C_{60}/C_{70} crystal obtained from supersoluted solvent (a); C_{60} (b) and C_{70} (c) single crystals obtained by sublimation of fullerene.

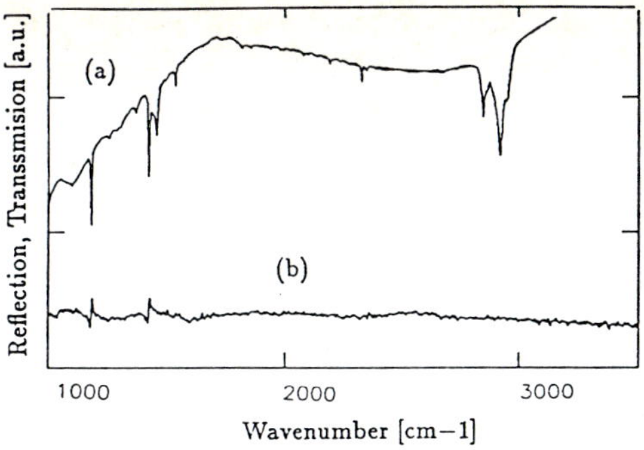

Fig. 2 IR measurement of a C_{60} film (a), and of a C_{60} single crystals (b).

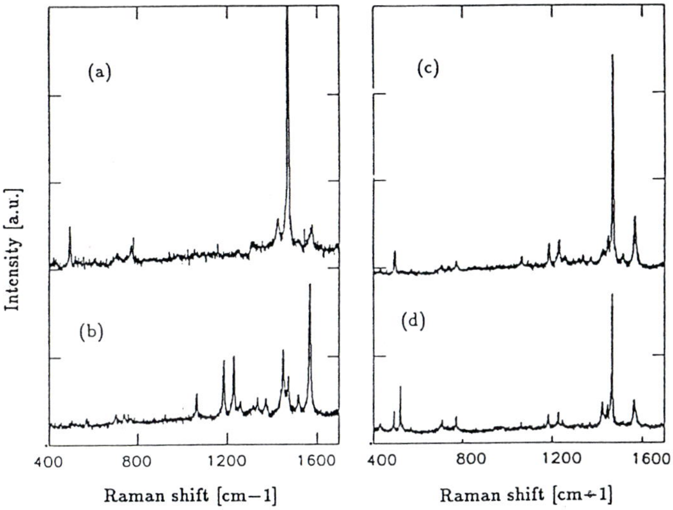

Fig. 3 Raman spectrum of a C_{60} single crystal (a); a C_{70} single crystal (b); a C_{60}/ C_{70} single crystal (c); and of a C_{60}/C_{70} film (d).

spectrum (c) and spectrum (d) indicates that about the same amount of C_{70} is incorporated into the crystal as it is abundant in the source material from which the crystal was grown. The Raman spectra of C_{70} showed no contamination with C_{60}.

4. Conclusion

Single crystals of fullerenes can be grown from the vapor phase with a moderate technical efford. After several steps of sublimation of the starting material the crystals are free from organic solvents. In order to obtain oxigen free material the vacuum for the sublimation must be at least better than 10^{-7} mbar.

Acknowledgment: This work was supported by the Osteuropa Förderung der BMfWF, project GZ 45.212/2-27691 and by the FFWF in Austria.

References

1. W. Krätschmer, L. D. Lamb, K. Fostiropoulos and D. R. Huffman, Nature, **347**, 354 (1990).
2. K. Kikuchi, S. Suzuki, K. Saito, H. Shiromaru, I. Ikemoto, Y. Achiba, Physica C, **185-189**, 415 (1991).
3. S. Pekker, G. Faigel, K. Fodor-Csorba, L. Granasy, E. Jakab and M. Tegze, submitted to Europhysics Lett.
4. R. L. Meng, D. Ramirez, X. Jiang, P. C. Chow, C. Diaz, K. Matsuishi, S. C. Moss, P. H. Hor, C. W. Chu, Appl.Phys.Lett., **59**, 3402 (1991).

Superconducting Properties of Fullerenes Doped with Binary Thallium Alloys

M. Baenitz[1], *M. Kraus*[1], *S. Gärtner*[1], *H.M. Vieth*[1], *H. Werner*[2], *R. Schlögl*[2], *W. Krätschmer*[3], *M. Kanowski*[1], *and K. Lüders*[1]

[1]Institut für Experimentalphysik, Freie Universität Berlin, Arnimallee 14, W-1000 Berlin 33, Fed. Rep. of Germany
[2]Institut für Anorganische Chemie der Universität, Niederurseler Hang, W-6000 Frankfurt, Fed. Rep. of Germany
[3]Max-Planck-Institut für Kernphysik, P.O. Box 103980, W-6900 Heidelberg, Fed. Rep. of Germany

Abstract. C_{60} powder samples have been prepared by using binary Tl-containing alloys of various compositions. Measurements of the dc magnetization, the ac susceptibility in magnetic fields up to 8 Tesla and ^{13}C NMR investigations are presented. The existence of a ternary Tl-containing C_{60} compound is discussed. The upper critical field $B_{c2}(T)$ shows a positive curvature near T_c.

1. Introduction

The recent discovery that doping of C_{60} with alkali metals like potassium or rubidium leads to superconducting compounds with transition temperatures of 18 − 20 K (onset) [1-4] and 28 − 30 K [5,6], respectively, provides the challenge to increase the number of superconducting C_{60} compounds and to enhance the transition temperature T_c to superconductivity by intercalating binary alloys. Combinations of the C_{60} molecule with alkali metals and a third component (e.g. K_xTl_y, Rb_xTl_y [7,8,4], $CsTl_2$, CsBi and $CsHg_{1.1}$ [9,10]) are reported to show superconductivity. By the use of dopants with different ionic radii [11] and by varying the pressure acting on the sample [12], the size of the A_3C_{60} ($A = K$, Rb, K_xTl_y, Rb_2Cs) unit cell can be changed. Both experiments show a well defined relationship between an increased volume of the unit cell and a rise in T_c. These findings can be explained on the basis of a simple picture. A larger unit-cell size corresponds to a narrower conduction band due to the decreased overlap between molecular orbitals and results in a higher density of states $N(\epsilon_F)$ since the number of states is not influenced in these experiments. According to the BCS theory, in the weak coupling case an increase of $N(\epsilon_F)$ finally results in a rise in T_c. Depending on the degree of ionisation thallium could be a suitable codopant to raise T_c [4]. In contrast to our previous findings [7,8] and to those of Kelty et al. [9] where T_c seems not to be altered by the use of thallium as a codopant, Iqbal et al. [4] claim the observation of T_c values up to 48 K in C_{60} samples doped with a rubidium-thallium alloy. The latter results, however, have not been reproduced yet independently.

2. Preparation

As described earlier [14], C_{60} molecules were synthesized from the soot of evaporated graphite. The C_{60} powder used for preparation of all samples investigated in this work containes an amount of about 10% C_{70}.

Alloys of various compositions as given in Table 1 were prepared by heating the respective amounts of metals sealed in pyrex glass tubes for typically 1 h. Based on early ideas suggesting a similarity of doped fullerenes and intercalated graphite we used $KTl_{1.5}$– and $RbTl_{1.5}$–alloys in our first doping experiments.

According to the findings of Iqbal et al. especially samples being doped with alloys consisting of a lower relative amount of Tl to Rb were more likely to provide an enhancement of T_c. Therefore, in the following preparations also alloys with less than 55 atomic percent Tl were prepared. The resulting alloys consist of liquid rubidium and the intermetallic compound Rb_4Tl_5 [15] and are therefore of solid and viscous consistence and cannot be pulverized. Hence the starting alloy compositions of the samples # 9, # 10 and # 13 (Table 1) are less well defined than the $KTl_{1.5}$– and $RbTl_{1.5}$–alloys.

The doping procedure was carried out as follows. Preweight amounts of C_{60} powders were annealed in close contact with the respective amount of the alloy. The annealing temperatures and times are given in Table 1. During the preparation the samples were either sealed in evacuated pyrex tubes or handled

Tab. 1. Nominal sample compositions, doping conditions and critical temperatures T_c of K–, K_xTl_y, Rb– and Rb_xTl_y doped C_{60}.

#	Nominal Sample Composition	Annealing Time(s) [hours]	Annealing Temperature(s) [°C]	T_c [K]
1	$K_3\ C_{60/70}$	3	300±5	19
2	$Rb_3\ C_{60/70}$	24	450±5	27.5
3	$Rb_3\ C_{60/70}$	20	450±5	24
4	$(KTl_{1.5})_3\ C_{60/70}$	62	340±5	17.6
5	$(KTl_{1.5})_3\ C_{60/70}$	16	400±5	18
6	$(KTl_{1.5})_3\ C_{60/70}$	7 17	405±5 420±5	 17
7	$(RbTl_{1.5})_3\ C_{60/70}$	18	450±5	27.5
8	$(RbTl_{1.5})_3\ C_{60/70}$	16 21	400±1 430±1	 23.0
9	$(Rb_{2.7}Tl_{2.2})\ C_{60/70}$	18.5	415±5	26.2
10	$(Rb_{2.7}Tl_{2.2})\ C_{60/70}$	40	415±5	26.3
11	$(RbTl_{1.5})_3\ C_{60/70}$ powder	11.5 11	420±5 410±5	 26
12	$(RbTl_{1.5})_3\ C_{60/70}$ pellet	11.5 11	420±5 410±5	 26
13	$(Rb_{1.2}Tl_{1.8})\ C_{60/70}$	16 20	400±5 430±5	 28

in an Ar atmosphere. The superconducting volume fractions as determined by dc-magnetization (zero-field-cooled-curve ZFC) and ac susceptibility measurements (Nb powder standard) are less or equal 10 % for most samples. The amount of the superconducting phase could be increased up to 30 % by pressing the samples and thus enhancing the contact between the alloy and the C_{60} powder during the doping process.

3. Results and Discussion

In order to determine the dc magnetization as a function of temperature (c.f. Fig. 1), a SQUID magnetometer (SHE) was employed in the way described earlier [7,8]. The external fields applied ranged between 10 and 500 G. The transition temperatures obtained are listed in Table 1.

Neither variing the annealing temperatures, the total metal concentration nor the ratio of alkali metal to thallium did result in a significant change of the T_c values compared to binary compounds. From the dc magnetization investigations there is no evidence for a second, possibly filamentary phase with a transition temperature above that of the binary non-Tl-containing compounds. In addition, by cooling the sample below 4.2 K, a second diamagnetic transition is observed at 2.4 K (Fig. 2). Which coincides with the transition temperature of metallic thallium [13]. An evaluation of the shielding fraction (Nb-powder standard) shows that (90±10) % of the thallium used for preparation becomes superconducting at this temperature.

Additionally, x-ray analysis of Rb_xTl_y doped C_{60} reveales lattice constants of both hexagonal and simple cubic thallium. In contrast, in the rubidium-

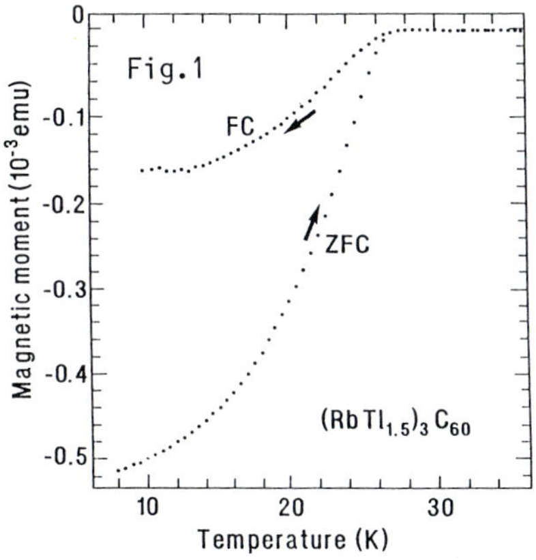

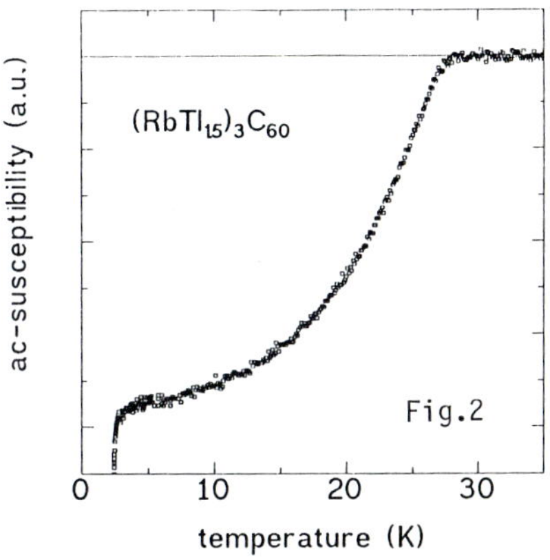

Fig. 1. DC magnetization of a $(RbTl_{1.5})_3C_{60}$ sample (60 mg) (# 7 in Table 1) as a function of temperature. Field-cooled (FC) and zero-field-cooled (ZFC) curves are indicated. The value of the applied field was 8 G.

Fig. 2. Temperature dependence of the ac susceptibility (ν = 107 Hz) of a $(RbTl_{1.5})_3C_{60}$ powder sample (220 mg)(# 7 in Table 1).

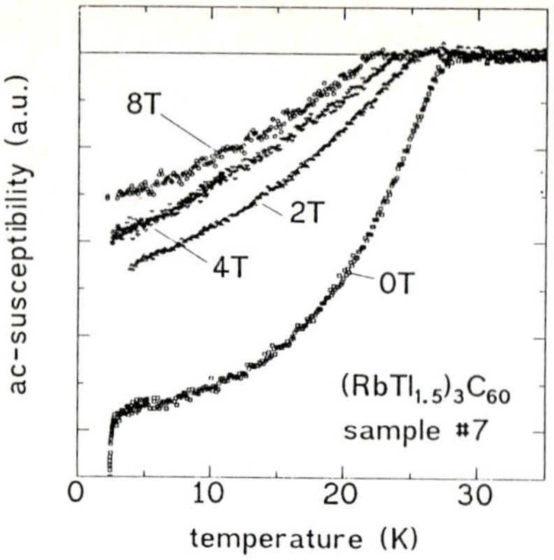

Fig. 3. Temperature dependence of the ac susceptibility in different external magnetic fields of a $(RbTl_{1.5})_3C_{60}$ powder sample (# 7 in Table 1).

thallium-alloys used for sample preparation no evidence for pure Tl has been found.

The ac susceptibility $\chi(T)$ and the upper critical field $B_{c2}(T)$ were measured using a standard Hartshorn induction coil arrangement in external magnetic fields up to 8 Tesla. Offsets and drift effects arising from the coils were taken into account in order to obtain the true signal. The measurements were performed in the frequency range up to 120 kHz. No frequency dependence of T_c has been observed. Fig. 3 shows the typical behavior of the ac susceptibility of a $(RbTl_{1.5})_3C_{60}$ powder sample in different external magnetic fields.

A comparison of the values for $B_{c2}(T)$ obtained for $(RbTl_{1.5})_3C_{60}$, K_3C_{60} [16] and Rb_3C_{60} [17,12] samples is shown in Fig. 4. Powder samples [16,17] and bulk samples [12] as well show a positive curvature of $B_{c2}(T)$ near T_c. This is not expected for a BCS superconductor.

A positive curvature of $B_{c2}(T)$ is observed in anisotropic lower dimensional superconductors like cuprate or organic superconductors. Here, this effect is caused by decoupling of the superconducting layers (for example CuO_2 layers in HTSC) at lower temperatures [18]. Theoretical calculations of $B_{c2}(T)$ for strong coupling superconductors with strong lattice anhamonics also predict a positive curvature near T_c but with a change to negative curvature at lower temperatures [19]. Grüner et al. [20] report a change in the sign of the curvature at higher magnetic fields for K_3C_{60} and Rb_3C_{60} samples.

A positive curvature of $B_{c2}(T)$ near T_c does not necessarily have to be due to a structural anisotropy or strong lattice anharmonics. Also the presence of different phases (with different transition temperatures) or the granular structure of the sample can cause this effect.

From the slope $(\partial B_{c2}/\partial T)$ near T_c (dotted line in Fig. 4) we calculated the $B_{c2}(0)$ value by application of the Werthamer-Helfand-Hohenberg theory [21,16]

$$B_{c2}(0) = -0.69 T_c (\partial B_{c2}/\partial T)_{T=T_c}. \qquad (1)$$

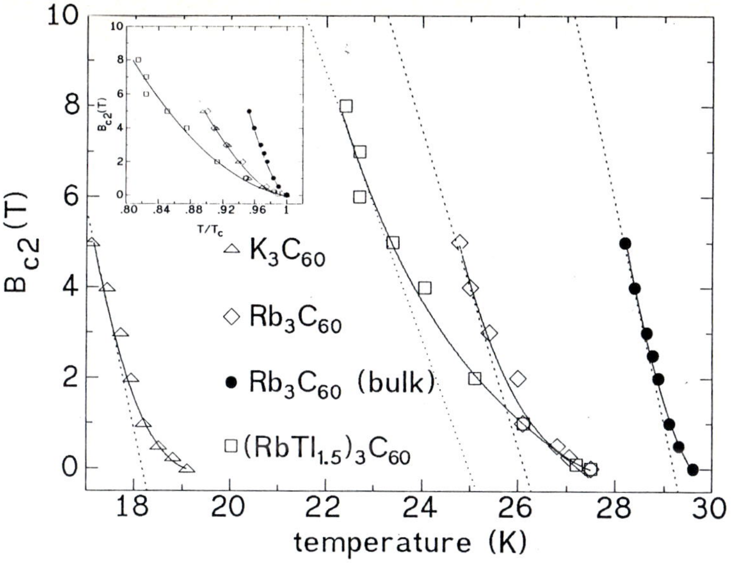

Fig. 4. Upper critical field $B_{c2}(T)$ of fullerenes doped with alkali metals [15,16,12] and a binary alloy as a function of temperature. The inset shows a presentation with reduced temperature.

The obtained values for $B_{c2}(0)$ are 46 T for K_3C_{60}, 61 T [17], 78 T [12] for Rb_3C_{60}, and 52 T for $(RbTl_{1.5})_3C_{60}$.

From $B_{c2}(0)$ we determined the coherence length ξ_0 using the relation [22]

$$B_{c2}(0) = \Phi_0/(2\pi\xi_0^2). \tag{2}$$

We find $\xi_0 = 26$ Å for K_3C_{60}, 23 Å [17], 20 Å [12] for Rb_3C_{60} and 25 Å for $(RbTl_{1.5})_3C_{60}$.

Furthermore, ^{13}C NMR measurements have been performed on both $KTl_{1.5}$– and $RbTl_{1.5}$–doped samples using a BRUKER CXP 300 spectrometer at an applied field of 7.04 T.

The undoped starting material shows the usual behavior as reported earlier (Fig. 5) [23,24]. Both, in $(KTl_{1.5})_3C_{60}$ (Fig. 5) and in $(RbTl_{1.5})_3C_{60}$ we find a single resonance line shifted by 34 ppm and 42 ppm, respectively, to higher values. The line width in both samples is increased by a factor of about 3 compared to pristine C_{60}. The narrowness of these lines indicates that the C_{60} molecules rotate rapidly on the NMR time scale in the undoped and as well in the doped substances. Additionally, the appearence of a single, shifted narrow line implies that the sample consists of a majority phase of doped C_{60}. There is only a small amount (roughly 1%) of residual undoped C_{60} (c.f. Fig. 6). A comparison with the results of ^{13}C NMR measurements by Tycko and coworkers [24] on potassium doped C_{60} shows that an identical chemical shift (186 ppm) and the same linewith (15 ppm) is obtained for a sample attributed to K_3C_{60}. Apparently there is no influence of thallium on the ^{13}C-NMR resonance line.

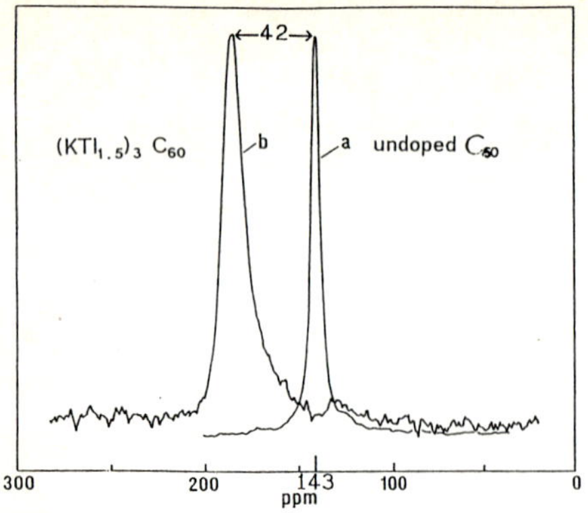

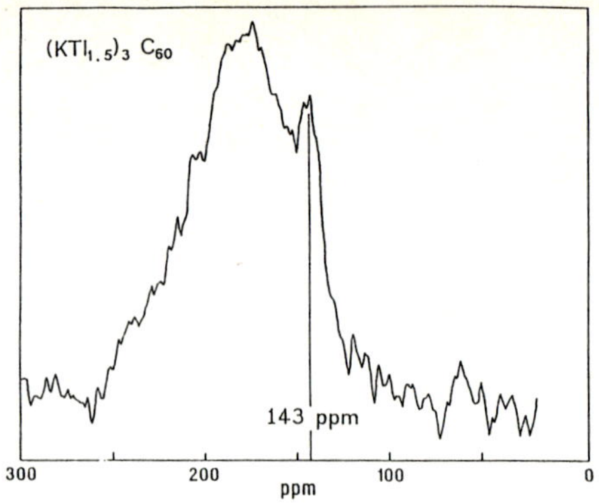

Fig. 5 and 6. ^{13}C NMR spectra of solid C_{60} (a) and of C_{60} doped with $KTl_{1.5}$ (b) at room temperature (left) and at 160 K (right). The line shifts are given with respect to TMS.

Therefore, the results obtained by ^{13}C NMR, ac susceptibility, dc magnetization and x-ray analysis can be explained by a non-Tl-containig majority phase in the samples investigated in this work.

Acknowledgement. We would like to thank G. Kaindl for placing the SQUID magnetometer to our disposal. The binary C_{60} compounds were prepared by V. Thommen at the University of Basel (CH).

References

[1] A.F. Hebard, M.J. Rosseinsky, R.C. Haddon, D.W. Murphy, S.H. Glarum, T.T.M. Palstra, A.P. Ramirez, and A.R. Kortan, Nature **350**, 600 (1991).

[2] P.W. Stephens, L. Mihaly, P.L. Lee, R.L. Whetten, S.-M. Huang, R.B. Kaner, F. Diederich, and K. Holczer, Nature **351**, 632 (1991).

[3] Y. Maruyama, T. Inabe, H. Ogata, Y. Achiba, S. Suzuki, K. Kikuchi, and I. Ikemoto, Chem. Lett., 1849 (1991).

[4] Z. Iqbal, R.H. Baughman, B.L. Ramakrishna, S. Khare, N.S. Murthy, H.J. Borneman, and D.E. Morris, Science **254**, 826 (1991).

[5] M.J. Rosseinsky, A.P. Ramirez, S.H. Glarum, D.W. Murphy, R.C. Haddon, A.F. Hebard, T.T.M. Palstra, A.R. Kortan, S.M. Zahurak, and A.V. Makhija, Phys. Rev. Lett. **66**, 2830 (1991).

[6] K. Holczer, O. Klein, S.-M. Huang, R.B. Kaner, K.-J. Fu, R.L. Whetten, and F. Diederich, Science **252**, 1154 (1991).

[7] M. Kraus, J. Freytag, S. Gärtner, H.M. Vieth, W. Krätschmer, and K. Lüders, Z. Phys. B - Condensed Matter **85**, 1 (1991).

[8] M. Kraus, S. Gärtner, M. Baenitz, M. Kanowski, H.M. Vieth, C.T. Simmons, W. Krätschmer, V. Thommen, H.P. Lang, H.-J. Güntherodt, and K. Lüders, Europhys. Lett. **17**, 419 (1992).

[9] S.P. Kelty, C.-C. Chen, and C.M. Lieber, Nature **352**, 223 (1991).
[10] C.-C. Chen, S.P. Kelty, and C.M. Lieber, Science **253**, 886 (1991).
[11] R.M. Fleming, A.P. Ramirez, M.J. Rosseinsky, D.W. Murphy, R.C. Haddon, S.M. Zahurak, and A.V. Makhija, Nature **352**, 787 (1991).
[12] G. Sparn, J.D. Thompson, R.L. Whetten, S.-M. Huang, R.B. Kaner, F. Diederich, G. Grüner, and K. Holczer, Phys. Rev. Lett. **68**, 1228 (1992).
[13] B. W. Roberts, J. Phys. Chem. Ref. Data **5**, 3 (1976).
[14] W. Krätschmer, D.L. Lamb, K. Fostiropoulos, and D.R. Huffman, Nature **347**, 354 (1990).
[15] R. Thümmel, Z. Anorg. und Allgem. Chemie **376**, 44 (1970).
[16] K. Holczer, O. Klein, G. Grüner, J.D. Thompson, F. Diederich, and R.L. Whetten, Phys. Rev. Lett. **67**, 271 (1991).
[17] C. Politis, V. Buntar, W. Krauss, and A. Gurevich, Eurohys. Lett. **17**, 175 (1992).
[18] P.H. Kes, Supercond. Sci. Technol. **5**, 41 (1992).
[19] T. Galbaatar, S.L. Drechsler, Physica C **191**, 377 (1992).
[20] G. Grüner, this issue
[21] N.R. Werthamer, E. Helfand, and P.C. Hohenberg, Phys. Rev. **147**, 295 (1966).
[22] M. Thinkham, Introduction to Superconductivity McGraw-Hill, New York 1975.
[23] C.S. Yannoni, R.D. Johnson, G. Meijer, D.S. Bethune, and J.R. Salem, J. Phys. Chem. **95**, 9 (1991).
[24] R. Tycko, G. Dabbagh, M.J. Rosseinsky, D.W. Murphy, R.M. Fleming, A.P. Ramirez, and J.C. Tully, Science **253**, 884 (1991).

Electronic Structure Studies of Fullerites and Fullerides

M. Merkel, E. Sohmen, A. Masaki, H. Romberg, M. Alexander, M. Knupfer, M.S. Golden, P. Adelmann, B. Renker, and J. Fink

Kernforschungszentrum Karlsruhe, Institut für Nukleare Festkörperphysik, Postfach 3640, W-7500 Karlsruhe, Fed. Rep. of Germany

Abstract: The electronic structure of fullerites and fullerides has been investigated by high-resolution photoemission and by high-energy electron energy-loss spectroscopy in transmission. Information on the occupied π and σ bands, on the unoccupied π^* and σ^* bands, and on the joint density of states has been obtained. In particular, we report on the changes of the electronic structure of fullerides as a function of dopant concentration.

1. Introduction

The discovery of fullerene molecules [1] has lead to a large number of experimental and theoretical investigations of these new allotropes of carbon. The synthesis of macroscopic amounts of fullerenes [2] has allowed the preparation of solids, known as fullerites and the discovery of the fullerite based compounds, A_xC_{60}, called fullerides. For certain compositions the fullerides form synthetic metals [3] and superconductivity has been discovered in A_3C_{60} compounds [4] (A=K, Rb) with remarkably high transition temperatures, T_c, of up to 33 K. It is a challenge to understand the electronic structure of these new and fascinating materials. In particular, knowledge of the electronic structure is a prerequisite for the understanding of the mechanism of high-T_c superconductivity. There have been numerous band structure calculations carried out on undoped and doped solid C_{60} within the local-density approximation (LDA) [5-7]. Using the same approximation, there have also been calculations of the optical properties of fullerites [8-11]. The question arises as to whether LDA calculations are adequate for this system, or whether electron-phonon coupling or electron-electron interactions are strong enough to cause serious deviations from the one-electron picture. Consequently, it is imperative that these theoretical calculations should be controlled by experimental studies. Previously, studies have been performed using photoemission spectroscopy (PES) [11-15], inverse photoemission (IPES) [12], X-ray absorption spectroscopy (XAS) [14, 16], optical spectroscopy [17], and high-resolution electron energy-loss spectroscopy (HREELS) [18]. In this contribution we review our own PES and electron energy-loss spectroscopy (EELS) studies on

Springer Series in Solid-State Sciences, Vol. 113 **Electronic Properties of High-T_c Superconductors**
Editors: H. Kuzmany, M. Mehring, J. Fink

fullerites and fullerides. Part of the EELS data have been published previously [19,20].

2. Experiment

A mixture of fullerenes was synthesized by the contact-arc method [2] under 100 torr of He. After extraction with toluene, C_{60}, C_{70}, and higher fullerenes were separated by column chromatography on neutral alumina with 5% toluene in hexane as eluant. The photoemission data were recorded with a commercial VSW spectrometer, using a helium discharge lamp. The overall energy resolution was set to 25 meV for the present measurements. Thin film samples were prepared *in-situ* on a freshly deposited Au film by evaporation of C_{60} from a Knudsen cell and K from a thoroughly degassed SAES getter source. The samples were subsequently annealed at 150°C for ~1h. The electron energy-loss data were recorded with a 170 keV spectrometer [21] in transmission. The energy and momentum resolution were set to 0.14eV and 0.04Å^{-1}, respectively. For core excitation spectra, the momentum resolution was reduced to 0.2Å^{-1}. For the EELS measurements, free-standing films with a thickness of about 1000Å were prepared by evaporation of fullerenes on NaCl crystals. The latter were dissolved in water and the fullerite films floated onto standard electron microscopy grids. Subsequently, the films were annealed under UHV conditions at 300°C and doping was achieved by evaporation of various amounts of alkali metals onto the films.

3. Fullerites

In Fig.1 we show the photoemission spectrum of the valence-band region of a C_{60} film recorded with a photon energy of $\hbar\omega$=21.2eV together with the theoretical density of states (DOS) calculated in the LDA approximation [7]. The band structure results have been broadened to account for finite temperature and experimental resolution and shifted so that the onset of the h_{1u}-derived bands matches the experimental result. The binding energy scale is referred to the Fermi level of a Au film. It can be seen that the widths and relative spacings of the bands are generally in good agreement between the calculation and experiment. The first two maxima at 2.3 and 3.6eV can be assigned to a group of 5 bands derived from the h_{1u} molecular levels, and a group of 9 bands derived from h_g and g_g states, respectively. Both have predominantly π electron character.

The h_{1u}-derived bands have a total measured width of about 1 eV which is reproduced by the band structure calculation. However, the three peaks of the h_{1u} bands of Fig. 1b are not observed in the experiment, although the splitting between the maxima is an order of magnitude greater than the experimental resolution. It is interesting to compare the spectrum in Fig.1a with photoemission spectra of gas phase C_{60} [22]. In

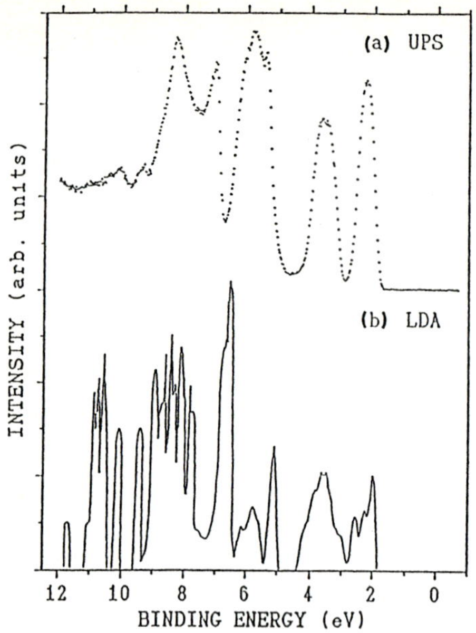

Fig. 1 a) Photoemission spectra of the valence-band region of solid C_{60}.
b) Theoretical DOS for solid C_{60} (fcc, uni-directional) broadened with a Lorentzian of FWHM 0.27eV. The effects of dimerization of C_{60} have not been included.

the latter, the line due to the h_{1u} state has a width of about 0.3 eV and a shoulder on the high binding energy side. This shoulder has been explained in terms of transitions within the vibrational manifold of the positive ion. An explanation in terms of a Jahn-Teller splitting in the positive ion has also been given, although the intensity of the shoulder relative to the primary peak does not seem consistent with this interpretation. The experimental width of the h_{1u} line in solid C_{60} may therefore be composed of a broadening due to band formation and due to excitations of intramolecular vibrations. In addition, there is a broadening due to lifetime effects, which can be estimated from the data on molecular C_{60} to be less than ~0.3 eV.

In the spectrum shown in Fig.1a there are very narrow peaks at 5.4eV and 7.1eV. These can probably be assigned to rather narrow σ bands. Since the overlap of the σ orbitals of adjacent molecules is much smaller than that of the π orbitals, the width of σ bands should be correspondingly reduced. The LDA calculation appears to underestimate the binding energy of these σ bands.

At 250K there is a phase transition from the fcc phase with free rotating molecules to a sc phase with hindered rotations. At ~90K the hindered rotations appear to freeze out. Various band structure calculations [6,7] predict considerable changes of the DOS due to

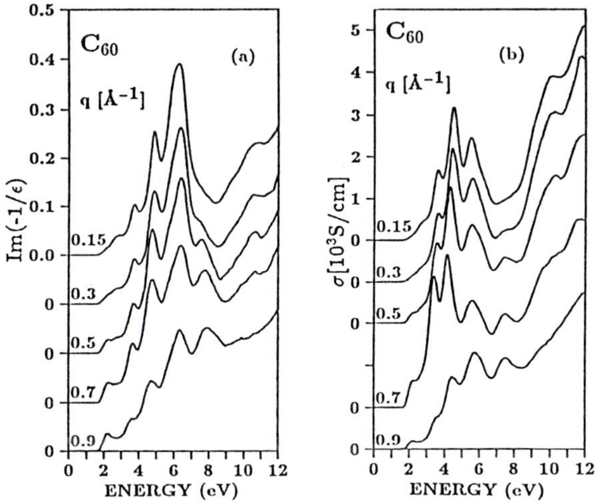

Fig.2 a) Low-energy loss function of C_{60} for various momentum transfers, **q** (in $Å^{-1}$) measured by EELS.
b) Optical conductivity, $\sigma = \omega\varepsilon_0\varepsilon_2$, of C_{60} as a function of momentum transfer, **q**.

structural changes at lower temperatures. Therefore, we have measured high resolution photoemission spectra as a function of temperature ($9K \leq T \leq 300K$). Within experimental accuracy, no changes of the spectra have been observed indicating that spectral broadening due to phonons is larger than changes of the DOS resulting from phase transitions.

In Fig. 2 we show the low-energy loss function, Im(-1/ε), of a C_{60} film measured by EELS, and the optical conductivity, $\sigma = \omega\varepsilon_0\varepsilon_2$, derived from a Kramers-Kronig analysis of the loss function for various momentum transfers, **q**. The low-energy loss function shows a **q**-independent onset at 1.7eV, with features at 2.2, 2.7 and 3.6eV. The peak at 2.2eV can probably be assigned as a singlet exciton related to the dipole forbidden h_{1u}-t_{1u} transition, which is enhanced at higher momentum transfer as a result of increasing excitation of monopole transitions. Similarly, the features at 2.7 and 3.6eV can be attributed to π-π* transitions which may possess a degree of excitonic character. The plasmon of all π electrons is observed at ~6eV. The **q**-dependent intensity variation of these features can clearly be seen in the optical conductivity data of Fig. 2b, as well as some higher lying π-π* transitions. Using parameters refined from the fitting of photoemission data such as is shown in Fig. 1a, we have found that a majority of the transitions observed in the EELS studies can be assigned within an effective Su-Schrieffer-Heeger model. However, the validity of such a model in a system where electronic correlation may play an important role requires further consideration.

Next, in Fig. 3 we show the low energy-loss function for solid C_{70} measured by EELS with a small momentum transfer (**q** = $0.1Å^{-1}$),

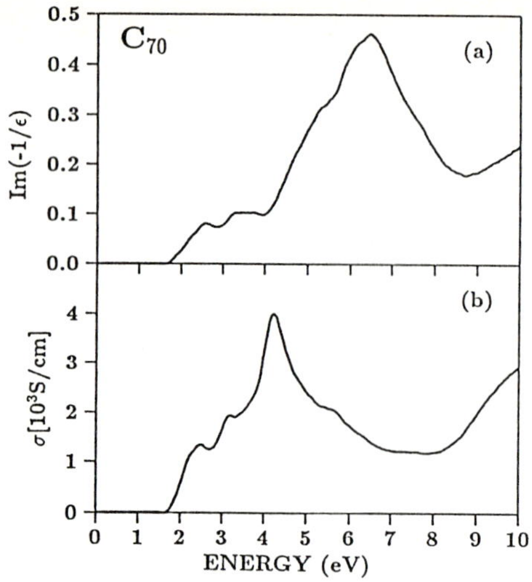

Fig. 3 Low-energy loss function for solid C_{70} measured by EELS.and the derived optical conductivity

together with the optical conductivity obtained by a Kramers-Kronig analysis of the loss function. The lower symmetry of the higher fullerite results in the partial lifting of the degeneracy of the electronic levels. This can be seen to result in a broadening of the spectral structure in comparison to C_{60}. However, in common with C_{60}, the onset of the loss function occurs at 1.7eV and the plasmon of all π electrons is observed in the loss function at ~6eV. In the optical conductivity, the direct gap transition (optically forbidden) can be observed as a weak shoulder at 1.9eV. Transitions from three main groups of states give rise to structure starting at 2.2, 3.1 and 4.3eV, with some fine structure observable due to the individual transitions within each group.

4. Fullerides

In Fig. 4 we show photoemission spectra in the valence band region of K_xC_{60}. Similar data have been published previously [13-15]. With increasing dopant concentration a new peak close to the Fermi level appears due to the filling of the t_{1u}-derived conduction bands. At intermediate dopant concentrations there is a clear Fermi edge. Assuming only 3 stable phases for $x = 0$, 3 and 6, the spectrum with the highest Fermi edge should correspond to that of the metallic phase ($x = 3$). On the other hand, assuming the highest doping concentration to be $x=6$, the dopant concentration for each of the other spectra can be derived from the intensity of the peak at lowest binding energy. The x values given in Fig. 4 have been determined using the latter approach, with the spectra normalized to the area of.the HOMO-derived peak. This would imply that

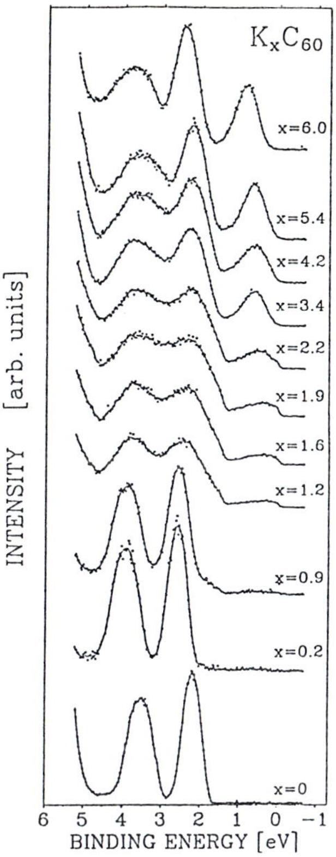

Fig. 4 Photoemission spectra of K_xC_{60} measured at room temperature.

the metallic phase is at a maximum for x = 1.6 and that for x = 3 the compound is insulating. Recently, an insulating phase due to correlation effects has been predicted for x = 3 [23], and the existence of a pseudo-gap has been derived from photoemission and inverse photoemission data [24]. However, the spectra shown in Fig. 4 may possibly result from the existence of several phases at the surface and a metallic phase with x = 3. Further studies of the surface structure and their relationship to bulk properties in A_xC_{60} are necessary.

In the metallic, intermediate-doped sample there is a considerable broadening of the HOMO (h_{1u})- and the (h_g, g_g)-derived bands compared to the undoped case. The occupied part of the LUMO-derived bands is also broad: assuming half-filling this yields a total LUMO width of ~2 eV which is considerably larger than expected from band structure calculations. In the fully doped case, the widths of the LUMO- and HOMO-derived bands are 1.2 and 1.3 eV, respectively. These are similar to the values expected from band structure calculations and very close to those of the undoped case.

There are several possible explanations for the broadening of the bands in the half-filled case. As a result of electron-phonon coupling, there may be a Jahn-Teller-like distortion of the C atoms within the C_{60}

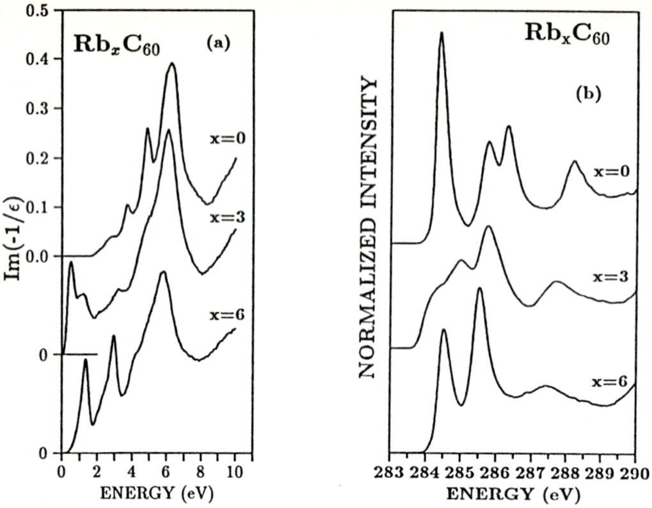

Fig. 5 a) Low-energy loss function measured by EELS for Rb_xC_{60}.
b) C 1s absorption edges for Rb_xC_{60} measured by EELS.

molecule, leading to a splitting of the molecular orbitals as a function of the filling of the LUMO level [25]. Calculations have been performed in the framework of a Su-Schrieffer-Heeger model leading to a maximal splitting of the molecular levels by some tenths of an eV for x=3 and a complete degeneracy for x=0 and x=6. In addition, the HOMO-LUMO gap is considerably reduced for x=6 in agreement with the experiment, which gives a value for the separation of the HOMO-LUMO maxima of 1.6eV. On the other hand, the anomalous broadening of the bands for intermediate x values could also be explained by correlation effects on the C sites. These cannot be ruled out as a consequence of the narrow bandwidth of the π bands and the large correlation energy, U, of 1.6 eV [23]. Finally, although surface degradation or a mixing of different phases at the surface seems unlikely, it cannot be dismissed at this stage.

Similar photoemission results have been obtained in this laboratory for the doping of C_{60} with Rb. In contrast, preliminary investigations of the Cs-C_{60} system were unable to observe a clear Fermi edge, indicating an absence of metallic behaviour at the surface at any doping level.

In Fig.5a we show the loss function of Rb_xC_{60} for x=0, 3 and 6, and in Fig. 5b the C 1s absorption edges of the same samples. In the loss function for x=3, the gap is filled with two transitions at 0.5eV and 1.2eV. The 0.5eV peak is assigned to a plasmon caused by an intraband transition within the LUMO-derived conduction bands. The second peak at 1.2eV is assigned to a transition between the partially filled LUMO-derived bands and the next group of π* bands derived from the molecular t_{1g} level. Due to the complete filling of the conduction bands, the lower energy peak has disappeared for x=6 and the peak at 1.2eV has increased in intensity. The

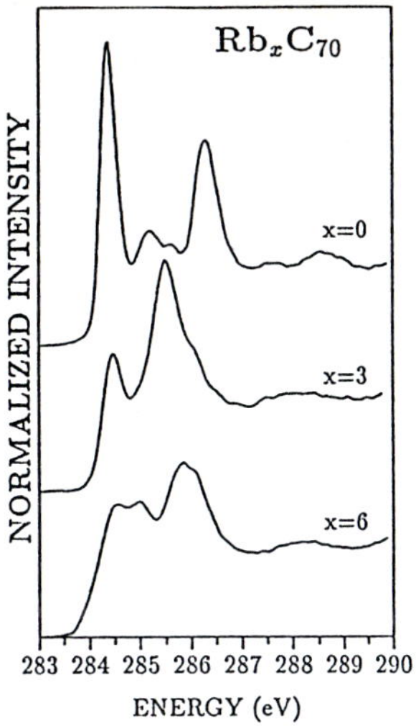

Fig. 6. C 1s absorption edges measured by EELS for Rb_xC_{70}. The curves are labelled with x.

data shown in Fig. 5a are qualitatively in agreement with recent calculations of the loss function [10]. It is interesting to note that on going from x=0 to x=6 the peak at 3.6eV moves to 2.9eV. This again indicates a shrinking of the energy difference between π and π* bands. This may be a result of a lowering of the dimerization in the doped case compared to the undoped case (where π electrons are localized in the bonds connecting the pentagons). This result is in agreement with theoretical calculations [25,26].

Neglecting core hole effects, the C 1s absorption edges shown in Fig. 5b represent the density of unoccupied states of the Rb-doped C_{60} fulleride. They clearly illustrate the progressive filling of the LUMO with doping. This is manifest in the systematic reduction of the first peak, which results from transitions from the C 1s level to unoccupied LUMO states. The chemical shift of the C 1s core level on doping results in the shift of the spectra to lower energies with increasing doping. A considerable broadening of the 1s-π* transitions is observed for x=3. This may be explained in terms of Jahn-Teller-like distortions such as were mentioned in the discussion of the photoemission data of Fig. 4.

Moving once again to the higher fulleride, Fig. 6 shows C 1s absorption edges for Rb_xC_{70} for x=0, 3, and 6. The results are similar to those of Rb_xC_{60} and once again indicate the gradual filling of the LUMO-derived states on successive Rb doping. Similar C 1s chemical shifts are observed as well as broadening of the spectral structure for the half-doped, x=3 fulleride.

5. Summary

The main result of the present investigation is the observation that upon n-type doping of both C_{60} and C_{70} there is a filling of the conduction bands. In C_{60} for $x=3$, whilst the EELS data are consistent with half filling of the conduction band and a metallic state, the photoemission results are more difficult to interpret within such a simple picture. For $x=6$, these bands are completely filled leading again to an insulating state. However, for both fullerites the changes of the electronic structure are not rigid-band like. There is a reduction of the energy difference between π and π* bands due to a reduction in the dimerization with increasing x. At half-filling there may also be a Jahn-Teller-like splitting of the molecular π levels leading to a broadening of π bands in the solid.

References

1. H.W. Kroto, J.R. Heath, S.C.O'Brien, R.F. Curl, and R. E. Smalley, *Nature* **318** (1985) 162 .
2. W. Krätschmer, L.D. Lamb, K. Fostiropoulos, and D. R. Huffman, *Nature* **347** (1990) 354.
3. R.C. Haddon, A.F. Hebard, M.J. Rosseinsky, D.W. Murphy, S.J. Duclos, K.B. Lyons, B. Miller, J.M. Rosamilia, R.M. Fleming, A.R. Kortan, S.H. Glarum, A.V. Makhija, A.J. Müller, R.H. Eick, S.M. Zahurak, R. Tycko, G. Dabbagh, and F.A. Thiel, *Nature* **350** (1991) 320.
4. A.F. Hebard, M.J. Rosseinsky, R.C. Haddon, D.W. Murphy, S.H. Glarum, T.T.M. Palstra, A.P. Ramirez, and A.R. Kortan, *Nature* **350** (1991) 600.
5. S. Saito and A. Oshima, *Phys. Rev. Lett.* **66** (1991) 2637.
6. S.C. Erwin and W.E. Pickett, *Science* **254** (1991) 842.
7. S. Satpathy, V.P. Antropov, O.K. Andersen, O. Jepsen, O. Gunnarsson, and A.I. Lichtenstein, *Phys. Rev.* **B**, in print and private communication
8. W.Y. Ching, M.-Z. Huang, Y.-N. Xu, W.G. Harter, and F.T. Chan, *Phys. Rev. Lett.* **67** (1991) 2045.
9. G.E. Bertsch, A. Bulgac, D. Tománek, and Y. Wang, *Phys. Rev. Lett.* **67** (1991) 2690.
10. Y.-N. Xu, M.-Z. Huang, and W.Y. Ching, *Phys. Rev.* **B**. **44** (1991) 13171.
11. J.H. Weaver, J.L. Martins, T. Komeda, Y. Chen, T.R. Ohno, G.H. Kroll, N. Troullier, R.E. Haufler, and R.E. Smalley, *Phys. Rev. Lett.* **66** (1991) 1741.
12. P.J. Benning, D.M. Poirier, T.R. Ohno, Y. Chen, M.B. Jost, F. Stepniak, G.H. Kroll, and J.H. Weaver, *Phys. Rev.* **B**, in press.

13. P.J. Benning, J.L. Martins, J.H. Weaver, L.P.F. Chibante, and R.E. Smalley, *Science* **252** (1991) 1417.
14. C.T. Chen, L.H. Tjeng, P. Rudolf, G. Meigs, J.E. Rowe, J. Chen, J.P. Mc Cauley Jr., A.B. Smith III., A.R. McGhie, W.J. Romanow, and E.W. Plummer, *Nature* **352** (1991) 603.
15. G.K. Wertheim, J.E. Rowe, D.N.E. Buchanan, E.E. Chaban, A.F. Hebard, A.R. Kortan, A.V. Makhija, and R.C. Haddon, *Science* **252** (1991) 1419.
16. L.J. Terminello, D.K. Shuh, F.J. Himpsel, D.A. Lapiano-Smith, J.Stöhr, D.S. Bethune, and G. Meijer, *Chem. Phys. Lett.* **182** (1991) 491.
17. T. Pichler, M. Matus, J. Kürti, and H. Kuzmany, *Solid State Commun.* in print.
18. G. Gensterblum, J.J. Pireaux, P.A. Thiry, R. Caudano, J.P. Vigneron, Ph. Lambin, A.A. Lucas, and W. Krätschmer, *Phys. Rev. Lett.* **67** (1991) 2171.
19. E. Sohmen, J. Fink, and W. Krätschmer, *Z.Phys.* **B 86** (1992) 87.
20. E. Sohmen, J. Fink, and W. Krätschmer, *Europhys. Lett.* **17** (1992) 51.
21. J. Fink, *Adv. Electron. Electron Phys.* **74** (1989) 121.
22. D.L. Lichtenberger, M.E. Jatcko, K.W. Nebesny, C.D. Ray, D.R. Huffman, and L.D. Lamb, *Mat. Res. Soc. Symp. Proc.* **206** (1991) 673.
23. R.W. Lof, M.A. von Veenendaal, B. Koopmans, H.T. Jonkman, and G.A. Sawatzky, *Phys. Rev. Lett.*, submitted
24. T.Takahashi, S. Suzuki, T. Morikawa, H. Katayama-Joshida, S. Hasegawa, H. Inokuchi, K. Seki, K. Kikuchi, S. Suzuki, K. Ikemoto, and Y. Achiba, *Phys. Rev. Lett.* **68**, 1232 (1992)
25. K. Harigaya, *J. Phys. Soc. Japan*, submitted
26. G. Stollhoff, *Phys. Rev.* **B**, submitted.

X-Ray Absorption Study of Iodine-Doped C_{60}

G. Wortmann[1], *J. Freund*[1], *G. Nowitzke*[1], *H. Werner*[2], *and R. Schlögl*[2]

[1]Fachbereich Physik, Universität GH Paderborn,
Postfach 1621, W-4790 Paderborn, Fed. Rep. of Germany

[2]Institut für Anorganische Chemie, Universität Frankfurt,
Niederurseler Hang, W-6000 Frankfurt 50, Fed. Rep. of Germany

Abstract: X-ray absorption spectroscopy at the iodine $L_{I,III}$ - thresholds was applied to study the structural and chemical properties of iodine-doped C_{60}. The studies were performed on a system of the chemical composition $C_{60}I_{3.66}$ prepared by gas-phase reaction. Both the iodine L_{III} - EXAFS and the L_I - XANES prove the molecular form of the iodine as I_2 , modified by an increase in the intramolecular bond length upon intercalation. The derived chemical properties are similar to that of graphite intercalation compounds formed with halogen molecules.

1. Introduction

The carbon molecule C_{60} , known as Buckminster-Fullerene, has been recognized as a third form of carbon beside diamond and graphite [1]. Among the fascinating properties of these molecules in their condensed form, when doped with alkali metals like K or Rb, is the appearance of superconductivity. K_3C_{60} and Rb_3C_{60} exhibit T_c values of 18 K and 28 K, respectively [2]. In many repects the doped C_{60} systems have similarities with graphite intercalation compounds, where donor systems (e.g. KC_8, RbC_8) with T_c values below 1 K and acceptor systems (with acceptor molecules like SbF_6^- and $SbCl_6^-$ or halogen molecules like Br_2, IBr, ICl) without superconducting properties exist. Interestingly, there were reports of the occurance of superconductivity around 60 K in iodine-doped C_{60} [3]. This prompted us to investigate the structural and chemical properties of iodine-doped C_{60} applying x-ray absorption spectroscopy at the L_I- and L_{III}-thresholds of iodine. We shall discuss the results of this investigation in comparison with our previous studies of halogen-intercalated graphites [4,5] and conducting polymers [6].

2. Sample Preparation and Experimental Details

The samples were prepared from highly purified C_{60} and elemental iodine at temperatures between 510 K and 580 K. An elemental analysis yielded a chemical composition of $C_{60}I_{3.66}$. The system, named $C_{60}(I_2)_2$ in the following, was also studied by x-ray diffraction (XRD) and exhibits a single-phase diffractogramme with a crystal symmetry lower than cubic [7]. The sample was encapsulated in a vacuum-tight absorber holder equipped with Be windows and investigated at both the iodine L_I- and L_{III}-thresholds in the temperature range 11 K - 300 K. As reference system served (BEDT-TTF)$_2I_3$ in its α-phase (non-superconducting) and β-phase (superconducting). It contains linear I_3^- acceptor molecules whose intramolecular spacings are well known [8]. The measurements were performed at the EXAFS-II beamline of HASYLAB (DESY, Hamburg) employing a Si(111) double crystal monochromator and a focusing mirror.

Springer Series in Solid-State Sciences, Vol. 113 Electronic Properties of High-T_c Superconductors
Editors: H. Kuzmany, M. Mehring, J. Fink

3. Results and Discussion

Fig. 1 shows a typical I-L_{III} EXAFS spectrum and its Fourier transform. Only one defined distance is observed, with a value typical for an intramolecular I-I distance. The usual EXAFS analysis yielded a distance, d_{I-I}, of 2.78(1) A, independent of temperature (see Fig. 2). The temperature dependence of σ^2, i.e. the variance of d_{I-I}, is also shown. This parameter is constant up to 60 K and shows then an increase with temperature. This behaviour can be fitted with a model assuming one eigenfrequency for the iodine system (Einstein model) [9]. The EXAFS analysis of the I_3^- anion in the reference system, $(BEDT\text{-}TTF)_2I_3$, yielded a value for d_{I-I} of 2.94(1) A, which is typical for an I_3^- anion and in agreement with known structural data [8]. The EXAFS analysis yielded also a considerable lower nearest-neighbour number for iodine-doped C_{60} than for $(BEDT\text{-}TTF)_2I_3$. Together with the above value of d_{I-I}, this points to the existence of molecular I_2 in the C_{60} lattice. The I_2 molecules experience an increase of the intramolecular bond length. The present value, d_{I-I} = 2.78 A, is larger than those of gaseous I_2 and solid I_2 with 2.666 A and 2.715 A, respectively.

These findings are confirmed by the near-edge structure (XANES) of the L_I-threshold. Fig. 3 shows spectra of $C_{60}(I_2)_2$ and of I_3^- in BEDT-TTF. Iodine L_I-spectra of halogen molecules exhibit a dominant pre-edge peak, which is called σ*-resonance due to the 2s-5p transitions into the unoccupied and antibonding molecular orbitals with σ-

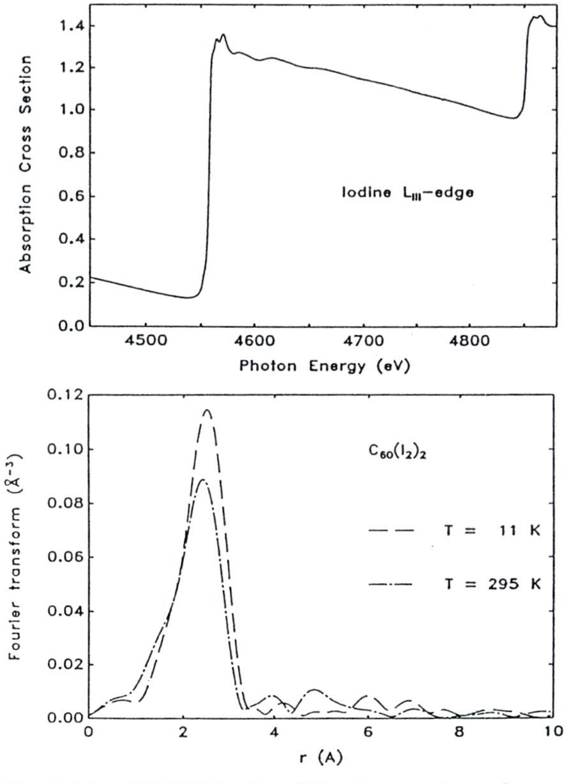

Fig. 1: I-L_{III} EXAFS (top) and Fourier transforms (bottom) of $C_{60}(I_2)_2$

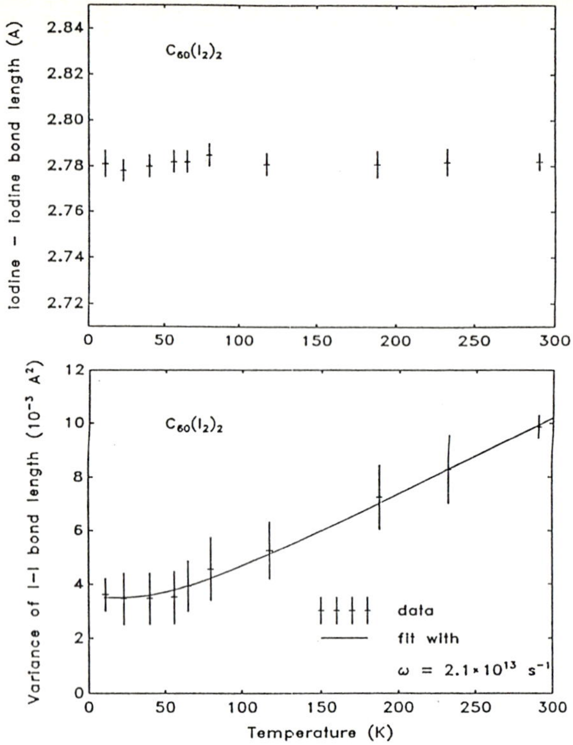

Fig. 2: Temperature dependence of the I-I intramolecular bondlength (top) and of its variance, σ^2, (bottom) in $C_{60}(I_2)_2$.

symmetry. It is known from our previous investigations of various halogen systems that the energy separation between the dominant pre-edge peak and the edge, labelled with A and B in Fig. 3, is inversely proportional to the intramolecular bond length [10]. Using this correlation, one derives a bondlength of 2.75(5) A, in agreement with the (more precise) EXAFS results. Beside the energy separation A-B, the height of the σ^*-resonance contains information about the chemical properties of the halogen system, since it is (roughly) proportional to the number of holes in the 5p shell. This number is 1 per iodine for an I_2 molecule and, averaged, 0.66 for an I_3^- anion. From the analysis of the L_I-spectra shown in Fig. 3, we obtain r = 1.47(5) for the ratio of the (normalized) areas of the σ^*-resonances of I_2 in C_{60} and I_3^- in BEDT-TTF, in agreement with the expected value of r = 1.5.

The value of the intramolecular bond length of iodine in C_{60}, $d_{I\text{-}I}$ = 2.78 A, determined directly in this study, is in sharp contrast with the value $d_{I\text{-}I}$ = 2.53 A, deduced from an XRD study of $C_{60}I_3$ [11]. The crystallographic space group reported in Ref. 11 is, in our opinion, not compatible with the local symmetry of the intercalated I_2 molecules. These questions will be discussed in detail in a forthcoming paper [7].

The present finding that molecular iodine is present in the C_{60} matrix parallels with previous investigations of the inter-halogen molecules ICl and IBr intercalated into graphite. X-ray absorption and Mössbauer studies prove that only molecular species are present in these acceptor systems [4,5]. After intercalation the ICl and IBr molecules exhibit an increase in molecular bond lengths of 0.05 to 0.10 A, respectively, in comparison

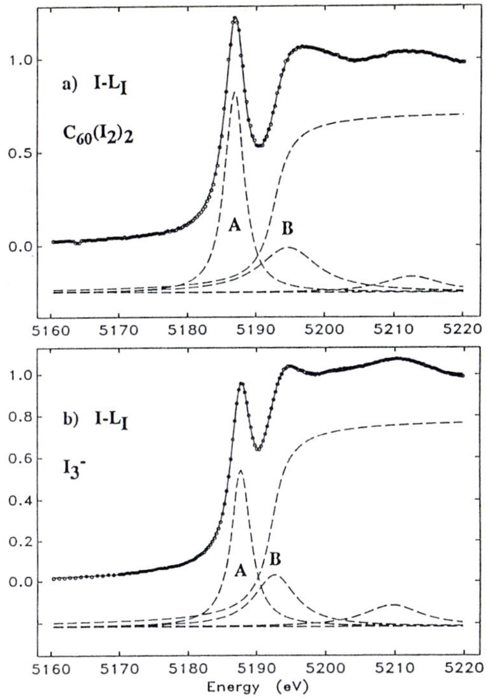

Fig. 3: I-L_I XANES of (a) $C_{60}(I_2)_2$ and (b) of the reference system α-(BEDT-TTF)$_2I_3$ containing linear I_3^- anions.

with their solid phases, which compares well with the present observations. The iodine positions were found to be in registry with the carbon hexagons, as reflected by defined I-C distances in the Fourier transform of the iodine L_{III}-EXAFS [4,10]. The absence of such well-defined I-C distances in the present system is easily explained by the multitude of possible I-C distances in the $C_{60}(I_2)_2$ system. This "incommensurate" position of iodine with respect to C neighbours leads to an averaging and thus extinction of the EXAFS amplitude. Similar observations were made in previous EXAFS investigations of iodine acceptor molecules (I_3^-, I_5^-) inserted into polyacetylene [6].

It is interesting to compare the charge transfer in systems as different as conducting polymers (with iodine-doped polyacetylene as best example) and radical-anion salts like (BEDT-TTF)$_2I_3$ on the one hand and halogen-graphites and iodine-doped C_{60} on the other hand. In the first case the charge transfer is determined by the relative number of *acceptor anions*. In the latter case, however, the charge transfer per *halogen molecule* is much smaller than for an anion and, to our opinion, better described as a charge redistribution within the overlapping π-orbital systems of the halogen molecules on the one hand and and the carbon planes or C_{60} molecules on the other hand. The electronic properties of the C_{60} molecules are much less modified by the intercalation of iodine molecules than by the intercalation of alkali metals. This was also proven by a variety of other spectroscopic investigations of the present sample [7]. $C_{60}(I_2)_2$ remains insulating and in a chemically stable state.

One should finally comment on the superconducting properties. First of all, the speculations reported in Ref. 3 have been withdrawn. Secondly, a susceptibility study of the sample down to 1.5 K did not give any evidence for such a behaviour [7], in agreement with Refs. 11 and 12. Finally, since the charge transfer is very small and there are no hole carriers, superconductivity is not expected to occur at all in $C_{60}(I_2)_2$.

This work was supported by the BMFT (Project Nr. 05 5PPACB) and the DFG (Sfb-337, TP B2).

References

1. W. Krätschmer, L.D. Lamb, K. Fostiropoulos, D.R. Huffman, Nature **347**, 354 (1990).
2. A.F. Hebard et al., Nature **350**, 32 (1991); K. Holczer et al., Science **252**, 1154 (1991); M.J. Rosseinsky et al., Phys. Rev. Lett. **66**, 2830 (1991).
3. T. Swinbanks, Nature **352**, 632 (1991); **353**, 377 (1991).
4. W. Krone, G. Wortmann, and G. Kaindl, Synthetic Metals, **29**, F 247 (1989).
5. M. Tiedtke and G. Wortmann, Synthetic Metals **34**, 404 (1989); Hyperfine Interactions **53**, 419 (1990).
6. G. Wortmann, W. Krone, V. Biebesheimer, and G. Kaindl, Springer Series in Solid-State Sciences **63**, 41 (1985).
7. H. Werner et al., submitted
8. e.g.: P.C.W. Leung et al., Solid State Commun. **57**, 93 (1986) and ref. cited therein.
9. J. Freund et al., in preparation
10. G. Wortmann, W. Krone, G. Kaindl, Physica **B 158**, 535 (1989).
11. Q. Zhu, D.E. Cox, J.E. Fischer, K. Kniaz, A.R. McGhie, O. Zhou, Nature **355**, 712 (1992).
12. M. Kobayashi et al., Solid State Commun. **81**, 93 (1992).

In-situ UV/VIS and Infrared Spectroscopy of Potassium-Doped C_{60}

T. Pichler, J. Kürti[2], *and H. Kuzmany*[1]

[1]Institut für Festkörperphysik, Universität Wien, A-1090 Vienna, Austria
[2]Department of Atomic Physics, R. Eötvös University, H-1088 Budapest, Hungary

Abstract. *In situ* optical and infrared transmission measurements are reported for K_xC_{60} ($0 \leq x \leq 6$). From a fit of the absorption spectra for the three stable phases C_{60}, K_3C_{60} and K_6C_{60} to a Kramers-Heisenberg DF a definite assignment of the electronic transitions was found, in excellent agreement with LHS and LDA calculations. In the infrared region the electronic background and the shift of the 4 T_{1u} modes with doping were studied. The strongest shift was observed for the T_{1u} mode at $1428\,cm^{-1}$.

1 Introduction

In the doping process of C_{60} alkali metal atoms are accommodated on octahedral and tetrahedral lattice sites which leeds to a metallic phase M_3C_{60} with fcc crystal structure [1] and, for further doping, to a semiconducting phase M_6C_{60} with a bcc lattice [2]. The electronic structure of the neutral compound was investigated in detail by spectroscopic techniques like optical absorption, resonance Raman, photoemission, inverse photoemission, and electron energy-loss spectroscopy [3].

We report detailed measurements of optical absorption in the spectral range between 0.5 and 6 eV for K_xC_{60} in a continuous doping range $0 \leq x \leq 6$. The obtained spectra were analysed using a Kramers-Heisenberg dielectric response function [4]. In addition we performed *in situ* potassium doping experiments in the infrared region to get information about the change of the electronic background and about the the 4 infrared active T_{1u} modes with increasing potassium concentration.

2 Experimental

Smooth films from purified C_{60} with a thickness of 0.4 μ were sublimated on a quartz slide for optical transmission measurements and films with a thickness of 0.5 μ were sublimated on a Si wafer for infrared transmission spectroscopy. Four electrical contacts were provided on the quartz for a van der Pauw conductivity measurement during the doping process. Doping in the HITACHI UV-vis spectrometer was performed *in situ* in a quartz tube by slowly evaporating metallic K in a dynamical vacuum of $2 \cdot 10^{-4}$ Pa. After each doping step the heater current was switched off until quasiequilibrium for the van der Pauw voltage was obtained. The doping process in the IR was done *in situ* in a home made IR cell inserted in a BRUKER 66V spectrometer by evaporating K in a dynamical vacuum of $1 \cdot 10^{-4}$ Pa. The transmission spectra of the C_{60} coated Si wafer was measured in the range of 5000 to $400\,cm^{-1}$ with a resolution of $0.5\,cm^{-1}$.

3 Results

Fig.1 shows the absorption spectra of a C_{60} film in the neutral, K_3C_{60} and K_6C_{60} state. The spectra were analysed by using a Kramers Heisenberg dielectric function. Since

Springer Series in Solid-State Sciences, Vol. 113 Electronic Properties of High-T_c Superconductors
Editors: H. Kuzmany, M. Mehring, J. Fink

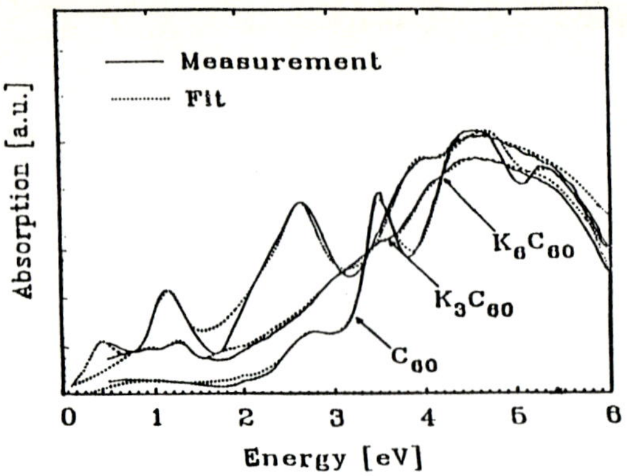

Fig.1: Absorbance of a pure C_{60} film and C_{60} doped to the stable phases K_3C_{60} and K_6C_{60} compared to an oscillator fit.

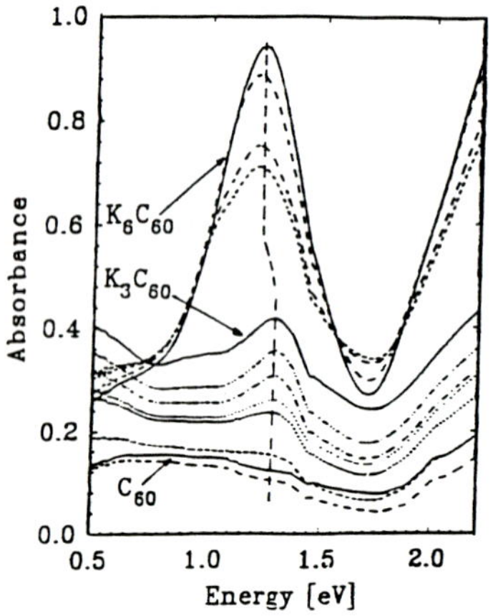

Fig. 2: Absorption spectra around 1.3 eV for increasing doping times.

the exact value plotted from the spectrometer is $-ln\langle T\rangle$, this was calculated for several electronic oscillators of the DF. The oscillators were selected from the spectrum by visual inspection. The dotted line is the result of this fit. No free carrier contribution was considered for this spectral range. For ϵ_∞ a value of 4 was used.The interferences of the quartz plate were corrected selfconsistently. Details for the change of the structures in the absorption spectra can be directly correlated to results from band structure calculations.

Several characteristic and well expressed changes in the spectra can be observed with increasing doping. Above 3.5 eV the characteristic features of the spectra for the doped material are broadened and slightly shifted rather than that peaks disappear or new peaks are created. The strong absorption peak at 3.5 eV is strongly bleached throughout the full doping process. In the spectral range between 2 and 2.7 eV a general broad increase of the absorption is observed and finally a strong peak at 2.7 eV appears. Most interesting changes appear on the low energy end of the spectrum as shown in detail in Fig.2. Around 1.3 eV a strong line with a characteristic shoulder grows continuously with doping but shifts discontinuously to lower energies at the transition from K_3 to K_6. At still lower energies the absorbance increases first with increasing doping until the K_3 state is reached and decreases for continuing doping.

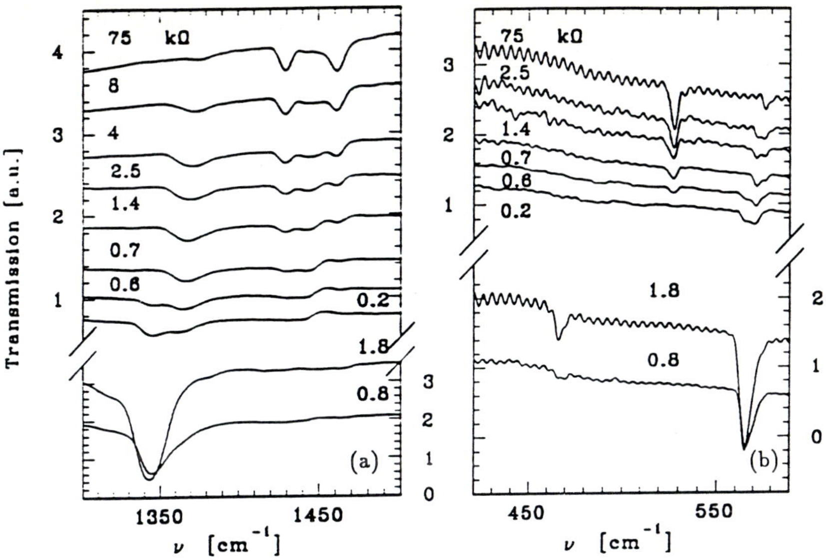

Fig.3: Shift of the T_{1u} mode at 1428 cm^{-1} (a) and shift of the T_{1u} modes at 527 cm^{-1} and 577 cm^{-1} (b) with increasing doping concentrations.

Below 0.5 eV the change of the spectra with doping was studied in the FTIR spectrometer. The background transmission of the coated Si waver decreased strongly as the concentration of K_3C_{60} is increased. This is shown in Fig.3 (a), (b). Finally, for doping to K_6C_{60} the background transmission increases again.

The response of the infrared active T_{1u} modes is remarkable. In Fig.3 (a) the change of the T_{1u} mode at 1428 cm^{-1} is shown. With increasing doping (decreasing resistance) the oscillator strength of the mode decreases and a new mode at 1362 cm^{-1} appears. This mode is characteristic for the K_3C_{60} phase. Finally, for the K_6C_{60} state the mode arrives at 1342 cm^{-1} . This behavior proves the phase separation between C_{60}, K_3C_{60} and K_6C_{60} because there is no continuous line shift for this mode. There is however, a slight shift of the T_{1u} mode of K_3C_{60} between 1370 cm^{-1} and 1362 cm^{-1} . Interestingly, in the pristine material we also observe the infraredactive part of the oxygen contaminated A_g pinch mode at 1462 cm^{-1} and the IR active part of the A_g pinch mode in K_3C_{60} at 1442 cm^{-1} .

The T_{1u} mode at 1182 cm^{-1} is not shifted with doping. Fig.3 (b) shows the shift of the two low energy T_{1u} modes. The line at 527 cm^{-1} is shifted very strongly between the pristine C_{60} and K_6C_{60}. The position of the mode in K_3C_{60} can not be observed as the oscillator strength is below the resulution limit. The second mode at 577 cm^{-1} shows a simiar behavior as the A_g pinch mode in the Raman spectra [5]. It shifts linear with the valency of the charged C_{60} molecules as summarized in Tab.1.

4 Discussion

The optical absorption spectrum for the neutral material and the doped material can be easily identified by comparison with LDA bandstructure calculations. The discrepancy for the assignment in the case of the neutral material concerns the position of the first allowed transition. Whereas originally the strong peak in the absorption at 3.5 eV was considered as the first allowed ($h_u \rightarrow t_{1g}$) transition more recent experiments suggest that this transition corresponds to the small peak around 2.7 eV. Since all features in the spectra for the doped systems are straightforwardly explained for this assignment the present results strongly support that the first allowed transition is at 2.7 eV. In this notation the strong increase of the oscillator strength at 1.3 eV is due to the lowest energy ($t_{1u} \rightarrow t_{1g}$) transition from the doping induced population in the t_{1u} level [4].

The IR experiments clearly demonstrate a phase separation between the three stable phases similar to observations by Raman spectroscopy [5]. In Tab.1 the observed positions of the infrared active T_{1u} modes together with the linestift per charge are listed.

Tab.1: Positions of the T_{1u} modes of the three stable phases C_{60}, K_3C_{60} and K_6C_{60}.

Mode nr.	C_{60} [cm^{-1}]	K_3C_{60} [cm^{-1}]	K_6C_{60} [cm^{-1}]	$\Delta\nu$/charge [cm^{-1} /EQ]
1	527	—	467	10
2	577	571	565	2 (linear)
3	1182	1182	1182	0
4	1428	1362	1342	14 (not linear)

The observed modes for the K_6C_{60} are in very good agreement with results presentated by H.J. Choi et. al. [6]. In various theoretical analyses [6,7] it is concluded that a strong line shift of vibrational modes is correlated to a strong electron phonon coupling. Thus these modes may contribute preferably to the pairing mechanism of superconductivity. The slight shift of the T_{1u} mode of K_3C_{60} with the highest energy between 1370 cm^{-1} and 1362 cm^{-1} with increasing K concentration may be explained by a cluster size effect of the K_3C_{60} phase or by small deviations from stochiometric conditions. The strength of the IR active mode at 1462 cm^{-1} strongly depends on the preparation.

Acknowledgement. Work supported by the FFWF, project P8172.

References

[1] P.W. Stephens, L. Mihaly, P.L. Lee, R.L. Whetten, S.M. Huang, R. Kaner, F. Deiderich, and K. Holczer, Nature **351**, 632 (1991).
[2] O. Zhou, J.E. Fisher, N. Coustel, S. Kycia, Q. Zhu, A.R. McGhie,W.J. Romanow, J.P. McCauley Jr,A.B. Smith III and D.E. Cox, Nature **351**, 462 (1991).
[3] J. Fink and E. Sohmen, Physikalische Blätter, Vol **48**, No. 1, 11 (1992).
[4] T. Pichler, M. Matus, J. Kürti, and H. Kuzmany SSC, Vol. **81**, No. 10, 859 (1992).
[5] T. Pichler, M. Matus, J. Kürti, and H. Kuzmany, to be published.
[6] H.J. Choi and M.J. Rice in this volume.
[7] C. M. Varma, J. Zaanen, and K. Raghavachari, Science **254**, 989 (1991).

Infrared Absorption by Charged Phonons in Doped C_{60}

H.-Y. Choi and M.J. Rice

Materials Research Laboratory, 0114-39D, Xerox Webster Research Center, Webster, NY 14580, USA

Abstract. The giant infrared activity observed in A_6C_{60} (A=K, Rb) by Fu *et al.* is interpreted as being due to a classic charged-phonon effect in which the T_{1u} molecular vibration modes of C_{60} acquire *electronic* oscillator strength via coupling to virtual $t_{1u}\rightarrow t_{1g}$ electronic transitions. The theory we introduce for the compounds A_xC_{60} (x = 3, 4, and 6), describes the A_6C_{60} data extremely well and enables values of the electron-molecular vibration coupling constants and the unsoftened T_{1u} frequencies to be deduced directly from the IR spectra. We note that the T_{1u} vibrations participate in the phonon mechanism of superconductivity in the A_3C_{60} compounds.

Fu *et al.* [1] have recently measured the infrared (IR) spectrum of A_6C_{60} (A=K, Rb) and find that several of the T_{1u} infrared-active modes that appear in the spectrum [2] of undoped crystalline C_{60} have acquired in the fully doped material anomalously large oscillator strengths and undergone softening. The oscillator strength enhancement of two of the modes is of order 10^2. These giant activities are associated with the appearance of a new low-lying electronic transition at 1.2 eV. In this paper, we interpret the giant IR activity as being due to a classic charged-phonon effect [3] in which the T_{1u} vibrational modes of molecular C_{60} acquire *electronic* oscillator strength via coupling to virtual electronic transitions between the C_{60} t_{1u} and t_{1g} molecular orbitals. [4] For weak electron-molecular-vibration (EMV) coupling, the theory we introduce to describe this effect predicts for the compounds A_xC_{60} (x = 3, 4, and 6) that the softening of the T_{1u} modes is proportional to x, but that the integrated oscillator strength of their absorption bands is proportional to the *square* of x. The theory, which describes the A_6C_{60} data extremely well, enables the values of the dimensionless EMV coupling constants and the unsoftened t_{1u} frequencies of $C_{60}{}^{-x}$ to be deduced directly from the IR spectra. The charged-phonon effect therefore yields key experimental data for testing theoretical calculations of the electronic and vibrational structure of ionic C_{60}, as well as providing a monitor of the charge state of the C_{60} molecule in doped fullerenes. [5] Since the T_{1u} vibrations enter the longitudinal dielectric constant they participate in the phonon mechanism of superconductivity in the A_3C_{60} compounds.

The charged phonon effect, or the borrowing of electronic oscillator strength by a vibrational mode from an electronic transition to which the mode has become coupled, is well known in physical chemistry [6] and in the physics of low-dimensional solids [7], where the conditions required to produce the coupling often

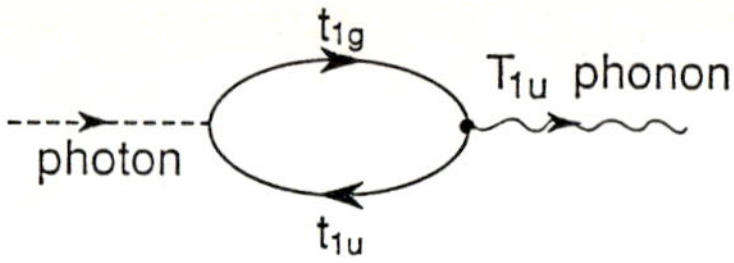

Fig. 1. Coupling of photon to a T_{1u} phonon via virtual electronic $t_{1u}\rightarrow t_{1g}$ excitation.

arise from symmetry-breaking effects.[3, 8] In discussing its theory for the A_xC_{60} compounds we will introduce, in the present paper, four simplifying assumptions. First, we take the widths of the electronic bands in A_xC_{60} to be zero. In this limit x electrons occupy the three-fold degenerate t_{1u} molecular orbitals of each C_{60} ion, while the higher lying t_{1g} orbitals remain empty in the ground state configuration. [4] Electron energy loss and solution spectroscopy studies [9] indicate that the $t_{1u}\rightarrow t_{1g}$ transition energy $\hbar\,\omega_e \sim 1.2$ eV for x = 3, x = 6, and x=1. Second, we assume that the $t_{1u}\rightarrow t_{1g}$ transition dipole moment couples only to C_{60} molecular vibrations whose displacements cause electronic polarization of the molecule. The latter are the T_{1u} modes, the only IR active modes [10] of C_{60}. We note that in icosahedral symmetry, $t_{1u} \times t_{1g} = A_u + T_{1u} + H_u$ so that this coupling is indeed a symmetry allowed coupling. Third, we will, for $x \neq 0$, assume that the intrinsic IR activity of the uncoupled T_{1u} modes is very weak by comparison to that which arises from the charged-phonon effect, and, consequently, will ignore it. A Feynman diagram illustrating the basic effect is drawn in Fig. 1. Fourth, we will work within the framework of a one-electron picture. Consequently, our theoretical description ignores explicit effects of electron-electron interactions on the spectral transitions. It will be interesting to see from future experiments the extent to which such effects could alter the dependencies on x that we find in the one-electron description.

Under these assumptions the frequency-dependent conductivity $\sigma(\omega)$ due to the $t_{1u}\rightarrow t_{1g}$ transition and the accompanying "charging" of the T_{1u} modes may be immediately written down on the basis of a standard formula: [3]

$$\sigma(\omega) = -i\omega N\{\chi(\omega) + \lambda x \chi(\omega)\tilde{\chi}(\omega) D_{ph}(\omega)\} \qquad (1)$$

where, in the present context, $\chi(\omega)=x\alpha\omega_e^2/(\omega_e^2-\omega^2-i\Gamma_e\omega)$, is the electronic polarizability of the C_{60}^{-x} ion contributed by the $t_{1u}\rightarrow t_{1g}$ transitions, $\tilde{\chi}(\omega)=\chi(\omega)/\chi(0)$, and $D_{ph}(\omega)$ is the composite phonon propagator $D_{ph}^{-1}(\omega)=D_0^{-1}(\omega) - x\lambda\chi(\omega)$ in which

$$D_0(\omega) = \Sigma_n(\lambda_n\omega_n^2/\lambda)/(\omega_n^2 - \omega^2 - i\omega\Gamma_n) \qquad (2)$$

In Eq. (2) ω_n denotes the frequency of the n-th T_{1u} molecular vibration (n = 1, --, 4) of the C_{60}^{-x} ion in the absence of the coupling of this mode to $t_{1u}\rightarrow t_{1g}$ transitions. λ_n is the dimensionless EMV coupling constant specifying the strength of the latter's coupling to the electronic transition, while $\lambda=\Sigma_n\lambda_n$ is the total EMV coupling constant. N denotes the number of C_{60} ions per unit volume and α is the static $t_{1u}\rightarrow t_{1g}$ electronic polarizability per added electron. Γ_e and Γ_n are the widths of the uncoupled electronic and vibrational excitations, respectively. It is readily seen from Eqs. (1) and (2) that the total static $t_{1u}\rightarrow t_{1g}$ polarizability of the C_{60}^{-x} ion, $\chi_{tot}(0)$, is enhanced by EMV coupling according to $\chi_{tot}(0) = \alpha x/(1-x\lambda)$. Evidently, the C_{60}^{-x} cage is stable provided that $x\lambda< 1$.

The second term of Eq. (1) describes the IR absorption by the charged T_{1u} modes. For $\omega_n^2 << \omega_e^2$, and in the limit that $\Gamma_n/\omega_n\rightarrow 0$, their frequencies Ω are determined by the solutions of

$$1-x\lambda\, D_0(\Omega) = 0, \qquad (3)$$

while the integrated oscillator strengths (IOS) of their absorption bands are given by

$$S(\Omega) = \int_{\Omega} d\omega\sigma_1(\omega) = (\pi N\alpha/2\lambda)\,(1/(\partial^2 D_0(\omega)/\partial\omega^2)_{\omega=\Omega}) \qquad (4)$$

For *weak* total EMV coupling, i.e., for $x\lambda << 1$, Eqs. (3) and (4) lead to $\Omega^2 \cong \Omega_n^2=\omega_n^2(1-x\lambda_n)$ and $S(\Omega_n) = (\pi/2)N\alpha\lambda_n\, x^2\omega_n^2$. Thus, for weak EMV coupling, the phonon softening $\Omega_n-\omega_n \cong -x\lambda_n\omega_n/2$, is proportional to x, but the integrated oscillator strength is proportional to x^2. The latter result contrasts with the x dependence of the IOS of the electronic transition $S_e = (\pi/2)N\alpha x\omega_e^2$ which is proportional to x. It also contrasts with the situation in doped conjugated polymers where the IOS's of the charged phonon bands of solitons [8] and polarons [11] $S_n=(\pi/2)N\alpha\lambda_n x\omega_n^2$ are proportional to the dopant concentration x. This different behavior reflects the property that for the doped fullerene problem the effective electron-phonon coupling constant is $x\lambda_n$ rather than λ_n since x electrons couple to the same phonon mode. For the soliton or polaron in a conjugated polymer the phonon mode couples to the charge of a single electron. We note that the charge, e^*_n, acquired by the mode Ω_n is proportional to x, specifically, $e^*_n \cong x(\lambda_n K_n\alpha)^{1/2}$, where K_n denotes the force constant of the unperturbed T_{1u} mode.

More generally, for arbitrary $x\lambda$, both Ω and $S(\Omega)$ are functions of all the values of λ_n and ω_n. The latter quantities are fundamental physical constants of C_{60}^{-x} and their experimental values are desirable. In fact, their experimental values may be obtained simply by solving Eqs. (3) and (4) for λ_n and ω_n in terms of the directly measured values of Ω and $S(\Omega)$. The value of α in Eq. (4) may be obtained experimentally from the observed IOS of the $t_{1u}\rightarrow t_{1g}$ transition. The charged-

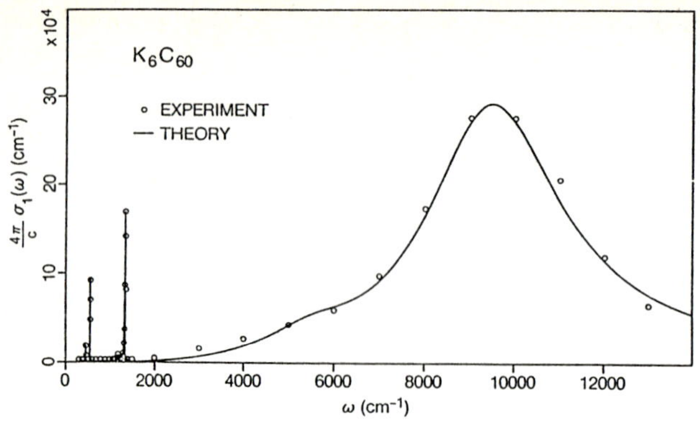

Fig. 2. Fit of Eq. (1) (full curve) to the converted conductivity data (circles) of Fu *et al.*[1]

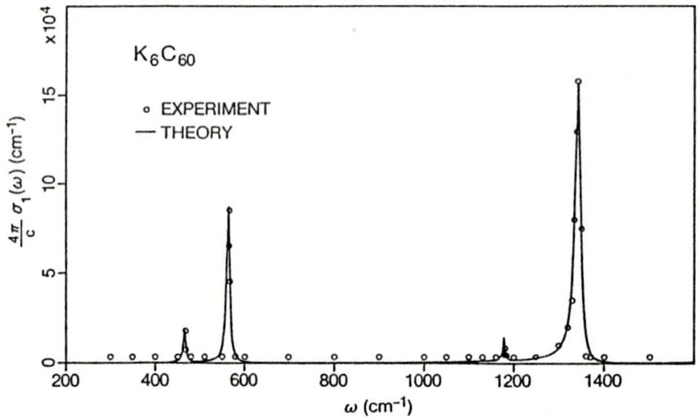

Fig. 3. Fit of Eq. (1) (full curve) to the converted conductivity data (circles) of Fu *et al.*[1] in the region of the T_{1u} frequencies.

phonon effect, therefore, offers the means of yielding key experimental data for testing theoretical computations of the electronic and vibrational structure of ionic C_{60}. The effect has, indeed, been similarly used in the past, in the development of the low dimensional metals based on the organic charge transfer salts. [12] For the present materials, the testing of theoretical calculations of $\{\lambda_n\}$ would be of particular interest.

The IR spectrum of Fu *et al.*, converted from absorbance A to conductivity data via the relation $A=(\sigma_1/4\pi c)d$, is shown in Figs. 2 and 3. A fit of Eq. (1) to this spectrum is equivalent to an experimental determination of all the unknown parameters in Eq. (1). The electronic band centered at 1.2 eV exhibits a shoulder at $\hbar\omega$ =0.7 eV, and we model this feature as an additional, weak, electronic transition (with parameters α', ω'_e, Γ'_e) in the electronic polarizability $\chi(\omega)$. A least squares fit of Eq. (1) to the data is shown in Figs. 2 and 3 as the

Table 1. Values of the dimensionless EMV coupling constants λ_n and unsoftened T_{1u} vibrational frequencies ω_n of C_{60}^{-6} as deduced from the data of Fu *et al.* on the basis of Eq. (1). Ω_n denote the observed T_{1u} frequencies in K_6C_{60}.

n	Ω_n (cm^{-1})	ω_n (cm^{-1})	$\lambda_n x 10^2$
1	467	476	0.43
2	565	612	4.2
3	1182	1186	0.07
4	1342	1411	2.9

continuous curve. The determined electronic parameters are $\alpha = (0.30/4\pi N)$, ω_e=9500 cm^{-1}, Γ_e=3600 cm^{-1}, and α'= $(0.07/4\pi N)$, ω'_e= 5548 cm^{-1}, Γ'_e=2600 cm^{-1}. The values determined for λ_n and ω_n are tabulated in Table 1 together with the corresponding observed values of Ω_n. The widths Γ_n were found to be $\Gamma_n \sim 6$ cm^{-1} for all n. It is seen that the theory provides an excellent fit of the data.

It is seen from Table 1 that while the individual coupling constants are small, their sum, $\lambda = 7.6x10^{-2}$, is sufficiently large to lead to a significant static total EMV coupling $x\lambda = 0.46$ for $x = 6$. Thus, EMV coupling leads to a considerable enhancement of the static $t_{1u} \rightarrow t_{1g}$ polarizability, $\chi_{tot}(0)/\chi(0) = 1.85$. The two modes $\omega_2 = 612$ cm^{-1} and $\omega_4 = 1411$ cm^{-1} are the strongest coupled modes with the former more strongly coupled than the latter. The IOS of the higher frequency mode is larger than that of the lower frequency mode, however, since $S(\Omega_n) \sim \lambda_n \omega_n^2$. Since the modes ω_1 and ω_2 lie close in frequency, the EMV coupling induces significant repulsion between them. Thus Ω_1 and Ω_2 appear more, and less softened, respectively, than the softening that their respective coupling constants would imply were the modes isolated modes.

We note that since the charged T_{1u} vibrations enter the longitudinal dielectric constant they will participate in the phonon mechanism of superconductivity in the metallic x=3 compounds. In this respect the T_{1u} modes behave as optical phonons, coupling to the conduction electrons via the long-range Coulomb interaction. Until now, couplings of the conduction electrons to the C_{60} Raman-active H_g and A_g vibrations have been considered [13-16] to be the only C_{60} EMV couplings relevant to superconductivity.

Finally, we mention that we have performed microscopic calculations of the IR activity of the C_{60}^{-6} ion employing a tight binding (SSH) model Hamiltonian.[17] These calculations confirm that although the $t_{1u} \rightarrow t_{1g}$ transitions also couple to the A_u and H_u vibrations, only the T_{1u} modes actually enter $\sigma(\omega)$. The large enhancement of the T_{1u} IOS's are also confirmed but the two strongest coupled modes are found to be ω_3 and ω_4 instead of ω_2 and ω_4. Details of these calculations will be reported elsewhere.

We thank the authors of reference 1 for communicating their results to us prior to publication.

References

1. K.-J. Fu, W. L. Karney, O. L. Chapman, S.-M. Huang, R. B. Kaner, F. Diederich, K. Holczer, and R. L. Whetten, preprint (1991).
2. D. S. Bethune, G. Meijer, W. C. Tang, H. J. Rosen, W. G. Golden, H. Seki, C. A. Brown, and M. S. de Vries, Chem. Phys. Lett. **179**, 181 (1991).
3. M. J. Rice, Phys. Rev. Lett. **37**, 36 (1976). A preliminary account of the present theory has been given by M. J. Rice and H.-Y. Choi, Phys. Rev. **B** May 1 (1992).
4. See, e.g., S. Saito and A. Oshiyama, Phys. Rev. Lett. **66**, 2647 (1991).
5. R. C. Haddon, A. F. Hebard, M. J. Rosseinsky, D. W. Murphy, S. J. Duclos, K. B. Lyons, B. Miller, J. M. Rosamilia, R. M. Fleming, A. R. Kortan, S. H. Glarum, A. V. Makhija, A. J. Muller, R. H. Eick, S. M. Zahurak, R. Tycko, G. Dabbagh, and F. A. Thiel, Nature **350**, 320 (1991).
6. E. E. Ferguson and F. A. Matsen, J. Chem. Phys. **29**, 105 (1958).
7. See, e.g., M. J. Rice, L. Pietronero, and P. Bruesch, Solid State Commun. **21**, 757 (1977); M. J. Rice, V. M. Yartsev, and C. S. Jacobsen, Phys. Rev. B **21**, 3437 (1980).
8. E. J. Mele and M. J. Rice, Phys. Rev. Lett. **45**, 926 (1980).
9. E. Sohmen, J. Fink, and W. Kratschmer, Europhysics Lett. **17**, 51 (1992); M. A. Greaney and S. M. Gorun, J. Phys. Chem. **95**, 7142 (1991).
10. R. E. Stanton and M. D. Newton, J. Phys. Chem. **92**, 2141 (1988).
11. J. C. Hicks and E. J. Mele, Phys. Rev. B **34**, 1100 (1986); H.-Y. Choi and E. J. Mele, Phys. Rev. B **34**, 8750 (1986).
12. N. O. Lipari, M. J. Rice, C. B. Duke, R. Bozio, A. Girlando, and C. Pecile, Int. J. Quantum Chemistry Symposium **11**, 583 (1977); M. J. Rice and N. O. Lipari, Phys. Rev. Lett. **38**, 437 (1977); M. J. Rice, Solid State Commun. **31**, 93 (1979).
13. J. L. Martins, N. Troullier, and M. Schubel, preprint (1991).
14. M. Schluter, M. Lannoo, M. Needels, G. A. Baraff, Phys. Rev. Lett. **68**, 526(1992).
15. C. M. Varma, J. Zaanen, and K. Raghavachari, Science, **254**, 989 (1991).
16. I. I. Mazin, S. N. Rashkeev, V. P. Antropov, O. Jepsen, A. I. Liechtenstein, and O. K. Andersen, preprint (1991).
17. H.-Y. Choi and M, J. Rice (to be published).

Van der Waals Cohesion and Plasmon Excitations in C_{60} Fullerite

Ph. Lambin and A.A. Lucas

Laboratoire de Physique du Solide, Facultés Universitaires
Notre-Dame de la Paix, Rue de Bruxelles 61, B-5000 Namur, Belgium

Abstract. The Van der Waals cohesive energy of C_{60} fullerite is evaluated from the zero-point energy of multipole plasmons fluctuating on the highly-polarizable Bucky balls. These hollow molecules are treated as dielectric shells. The shell material is an isotropic continuum with a dielectric function designed to exhibit the plasmon resonances observed in other forms of solid carbon in the ultraviolet.

1. Introduction

Since the development of a method for producing weighable quantities of C_{60} molecules [1], the question has been raised whether collective electronic excitations in these giant, quasi-spherical hollow molecules could be detected by experimental techniques [2]. There are now clear evidences from, e.g., photo-ionization [3] and electron-energy-loss spectroscopy (EELS) [4] testifying to the existence of plasma oscillations in C_{60}. This is briefly discussed below.

In the solid phase, the fullerene molecules are packed together by Van der Waals interactions, which have often been estimated by summing inter-cluster C-C pair potentials [5]. In the present paper, by contrast, the Van der Waals attraction in C_{60} fullerite is constructed from the more fundamental point of view of fluctuating multipoles [6]. The starting point in the present description of the cohesion is a set of equations that we now derive giving the excitation energies of collective electron oscillations in coupled C_{60} clusters.

2. Van der Waals Attraction and Coupled Plasmons in Fullerite

The basic ingredient in the following formulation of Van der Waals cohesion is the collective response of the valence electrons of C_{60} to an external potential of the form $A_L r^l Y_L(\hat{\mathbf{r}}) e^{-i\omega t}$, with Y_L a usual spherical harmonics and $L = (l,m)$. The potential induced outside the polarized molecule satisfies Laplace's equation and a spherical-harmonics component of it can be written as $B_L r^{-l-1} Y_L(\hat{\mathbf{r}}) e^{-i\omega t}$.

A multipole plasmon excitation develops a macroscopic potential of this sort. For a collection of N molecules, the potential around site I at $\mathbf{r}_I$ set up by the multipole plasmons fluctuating on the other molecules is

$$\sum_{J\neq I}\sum_{L'} B_{J,L'} |\mathbf{r}-\mathbf{r}_J|^{-l'-1} Y_{L'}(\widehat{\mathbf{r}-\mathbf{r}_J})\, e^{-i\omega t} = \sum_{L} |\mathbf{r}-\mathbf{r}_I|^{l}\, Y_L(\widehat{\mathbf{r}-\mathbf{r}_I}) \sum_{J\neq I}\sum_{L'} \frac{S_{L,L'}(\mathbf{r}_J-\mathbf{r}_I)}{2(2l+1)}\, B_{J,L'}\, e^{-i\omega t} \quad (1)$$

where the coefficients $S_{L,L'}$, which only depend on the geometrical vectors $\mathbf{r}_J$-$\mathbf{r}_I$, come from an addition formula for the spherical harmonics [7]. The right-hand side of eq. (1) identifies with a sum over L of excitation terms having the form assumed above, $A_{I,L}|\mathbf{r}-\mathbf{r}_I|^l Y_L(\mathbf{r}\hat{\ }\mathbf{r}_I)e^{-i\omega t}$. In a linear-response theory, $A_{I,L} = -B_{I,L}/\alpha_l(\omega)$, where $\alpha_l(\omega)$ is a dynamical multipole polarizability, and one is left with a set of equations for the amplitudes B of the fluctuating multipole fields :

$$-\frac{2l+1}{\alpha_l(\omega)} B_{I,L} + \frac{1}{2}\sum_{J\neq I}\sum_{L'} S_{L,L'}(\mathbf{r}_J\text{-}\mathbf{r}_I)\, B_{J,L'} = 0\,,\quad I,J = 1, 2 \ldots N\,. \tag{2}$$

The non-trivial solutions of these equations correspond to the coupled plasmons of the system, whose frequencies are the roots of the secular equation. For an isolated molecule (N=1), the eigenfrequencies coincide with the poles of the polarizability functions $\alpha_l(\omega)$. The Van der Waals cohesion is the change in zero-point energy $\sum \hbar\Delta\omega/2N$, where the $\Delta\omega$'s are frequency shifts brought about by coupling the plasmons fields, and the sum is over all the polarization modes of the N molecules.

In a crystal, the amplitudes B of the fluctuating multipoles satisfy Bloch's theorem. The solutions of eq. (2) obtained in this way are called polarization waves, a concept that has first been applied to rare-gas solids [8] with the sole dipole terms (l=1). For C_{60} fullerite, higher multipole contributions must be included because of the large size of the molecules [9].

3. A Dielectric Shell Model

As a simple model of the electronic response of C_{60}, we consider a spherical shell (see Fig. 1) with inner and outer radii a_1 and a_2. We take $a_1 = 2.7$ and $a_2 = 4.4$ Å, which average to the radius of the carbon cage. By contrast with the hydrodynamic model of ref. [2], where the electrons were confined on a two-dimensional surface, the thickness of the shell is finite in the present approach (1.7 Å ≈ half the interlayer spacing of graphite). We envision that the shell is composed of a continuous medium characterized by the dielectric function

$$\varepsilon(\omega) = 1 + \frac{1}{4}\frac{\omega_p^2}{\omega_\pi^2 - \omega^2} + \frac{3}{4}\frac{\omega_p^2}{\omega_\sigma^2 - \omega^2} \tag{3}$$

having two oscillators associated to collective π-π^* and σ-σ^* electronic transitions. The resonant frequencies ω_π and ω_σ are taken from the dielectric properties of graphite : 5 and 15 eV, respectively [10], and $\hbar\omega_p = 32$ eV. In eq. (3), the ratio 1:3 between the oscillator strengths of the π and σ resonances reflects the same ratio between the numbers of π and σ electronic bands.

The polarizability of the dielectric shell is easily derived at any order [9] :

$$\alpha_l(\omega) = (\varepsilon-1)\frac{l(1-\rho_l)[(l+1)\varepsilon+l]}{[(l+1)\varepsilon+l][l\varepsilon+l+1] - l(l+1)\rho_l(\varepsilon-1)^2}\, a_2^{2l+1}\,,\quad \rho_l = (a_1/a_2)^{2l+1}\,. \tag{4}$$

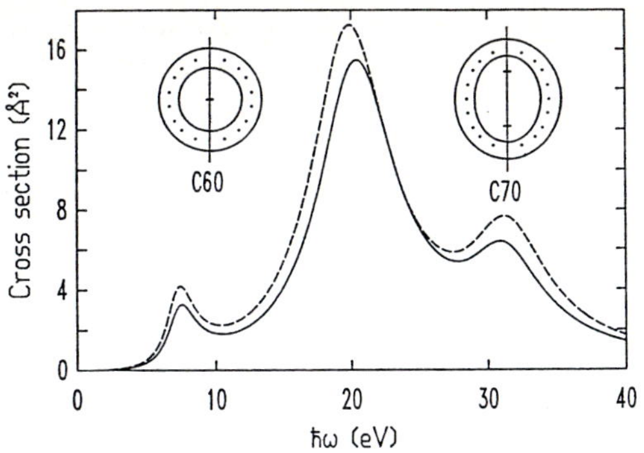

Fig. 1. The UV absorption cross sections of C_{60} (full curve) and C_{70} (dashed curve) have been computed for the spherical or spheroidal dielectric shells represented above, where the dots visualize the positions of the carbon atoms.

The dipole polarizability is of particular interest since its imaginary part is related to the light absorption coefficient. For this particular application, we have generalized the l=1 expression of eq. (4) to a hollow spheroid, having in mind the shape of C_{70}. The boundaries of the C_{70} dielectric shell are confocal ellipsoids of revolution (see Fig. 1) with length $2a_i$ and diameter $2b_i$, where i=1 or 2 refers to the internal or the external surface, respectively. The dipole polarizability is

$$\alpha_1(\omega) = \frac{\varepsilon-1}{3} \frac{n_1+(1-n_1)\varepsilon - \rho\,[n_2+(1-n_2)\varepsilon]}{[n_1+(1-n_1)\varepsilon][1-n_2+n_2\varepsilon] - \rho n_2(1-n_2)(\varepsilon-1)^2}\, a_2 b_2^2\,, \quad \rho = \frac{a_1 b_1^2}{a_2 b_2^2}\,. \qquad (5)$$

In this expression, n_1 and n_2 are the depolarization coefficients of the inner and outer spheroidal surfaces : for a field parallel or perpendicular to the axis of revolution of a prolate ellipsoid with eccentricity e, $n^{//} = (1-e^2)(\tanh^{-1}e-e)/e^3$ or $n^{\perp} = (1-n^{//})/2$. For a spherical shell, $n_1 = n_2 = 1/3$ in any direction.

The same dielectric function (eq. 3) has been used to describe the dipolar activity of C_{60} and C_{70} in the UV, assuming that the volume of the dielectric shell for C_{70} represents 70/60 of that of C_{60}. Another geometrical constraint for the model C_{70} molecule is that the focal points of the inner and outer surfaces coincide with the ones of the ellipsoid that best fit the carbon frame [11]. Taking finally for b_2-b_1 the thickness of the spherical shell used for C_{60}, the following parameters were obtained : $a_1 = 3.69$, $b_1 = 2.86$, $a_2 = 5.12$ and $b_2 = 4.56$ Å.

The static polarizability of C_{60} deduced from the geometrical and dielectric parameters of the model is 64.8 $Å^3$, reproducing a quantum-mechanical result [12]. For C_{70}, eq. (5) yields $\alpha_1^{//}(0) = 85.8$ and $\alpha_1^{\perp}(0) = 76.1$ $Å^3$. The UV absorption cross sections $\sigma_a(\omega) = 4\pi\omega/c\, \mathrm{Im}[\mathrm{Tr}\,\alpha_1(\omega)/3]$ of C_{60} and C_{70} are compared in Fig. 1. The peak at 7 eV is due to the π plasmon and could possibly correspond to the absorption line observed experimentally at 5.8 eV [13]. The broad structure around 20 eV well reproduces the giant Mie resonance recorded in the photoionization spectra of both molecules [3] and predicted by quantum-mechanical calculations [14]. There is in Fig. 1 a secondary σ absorption peak at 32 eV. This mode as a direct consequence of the hollow structure and the sharp discontinuities of the electron density at the boundaries of the molecular shell models [9].

4. Polarization Waves in C_{60} Fullerite

Using the expression (4) of the polarizability, the eigenfrequencies of coupled plasma oscillations in fullerite can be determined by solving eq. (2) for Bloch wave amplitudes B. Fig. 2 illustrates the dispersion curves of polarization waves in a fcc crystal of C_{60} molecules. The dashed lines have been obtained at the dipole level (l=1) : there are six modes per molecule (three dipole components for each of the inner and outer surface polarizations) and twice as many frequency branches arising from the two poles in the dielectric function. Collective π-π* excitations yield narrow polarization bands around 7 eV. The dashed curves at higher frequencies derive from the slow and fast σ dipole modes that led to the absorption peaks at 21 and 32 eV in Fig. 1. Including higher multipoles markedly affects the polarization band structure, as shown by the full curves in Fig. 2 that represent coupled σ plasmon waves developed at the octopole level (l=3). Signatures of coupled π and σ plasmons have been detected by EELS in the form of a narrow peak at 6.3 eV and a broad structure around 28 eV [4].

Van der Waals attraction is the consequence of lowering the zero-point energy of the (quantized) plasma oscillations on the interacting molecules. The zero-point energy shift ΔE has been computed from the polarization-wave band structure of C_{60}. For both the fcc and hcp structures with the nearest-neighbor center-to-center distance fixed at 10.04 Å, the dielectric model of Sect. 3 yields ΔE = -2.1 eV/molecule. This value, to which a repulsive potential should be added, is consistent with the observed heat of sublimation of about 1.7 eV per C_{60} molecule. In the Van der Waals attraction, the dipole plasmons alone contribute -0.3 eV/molecule. With l=3, ΔE = -1.3 and values of l as high as 7 are required to reach -2.0 eV/molecule. Higher multipole terms contribute little to the

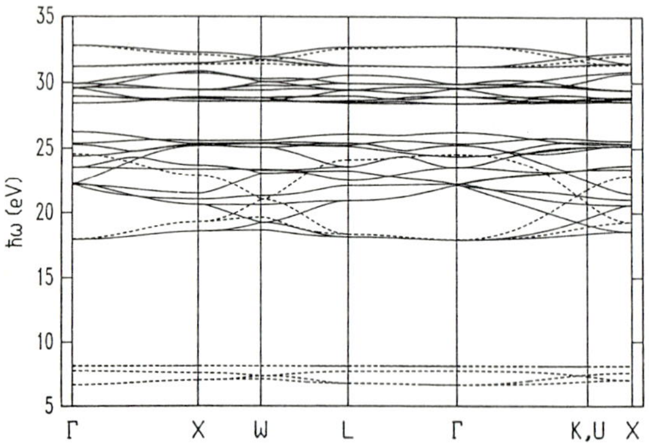

Fig. 2. Dispersion curves of dipole (dashed curves) and multipole (l≤3, full curves) polarization waves in a fcc crystal (a_{fcc} = 14.2 Å) of C_{60} molecules.

cohesion. This is fortunate for the present approach since rapid variations of the polarization charges, such as realized with $l \approx 10$ or more (the number of atom along a circumference), require a fully microscopic description.

Acknowledgements. This work has been supported by the Impulse Program in High-Temperature Superconductivity, a national program initiated by the Science Policy Programming Services. Ph. L. acknowledges the Belgian National Fund for Scientific Research (FNRS).

References

1 W. Krätschmer, L.D. Lamb, K. Fostiropoulos and D.R. Huffman, Nature 347, 354 (1990).
2 G. Barton and C. Eberlein, J. Chem. Phys. 95, 1512 (1991).
3 I.V. Vertel, H. Steger, J. de Vries, B. Weisser, C. Menzel, B. Kamke and W. Kamke, Phys. Rev. Lett. 68, 784 (1992).
4 Y. Saito, H. Shinohara and A. Ohshita, Japn. J. Appl. Phys. 30, L1068 (1991) ; G. Gensterblum, J.J. Pireaux, P.A. Thiry, R. Caudano, J.P. Vigneron, Ph. Lambin, A.A. Lucas and W. Krätschmer, Phys. Rev. Lett. 67, 2171 (1991) ; E. Sohmen, J. Fink and W. Krätschmer, Europhys. Lett. 17, 51 (1992).
5 Y.G. Guo, N.K. Karasawa and W. A. Goddard III, Nature 351, 464 (1991).
6 D. Langbein, "Van der Waals Attraction" (Springer-Verlag, Berlin, 1974).
7 O.K. Andersen, Phys. Rev. B 12, 3060 (1975).
8 A.A. Lucas, Physica 35, 353 (1967).
9 Ph. Lambin, A.A. Lucas and J.P. Vigneron, Phys. Rev. B (1992, in press).
10 R. Klücker, M. Skibowski and W. Steinmann, Phys. Stat. Sol. b 65, 703 (1974).
11 Data of K. Raghavachari and C. M. Rohlfing, J. Phys. Chem. 95, 5768 (1991) are best fitted by a spheroid with length 8.54 Å and diameter 7.17 Å.
12 P.W. Fowler, P. Lazaretti and R. Zanasi, Chem. Phys. Lett. 165, 79 (1990).
13 W. Krätschmer, K. Fostiropoulos and D.R. Huffman, Chem. Phys. Lett. 170, 167 (1990).
14 G.F. Bertsch, A. Bulgac, D. Tománek and Y. Wang, Phys. Rev. Lett. 67, 2690 (1991) ; A. Bulgac and N. Ju, Phys. Rev. Lett. (Submitted).

Fullerene Field-Effect Transistors

J. Kastner[1], *J. Paloheimo*[2], *and H. Kuzmany*[1]

[1]Institut für Festkörperphysik, Universität Wien and Ludwig-Boltzmann Institut für Festkörperphysik, Strudlhofgasse 4, A-1090 Vienna, Austria
[2]Semiconductor Laboratory, Technical Research Centre of Finland, Otakaari 7B, SF-02150 Espoo, Finland

Abstract. Undoped C_{60} and C_{60}/C_{70} fullerenes have been used as the active material in thin-film field-effect transistors (FET). All FETs turned out to be n-channel devices operating in the accumulation mode with a field-effect mobility around 10^{-4} cm^2/Vs. The conductance-activation energy is a function of the gate voltage. Like in amorphous silicon localized states have a strong influence on the transport properties. These localized states can either originate from disorder or from a self-trapping of the induced carriers in the fullerene.

1. Introduction

The crystalline form of C_{60} covers conductivity ranges from semiconducting to metallic and even superconducting [1]. Undoped C_{60} is a semiconductor with a direct energy gap, E_g. Calculations [2], measurements of conductivity [3] and UV-visible absorption [2] give values around 2 eV for E_g. This paper presents a field-effect transistor utilizing fullerenes. FET structures can be used to study the basic transport properties [4,5]. In systems like amorphous semiconductors the density of states around the Fermi energy can be investigated [6]. The field-effect mobility μ can be obtained from the initial linear region of the current-voltage characteristics. The drain current for $V_{DS} \ll (V_G\text{-}V_T)$ is typically written in the form [4]

$$I_D = (W\,\mu\,C\,/\,L)\,[(V_G\text{-}V_T)\,V_{DS}]$$

W and L are the channel width and length, C the gate oxide capacitance, V_G, V_{DS} and V_T are the gate, drain and threshold voltages, respectively.
In addition to the described basic information obtainable from FETs these systems may be interesting from a technological point of view as a possible application of fullerenes in sensor technology.

2. Experimental

A schematic cross-section of the FET is shown in Fig.1. The insulator is 300 nm silicon dioxide thermally grown on a highly doped n-type silicon wafer. The drain and source electrodes were made by evaporation of chromium (20 nm) and gold (30 nm) using photolithographic techniques. The electrodes were fingershaped with a seperation L of 5 μm and an effective channel width W of 8 cm. The fullerene films were prepared by evaporating chromatographically purified C_{60} or a mixture of C_{60} and C_{70} at 400°C in dynamical vacuum of $2\text{x}10^{-4}$ Pa for several hours. The film thicknesses were 80 nm and 120 nm. The current-voltage characteristics were measured using a HP4142B parameter analyzer.

Springer Series in Solid-State Sciences, Vol. 113 Electronic Properties of High-T_c Superconductors
Editors: H. Kuzmany, M. Mehring, J. Fink

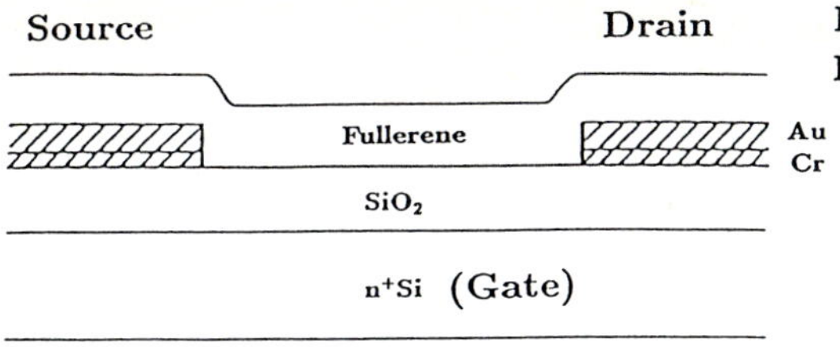

Fig.1: Cross section of the fullerene FET structure.

3. Results and Discussion

The Current-voltage characteristics of a C_{60}/C_{70} transistor at various gate voltages (0, 30, 40, 50, 60 V) is shown in Fig.2. The conductivity without applying a gate voltage is very low. When an appropriate positive voltage V_g is applied, the current I_D increases which indicates that an accumulation layer is formed near the fullerene/insulator interface. The drain current turned out to be a function of time for nonzero gatevoltages. At 295 K it decreases in 50 s towards a value, which is about one sixth of the initial current. The measurement time was optimized to minimize the effect of this phenomenon.

A change of I_D with the time has been observed earlier in Poly(alkylthiophene) transistors [7]. It is even larger in fullerene films and can be related to diffusion of charged molecules in the strong electric field or trapping phenomena at the fullerene-oxide interface.

Even with high negative voltages no signs for an inversion mode operation could be found. FETs with a film of pure C_{60} have qualitatively similar I_D-V_{DS} characteristics. The drain current is also increasing by applying a positive voltage.

Since I_D is increasing by applying a positive V_G, all transistors are n-channel devices. The field-effect mobility obtained from the linear region of the I_D-V_{DS}-characteristics is not a constant, but a function of V_g. It decreases from $\approx 5\text{x}10^{-7}$ cm^2/Vs to $\approx 5\text{x}10^{-4}$ cm^2/Vs when V_G is varied from 0 V to 100 V. This behavior shows that the electrons accumulated in the fullerene film have, in contrast to normal crystalline semiconductors, more than one possible state having different charge transport properties.

μ is of the same order of magnitude as in conjugated polymers like polyacetylene or poly-(alkylthiophene) [5], but considerably lower than in a-Si:H (1 cm^2/Vs) [6] or crystalline semiconductors (10^3 cm^2/Vs) [4]. The low mobility could originate from a self trapping of the induced carriers, as it is well known from conducting polymers. The main carriers in slightly doped C_{60} might be localized polarons and bipolarons, as it was recently proposed [8].

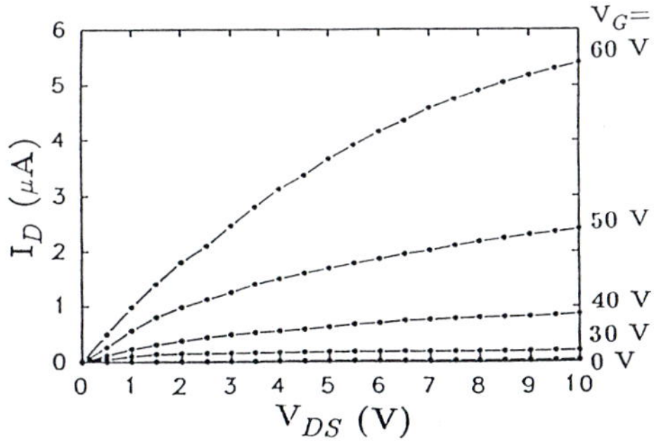

Fig.2: The Current-voltage characteristics of a C_{60}/C_{70} transistor with a 120 nm C_{60}/C_{70} film at various gate voltages (0, 30, 40, 50, 60 V) measured at 295 K.

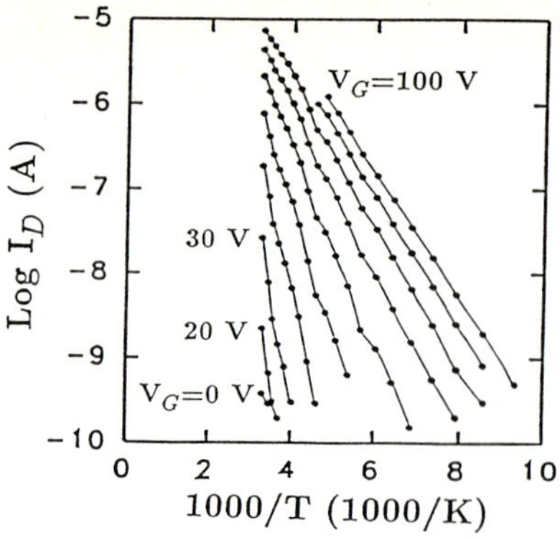

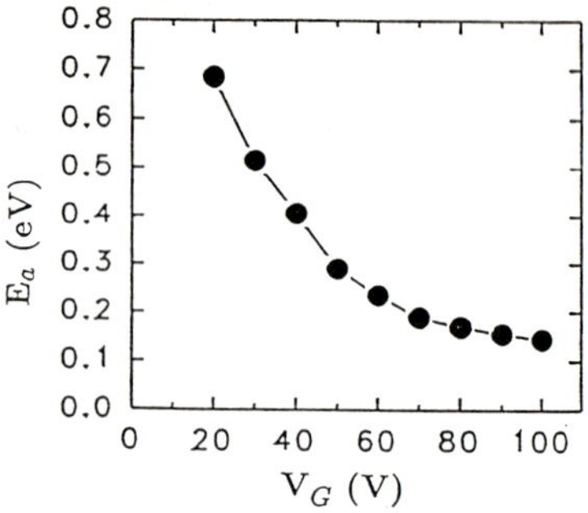

Fig.3: Drain current versus 1/T for different gate voltages (V_G=0,20,30,..., 90, 100 V) and a constant V_{DS}=2 V for a C_{60}/C_{70} film of 120 nm.

Fig.4: Activation energy versus gate voltage obtained from Fig.3.

An estimation for the carrier concentration for zero gate voltage gives $\approx 5\text{x}10^{15}$ cm^{-3}, when a μ of $5\text{x}10^{-7}$ cm^2/Vs is used. The n-type character of the pristine fullerene may originate from structural defects or residual solvents. Undoped conducting polymers are normally p-type [5,7], whereas undoped amorphous silicon or germanium is n-type [6]. In this respect fullerenes resemble to amorphous semiconductors.

The drain current turned out to be strongly temperature dependent. Experimental results are shown in Fig. 3. From the nearly linear behavior in the logarithmic plot an activation energy E_a can be obtained:

$$G=G_0 \exp(-E_a/kT) \qquad G=I_D/V_{DS}$$

G is the conductance and G_0 the conductance prefactor. E_a turned out to be a function of the gate voltage as one can see in Fig.4. It is decreasing with increasing V_G and saturates towards a minimum value of $\approx$ 0.14 eV. This behaviour can be attributed to the existence of band tail states, as it is known from a-Si [9]. The saturation value of E_a can be interpreted as the penetration depth of the conduction band states into the gap. Another possible interpretation is a relation to the polaron hopping energy, if electronic transport is dominated by polarons.

The Meyer-Neldel rule for the conductance prefactor was checked and found to be obeyed. This rule has been observed in all kinds of disordered materials (a-Si or a-Ge) for different properties (conductivity, thermoelectric power etc.) and is generally regarded as an intrinsic property [6,9]. This shows again the strong resemblance of fullerenes to amorphous Si.

4. Conclusions

Fullerenes can be used as the active material in field-effect transistors. The electrical properties show a strong resemblance to a-Si. The carriers are found to be n-type. Localized states play an important role in the electronic conduction. The performances of fullerene FETs may be improved by epitaxial growth or Langmuir-Blodgett techniques.

Acknowledgement. This work was supported by the Osteuropa Förderung des BMfWF project GZ 45.212/2-27b91, and the Technology Development Centre, Finland (TEKES).

References

1. A. F. Hebard, M. J. Rosseinsky, R. C. Haddon, D. W. Murphy, S. H. Glarum, T. T. M. Palstra, A. P. Ramirez, and A. R. Kortan, Nature **350**, 600 (1991)
2. T. Pichler, M. Matus, J. Kürti, and H. Kuzmany, Solid State Comm. **81**, 859 (1992)
3. Y. Saito, H. Shinohara, M. Kato, H. Nagashima, M. Ohkohchi, and Y. Ando, Chem. Phys. Lett. **189**, 236 (1992)
4. S. M. Sze, Physics of Semiconductor Devices (Wiley, New York, 1969)
5. J. Paloheimo, P. Kuivalainen, H. Stubb, E. Vuorimaa, and P. Yli-Lahti, Appl. Phys. Lett. **56**, 1157 (1990)
6. H. Overhof and P. Thomas, Springer Tracts in Modern Physics **114** (Springer, Berlin, 1989)
7. J. Paloheimo, H. Stubb, P. Yli-Lahti and P. Kuivalainen, Synth. Met. **41**, 563 (1991)
8. B. Friedmann, Phys. Rev. Lett. **45**, 1454 (1992)
9. C. A. Dimitriadis, N. Economou, and P. Coxon, Appl. Phys. Lett. **59**, 172 (1991)

High-Resolution Electron Energy Loss Spectroscopy of Thin C_{60} Films

G. Gensterblum, J.J. Pireaux, P.A. Thiry, R. Caudano, Ph. Lambin, and A.A. Lucas

LISE-LPS, FUNDP, 61 rue de Bruxelles, B-5000 Namur, Belgium

Abstract. The elementary excitations of C60 thin films deposited on Si(100) have been studied by high resolution electron energy loss spectroscopy. The spectrum extending from the far IR to the far VUV has been investigated. Many spectral features are comparable to earlier observations by photon, photoelectron, and neutron spectroscopies but several new molecular excitations are revealed.

1. Introduction.

The fullerene discovery [1] and the development of a technique for producing sizeable quantities of the C60 prototype have stimulated intense experimental and theoretical works. The excitement became even bigger after the discovery of superconductivity in alkali-metal doped C60 films [3]. The explanation of the origin of superconductivity in these systems necessitates a thorough understanding of the vibrational and electronic structure of the undoped system.

In this study we report on spectroscopic results on C60 obtained by high resolution electron energy loss spectroscopy (HREELS). We have detected 10 of the 46 vibrational modes in the infrared and 19 bound-bound and bound-free electronic resonances from 1.5 to 30 eV. In particular, we have observed two new features at energies lower than any features ever observed by other electron spectroscopies. They can be attributed to excitons and polarons. We further argue that a single molecule can support collective electron oscillations, similar to those of graphite, whose quanta occur at 6.3 eV for the π electrons (π-plasmons) and around 28 eV for the complete valence shell (σ-plasmons).

2. Experimental.

The fullerene powder was provided by W. Krätschmer. The powder which contained approximately 85% C60 and 15% C70 was then sublimed in UHV at about 300°C onto a clean surface of Si(100) at room temperature. The deposition rate was about 4Å per minute. The thickness of the deposited film was estimated with a quartz crystal oscillator to be about 60Å. The HREELS spectra were recorded with a commercial electron energy loss spectrometer (ISA-Riber).

3. Experimental Results.

3.1 Infrared.

Fig. 1 shows the energy losses in the infrared range. There are four outstanding peaks at 66, 94, 156 and 194 meV and six weaker bands or shoulders. The 66 meV

Springer Series in Solid-State Sciences, Vol. 113 Electronic Properties of High-T_c Superconductors
Editors: H. Kuzmany, M. Mehring, J. Fink

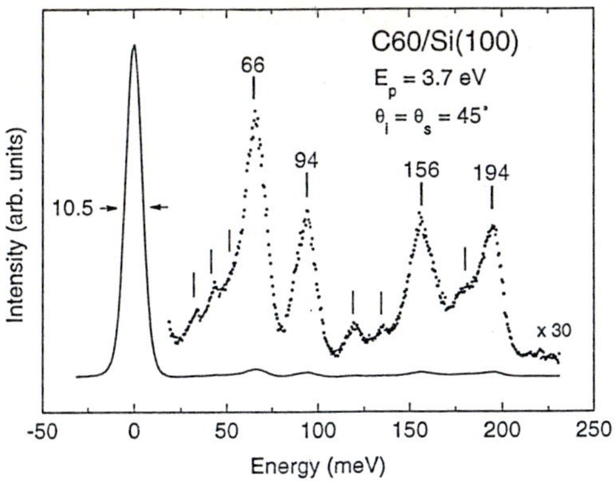

Fig. 1. HREELS spectrum of C60/Si(100) in the infrared.

band correlates very well with two of the four T_{1u} dipole active modes at 526 and 576 cm^{-1} [4] which are to close to be resolved here. The other three strong bands correlate better with dipole inactive, Raman [4] or Neutron lines [5].

One should expect that the dipole active modes make a larger contribution to the loss spectrum than the impact modes. However due to the high symmetry of the C60 molecule, the dipoles induced by the vibrational modes are very weak. The strongest dipole mode at 526 cm^{-1} responsible for the band at 66 meV has an oscillator strength of only 0.07 compared to normal values of about unity [6]. The strength of the two weakest T_{1u} modes at 1183 and 1430 cm^{-1} is even 20 times smaller. Under such circumstances the cross section for impact scattering becomes comparable to the dipole scattering one and it is not astonishing that the spectrum is mainly composed of impact scattering events. Furthermore this effect is enhanced by the observation that the surface is disordered: the dipole scattered electrons are no longer confined in a narrow lobe around the specular direction but are scattered nearly isotropically in all directions by the surface roughness. The disordered structure of the films is in fact demonstrated by different observations. First, there is no LEED pattern. Second, the off-specular elastic and inelastic intensities were not very different from the specular ones. If the film were ordered the off-specular spectrum would exclude the dipole scattering intensities and at least the 66 meV peak intensity should strongly decrease, which it did not.

3.2 Visible-Ultraviolet.

Fig.2 shows a spectrum taken with a primary energy of 10 eV and a resolution of 0.04 eV. The electronic gap in the excitation spectrum is followed by a clear peak at 1.55 eV and a weaker structure at 1.72 eV, which had never been observed by any other electron [7] or photoelectron [8] spectroscopy. The assignment of these two structures to the fullerenes (and not to residual solvent) was confirmed by repeating the experiment on chromatographically purified C60. Only recently similar structures were reported in the photoluminescence spectra of C60 [9] and were assigned to excitons or polarons. The first strong peak at 2.2 eV corresponds to a transition across the fundamental gap between HOMO- and LUMO derived states.

The HREELS visible-UV spectrum shown in Fig. 3 comprises several further peaks or shoulders up to 7 eV. The strong peaks of nearly constant intensity (with respect to the primary energy) at 3.7 eV and 4.8 eV as well as the nearby weaker structures represent impact excited single electron π–π^* transitions. The strong peak at 4.8 eV together with the 6.3 eV shouldered band form the familiar "camel back" structure so characteristic of the C60 absorption spectrum [10]. The energy

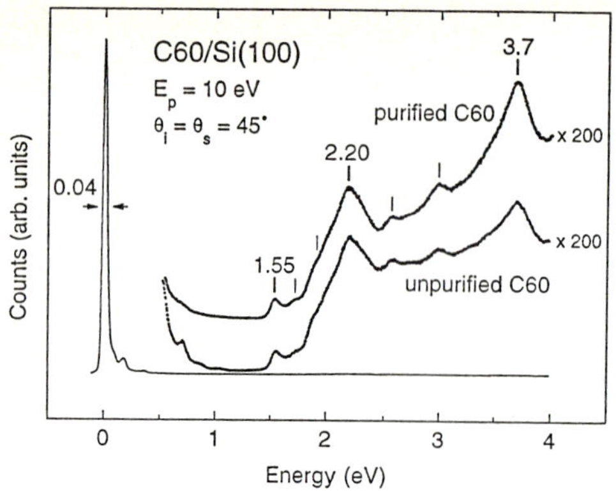

Fig. 2. HREELS spectra of C60/Si(100) in the visible.

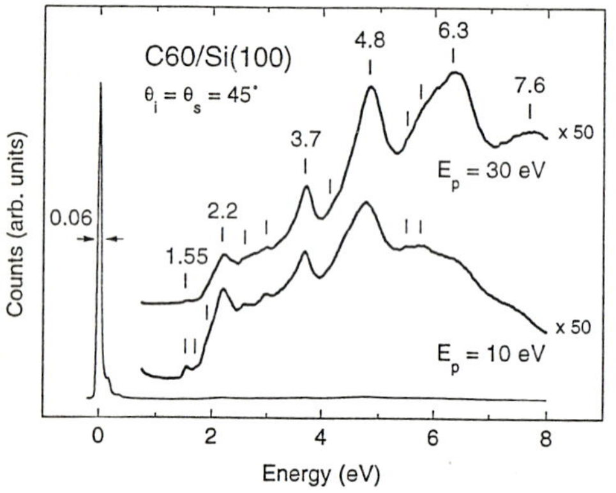

Fig. 3. HREELS spectra of C60/Si(100) in the visible-ultraviolet.

dependance of the intensity of the peak at 6.3 eV indicates the dipole nature of the excitation mechanism. In fact, in the case of dipole interaction the width of the dipole lobe increases with decreasing energy, so that at low primary energy most of the inelastically scattered electrons miss the narrow spectrometer aperture. When the energy increases the dipole lobe shrinks down into the spectrometer aperture and the intensity increases. By comparison with the value of the π-plasmon in crystalline graphite (7 eV) the peak at 6.3 eV can then be interpreted as the quantum of the collective excitation in the molecular π-electron subsystem. A more detailed discussion is given in reference [11].

3.3 Vacuum Ultraviolet.

Moving to the VUV region, two spectra taken with primary electron energies of 70 and 150 eV are shown in Fig. 4. Following the "camel back" structure, the first peak at 7.6 eV correlates very well with the lowest ionization energy of the C60 molecule [12]. The next five peaks reflect π–σ^* and σ–σ^* one-electron transitions of the N-electron system. They compare to similar structures in the UPS spectra, but do not exactly coïncide with the UPS lines which measure the occupied density of states of the N-1 electron system.

The broad peak around 28 eV is identified as a collective excitation by the sensitivity of its intensity to the primary energy. A similar feature appears as a strong shake up satellite of the XPS C1s core line [8] and has also been observed in

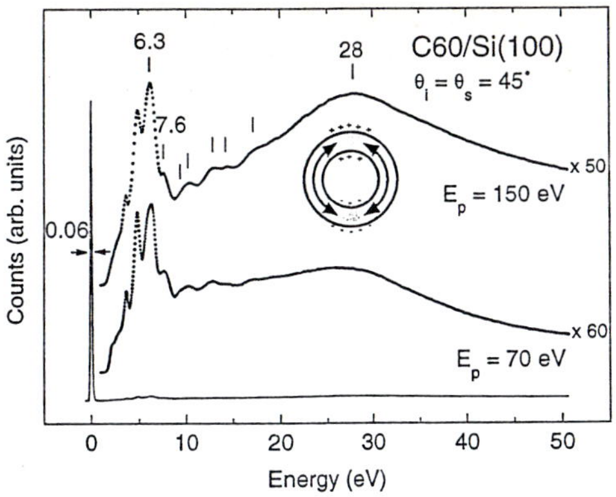

Fig. 4. HREELS spectra of C60/Si(100) in the vacuum ultraviolet.

transmission EELS [7]. It is interpreted as due to the excitation of multipolar "σ-plasmons" (essentially the l=1 modes), the quanta of collective motions of the entire 240 electrons of the molecular valence shell. The molecular character of the collective excitation was further confirmed by the detection of a giant optical resonance around 21 eV in the photoionization spectra of C60 [13]. In the fullerite, this resonance is blue shifted by solid state effects and appears at 28 eV in EELS.

References

[1] H.W. Kroto, J.R. Heath, S.C. O'Brien, R.F. Curl, and R.E. Smalley, Nature **318**, 162 (1985).
[2] W. Krätschmer, L.D. Lamb, K. Fostiropoulos, and D.R. Huffman, Nature **347**, 354 (1990).
[3] A.F. Hebard, M.J. Rosseinsky, R.C. Haddon, D.W. Murphy, S.H. Glarum, T.T.M. Palstra, A.P. Ramirez, and A.R. Kortan, Nature **350**, 600 (1991).
[4] D.S. Bethune, G. Meijer, W.C. Tang, H.J. Rosen, W.G. Golden, H. Seki, C.A. Brown, and M.S. Devries, Chem. Phys. Lett. **179**, 183 (1991).
[5] R.L. Cappelletti, J.R.D. Copley, W.A. Kamitakahara, Fand Li, J.S. Lannin, and D. Ramage, Phys. Rev. Lett. **66**, 3261 (1991).
[6] G. Gensterblum, Li-Ming Yu, J.J. Pireaux, P.A. Thiry, R. Caudano, Ph. Lambin, A.A. Lucas, W. Krätschmer, and J.E. Fischer, J. Phys. Chem. Solid Surf. (in press).
[7] E. Sohmen, J. Fink, and W. Krätschmer, Europhys. Lett. **17**, 51 (1992).
[8] J.H. Weaver, J.L. Martins, T. Komeda, Y. Chen, T.R. Ohno, G.H. Kroll, N. Troullier, R.E. Haufler, and R.E. Smalley, Phys. Rev. Letters **66**, 1741 (1991).
[9] P.A. Lane, L.S. Swanson, Q.-X. Ni, J. Shinar, J.P. Engel, T.J. Barton, and L. Jones, Phys. Rev. Lett. **68**, 887 (1992).
[10] W. Krätschmer, K. Fostiropoulos, and D.R. Huffman, Chem. Phys. Lett. **170**, 167 (1990).
[11] G. Gensterblum, J.J. Pireaux, P.A. Thiry, R. Caudano, J.P. Vigneron, Ph. Lambin, A.A. Lucas, and W. Krätschmer, Phys. Rev. Lett. 67, 2171 (1991).
[12] D.L. Lichtenberger, K.W. Nebesny, Ch.D. Ray, D.R. Huffman and L.D. Lamb, Chem. Phys. Lett. **176**, 203 (1991).
[13] I.V. Vertel, H. Steger, J. de Vries, B. Weisser, C. Menzel, B. Kamke, and W. Kamke, Phys. Rev. Lett. **68**, 784 (1992).

Electronic Structure of Alkali-Metal Doped C_{60}: Dependence of the Fermi-Level Densities of States on the Lattice Parameter

R.P. Gupta[1] *and M. Gupta*[2]

[1]Section de Recherches de Métallurgie Physique, Centre d'Etudes de Saclay, F-91191 Gif-sur-Yvette Cedex, France
[2]Institut des Sciences des Matériaux, UA 446 du CNRS, Bât. 415, Université de Paris-Sud, F-91405 Orsay, France

Abstract : Since the discovery of superconductivity in the alkali metal doped Fullerenes A_3C_{60} (where A is an alkali atom), it is known that the critical temperature T_c depends strongly on the size of the alkali atom. T_c increases with the increasing size of the atom. There is simultaneously an increase in the lattice parameter. It has generally been assumed that this increase in the lattice parameter results in an increase in the densities of states at the Fermi level which in turn leads to an increase in T_c. We present the results of our electronic structure calculations for A_3C_{60} as a function of lattice parameter. Our calculations show that the densities of states in this compound are highly structured in the vicinity of the Fermi level, and vary strongly as a function of lattice parameter. As a result the value of $N(E_F)$ cannot be scaled in a simple manner with the lattice parameter. This result casts a serious doubt on the assumed direct relationship between T_c and the densities of states in these compounds.

The recent discovery [1] of superconductivity in the alkali-doped C_{60} has generated an intense interest in understanding the mechanisms responsible for superconductivity in these molecular crystals. The crystal structure of these compounds is established to be face-centered-cubic (fcc) in which the alkali metal atoms occupy the interstitial sites (see Fig. 1). The maximum T_c is obtained when both octahedral and tetrahedral sites are fully occupied. In fact the compounds are superconducting only when large alkali atoms K, Rb, Cs (or their combinations) are used and efforts to induce superconductivity by Li or Na doping have not been successful so far.

It has been observed [2] that the T_c increases monotonically with the increasing size of the alkali atom which also results in an increase in the lattice parameter of the unit cell. Within the BCS theory of superconductivity, where T_c is directly related to the value of the densities of states $N(E_F)$ at the Fermi level, this increase in T_c has been interpreted [2] as resulting directly from an increase in the $N(E_F)$ due to a narrowing of the bands at the Fermi level with the increase in the lattice parameter. In this paper the results of our electronic structure calculations are presented where we have studied the dependence of $N(E_F)$ on the lattice parameter. Our calculations show that the densities of states in the vicinity of the Fermi level are highly structured and this renders the simple scaling of the $N(E_F)$ with the lattice parameter hazardous.

A C_{60} cluster is formed of a truncated icosahedron and consists of twenty hexagons and twelve pentagons as in a football. There are two different types of

Springer Series in Solid-State Sciences, Vol. 113 Electronic Properties of High-T_c Superconductors
Editors: H. Kuzmany, M. Mehring, J. Fink

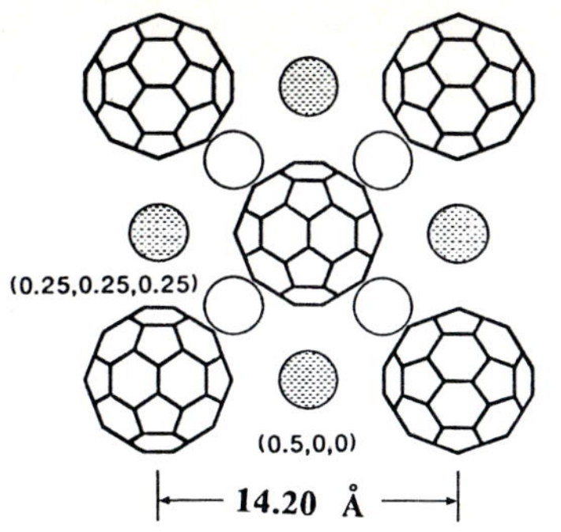

Fig. 1 : Crystal structure of K_3C_{60}

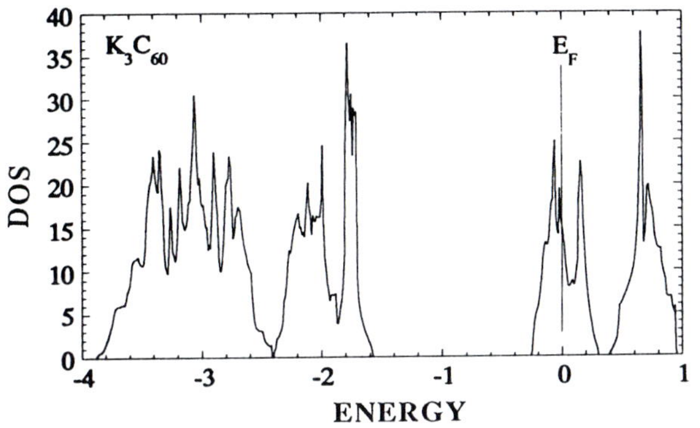

Fig. 2 : Densities of states (states/eV-molecule) of K_3C_{60} with the lattice parameter a = 14.20 Å.

bonds within this cluster ; one constituting the pentagons, and the other shared by two hexagons. These bonds differ only slightly in length in an actual crystal. In this paper we have assumed them to be identical in length (1.42 Å) which gives us a cluster with an ideal icosahedral symmetry. The C_{60} clusters are placed on the fcc lattice in a manner so that each cluster has twelve equivalent nearest neighbours. In this case each crystal axis of the fcc lattice bisects a bond shared by two hexagons. With this choice two orientations of the C_{60} clusters are possible due to their icosahedral symmetry. Recent experiments [3] have suggested that the C_{60} clusters are rotating rapidly at room temperature, and that there is an orientational disorder in the fcc lattice. This disorder has been ignored in the present calculations.

Our electronic structure calculations were performed using the linear combination of atomic orbitals (LCAO) method. The parameters for these calculations were taken from the work of Tomanek and Schluter [4] on carbon clusters. The densities of states (DOS) were calculated using the accurate tetrahedron method from ~ 6000 tetrahedrons in the Brillouin zone, and are shown in Fig. 2 for the lattice parameter a = 14.20 Å which corresponds to the lattice parameter for K_3C_{60}. These DOS are in excellent agreement with those reported earlier by several authors [5, 6]. The band gap between the highest occupied valence band and the conduction band is found to be direct at the point X in the Brillouin zone with a value Eg = 1.318 eV. We have assumed in our calculations that the alkali atom acts

Table I : Variation of the band gap Eg and the densities of states $N(E_F)$ (in states/eV-molecule) at the Fermi level E_F as a function of lattice parameter a in A_3C_{60} (A = an alkali atom). The last column shows the Gaussian broadened densities of states at E_F with the broadening parameter $\sigma = 0.05$ eV.

a (Å)	Eg (eV)	$N(E_F)$	Gaussian broadened $N(E_F)$
14.00	1.467	38.6	31.2
14.10	1.452	25.1	23.8
14.20	1.318	15.1	13.9
14.30	1.424	12.3	14.2
14.40	1.456	13.5	14.9
14.50	1.485	14.7	15.9

essentially as an electron donor which simply pushes the Fermi level E_F in the conduction band. The Fermi level so obtained for K_3C_{60} is also shown in Fig. 2 ; all energies in this Figure are measured relative to the Fermi energy.

Fig. 2 shows that there is substantial structure in the densities of states in the vicinity of the Fermi level. The Fermi level for this value of the lattice parameter falls in a rapidly varying portion of the densities of states. The structure found in this calculation is similar to the one which was found by Erwin and Pickett [5]. We obtain a value of $N(E_F) = 15.1$ states/eV-molecule at a = 14.2 Å, which is also in good agreement with the value obtained by these authors. Similar calculations were performed for several lattice parameters in order to find the variation of $N(E_F)$ as a function of the lattice parameter a. These results are summarized in Table I. This Table shows that $N(E_F)$ does not increase monotically as a function of the lattice parameter. A minimum in $N(E_F)$ occurs at a = 14.3 Å and away from this value the DOS increases. The increase in $N(E_F)$ away from this lattice parameter as one increases the lattice parameter would apparently be in agreement with the increase in T_c. It is, however, known [7] that under pressure there is a considerable decrease in T_c. Zhou et al. [8] found that at a pressure of 28 kbar the T_c in K_3C_{60} decreases to 6 K while the lattice parameter decreases to 13.9 Å. They interpreted this result in terms of a decrease in $N(E_F)$ due to a decrease in the lattice parameter. Table I shows that this assumption is not correct, since $N(E_F)$ increases as the lattice parameter a decreases.

Of course, the value of $N(E_F)$ can be very sensitive to the structure of the peaks and the position of E_F. This structure can be affected by orientational disorder which exists in these compounds. We have included this effect approximately by broadening the DOS with a Gaussian with a broadening parameter $\sigma = 0.05$ eV. The values of $N(E_F)$ are somewhat affected and the minimum in $N(E_F)$ now occurs at a = 14.2 Å. However, the general conclusions remain unchanged.

In summary, our calculations have shown that $N(E_F)$ is not a monotonically varying function of the lattice parameter a. The change in a affects the intermolecular interaction which in turn affect all molecular orbitals. The structure in the DOS in the vicinity of the Fermi level is determined by this cooperative interaction and cannot be *a priori* predicted without a detailed calculation of the electronic structure.

References

[1] A.F. Hebard, M.J. Rosseinsky, R.C. Haddon, D.W. Murphy, S.H. Glarum, T.M. Paistra, A.P. Ramirez, and A.R. Kortan, Nature 350, 600 (1991).

[2] R.M. Fleming, A.P. Ramirez, M.J. Rosseinsky, D.W. Murphy, R.C. Haddon, S.M. Zahurek, and A.V. Mukhija, Nature 352, 787 (1991).

[3] P.A. Heiney, J.E. Fischer, A.R. McGhie, W.J. Romanow, A.M. Denenstein, J.P. McCauley,Jr., and A.B. Smith III, Phys. Rev. Lett. 66, 2911 (1991).

[4] D. Tomanek and M.A. Schluter, Phys. Rev. Lett. 67, 2331 (1991).

[5] S.C. Erwin and W.E. Pickett, Science 254, 842 (1991).

[6] W.Y. Ching, M. Huang, Y. Xu, W.G. Harter, and F.T. Chan, Phys. Rev. Lett. 67, 2045 (1991).

[7] J.E. Schirder, D.L. Overmyer, H.H. Wang, J.M. Williams, K.D. Carlson, A.M. Kini, U. Welp, and W.K. Kwok, Physica C 178, 137 (1991).

[8] O. Zhou, G.M. Vaughan, Q. Zhu, J.E. Fischer, P.A. Heiney, N. Coustel, J.P. McCauley,Jr., and A.B. Smith III, Science 255, 833 (1992).

Index of Contributors

Springer Series in Solid-State Sciences

Editors: M. Cardona P. Fulde K. von Klitzing H.-J. Queisser

1 **Principles of Magnetic Resonance** 3rd Edition By C. P. Slichter
2 **Introduction to Solid-State Theory** 2nd Printing By O. Madelung
3 **Dynamical Scattering of X-Rays in Crystals** By Z. G. Pinsker
4 **Inelastic Electron Tunneling Spectroscopy** Editor: T. Wolfram
5 **Fundamentals of Crystal Growth I** Macroscopic Equilibrium and Transport Concepts. 2nd Printing By F. Rosenberger
6 **Magnetic Flux Structures in Superconductors** By R. P. Huebener
7 **Green's Functions in Quantum Physics** 2nd Edition By E. N. Economou
8 **Solitons and Condensed Matter Physics** 2nd Printing Editors: A. R. Bishop and T. Schneider
9 **Photoferroelectrics** By V. M. Fridkin
10 **Phonon Dispersion Relations in Insulators** By H. Bilz and W. Kress
11 **Electron Transport in Compound Semiconductors** By B. R. Nag
12 **The Physics of Elementary Excitations** By S. Nakajima, Y. Toyozawa, and R. Abe
13 **The Physics of Selenium and Tellurium** Editors: E. Gerlach and P. Grosse
14 **Magnetic Bubble Technology** 2nd Edition By A. H. Eschenfelder
15 **Modern Crystallography I** Symmetry of Crystals. Methods of Structural Crystallography By B. K. Vainshtein
16 **Organic Molecular Crystals** Their Electronic States. By E. A. Silinsh
17 **The Theory of Magnetism I** Statics and Dynamics. 2nd Printing By D. C. Mattis
18 **Relaxation of Elementary Excitations** Editors: R. Kubo and E. Hanamura
19 **Solitons.** Mathematical Methods for Physicists. 2nd Printing By G. Eilenberger
20 **Theory of Nonlinear Lattices** 2nd Edition By M. Toda
21 **Modern Crystallography II** Structure of Crystals By B. K. Vainshtein, V. M. Fridkin, and V. L. Indenbom
22 **Point Defects in Semiconductors I** Theoretical Aspects By M. Lannoo and J. Bourgoin
23 **Physics in One Dimension** Editors: J. Bernasconi, T. Schneider
24 **Physics in High Magnetic Fields** Editors: S. Chikazumi and N. Miura
25 **Fundamental Physics of Amorphous Semiconductors** Editor: F. Yonezawa
26 **Elastic Media with Microstructure I** One-Dimensional Models. By I. A. Kunin
27 **Superconductivity of Transition Metals** Their Alloys and Compounds By S. V. Vonsovsky, Yu. A. Izyumov, and E. Z. Kurmaev
28 **The Structure and Properties of Matter** Editor: T. Matsubara
29 **Electron Correlation and Magnetism in Narrow-Band Systems** Editor: T. Moriya
30 **Statistical Physics I** Equilibrium Statistical Mechanics 2nd Edition By M. Toda, R. Kubo, N. Saito
31 **Statistical Physics II** Nonequilibrium Statistical Mechanics 2nd Edition By R. Kubo, M. Toda, N. Hashitsume
32 **Quantum Theory of Magnetism** 2nd Edition By R. M. White
33 **Mixed Crystals** By A. I. Kitaigorodsky
34 **Phonons: Theory and Experiments I** Lattice Dynamics and Models of Interatomic Forces. By P. Brüesch
35 **Point Defects in Semiconductors II** Experimental Aspects By J. Bourgoin and M. Lannoo
36 **Modern Crystallography III** Crystal Growth 2nd Edition By A. A. Chernov
37 **Modern Crystallography IV** Physical Properties of Crystals Editor: L. A. Shuvalov
38 **Physics of Intercalation Compounds** Editors: L. Pietronero and E. Tosatti
39 **Anderson Localization** Editors: Y. Nagaoka and H. Fukuyama
40 **Semiconductor Physics** An Introduction 5th Edition By K. Seeger
41 **The LMTO Method** Muffin-Tin Orbitals and Electronic Structure By H. L. Skriver
42 **Crystal Optics with Spatial Dispersion, and Excitons** 2nd Edition By V. M. Agranovich and V. L. Ginzburg
43 **Structural Analysis of Point Defects in Solids** An Introduction to Multiple Magnetic Resonance Spectroscopy By J.-M. Spaeth, J. R. Niklas, and R. H. Bartram
44 **Elastic Media with Microstructure II** Three-Dimensional Models By I. A. Kunin
45 **Electronic Properties of Doped Semiconductors** By B. I. Shklovskii and A. L. Efros
46 **Topological Disorder in Condensed Matter** Editors: F. Yonezawa and T. Ninomiya
47 **Statics and Dynamics of Nonlinear Systems** Editors: G. Benedek, H. Bilz, and R. Zeyher
48 **Magnetic Phase Transitions** Editors: M. Ausloos and R. J. Elliott
49 **Organic Molecular Aggregates** Electronic Excitation and Interaction Processes Editors: P. Reineker, H. Haken, and H. C. Wolf

Springer Series in Solid-State Sciences

Editors: M. Cardona P. Fulde K. von Klitzing H.-J. Queisser

50 **Multiple Diffraction of X-Rays in Crystals**
By Shih-Lin Chang

51 **Phonon Scattering in Condensed Matter**
Editors: W. Eisenmenger, K. Laßmann, and S. Döttinger

52 **Superconductivity in Magnetic and Exotic Materials** Editors: T. Matsubara and A. Kotani

53 **Two-Dimensional Systems, Heterostructures, and Superlattices**
Editors: G. Bauer, F. Kuchar, and H. Heinrich

54 **Magnetic Excitations and Fluctuations**
Editors: S. Lovesey, U. Balucani, F. Borsa, and V. Tognetti

55 **The Theory of Magnetism II** Thermodynamics and Statistical Mechanics By D. C. Mattis

56 **Spin Fluctuations in Itinerant Electron Magnetism** By T. Moriya

57 **Polycrystalline Semiconductors,**
Physical Properties and Applications
Editor: G. Harbeke

58 **The Recursion Method and Its Applications**
Editors: D. Pettifor and D. Weaire

59 **Dynamical Processes and Ordering on Solid Surfaces** Editors: A. Yoshimori and M. Tsukada

60 **Excitonic Processes in Solids**
By M. Ueta, H. Kanzaki, K. Kobayashi, Y. Toyozawa, and E. Hanamura

61 **Localization, Interaction, and Transport Phenomena** Editors: B. Kramer, G. Bergmann, and Y. Bruynseraede

62 **Theory of Heavy Fermions and Valence Fluctuations** Editors: T. Kasuya and T. Saso

63 **Electronic Properties of Polymers and Related Compounds**
Editors: H. Kuzmany, M. Mehring, and S. Roth

64 **Symmetries in Physics** Group Theory Applied to Physical Problems
By W. Ludwig and C. Falter

65 **Phonons: Theory and Experiments II**
Experiments and Interpretation of Experimental Results By P. Brüesch

66 **Phonons: Theory and Experiments III**
Phenomena Related to Phonons
By P. Brüesch

67 **Two-Dimensional Systems: Physics and New Devices**
Editors: G. Bauer, F. Kuchar, and H. Heinrich

68 **Phonon Scattering in Condensed Matter V**
Editors: A. C. Anderson and J. P. Wolfe

69 **Nonlinearity in Condensed Matter**
Editors: A. R. Bishop, D. K. Campbell, P. Kumar, and S. E. Trullinger

70 **From Hamiltonians to Phase Diagrams** The Electronic and Statistical-Mechanical Theory of sp-Bonded Metals and Alloys By J. Hafner

71 **High Magnetic Fields in Semiconductor Physics**
Editor: G. Landwehr

72 **One-Dimensional Conductors**
By S. Kagoshima, H. Nagasawa, and T. Sambongi

73 **Quantum Solid-State Physics**
Editors: S. V. Vonsovsky and M. I. Katsnelson

74 **Quantum Monte Carlo Methods** in Equilibrium and Nonequilibrium Systems Editor: M. Suzuki

75 **Electronic Structure and Optical Properties of Semiconductors** 2nd Edition
By M. L. Cohen and J. R. Chelikowsky

76 **Electronic Properties of Conjugated Polymers**
Editors: H. Kuzmany, M. Mehring, and S. Roth

77 **Fermi Surface Effects**
Editors: J. Kondo and A. Yoshimori

78 **Group Theory and Its Applications in Physics**
By T. Inui, Y. Tanabe, and Y. Onodera

79 **Elementary Excitations in Quantum Fluids**
Editors: K. Ohbayashi and M. Watabe

80 **Monte Carlo Simulation in Statistical Physics**
An Introduction 2nd Edition
By K. Binder and D. W. Heermann

81 **Core-Level Spectroscopy in Condensed Systems**
Editors: J. Kanamori and A. Kotani

82 **Introduction to Photoemission Spectroscopy**
By S. Hüfner

83 **Physics and Technology of Submicron Structures**
Editors: H. Heinrich, G. Bauer, and F. Kuchar

84 **Beyond the Crystalline State** An Emerging Perspective By G. Venkataraman, D. Sahoo, and V. Balakrishnan

85 **The Fractional Quantum Hall Effect**
Properties of an Incompressible Quantum Fluid
By T. Chakraborty and P. Pietiläinen

86 **The Quantum Statistics of Dynamic Processes**
By E. Fick and G. Sauermann

87 **High Magnetic Fields in Semiconductor Physics II**
Transport and Optics Editor: G. Landwehr

88 **Organic Superconductors**
By T. Ishiguro and K. Yamaji

89 **Strong Correlation and Superconductivity**
Editors: H. Fukuyama, S. Maekawa, and A. P. Malozemoff

Springer-Verlag and the Environment

We at Springer-Verlag firmly believe that an international science publisher has a special obligation to the environment, and our corporate policies consistently reflect this conviction.

We also expect our business partners – paper mills, printers, packaging manufacturers, etc. – to commit themselves to using environmentally friendly materials and production processes.

The paper in this book is made from low- or no-chlorine pulp and is acid free, in conformance with international standards for paper permanency.

Printing: Mercedesdruck, Berlin
Binding: Buchbinderei Lüderitz & Bauer, Berlin